Understanding Statistics in Psychology with SPSS

Pearson

At Pearson, we have a simple mission: to help people make more of their lives through learning.

We combine innovative learning technology with trusted content and educational expertise to provide engaging and effective learning experiences that serve people wherever and whenever they are learning.

From classroom to boardroom, our curriculum materials, digital learning tools and testing programmes help to educate millions of people worldwide – more than any other private enterprise.

Every day our work helps learning flourish, and wherever learning flourishes, so do people.

To learn more, please visit us at **www.pearson.com/uk**

Understanding Statistics in Psychology with SPSS

Eighth edition

Dennis Howitt   Loughborough University

Duncan Cramer   Loughborough University

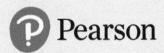

Harlow, England • London • New York • Boston • San Francisco • Toronto • Sydney • Dubai • Singapore • Hong Kong
Tokyo • Seoul • Taipei • New Delhi • Cape Town • São Paulo • Mexico City • Madrid • Amsterdam • Munich • Paris • Milan

PEARSON EDUCATION LIMITED
KAO Two
KAO Park
Harlow CM17 9SR
United Kingdom
Tel: +44 (0)1279 623623
Web: www.pearson.com/uk

First published 1997 (print)
Second edition published 2000 (print)
Revised second edition published 2003 (print)
Third edition published 2005 (print)
Fourth edition published 2008 (print)
Fifth edition published 2011 (print)
Sixth edition published 2014 (print and electronic)
Seventh edition published 2017 (print and electronic)
Eighth edition published 2020 (print and electronic)

ISBN: 978-1-292-28230-5 (print)
        978-1-292-28233-6 (PDF)
        978-1-292-28232-9 (ePub)

British Library Cataloguing-in-Publication Data
A catalogue record for the print edition is available from the British Library

Library of Congress Cataloging-in-Publication Data
Names: Howitt, Dennis, author. | Cramer, Duncan, 1948- author.
Title: Understanding statistics in psychology with SPSS / Dennis Howitt,
    Loughborough University, Duncan Cramer, Loughborough University.
Description: Eighth edition. | Harlow, England ; New York : Pearson, 2020.
    | "First published 1997"—Title page verso. | Includes bibliographical
    references and index.
Identifiers: LCCN 2019059735 (print) | LCCN 2019059736 (ebook) | ISBN
    9781292282305 (paperback) | ISBN 9781292282336 (ebook) | ISBN
    9781292282329 (epub)
Subjects: LCSH: Psychometrics.
Classification: LCC BF39 .H74 2020 (print) | LCC BF39 (ebook) | DDC
    150.1/5195—dc23
LC record available at https://lccn.loc.gov/2019059735
LC ebook record available at https://lccn.loc.gov/2019059736

A catalog record for the print edition is available from the Library of Congress

10 9 8 7 6 5 4 3 2 1
24 23 22 21 20

Front cover image: Scott Partridge/Moment Open/Getty Images

Print edition typeset in 9.5/12 pt Sabon LT Pro by SPi Global

NOTE THAT ANY PAGE CROSS REFERENCES REFER TO THE PRINT EDITION

Brief contents

Contents   *vii*

Guided tour   *xx*

Introduction   *xxv*

Acknowledgements   *xxvii*

  1 Why statistics?   1

Part 1 Descriptive statistics   19

  2 Some basics: Variability and measurement   21
  3 Describing variables: Tables and diagrams   31
  4 Describing variables numerically: Averages, variation and spread   46
  5 Shapes of distributions of scores   62
  6 Standard deviation and z-scores: Standard unit of measurement in statistics   75
  7 Relationships between two or more variables: Diagrams and tables   90
  8 Correlation coefficients: Pearson's correlation and Spearman's rho   102
  9 Regression: Prediction with precision   122

Part 2 Significance testing   135

 10 Samples from populations   137
 11 Statistical significance for the correlation coefficient: A practical introduction to
statistical inference   144
 12 Standard error: Standard deviation of the means of samples   158
 13 Related t-test: Comparing two samples of related/correlated/paired scores   166
 14 Unrelated t-test: Comparing two samples of unrelated/
uncorrelated/independent scores   180
 15 What you need to write about your statistical analysis   197
 16 Confidence intervals   204
 17 Effect size in statistical analysis: Do my findings matter?   215
 18 Chi-square: Differences between samples of frequency data   225
 19 Probability   244
 20 One-tailed versus two-tailed significance testing   250
 21 Ranking tests: Nonparametric statistics   256

Part 3 Introduction to analysis of variance   271

 22 Variance ratio test: F-ratio to compare two variances   273
 23 Analysis of variance (ANOVA): One-way unrelated or uncorrelated ANOVA   282
 24 ANOVA for correlated scores or repeated measures   300
 25 Two-way or factorial ANOVA for unrelated/uncorrelated scores: Two studies for
the price of one?   315
 26 Multiple comparisons within ANOVA: *A priori* and *post hoc* tests   342
 27 Mixed-design ANOVA: Related and unrelated variables together   353

28   Analysis of covariance (ANCOVA): Controlling for additional variables   370
29   Multivariate analysis of variance (MANOVA)   386
30   Discriminant (function) analysis – especially in MANOVA   402
31   Statistics and analysis of experiments   416

Part 4   More advanced correlational statistics   429

32   Partial correlation: Spurious correlation, third or confounding variables, suppressor variables   431
33   Factor analysis: Simplifying complex data   444
34   Multiple regression and multiple correlation   467
35   Path analysis   484

Part 5   Assorted advanced techniques   501

36   Meta-analysis: Combining and exploring statistical findings from previous research   503
37   Reliability in scales and measurement: Consistency and agreement   522
38   Influence of moderator variables on relationships between two variables   536
39   Statistical power analysis: Getting the sample size right   558

Part 6   Advanced qualitative or nominal techniques   581

40   Log-linear methods: Analysis of complex contingency tables   583
41   Multinomial logistic regression: Distinguishing between several different categories or groups   609
42   Binomial logistic regression   626
43   Data mining and big data   643

Appendices   *653*
Glossary   *689*
References   *697*
Index   *704*

Contents

	Guided tour	*xx*
	Introduction	*xxv*
	Acknowledgements	*xxvii*

1	Why statistics?	1
	Overview	1
1.1	Introduction	2
1.2	Research on learning statistics	3
1.3	Why is learning statistics difficult?	4
1.4	The importance of understanding research designs	6
1.5	Positive about statistics	7
1.6	What statistics can't do	9
1.7	Easing the way	10
1.8	What do I need to know to be an effective user of statistics?	12
1.9	A few words about SPSS	13
1.10	Quick guide to the book's procedures and statistical tests	14
	Key points	16
	Computer analysis: SPSS Analyze, Graphs and Transform drop-down menus	17

Part 1   Descriptive statistics   19

2	Some basics: Variability and measurement	21
	Overview	21
2.1	Introduction	22
2.2	Variables and measurement	23
2.3	Major types of measurement	24
	Key points	28
	Computer analysis: Some basics of data entry using SPSS	29
3	Describing variables: Tables and diagrams	31
	Overview	31
3.1	Introduction	32

3.2	Choosing tables and diagrams	33
3.3	Errors to avoid	41
	Key points	42
	Computer analysis: Tables, diagrams and recoding using SPSS	42
4	Describing variables numerically: Averages, variation and spread	46
	Overview	46
4.1	Introduction	47
4.2	Typical scores: mean, median and mode	48
4.3	Comparison of mean, median and mode	51
4.4	Spread of scores: range and interquartile range	51
4.5	Spread of scores: variance	55
	Key points	59
	Computer analysis: Descriptive statistics using SPSS	60
5	Shapes of distributions of scores	62
	Overview	62
5.1	Introduction	63
5.2	Histograms and frequency curves	63
5.3	Normal curve	64
5.4	Distorted curves	66
5.5	Other frequency curves	68
	Key points	72
	Computer analysis: Frequencies using SPSS	73
6	Standard deviation and z-scores: Standard unit of measurement in statistics	75
	Overview	75
6.1	Introduction	76
6.2	Theoretical background	76
6.3	Measuring the number of standard deviations – the z-score	80
6.4	Use of z-scores	82
6.5	Standard normal distribution	83
6.6	Important feature of z-scores	86
	Key points	87
	Computer analysis: Standard deviation and z-scores using SPSS	88
7	Relationships between two or more variables: Diagrams and tables	90
	Overview	90
7.1	Introduction	91
7.2	Principles of diagrammatic and tabular presentation	92
7.3	Type A: both variables numerical scores	93
7.4	Type B: both variables nominal categories	95

7.5	Type C: one variable nominal categories, the other numerical scores	97
	Key points	99
	Computer analysis: Crosstabulation and compound bar charts using SPSS	99
8	**Correlation coefficients: Pearson's correlation and Spearman's rho**	**102**
	Overview	102
8.1	Introduction	103
8.2	Principles of the correlation coefficient	104
8.3	Some rules to check out	111
8.4	Coefficient of determination	112
8.5	Significance testing	113
8.6	Spearman's rho – another correlation coefficient	113
8.7	Example from the literature	116
	Key points	117
	Computer analysis: Correlation coefficients using SPSS	118
	Computer analysis: Scattergram using SPSS	120
9	**Regression: Prediction with precision**	**122**
	Overview	122
9.1	Introduction	123
9.2	Theoretical background and regression equations	125
9.3	Confidence intervals and standard error: how accurate are the predicted score and the regression equations?	130
	Key points	132
	Computer analysis: Simple regression using SPSS	133

Part 2   Significance testing   135

10	**Samples from populations**	**137**
	Overview	137
10.1	Introduction	138
10.2	Theoretical considerations	138
10.3	Characteristics of random samples	140
10.4	Confidence intervals	141
	Key points	142
	Computer analysis: Selecting a random sample using SPSS	142
11	**Statistical significance for the correlation coefficient: A practical introduction to statistical inference**	**144**
	Overview	144

11.1	Introduction	145
11.2	Theoretical considerations	145
11.3	Back to the real world: null hypothesis	147
11.4	Pearson's correlation coefficient again	149
11.5	Spearman's rho correlation coefficient	153
	Key points	155
	Computer analysis: Correlation coefficients using SPSS	156
12	**Standard error: Standard deviation of the means of samples**	**158**
	Overview	158
12.1	Introduction	159
12.2	Theoretical considerations	159
12.3	Estimated standard deviation and standard error	161
	Key points	163
	Computer analysis: Standard error using SPSS	164
13	**Related *t*-test: Comparing two samples of related/correlated/paired scores**	**166**
	Overview	166
13.1	Introduction	167
13.2	Dependent and independent variables	169
13.3	Some basic revision	169
13.4	Theoretical considerations underlying the computer analysis	170
13.5	Cautionary note	175
	Key points	177
	Computer analysis: Related/correlated/paired *t*-test using SPSS	178
14	**Unrelated *t*-test: Comparing two samples of unrelated/uncorrelated/independent scores**	**180**
	Overview	180
14.1	Introduction	181
14.2	Theoretical considerations	182
14.3	Standard deviation and standard error	186
14.4	Cautionary note	192
	Key points	193
	Computer analysis: Unrelated/uncorrelated/independent *t*-test using SPSS	194
15	**What you need to write about your statistical analysis**	**197**
	Overview	197
15.1	Introduction	198
15.2	Reporting statistical significance	199
15.3	Shortened forms	199
15.4	APA (American Psychological Association) style	200
	Key points	203

16	Confidence intervals	204
	Overview	204
16.1	Introduction	205
16.2	Relationship between significance and confidence intervals	208
16.3	Regression	211
16.4	Writing up a confidence interval using APA style	213
16.5	Other confidence intervals	213
	Key points	214
	Computer analysis: Examples of SPSS output containing confidence intervals	214

17	Effect size in statistical analysis: Do my findings matter?	215
	Overview	215
17.1	Introduction	216
17.2	Statistical significance and effect size	216
17.3	Size of the effect in studies	217
17.4	Approximation for nonparametric tests	219
17.5	Analysis of variance (ANOVA)	219
17.6	Writing up effect sizes using APA style	221
17.7	Have I got a large, medium or small effect size?	221
17.8	Method and statistical efficiency	222
	Key points	224

18	Chi-square: Differences between samples of frequency data	225
	Overview	225
18.1	Introduction	226
18.2	Theoretical issues	227
18.3	Partitioning chi-square	233
18.4	Important warnings	234
18.5	Alternatives to chi-square	235
18.6	Chi-square and known populations	237
18.7	Chi-square for related samples – the McNemar test	239
18.8	Example from the literature	239
	Key points	241
	Computer analysis: Chi-square using SPSS	241
	Recommended further reading	243

19	Probability	244
	Overview	244
19.1	Introduction	245
19.2	Principles of probability	245
19.3	Implications	247
	Key points	249

20	One-tailed versus two-tailed significance testing	250
	Overview	250
20.1	Introduction	251
20.2	Theoretical considerations	251
20.3	Further requirements	253
	Key points	254
	Computer analysis: One- and two-tailed statistical significance using SPSS	255
21	Ranking tests: Nonparametric statistics	256
	Overview	256
21.1	Introduction	257
21.2	Theoretical considerations	257
21.3	Nonparametric statistical tests	259
21.4	Three or more groups of scores	267
	Key points	268
	Computer analysis: Two-group ranking tests using SPSS	268
	Recommended further reading	270

Part 3   Introduction to analysis of variance   271

22	Variance ratio test: *F*-ratio to compare two variances	273
	Overview	273
22.1	Introduction	274
22.2	Theoretical issues and application	275
	Key points	279
	Computer analysis: *F*-ratio test using SPSS	280
23	Analysis of variance (ANOVA): One-way unrelated or uncorrelated ANOVA	282
	Overview	282
23.1	Introduction	283
23.2	Some revision and some new material	283
23.3	Theoretical considerations	284
23.4	Degrees of freedom	288
23.5	Analysis of variance summary table	294
	Key points	296
	Computer analysis: Unrelated one-way analysis of variance using SPSS	297
24	ANOVA for correlated scores or repeated measures	300
	Overview	300
24.1	Introduction	301

24.2	Theoretical considerations underlying the computer analysis	303
24.3	Examples	304
	Key points	312
	Computer analysis: Related analysis of variance using SPSS	313
25	**Two-way or factorial ANOVA for unrelated/uncorrelated scores: Two studies for the price of one?**	**315**
	Overview	315
25.1	Introduction	316
25.2	Theoretical considerations	317
25.3	Steps in the analysis	318
25.4	More on interactions	331
25.5	Three or more independent variables	334
	Key points	338
	Computer analysis: Unrelated two-way analysis of variance using SPSS	339
26	**Multiple comparisons within ANOVA: *A priori* and *post hoc* tests**	**342**
	Overview	342
26.1	Introduction	343
26.2	Planned (*a priori*) versus unplanned (*post hoc*) comparisons	344
26.3	Methods of multiple comparisons testing	345
26.4	Multiple comparisons for multifactorial ANOVA	345
26.5	Contrasts	346
26.6	Trends	348
	Key points	349
	Computer analysis: Multiple comparison tests using SPSS	350
	Recommended further reading	352
27	**Mixed-design ANOVA: Related and unrelated variables together**	**353**
	Overview	353
27.1	Introduction	354
27.2	Mixed designs and repeated measures	354
	Key points	367
	Computer analysis: Mixed design analysis of variance using SPSS	367
	Recommended further reading	369
28	**Analysis of covariance (ANCOVA): Controlling for additional variables**	**370**
	Overview	370
28.1	Introduction	371
28.2	Analysis of covariance	372
	Key points	382
	Computer analysis: Analysis of covariance using SPSS	383
	Recommended further reading	385

29   Multivariate analysis of variance (MANOVA)   386
      Overview   386
29.1 Introduction   387
29.2 MANOVA's two stages   390
29.3 Doing MANOVA   392
29.4 Reporting your findings   397
      Key points   398
      Computer analysis: Multivariate analysis of variance using SPSS   399
      Recommended further reading   401

30   Discriminant (function) analysis – especially in MANOVA   402
      Overview   402
30.1 Introduction   403
30.2 Doing the discriminant function analysis   405
30.3 Reporting your findings   411
      Key points   412
      Computer analysis: Discriminant function analysis using SPSS   413
      Recommended further reading   415

31   Statistics and analysis of experiments   416
      Overview   416
31.1 Introduction   417
31.2 The Patent Stats Pack   417
31.3 Checklist   418
31.4 Special cases   422
      Key points   422
      Computer analysis: Selecting subsamples of your data using SPSS   424
      Computer analysis: Recoding groups for multiple comparison tests using SPSS   426

Part 4   More advanced correlational statistics   429

32   Partial correlation: Spurious correlation, third or confounding variables,
      suppressor variables   431
      Overview   431
32.1 Introduction   432
32.2 Theoretical considerations   433
32.3 Doing partial correlation   435
32.4 Interpretation   436

32.5	Multiple control variables	437
32.6	Suppressor variables	437
32.7	Example from the research literature	438
32.8	Example from a student's work	439
	Key points	440
	Computer analysis: Partial correlation using SPSS	441
33	**Factor analysis: Simplifying complex data**	**444**
	Overview	444
33.1	Introduction	445
33.2	A bit of history	446
33.3	Basics of factor analysis	447
33.4	Decisions, decisions, decisions	449
33.5	Exploratory and confirmatory factor analysis	457
33.6	Example of factor analysis from the literature	458
33.7	Reporting the results	461
	Key points	463
	Computer analysis: Principal components analysis using SPSS	464
	Recommended further reading	466
34	**Multiple regression and multiple correlation**	**467**
	Overview	467
34.1	Introduction	468
34.2	Theoretical considerations	468
34.3	Assumptions of multiple regression	474
34.4	Stepwise multiple regression example	475
34.5	Reporting the results	478
34.6	Example from the published literature	479
	Key points	481
	Computer analysis: Stepwise multiple regression using SPSS	481
	Recommended further reading	483
35	**Path analysis**	**484**
	Overview	484
35.1	Introduction	485
35.2	Theoretical considerations	485
35.3	Example from published research	492
35.4	Reporting the results	494
	Key points	496
	Computer analysis: Hierarchical multiple regression using SPSS	497
	Recommended further reading	499

Part 5   Assorted advanced techniques   501

36	Meta-analysis: Combining and exploring statistical findings from previous research	503
	Overview	503
36.1	Introduction	504
36.2	Pearson correlation coefficient as the effect size	506
36.3	Other measures of effect size	506
36.4	Effects of different characteristics of studies	507
36.5	First steps in meta-analysis	508
36.6	Illustrative example	514
36.7	Comparing a study with a previous study	517
36.8	Reporting the results	518
	Key points	520
	Computer analysis: Some meta-analysis software	520
	Recommended further reading	521
37	Reliability in scales and measurement: Consistency and agreement	522
	Overview	522
37.1	Introduction	523
37.2	Item-analysis using item–total correlation	523
37.3	Split-half reliability	525
37.4	Alpha reliability	526
37.5	Agreement among raters	529
	Key points	533
	Computer analysis: Cronbach's alpha and kappa using SPSS	534
	Recommended further reading	535
38	Influence of moderator variables on relationships between two variables	536
	Overview	536
38.1	Introduction	537
38.2	Statistical approaches to finding moderator effects	541
38.3	Hierarchical multiple regression approach to identifying moderator effects (or interactions)	541
38.4	ANOVA approach to identifying moderator effects (i.e. interactions)	551
	Key points	555
	Computer analysis: Regression moderator analysis using SPSS	556
	Recommended further reading	557

39	Statistical power analysis: Getting the sample size right	558
	Overview	558
39.1	Introduction	559
39.2	Types of statistical power analysis and their limitations	568
39.3	Doing power analysis	571
39.4	Calculating power	572
39.5	Reporting the results	576
	Key points	577
	Computer analysis: Power analysis with G*Power	578

Part 6   Advanced qualitative or nominal techniques   581

40	Log-linear methods: Analysis of complex contingency tables	583
	Overview	583
40.1	Introduction	584
40.2	Two-variable example	586
40.3	Three-variable example	593
40.4	Reporting the results	604
	Key points	605
	Computer analysis: Log-linear analysis using SPSS	606
	Recommended further reading	608

41	Multinomial logistic regression: Distinguishing between several different categories or groups	609
	Overview	609
41.1	Introduction	610
41.2	Dummy variables	612
41.3	What can multinomial logistic regression do?	613
41.4	Worked example	615
41.5	Accuracy of the prediction	616
41.6	How good are the predictors?	617
41.7	Prediction	620
41.8	Interpreting the results	622
41.9	Reporting the results	622
	Key points	623
	Computer analysis: Multinomial logistic regression using SPSS	624

| 42 | Binomial logistic regression | 626 |
| | Overview | 626 |

42.1	Introduction	627
42.2	Typical example	631
42.3	Applying the logistic regression procedure	634
42.4	Regression formula	638
42.5	Reporting the results	639
	Key points	640
	Computer analysis: Binomial logistic regression using SPSS	641

43	Data mining and big data	643
	Overview	643
43.1	Introduction	644
43.2	Adopting a new thinking mode	646
43.3	Dissatisfactions with traditional psychology	647
43.4	Web scraping	648
43.5	Data mining and statistical techniques	649
	Key points	651

	Appendices	
Appendix A	Testing for excessively skewed distributions	653
Appendix B1	Large-sample formulae for the nonparametric tests	656
Appendix B2	Nonparametric tests for three or more groups	658
	Computer analysis: Kruskal–Wallis and Friedman nonparametric tests using SPSS	662
Appendix C	Extended table of significance for the Pearson correlation coefficient	664
Appendix D	Table of significance for the Spearman correlation coefficient	667
Appendix E	Extended table of significance for the t-test	670
Appendix F	Table of significance for chi-square	673
Appendix G	Extended table of significance for the sign test	674
Appendix H	Table of significance for the Wilcoxon matched pairs test	677
Appendix I	Tables of significance for the Mann–Whitney U-test	680
Appendix J	Tables of significance values for the F-distribution	683
Appendix K	Table of significance values for t when making multiple t-tests	686

Glossary	689
References	697
Index	704

Companion Website

For open-access **student resources** specifically written
to complement this textbook and support your learning,
please visit **go.pearson.com/uk/he/resources**

Lecturer Resources

For password-protected online resources tailored to support
the use of this textbook in teaching, please visit
go.pearson.com/uk/he/resources

Guided tour

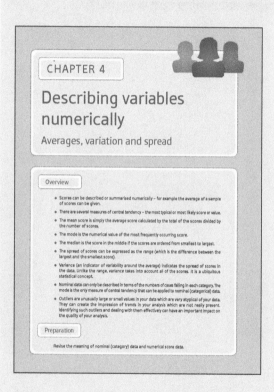

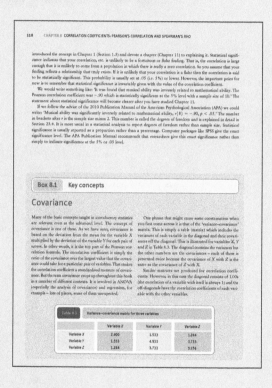

Clear overview

Introduce the chapter to give students a feel for the topics covered.

Key concepts

Offer guidance on the important concepts and issues discussed in the text.

11.4 PEARSON'S CORRELATION COEFFICIENT AGAIN   149

Box 11.1   Focus on

Do correlations differ?

Notice that throughout this chapter we are comparing a particular correlation coefficient obtained from our data with the correlation coefficient that we would expect to obtain if there were no relationship between the two variables at all. In other words, we are calculating the likelihood of obtaining the correlation coefficient based on our sample of data if, in fact, the correlation between these two variables in the population from which the sample was taken is actually .0. However, there are circumstances in which the researcher might wish to assess whether two correlations obtained in their research are significantly different from each other. Imagine, for example, that the researcher is investigating the relationship between satisfaction with one's marriage and the length of time that

individuals have been married. The researcher notes that the correlation between satisfaction and length of marriage is .25 for male participants but .53 for female participants. There is clearly a difference here, but is it a statistically significant one? So essentially the researcher needs to know whether a correlation of .53 is significantly different from a correlation of .25 (the researcher has probably already tested the significance of each of these correlations separately but, of course, this does not answer the question of whether the two correlation coefficients differ from each other). It is a relatively simple matter to do this calculation. It has to be done by hand, unfortunately. The procedure for doing this is described in Section 37.7 Comparing a study with a previous study.

11.4   Pearson's correlation coefficient again

Computer programs such as SPSS give exact significance levels for your correlation coefficient. Nevertheless, originally one would have used tables of the distribution of the correlation coefficient to find the significance level. Occasionally you still might need to consult such a table:

*   For example, imagine that you are reviewing the research literature and find that one old study reports a correlation of .66 between two variables but fails to give the significance level, then what do you do? This sort of situation can occasionally happen since not every research paper is exemplary in its statistical analysis. Or you wish to check that there is not a typographical error for the given significance level then what do you do? SPSS will not be of help in these situations.

*   What if you wanted to know the size of correlation which would be statistically significant for a given sample size? If, for example, you are expecting a small correlation of say .2 then how big a sample would be needed for this to be statistically significant? The only way to find out is to consult tables.

Since SPSS does not help here, in this section we will explain how significance levels may be obtained from tables. But you need to the size of the correlation coefficient and the sample size (or in some tables the degrees of freedom) involved.

The null hypothesis for research involving the correlation coefficient is that there is no relationship between the two variables. In other words, the null hypothesis states that the correlation coefficient between the two variables is .00 in the population (defined by the null hypothesis). So what if, in a sample of 10 pairs of scores, the correlation is .94 as for the data in Table 11.3? Do we accept or reject the null hypothesis?

Focus on

Explore particular concepts in more detail.

---

162   CHAPTER 12 STANDARD ERROR: STANDARD DEVIATION OF THE MEANS OF SAMPLES

Explaining statistics 12.1

How the estimated standard error works

Table 12.3 is a sample of six scores taken at random from the population: 5, 7, 3, 6, 4, 5.

Table 12.3	Steps in calculating the standard error
X (scores)	X^2 (squared scores)
5	25
7	49
3	9
6	36
4	16
5	25
$\sum X = 30$	$\sum X^2 = 160$

Step 1   Using this information we can estimate the standard error of samples of size 6 taken from the same population. Taking our six scores (X), we need to produce Table 12.3, where $N = 6$.

Step 2   Substitute these values in the standard error formula:

$$\text{(estimated) standard error} = \frac{\sqrt{\dfrac{\sum X^2 - \dfrac{(\sum X)^2}{N}}{N-1}}}{\sqrt{N}} = \frac{\sqrt{\dfrac{160 - \dfrac{30^2}{6}}{6-1}}}{\sqrt{6}} = \frac{\sqrt{\dfrac{160 - \dfrac{900}{6}}{5}}}{2.449}$$

$$= \frac{\sqrt{\dfrac{160 - 150}{5}}}{2.449} = \frac{\sqrt{\dfrac{10}{5}}}{2.449}$$

$$= \frac{\sqrt{2}}{2.449} = \frac{1.414}{2.449} = 0.58$$

Note that this is the same value as that given by SPSS in Screenshot 12.5.

Interpreting the results

The standard error is 0.58. This is a measure of deviation of sample means from the population mean. It is a difficult concept to make concrete. Very roughly speaking, we could say that the standard deviation is the typical amount by which sample means deviate from the population mean. Some statisticians (e.g. Huck, 2009) dislike this sort of explanation though they offer no easily understood alternative for non-statisticians. It is possible to use a special mathematical distribution, the t-distribution, to indicate the proportions of sample means which lie between the population mean and any number of standard errors away from it. This is discussed in the following two chapters.

Explaining statistics

Take students through a statistical test with a detailed step-by-step explanation.

Research examples

Multiple comparison tests

Ivancevich (1976) conducted a field experiment in which sales personnel were assigned to various goal setting groups. One was a participative goal-setting situation, another was an assigned goal group, and a third group served as a comparison group. Various measures of performance and satisfaction were collected at various data collection points which included a before training baseline, then 6 months, 9 months and 12 months after training. ANOVA was used together with the Duncan's multiple range test to examine where the significant differences were to be found between the experimental and control conditions. The results suggested that for up to nine months both the participative and assigned goal setting groups had higher performance and satisfaction levels. At 12 months, this advantage no longer applied.

Touliatos and Lindholm (1981) compared the ratings on the Behavior Problem Checklist for parents and teachers. Some of the children rated were in counselling and others were not in counselling. Using ANOVA, it was found that the youngsters in counselling were more likely to exhibit deviant behaviour. The independent variables for the ANOVA were counselling versus not in counselling and ratings by mothers versus fathers versus teachers. The researchers wanted to know just where in their data the differences lay. So they used Duncan's Multiple Range Test which showed that more behavioural problems were seen by parents than by the children's teachers.

Yildirim (2008) investigated the relationship between occupational burnout and the availability of various sources of social support among school counsellors in Turkey. The analysis included other sociodemographic variables. There was a significant negative relationship between burnout and sources of social support. However, burnout was not related to age, gender or marital status in this study. Some of the subdimensions of burnout were related to some of these variables. The Scheffé test was employed to make finer comparisons between the conditions of the ANOVA. For example, it was found that counsellors with only up to three years of experience had higher levels of depersonalisation of burnout than those with more experience in this sort of counselling.

Key points

- If you have more than two sets of scores in the analysis of variance (or any other test for that matter), it is important to employ one of the procedures for multiple comparisons.

- Even simple procedures such as multiple *t*-tests are better than nothing, especially if the proper adjustment is made for the number of *t*-tests being carried out and you adjust the critical values accordingly.

- Modern computer packages, especially SPSS, have a range of multiple comparison tests. It is a fine art to know which is the most appropriate for your particular circumstances. Usually it is expedient to compare the results from several tests; often they will give much the same results, especially where the trends in the data are clear.

Research examples

Demonstrate how the statistical tests have been used in real research.

Key points

- The related or correlated *t*-test is merely a special case of the one-way analysis of variance for related samples (Chapter 24). Although it is frequently used in psychological research it tells us nothing more than the equivalent analysis of variance would do. Since the analysis of variance is generally a more flexible statistic, allowing any number of groups of scores to be compared, it might be your preferred statistic. However, the common occurrence of the *t*-test in psychological research means that you need to have some idea about what it is.

- The related *t*-test assumes that the distribution of the difference scores is not markedly skewed. If it is then the test may be unacceptably inaccurate. Appendix A explains how to test for skewness.

- If you compare many pairs of samples with each other in the same study using the *t*-test, you should consult Chapter 26 to find out about appropriate significance levels. There are better ways of making multiple comparisons, as they are called, but with appropriate adjustment to the critical values for significance, multiple *t*-tests can be justified.

- If you find that your related *t*-test is not significant, it could be that your two samples of scores are not correlated, thus not meeting the assumptions of the related *t*-test.

- Significance Table 13.1 applies whenever we have estimated the standard error from the characteristics of a sample. However, if we had actually known the population standard deviation and consequently the standard error was the actual standard error and not an estimate, we should not use the *t*-distribution table. In these rare (virtually unknown) circumstances, the distribution of the *t*-score formula is that for the *z*-scores.

- Although the correlated *t*-test can be used to compare any pairs of scores, it does not always make sense to do so. For example, you could use the correlated *t*-test to compare the weights and heights of people to see if the weight mean and the height mean differ. Unfortunately, it is a rather stupid thing to do since the numerical values involved relate to radically different things which are not comparable with each other. It is the comparison which is nonsensical in this case. The statistical test is not to blame. On the other hand, one could compare a sample of people's weights at different points in time quite meaningfully.

Key points

Each chapter concludes with a set of the key points to provide a useful reminder when revising a topic.

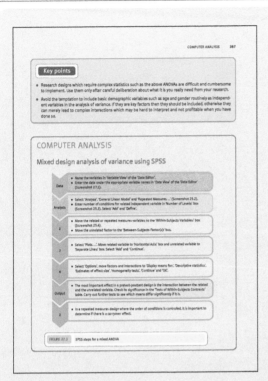

Computer analysis

Step-by-step advice and instruction on analysing data using SPSS Statistics are provided at the end of each chapter.

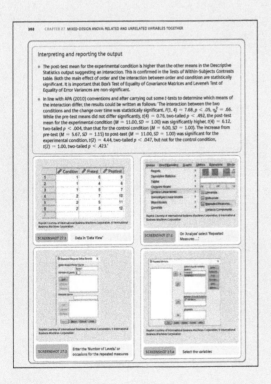

SPSS screenshots

The guidance on how to use SPSS for each statistical test is accompanied by screenshots, so the processes can be easily followed.

Introduction

This is the eighth edition of *Understanding Statistics in Psychology with SPSS*. Hopefully, this is even more helpful to the student learning experience. One thing that has not changed which sets this book apart from others aimed at students: it continues to provide an accessible introduction to the wide range of statistics that are employed by professional researchers. Students using earlier editions of the book will by now often be well into teaching and research careers of their own. We hope that this edition will be permanently on their desks while they instruct their students how to do statistics properly. In the distant past, the abbreviation SPSS stood for Statistical Software for the Social Sciences. Although the official name of the latest release at the time of publication is IBM SPSS Statistics 25.0 we shall refer to it throughout this book as SPSS because it is shorter, most users refer to it this way and the first letter of the original acronym actually refers to Statistical and so to add Statistics again seems repetitive. For most users of SPSS, SPSS versions have changed little since SPSS 13 came out in 2005, so this book will also be suitable for those using these earlier releases. Real changes in SPSS only slowly emerge.

We have considered very carefully the need for instruction into how to compute statistics using SPSS and other computer programs. Our approach in this book is to provide the basic steps needed for the computation but we have added a number of screenshots to help the reader with the analysis. Students of today are very familiar with computers and many do not need overly detailed instructions. Too much detailed step-by-step instruction tends to inhibit exploration of the program – trying things out simply to see what happens and using one's intelligence and a bit of knowledge to work out what things mean. Students can become fixated on the individual steps and fail to get a complete picture of the process of doing statistics with SPSS or other computer programs. In the end, learning to use a computer program is quicker if the user takes some responsibility for their learning.

Much of our daily use of computers in general is on a trial and error basis (we don't need step-by-step instructions to use Facebook or eBay) so why should this be different for statistics programs? How many of us read instructions for the iPhone in detail before trying things out? Of course, there is nothing unusual about tying statistics textbooks to computer packages such as SPSS. Unfortunately, SPSS is not the complete answer to the statistical needs of psychologists. It simply does not do everything that students (and professionals for that matter) need to know. Some of these things are very simple and easily computed by hand if instructions are provided. Other things do require computer programs other than SPSS when procedures are not available on SPSS. We think that ideally psychologists should know the statistics which their discipline needs and not simply those that SPSS provides.

SPSS is very good at what it does but there are times when additional help is needed. This is why we introduce students to other programs which will be helpful to them when necessary. One of the most important features of SPSS is that it is virtually universally available to students for little or no cost thanks to site licensing agreements. Unfortunately, this is not true of all other commercial statistics software. For that reason we have suggested and recommended programs which are essentially free for the user. The Web has a surprisingly large amount of such software to carry out a wide range of statistical routines. A few minutes using Google or some other search engine will often be bountifully productive. Some of these programs are there to be downloaded but others, applets, are instantly available for calculations. We have added, at the end of each chapter, advice on the use of software.

This does not mean that we have abandoned responsibility for teaching how statistics works in favour of explaining how to press keys on a computer keyboard. Although we think it best that statistics are computed using statistics programs because the risk of simple calculation errors is reduced, it seems to us that knowing how to go about doing the calculations that computer programs will do for you leads to an understanding of statistics which relying on computers alone does not. So we have included sections entitled 'Explaining statistics' which are based on hand calculation methods which should help students understand better what the computer program does (more or less) when it is used to do that calculation. Statistical techniques, after all, are little more than the mathematical steps involved in their calculation. Of course, they may be ignored where this level of knowledge is not required.

The basic concept of the book remains the same – a modular statistics package that is accessible throughout to a wide ability range of students. We have attempted to achieve this while being as rigorous as possible where rigour is crucial. Ultimately this is a book for students, though its emphasis on statistics in practice means that it should be valuable to anyone seeking to familiarise themselves with the vast majority of common statistical techniques employed in modern psychology and related disciplines. Not all chapters will be useful to everyone but the book, taken as a whole, provides a sound basis for learning the statistics which professional psychologists use. In this sense, it eases the transition from being a student to being a professional.

For this edition, we have added a chapter on 'big data' and its analysis. Not only does this contrast with more traditional approaches to psychological research but it offers radically new data sets of importance to psychologists. We have also revised every chapter to improve readability and ease the study load wherever possible. Changes have been made to encourage the student to reflect on the special demands of studying the somewhat alien topic of statistics.

Dennis Howitt and Duncan Cramer

Acknowledgements

Working on a book with the team at Pearson is one of the most pleasurable experiences imaginable even when things do not run smoothly. We are in the debt to many people for their talents which contributed to the production of this edition. A few people warrant special mention.

For more years than usual in publishing we worked with Janey Webb who was exceptional in so many ways and is greatly missed now that she has departed from Pearson. Her support was constant and generous. Her official title changed over the years but ended as Publisher though we prefer to think of her just as Janey. We welcome Catherine Yates as the new Publisher. Goodbye also to Saraswati Banerjee who was Acquisitions Editor. She was always superb support and good wishes to her on her new path.

Akanksha Marwah was the Assistant Content Producer who took our manuscript pressed the metaphorical buttons needed to make ready for production. With a statistics book this is a task not to be envied, we guess, but somehow it worked out just fine

The Copy Editor was Marie Gill. She did excellent work imposing the text design on our manuscript. Remarkably she also found time to spot our mistakes and references we forgot. It was great to be working with her.

Kevin Ancient did the text design and the cover design. It is difficult to write anything new about Kevin's work as we have thanked him in numerous books and editions. His contribution has always been brilliant.

Proof reading is a magical skill to us as we have no talent at all for it. Wendy Telfer took on the task for this book. Anyone but a super human would see it as a living nightmare. As we type these acknowledgements we have crossed fingers for her sanity.

A good index makes any book better. The index compiled by Kim Stringer for this edition is unbeatable, we think. She has made the book infinitely easier to use.

Finally, we would be lost without Sweda (or Ms Sweda) who was the Editorial Project Manager for this edition. No we don't know what this means either. It seems to involve everything that needs to be done and more. She has been a rock throughout and deserves to be lavished with the greatest praise. It has been a pleasure working with her. We wish we could be as nice.

Dennis Howitt

Duncan Cramer

◼ Publisher's acknowledgements

Text:

3–4 American Statistical Association: Gordon, S. (1995). A theoretical approach to understanding learners of statistics. *Journal of Statistics Education* [Online], *3*(3) http://www.amstat.org/publications/jse/v3n3/gordon.html, para 18; **5 Hogrefe Verlag:** Zimprich, D. (2012). Attitudes toward statistics among Swiss psychology students. *Swiss Journal of Psychology*, *71*, 149–155; **58 Ingenta:** Cetinkalp, Z. K. (2012). Achievement goals and physical self-perceptions of adolescent athletes. *Social Behaviour and Personality*, *40*, 473–480; **59 Taylor & Francis:** Otgaar, H., Horselenberg, R., van Kampen, R., & Lalleman, K. (2012). Clothed and unclothed human figure drawings lead to more correct and incorrect reports of touch in children. *Psychology, Crime & Law*, *18*, 641–653; **59 Taylor & Francis:** van Schaik, P., & Ling, J. (2012). An experimental analysis of experiential and cognitive variables in web navigation. *Human Computer Interaction*, *27*, 199–234; **87 Taylor & Francis:** Contador, I., Fernández-Calvo, B., Cacho, L. J., Ramos, F., & López-Rolón, A. (2010). Non-verbal memory tasks in early differential diagnosis of Alzheimer's disease and unipolar depression. *Applied Neuropsychology*, *17*, 251–261; **87 Taylor & Francis:** Di Filippo, G., de Luca, M., Judica, A., Spinelli, D., & Zoccolotti, P. (2006). Lexicality and stimulus length effects in Italian dyslexics: Role of overadditivity effect. *Child Neuropsychology*, *12*, 141–149; **117 The British Psychological Society:** Blom, D., van Middendorp, H., & Geenen, R. (2012). Anxious attachment may be a vulnerability factor for developing embitterment. *Psychology and Psychotherapy: Theory, Research and Practice*, *85*, 351–355; **155 The British Psychological Society:** Rohmer, O., & Louvet, E. (2012). Implicit measures of the stereotype content associated with disability. *British Journal of Social Psychology*, *51*, 732–740; **155 John Wiley & Sons:** Gannon, T. A., & Barrowcliffe, E. (2012). Firesetting in the general population: The development and validation of the Fire Setting and Fire Proclivity Scales. *Legal and Criminological Psychology*, *17*, 105–122; **155 Taylor & Francis:** Vallat-Azouvi, C., Pradat-Diehl, P., & Azouvi, P. (2012). The Working Memory Questionnaire: A scale to assess everyday life problems related to deficits of working memory in brain injured patients. *Neuropsychological Rehabilitation: An International Journal*, *22*, 634–649; **163 American Psychological Association:** Mercer, S. H., Harpole, L. L., Mitchell, R. R., McLemore, C., & Hardy, C. (2012). The impact of probe variability on brief experimental analysis of reading skills. *School Psychology Quarterly*, *27*, 223–235; **201 American Psychological Association:** Critcher, C. R., & Dunning, D. (2013). Predicting persons' versus a person's goodness: Behavioral forecasts diverge for individuals versus populations. *Journal of Personality and Social Psychology*, *104*, 28–44; **201 American Psychological Association:** Siy, J. O., & Cheryan, S. (2013). When compliments fail to flatter: American individualism and responses to positive stereotypes. *Journal of Personality and Social Psychology*, *104*, 87–102; **203 American Psychological Association:** Mitsumatsu, H. (2013). Stronger discounting of external cause by action in human adults: Evidence for an action-based hypothesis of visual collision perception. *Journal of Experimental Psychology: General*, *142*, 101–118; **203 John Wiley & Sons:** Rowe, M. L. (2012). A longitudinal investigation of the role of quantity and quality of child-directed speech in vocabulary development. *Child Development*, *83*, 1762–1774; **213 Elsevier:** Huisman, A., van Houwelingen, C. A. J., & Kerkhof, A. J. F. M. (2010). Psychopathology and suicide method in mental health care. *Journal of Affective Disorders*, *121*, 94–99; **213 American Psychological Association:** Abeyta, A. A., Routledge, C., & Juhl, J. (2015). Looking back to move forward: Nostalgia as a psychological resource for promoting relationship goals and overcoming relationship challenge. *Journal of Personality and Social Psychology*, *109*, 1029–1044; **213 American Psychological Association:** Rubin, J., Wynn, J., & Moscovitch, M. (2016). The spatial scaffold: The effects of spatial context on memory for events. *Journal of Experimental*

Psychology: Learning, Memory, and Cognition, 42, 308–315; **221 American Psychological Association:** Meyer, M. M., Bell, R., & Buchner, A. (2015). Remembering the snake in the grass: Threat enhances recognition but not source memory. *Emotion*, 15, 721–730; **221 American Psychological Association:** Zhang, Y., & Risen, J. L. (2014). Embodied motivation: Using a goal systems framework to understand the preference for social and physical warmth. *Journal of Personality and Social Psychology*, 107, 965–977; **223 John Wiley & Sons:** Gervais, S. J., Vescio, T. K., & Allen, J. (2012). When are people interchangeable sexual objects? The effect of gender and body type on sexual fungibility. *British Journal of Social Psychology*, 51, 499–513; **223 John Wiley & Sons:** Lautamo, T., Laakso, M. L., Aro, T., Ahonen, T., & Törmäkangas, K. (2011). Validity of the play assessment for group settings: An evaluation of differential item functioning between children with specific language impairment and typically developing peers. *Australian Occupational Therapy Journal*, 58, 222–230; **254 John Wiley & Sons:** Hoicka, E., & Akhtar, N. (2012). Early humour production. *British Journal of Developmental Psychology*, 30, 586–603; **266 McGraw-Hill Education:** Adapted and extended from Table I of R.P. Runyon and A. Haber (1989). *Fundamentals of behavioral statistics*. New York: McGraw-Hill; **296 John Wiley & Sons:** Frank, G. K. W., Roblek, T., Shott, M. E., Jappe, L. M., Rollin, M. D. H., Hagman, J. O., & Pryor, T. (2012). Heightened fear of uncertainty in anorexia and bulimia nervosa. *International Journal of Eating Disorders*, 45, 227–232; **397 American Psychological Association:** APA (2010). *Publication Manual of the American Psychological Association* (6th ed.). Washington, DC: American Psychological Association; **398 Taylor & Francis:** Casidy, R. (2012). Discovering consumer personality clusters in prestige sensitivity and fashion consciousness context. *Journal of International Consumer Marketing*, 24, 291–299; **439 Butler, C:** Butler, C. (1995a). Teachers' qualities, resources and involvement of special needs children in mainstream classrooms. Unpublished thesis, Department of Social Sciences, Loughborough University; **459, 461 American Psychological Association:** Butler, R. (1995b). Motivational and informational functions and consequences of children's attention to peers' work. *Journal of Educational Psychology*, 87, 347–360; **462 The British Psychological Society:** Gibbs, S., & Powell, B. (2012). Teacher efficacy and pupil behaviour: The structure of teachers' individual and collective beliefs and their relationship with numbers of pupils excluded from school. *British Journal of Educational Psychology*, 82, 564–584; **479 SAGE Publications:** Munford, M. B. (1994). Relationship of gender, self-esteem, social class and racial identity to depression in blacks. *Journal of Black Psychology*, 20, 157–174; **479 SAGE Publications:** Data from Munford, M. B. (1994). Relationship of gender, self-esteem, social class and racial identity to depression in blacks. *Journal of Black Psychology*, 20, 157–174; **495 John Wiley & Sons:** Wagner, U., & Zick, A. (1995). The relation of formal education to ethnic prejudice: Its reliability, validity and explanation. *European Journal of Social Psychology*, 25, 41–56; **495 The British Psychological Society:** Kuhnle, C., Hofer, M., & Kilian, B. (2012). Self-control as predictor of school grades, life balance, and flow in adolescents. *British Journal of Educational Psychology*, 82, 533–548; **496 American Psychological Association:** Lamoureux, B. E., Palmieri, P. A., Jackson, A. P., & Hobfoll, S. E. (2012). Child sexual abuse and adulthoodinterpersonal outcomes: Examining pathways for intervention. *Psychological Trauma: Theory, Research, Practice, and Policy*, 4, 605–613; **497 American Psychological Association:** APA (2010). *Publication Manual of the American Psychological Association* (6th ed.). Washington, DC: American Psychological Association; **578 Prof. Dr. Axel Buchner:** G*Power, © Copyright 2010–2016 Heinrich-Heine-Universität Düsseldorf; **605 EBSCO Industries:** Bridges, F. S., Williamson, C. B., Thompson, P. C., & Windsor, M. A. (2001). Lost letter technique: Returned responses to battered and abused women, men, and lesbians. *North American Journal of Psychology*, 3, 263–276; **605 American Psychological Association:** Tracey, T. J., Sherry, P., Bauer, G. P., Robins, T. H., Todaro, L., & Briggs, S. (1984). Help seeking as a function of student characteristics and program description: A logit-loglinear analysis. *Journal of Counseling*

Psychology, 31, 54–62; **623 The British Psychological Society:** Griffin, B., & Hesketh, B. (2008). Post-retirement work: The individual determinants of paid and volunteer work. *Journal of Occupational and Organizational Psychology, 81,* 101–121; **623 Elsevier:** Huisman, A., van Houwelingen, C. A. J., & Kerkhof, A. J. F. M. (2010). Psychopathology and suicide method in mental health care. *Journal of Affective Disorders, 121,* 94–99; **623 Elsevier:** Kogan, S. M. (2004). Disclosing unwanted sexual experiences: Results from a national sample of adolescent women. *Child Abuse & Neglect, 28,* 147–165; **640 Taylor & Francis:** Kenne, D. R., Boros, A. P., & Fischbein, R. L. (2010). Characteristics of opiate users leaving detoxification treatment against medical advice. *Journal of Addictive Diseases, 29,* 283–294; **650 SAGE Publications:** Hao, J., & Ho, T. K. (2019) Machine learning made easy: A review of Scikit-learn Package in Python Programming Language. *Journal of Educational and Behavioral Statistics, 44,* 348–361; **681–682 McGraw-Hill Education:** Adapted from Runyon, R.P. and Haber, A., (1989) *Table I of Fundamentals of behavioral statistics,* The McGraw Hill Companies Inc.

Photo:

Chapter/Part Openers: Getty Images: Logorilla/DigitalVision Vectors/Getty Images; **23 Getty Images:** HishamIbrahim/Stockbyte/Getty Images

Screenshots:

Screenshots of IBM SPSS: Reprint Courtesy of International Business Machines Corporation, © International Business Machines Corporation; **521 Larry C. Lyons:** From The Meta-Analysis Calculator, http://www.lyonsmorris.com/lyons/metaAnalysis/index.cfm, Reproduced by permission of Larry C. Lyons; **573–580 Prof. Dr. Axel Buchner:** Screenshot of G*Power, © Copyright 2010–2016 Heinrich-Heine-Universität Düsseldorf.

CHAPTER 1

Why statistics?

Overview

- Students often approach learning statistics rather negatively. Everyone knows this but research demonstrates it too. Importantly, this leads to poor learning. Student culture tends to reinforce this already bad learning environment for statistics.

- The school environment is an especially important determinant of our attitudes to mathematics, which then impacts expectations concerning learning statistics.

- Mistakenly, some students believe that statistics is peripheral to professional psychology and other related careers. The truth is quite different. Professional psychologists rely on research based on quantitative methods and statistics to inform their work.

- Psychologists, practitioners included, are usually expected to carry out research as part of their work role.

- Knowledge-based practice characterises most modern professions which psychology graduates enter. So a good working knowledge of statistics is an advantage in the job market.

- Old and outmoded statistical ideas can make learning statistics unnecessarily difficult. Some of these ideas are unworkable. This contributes to a fog of confusion surrounding statistics. Unfortunately, textbook writers can be guilty of this.

- Null hypothesis significance testing receives far too much attention in psychology to the exclusion of more useful approaches. It is important to understand the much more varied contribution that statistics makes to psychological knowledge. There is growing dissatisfaction with aspects of statistics as practised by some psychologists.

- Few mathematical skills are needed to develop a good working knowledge of statistics. All but a few students have these skills. Even where these skills have got a little rusty, they can be quickly relearned by motivated students.

1.1   Introduction

For many psychology students the formula is simple: statistics = punishment. Statistics is 'sadistics'. Most would avoid statistics given the chance. This makes a very unpromising learning environment. And an unenviable teaching environment for the poor soul teaching such reluctant students. Student ratings for statistics modules are enough to bring tears to the eyes of all but the most hardened of professors and lecturers. Little could be less satisfactory. Couldn't statistics simply be omitted from psychology degrees? Well yes, but that is unlikely to happen. Statistics is central to most research that is studied on psychology courses. Surely many practitioners do much good without needing statistics? Even if this were once true, it is not so nowadays. Once research and practice were largely separate but modern practitioners combine practice with research. Wherever psychologists work, they are almost certain to have research as part of their job description. We are living in an information-based society and a great deal of this comes from statistical findings. So the bottom line is that some knowledge of statistics is professionally important – and not just in psychology.

Culturally, mathematics and consequently statistics are seen in a negative light. Remarkably, the average person has a poor opinion of statistics even without knowing much about what it involves. People groan when statistics is mentioned. They critique it with hackneyed phrases like 'you can prove anything with statistics' and 'lies, damned lies and statistics'. Statistics can be used misleadingly but that is not the usual intention. Of course, minor adjustments to a graph can distort whatever trend is found. A modest growth or decline in a graph may be presented as dramatic or calamitous simply by choosing what to show and how to show it. Nevertheless, statistics deserves greater respect than its reputation suggests. In contrast, the great majority of the general public have a positive attitude towards and interest in science (Castell, Charlton, Clemence, et al., 2014).

The word statistics derives from the Latin for state (as in nation). Statistics is the information collected by the State to help guide government decision-making. The government's appetite for statistical information is prodigious. Most areas of government planning are guided by statistical data – pay, pensions, taxes, health services, prisons, the police and so forth. Big supermarkets use it, charities use it, the health service uses it, industrialists use it – you name it and they probably use statistics though not quite the same statistics as psychologists. Sound statistical knowledge is fundamental to understanding, planning and analysing research. Nevertheless, students study psychology to learn about psychology – not statistics. However, the psychology they learn almost certainly involves statistics at some point. Of course there is qualitative research not involving statistics but this is a fraction of psychology's output. Statistics and psychology are intertwined.

Statistics, then, has a central role in psychology. It is not there to punish students – no matter how it feels. So why not try to see statistics as a sort of cuddly friend which will help you in all sorts of ways? We are serious here. Criticisms of the dominance of statistics in psychology are common, of course. As much as anyone else, we are against the mindless application of statistics in psychology for its own sake. Psychology may seem obsessed with a few limited statistical topics such as significance testing but this is to overlook the myriad of more far-reaching positive benefits to be gained from the proper application of modern statistical ideas. In recent years, the dominance of null hypothesis significance testing has been critiqued and calls for a new approach to statistics (Cumming & Calin-Jageman, 2017). We have incorporated these newer approaches into this text. Our view is that statistics provides a means of finding order in otherwise confusing data. Some of the various ways of doing this are illustrated in Figure 1.1.

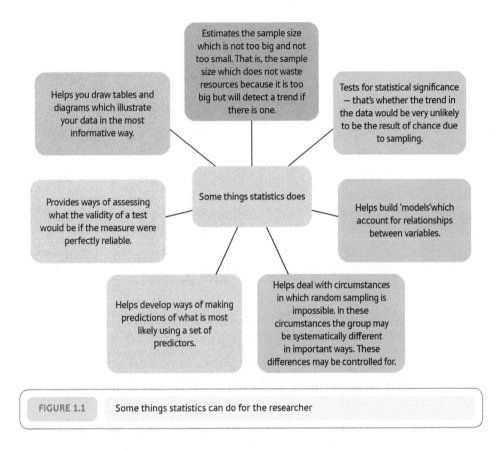

Estimates the sample size which is not too big and not too small. That is, the sample size which does not waste resources because it is too big but will detect a trend if there is one.

Tests for statistical significance – that's whether the trend in the data would be very unlikely to be the result of chance due to sampling.

Helps you draw tables and diagrams which illustrate your data in the most informative way.

Some things statistics does

Helps build 'models' which account for relationships between variables.

Provides ways of assessing what the validity of a test would be if the measure were perfectly reliable.

Helps develop ways of making predictions of what is most likely using a set of predictors.

Helps deal with circumstances in which random sampling is impossible. In these circumstances the group may be systematically different in important ways. These differences may be controlled for.

FIGURE 1.1   Some things statistics can do for the researcher

1.2   Research on learning statistics

Given society's endemic dislike of statistics, not surprisingly the research on psychology students and statistics makes generally depressing reading (e.g. Chew & Dillon, 2014). Trepidation and anxiety are characteristic responses to the prospect of studying statistics. Gordon (2004) talked to a large sample of Australian psychology students about their experience of statistics lectures. Three-quarters would not have studied it but it was compulsory. Statistics they saw as boring and difficult and felt that psychology and psychologists do not need it. They treated statistics as if it were a few mechanical procedures to be applied without understanding why. One student put it this way to Gordon (1995):

> I have a very pragmatic approach to university, I give them what they want. . . I really do like knowledge for knowledge's sake, but my main motivation is to pass the course. (paragraph numbered 18)

Even students who tried to master statistical methods and concepts had difficulty seeing its importance. Students who saw statistics as more personally meaningful in their studies said things like 'It would probably be useful in whatever job I do' (Gordon, 1995). As one might expect, the more positively orientated students did a bit better in statistics tests and examinations. Students with a negative orientation to statistics were generally not less able students and performed much the same as other students on other modules. But not seeing the point of statistics impacted their studies negatively. Figure 1.2 provides a broad classification of students in terms of how they see the relevance of statistics and their personal assessment of the discipline.

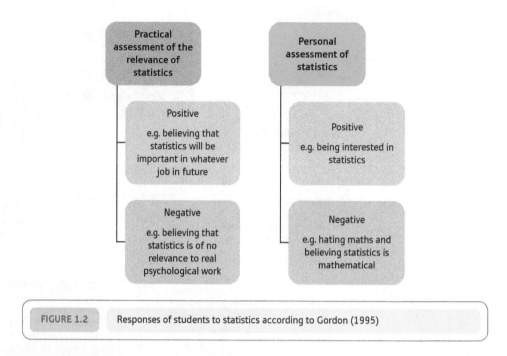

FIGURE 1.2   Responses of students to statistics according to Gordon (1995)

1.3   Why is learning statistics difficult?

Students tend to blame themselves for finding statistics a rather difficult subject. It makes them feel inadequate. Conscientious students should not blame themselves. Nor should they blame their lecturer for being a bad teacher. The villain of the piece is statistics itself quite patently. It has been argued that statistics with its primary concern with probability has fundamental unresolved issues which make learning difficult. Certainly, the evidence is that people do not think probabilistically at all well (Aksentijevic, 2015). Another problem is the fact that most statistical concepts are defined by a mathematical formula rather than in words. This makes it difficult to explain statistics in everyday language. Attempts to do so may be a little misleading but, worse still, criticised for being wrong. Statistics is a unique and distinctive way of thinking (Ben-Zvi & Garfield, 2004; Ruggeri, Dempster & Hanna, 2011). It has its own language and concepts. Some would say that many statistical ideas are decidedly odd. Grasping the statistical way of thinking and learning to speak statistical language takes some effort. Students in all sorts of disciplines struggle somewhat with statistics, it is not just psychology students. Statistical thinking is a different way of thinking. It also requires a rather different way of learning than most modules on a psychology degree. You can't afford to miss statistics lectures, much as this seems desirable, since statistical knowledge builds gradually in crucial steps. Miss any of these out and you are in trouble.

Learning statistics involves many emotional factors. University staff, for the most part, recognise that teaching statistics is made difficult because of students' anxieties, beliefs and negative attitudes concerning the subject (Schau, 2003). University life can be an experience full of emotion, and emotion affects learning – especially learning statistics. Real tears are shed. One student told Gordon (1995), 'I was drowning in statistics' – affective and extreme words but real. Being at university and studying statistics follows a long period of personal development through schooling (and for some at work). Personal histories, experiences, needs and goals are reflected in our strategies for coping with statistics (Gordon, 2004). These influence the way that we think about our learning processes and education more generally. Beliefs such as 'I'm no good at maths' will impact

| FIGURE 1.3 | Formula for doing well in statistics based on research findings |

In other words, students often bring baggage to learning statistics which seriously interferes with their studies. Issues concerning their mathematical ability are common. Some students incorrectly assume that their poor maths skills make statistics too hard for them. This view is reinforced by those departments which require good maths grades for admission. Given other time pressures, such students may adopt avoidance tactics such as skipping lectures rather than putting the time into studying statistics. Procrastination over one's work is known to be related to variables reflecting problems with statistics (Onwuegbuzie, 2004). Furthermore, every statistics class has its own culture in which students influence each other's attitudes to learning statistics. A class dominated by students antagonistic to statistics is not a good learning environment. Acting silly, talking in class or plagiarising the work of other students just does not help.

Whether mathematical ability is important to making a good statistics student is doubtful. There is, however, evidence that believing that good maths ability is needed to do well in statistics is undesirable. For example, Siew, McCartney and Vitevitch (2019) suggest on the basis of their research that students with high levels of anxiety about statistics should be specifically taught that there is no evidence of such a relationship. This aside, research strongly indicates that three factors – anxiety, attitudes and ability (see Figure 1.3) – are involved in learning statistics (Lalonde & Gardner, 1993). A negative attitude towards statistics is associated with poorer performances in statistics to some extent. Anxiety plays its part primarily through a specific form of anxiety known as mathematics (math) anxiety. Mathematics anxiety is common among psychology students. Those with higher levels of mathematics anxiety tend to do worse in statistics. This is more important in this context than trait or general anxiety which is when someone has a generally anxious personality in all sorts of situations. To be sure, mathematical ability is associated with better test and examination results, but not to a major extent. Poor mathematical ability has its influence largely because it is associated with increased levels of mathematical anxiety. That is, in itself, poor mathematical ability is not primarily a cause of worse results.

If more research evidence is needed, using a formal measure known as the Survey of Attitudes toward Statistics, Zimprich (2012) showed that attitudes towards statistics are made up of four components:

- Affect: How positive or negative a student is about statistics such as liking the subject.

- Cognitive competence: A student's beliefs about their ability and competence to do statistics

- Value: Attitudes concerning the relevance and usefulness of statistics such as using statistics in everyday life.

- Difficulty: The student's views about how difficult or easy statistics is.

Every one of these were interrelated, as one might expect. They also correlated with actual achievement in statistics. These attitudes were much more important than actual maths ability in terms of how well students do in statistics. In other words, how a student feels about statistics has a far more tangible effect on their performance in statistical tests and examinations than their mathematical ability. The lack of relationship between maths and statistics ability applies also to other aspects of studying for a psychology degree. Bourne (2018) investigated whether various mathematical abilities were related to performance on a British psychology degree. There was little relationship between maths ability and performance on the research component of the degree. One exception was that good graphical abilities were related to marks on aspects of research methods but only in the first year of study. Otherwise there was no relationship.

Along with others, we would argue that the level of mathematical ability needed to cope with the mathematical part of statistics is not great – fairly minimal in fact. Mostly, though, the statistical analyses you need are available on SPSS and other statistics programs. Generally speaking, rarely will you need to do calculations by hand and then these are usually simple. Often you will find websites which will calculate the few things which SPSS does not do. Diligence in making sure that your data has been correctly entered plus some knowledge of the appropriate statistical analysis are the important things. Some basic mathematics is helpful in that numbers and symbols can be daunting, at first. Statistics is a maths-based discipline and its concepts are generally defined by formulae rather than words. So if you are good at understanding mathematical formulae then this is an advantage, though far from necessary. Professional researchers differ widely in their mathematical skills and many do not regard themselves as at all mathematical. Yet they have learned to use statistics appropriately and intelligently, which is very much the task facing students. You need to understand the purpose of a statistical test and why it was developed, understand a little about how it works, know when to use it and most of all be able to make sense of the computer output. Maths is peripheral for the most part.

If you understand the concepts of addition, subtraction, multiplication and division then you have the basics for coping with statistics. You may not always get the right answer but the important thing is that you understand what these mathematical operations do. What might you need beyond this? Probably just the following:

- You need to understand the concept of squaring (that is multiplying a number by itself).

- You need to understand the concept of square root (the square root of a number is that number which when multiplied by itself gives the original number).

- It is good too if you understand negative numbers – such as that when multiplying two negative numbers you get a positive number but when you multiply a positive number by a negative number then the result is a negative number. A short time spent trying out positive and negative calculations on a calculator is a good way to refresh yourself of these basics.

- It is preferable if you understand the underlying principles or 'rules' governing mathematical formulae as these are used in statistical formulae, but if you don't, your computer does.

Little else is necessary – if you know what a logarithm is then you are in the ultra-advanced class. All in all, the requirements are not very demanding. Anything that has been forgotten or never learned will be quickly picked up by a motivated student. Not all lecturers will share this opinion. Nevertheless, the overwhelming majority know that students can really struggle with statistics for any number of reasons. So they provide teaching which serves the needs of all students taking the psychology programme, not just the maths-able ones. Interestingly, research suggests that the more approachable the statistics lecturer is the less statistics anxiety manifested by their students (Tonsing, 2018).

1.4   The importance of understanding research designs

Broadly speaking, different research designs require different statistical techniques. So a fundamental requirement is that you appreciate the different kinds of research design and what they can achieve. Statistical problems in research are often fundamentally research design problems. You really do have to formulate your research question, your hypotheses and your research design carefully for the statistical analysis to fall into place. If you don't have confidence that your research design is capable of addressing your research question, statistics cannot redress the problem. As you study statistics, you should gradually see ever more clearly that most statistical techniques are appropriate for particular research designs. For example, analysis of variance statistics are ideally suited to analysing randomised experiments.

Every degree course will give you a grounding in research methods and how research is done. But such knowledge will not translate directly into an ability to do research. This is developed through practical or lab classes in which you experience the process of doing research. Although research skills build up quite slowly over the course of your degree, these skills are little or nothing to do with mathematics. They are about the application of logic and thought to the research process. That is why being comfortable with your ability to design valid research comes before being able to choose suitable statistics. If you are confused about your research question, your hypotheses and your research design, it follows that you will be confused about the appropriate statistical analysis. So statistical analysis takes a minor role compared to the more general research skills involved in a quantitative study. You will find that once you can identify the type of research design you are using, the task of choosing appropriate statistical techniques for its analysis becomes almost self-evident.

1.5   Positive about statistics

It is clear that having a negative attitude towards statistics, although somewhat understandable, is counterproductive in many ways. Many of your fellow students will feel much the same. Professional researchers often make little claim to having any statistical expertise (Aksentijevic, 2015) but they still do excellent work. Nevertheless, it is important to deal with bad study techniques in relation to statistics such as avoiding or day dreaming through lectures. So how is it possible to be positive about statistics? Having an appreciation of what statistics contributes will help. Just why did statistics become so important in modern research when for centuries people did experiments and other research without statistics procedures such as significance testing? One of the most well-known statistical techniques used by psychologists is the *t*-test (see Chapters 13 and 14) or the Student *t*-test as it is also known. For decades, psychology students have learned to do the *t*-test. Student was the pen name of William Gosset who had studied chemistry and mathematics at university. He was employed by the Guinness Brewery in Dublin as a 'bright young thing' in the 1890s.

Quality control was important to the company. Obvious practical problems would follow if every bottle or barrel of beer had to be tested perhaps to see if the alcoholic strength was constant. One solution would have been to use just a small number of samples. Gosset worked on the extent of error likely to occur when sampling is employed and developed a mathematical way of calculating the likely error. For example, if a sample of just 10 bottles is taken, to what extent are these likely to mislead quality controllers about the alcoholic strength of the product in general?

Of course, you will never know from a sample exactly what the error will be but Gosset was able to estimate the likely error from the variability within the sample of bottles. Put into a formula, this is the idea of standard error which plagues many students on introductory statistics courses for countless decades. The *t*-test is based on standard error. Gosset had laid down a systematic basis for research to use samples rather than everything. Think about it: if it had not been for Gosset's innovation then you would spend your lifetime carrying out your first research study simply because you need to test everyone or everything (the population).

So rather than considering William Gosset as some sort of alien, would it not be better to see him as one of the statistical cuddly friends we mentioned earlier?!

■ Is it statistically significant?

The point of Gosset's revolutionary ideas is probably easy to see when explained in this way. But instead students are introduced to what to them are rather complex formulae and the question 'Are your findings statistically significant?' The question 'Is it significant?' is one of the fixations of many psychologists – the question probably sounds like a mantra to students when they first begin to study psychology. So intrusive is the question that for most students, statistics in psychology is about knowing what test of statistical significance to apply to their data. A test of statistical significance merely addresses the possibility that a trend that we find in our sample might have occurred by chance when there is no trend in reality. That is, how likely is it that the trend is simply the result of a fortuitous selection of a sample which appears to show a trend? (A trend might be, say, athletes scoring more highly on a measure of personal ambition than non-athletes or a relationship between a measure of ability to speak foreign languages and a measure of sociability.) But significance testing is only a small part of statistics, which provides a whole range of tools to help researchers (and students) address the practical problems of data analysis. Over the years, psychology has been criticised for the way statistics is used. A central focus of the criticism is the fixation of significance testing.

■ What sample size do I need?

Gosset's focus on small samples begs the question of how small a sample can be used. There would be something perverse about planning research which involved a sample size so small that our findings could never be statistically significant. But that is done inadvertently all of the time simply because researchers (including students) do not address the question of sample size properly. Often the advice given to those asking what sample size to use is that they should get as big a sample as they can. But this is a crude way of going about deciding sample size. Even the smallest trend will be statistically significant if the sample size is large enough. However, there is little point in using large samples when smaller ones would be adequate. The optimum sample size depends on the size of the effect the researcher thinks is worthwhile investigating, the statistical significance level required and the risk of not supporting the hypothesis when it is in fact true that the researcher is prepared to take. There are conventional values for the latter two but the researcher may wish to vary these.

There are no objective criteria which tell us what potential size of effect is worth studying which apply irrespective of circumstances. It might appear obvious that research should prioritise large trends but it is not as simple as that. In medical research, for instance, there are examples of very small trends which nevertheless save lives. Taking aspirin has a small effect on reducing the risk of heart attacks but saves lives in aspirin takers compared with a control group. The size of a trend worth the research effort therefore depends on what is being considered. A pill which prevents cancer in 10% of people would be of more interest than a pill which prevents flatulence in 10% of people, for example. So if a researcher designs a study which has a sample size too low to establish a statistically significant trend then this would be more worrisome in the case of the cancer cure than the flatulence cure. Chapter 39 explains how to go about deciding sample size in a considered, rational way. This area of statistics is known as *statistical power analysis*. So the apparently simple question of the sample size needed is rather more complex than at first appears.

This is not the place to give a full overview of the role of statistics in psychological research. It is important, though, to stress that statistics can help research in many ways.

researchers face in their quantitative research. Now this book is just about as comprehensive as understandable statistics texts get but not everything that statistics can do is represented. Nevertheless, you will find a great deal which goes far beyond the issue of statistical significance. Take, for example, factor analysis (Chapter 33). This is not at all about statistical significance but a way of finding or identifying the basic dimensions in your data. So, for example, many famous theories of personality and theories of intelligence have emerged out of factor analysis – for instance, the work of Hans Eysenck (Eysenck & Eysenck, 1976). This suggests that extraversion, neuroticism and psychoticism are the major underlying dimensions or components of personality on which people differ. There is no way that a researcher can simply look at their data, which can be enormously complex, and decide what its underlying structure is. It is not possible to identify extraversion, neuroticism and psychoticism simply by looking at the scores from a 50-item questionnaire that has been completed by 2000 participants. Nevertheless, statisticians (and psychologists) developed factor analysis as a method of doing just that.

Statistics also has a very important role in model building. This sounds complicated but it isn't too difficult. A model is simply a proposed set of relationships between variables. So, for instance, the relationships shown in Figure 1.3 between various characteristics of students studying statistics and their achievement in tests and examinations is a sort of model. Statistics addresses just how well the data fits the proposed model – there may be other characteristics of students to be considered in addition to those in Figure 1.3 to fully account for how well students do in statistics. The researcher may propose models but, equally, statistical techniques can also suggest them.

Some of the other things which statistics can help you with include:

- Is the trend that I have just found in my data big or small?

- Does this line of research show potential for further development?

- Are the measures that I am using sufficiently reliable and valid to detect a trend that I am interested in?

- Is it possible to amalgamate a number of variables into a single, more readily understood one?

- Can I eliminate competing explanations of my findings so as to give more credence to my hypothesis?

- How best can I present my data graphically in order to visually present my findings to an audience at a conference?

- Can I combine the findings of different studies so as to have a good idea of the typical findings of past research?

Statistics is just one aspect of the decision-making processes which underlie psychological research. It should not dominate a researcher's thinking exclusively. It is not even the most important part of research. But without it your decision-making may be sub-optimal.

1.6   What statistics can't do

Years of experience teaching statistics means, of course, that we were the statistics doctors that students having problems with their data analysis data came to – or even got sent to. These encounters vary widely. Some students appear to want help but really they are seeking confirmation that their ideas for their analysis are correct or that they have understood their data correctly. Yet others have designed their research so badly that either it is difficult to analyse at all or it is difficult to analyse using the statistics that the student knows at this point. A few students

Don't blame your poor lack of statistical knowledge when it is your research design which is at fault. Some research designs simply cannot address certain research questions. It is easy to get into a muddle so try to think carefully about what your research design can achieve prior to collecting data. Always ask yourself just how you will go about addressing your research questions with the data you are collecting. This requires pinpoint clarity as to what your research question is. You may find this difficult but a lack of statistical knowledge is not the reason for this.

You do need to plan research as early as you possibly can if you are to avoid the risk of confusions like these. Approaching deadlines for research proposal submission should not be the signal to start planning. This is likely to result in a research plan which you are less than clear about. That is why it is a good idea to pencil in the steps in your analysis even before you have collected any data. Just how will you go about doing your analysis? You could make up some data to insert into your data spreadsheet and then do the analysis on this. What tables would you need? What statistical techniques would be employed? But the temptation to leave the statistics until last in the hope that something or someone will come to your rescue can be overwhelming. However, such pre-planning would pay off when you have collected your actual data. You will know exactly what you need to do.

So some students may be unclear about their proposed research. The sooner they can sort their thoughts out the better. Confusion can be caused by trying to achieve too much in one study so do not be too ambitious about the scope of your research. However, insufficient preparation may also be responsible. It is difficult for any of us to be clear about our ideas without investing the time to think carefully. You should talk to anyone prepared to listen. There is no quicker way of recognising problems with your research proposals than finding yourself unable to explain clearly to a friend or lecturer just what you intend to do or how the data you collect will help answer the research question. The message is that you should try to identify the real problem which is the cause of the grief that you are experiencing.

Few researchers, if any, are trailblazers generating ideas and methods which have no bearing on what has gone before. Often there is a wealth of available research which will be of enormous benefit to you as you plan your research. For example, just how is it possible to measure 'love', religious beliefs, preferences and so forth? In all likelihood others have thought long and hard about these. Ignore what they have written at your peril. Past research helps you decide what the appropriate research designs are for research like yours. Similarly, you will see what statistical techniques were used to analyse data which are not dissimilar to yours? This is not to suggest that you slavishly follow what others have done but that you build on their achievements. Copious reading is required. This can be hard, and time consuming. Gradually your reading will pick up speed. You will learn what is essential to read through experience but sometimes this will include hard bits. Simply concocting a research proposal on the back of an envelope without the necessary spade work is far more difficult and risky than building upon past research.

1.7   Easing the way

Is there an easy way of learning statistics? Yes and no is the answer – we are psychologists after all. It clearly would take much effort to become a specialist in statistics developing statistical knowledge and theory. However, it is far less demanding to achieve a working knowledge of statistics as opposed to expertise. Using statistics correctly and effectively, but no more than that, is an achievable target for most of us. This is not cheating in any way. You don't need to know all of the intricacies of a car's mechanics to drive it and you don't need a degree in electronics to use your mobile phone.

One problem learning statistics is misleading or unhelpful advice from those around you.

statistical knowledge around. Many psychologists obtained much of their statistical knowledge when they were students. This may have been state-of-the-art then (though we suspect not) and has not been brought up to date since by some of them. Survey research on psychology degrees in the USA has shown the statistics teaching to be somewhat moribund and stuck on older ideas (Friedrich, Childress, & Cheng, 2018). Being obsessed with statistical significance is a good example but others include the following in our experience:

- *Many statistical tests require that your data are normally distributed* This means that your data should follow a bell-shaped distribution curve (known as the normal curve). The problem is that this assumption was built into working out the formulae for the statistics. However, even though this assumption may not be met, the test may still do an adequate job. Few psychologists know the extent to which assumptions may be violated without materially altering the value of the test. Even if your data violate a test's assumptions there are ways of dealing with this. For example, you could try bootstrapping versions (see Chapter 21). In bootstrapping, many random samples are taken from your data and the distribution of samples is based on these, not on a theoretical distribution. SPSS will calculate statistical tests using bootstrapping if requested.

- *There are three types of scores – ordinal (rankable), interval and ratio* These can be differentiated conceptually (see Chapter 2) but rarely can a psychologist say to which category their scores belong. Students struggle to differentiate the three and, not surprisingly, they fail but see the problem lying in the futility of the task. The distinction is practically ubiquitous in statistics textbooks. However, for nearly every purpose these three different types of data can be analysed using the same statistics. Worrying too much about the sort of scores you have can be counterproductive given that there is little practical consequence in terms of the analysis. Nominal data is materially different and consists of frequencies of cases in different named categories. The categories are not scores.

- *If your data do not meet the assumptions that the data are normally distributed, then you need a distribution free (or nonparametric) test* There are a number of problems with this. One is that nonparametric tests are not as versatile and effective as the parametric tests which assume the data are bell-shaped in distribution overall. That is, there may be no substitute to use when your data do not meet the parametric assumptions. The second problem is that it is not necessarily true that a nonparametric test works better than a parametric test when the latter's requirements are not met. Thirdly, bear in mind the first bullet point above and consider using bootstrapping methods. Tests of normality of the distribution are frequently missing in published research. We explain how these tests can be done in Chapter 5, however.

These are just examples which will make more sense when you read later chapters.

The reverse sort of problem arises when psychologists fail to exercise caution when they really ought to. A good example of this is the analysis of variance. In this, things called main effects and interactions are sought. But great care is needed since the technique prioritises finding main effects and interactions are secondary. What this means is that interactions may be subsumed by main effects when a little common sense would show that the main effects are really interactions. Details are in Chapter 25.

The point is that the environment in which students learn statistics is an intrinsically confusing one. There is a good chance that for one reason or another students will be exposed to mixed messages about statistics. Curiously, the fact that there may be several distinct but appropriate ways of analysing the same data adds to the difficulty. So students may find it difficult to know which statistical test to apply since they have been given superficially different advice. So when we explain that the *t*-test and the correlation coefficient yield fundamentally the same answer when they are applied to the same data, this

1.8   What do I need to know to be an effective user of statistics?

So what really needs to be known in order to use statistics effectively? The essentials have nothing to do with mathematics: they concern basic concepts in research. If you can apply these key ideas to your data then the statistical analysis usually follows from that. Statistical procedures all have limits to where and when they are applicable. These limitations largely concern the nature of the research design or the data. There are statistical techniques which are used for related designs and statistical techniques which are used for nominal data. So choosing an appropriate statistical analysis requires recognising the essential features of your research design – what sort of research design you have. Most of what you need to know is probably covered by the following list:

● The difference between a score and a category variable. Overwhelmingly psychologists use score variables.

  ● Score variables are ones which imply a quantity of something. An IQ of 120 implies something quantitatively different from an IQ of 80. Most psychological tests give quantitative scores, for example.

  ● Categorical variables (category variables or nominal variables) are ones where the categories have no implications of quantity. For example, male versus female is a category variable which we would refer to as gender. Similarly, Manchester United Football Supporter, Liverpool Football Supporter and Chelsea Football Supporter is also a category variable which we might refer to as football team supporter. This sort of data usually consists of the frequency (total number) of people (or things) which fall into each category. So the data might be 50 Manchester United supporters, 23 Liverpool supporters and 70 Chelsea supporters, for example.

  ● It is important to classify each of your variables as scores or category (categorical) variables. This allows you to decide the possible statistical techniques. Some statistical techniques work only for scores, some work only for category variables, and others use both. (Very occasionally, a category variable may be treated as a score variable but for now that is too sophisticated – it is explained in Chapter 41.)

● Almost without exception, score variables in psychology simply indicate increasing quantities of something. Although many psychology students have anguished over whether their variables are on what they call a ratio or equal interval scale, it is almost always impossible to say things like 'Jean is twice as intelligent as John' which implies a ratio scale. (This is discussed more in Chapter 2.) Statistically, these issues do not matter. As we pointed out earlier, the problem is that deciding what sort of scores you have is beset with difficulties and is a hopeless task. It is a total conundrum which is perplexing and unnecessary. The important thing to remember is that, almost without exception, it is impossible to claim that scores on variables can be expressed as ratios of each other. That is, it is meaningless to claim that one person is twice as, three times as, half as, etc. intelligent, sociable, withdrawn or whatever as another person. If you avoid making such claims, you won't go far wrong.

● The difference between a related and an unrelated research design. Related designs tend to be more efficient in terms of data but are less common in psychology. In a related design, people are measured twice (or more) using a particular measure or alternative versions of the same measure. So studies where people are measured at two or more different points in time are related designs. There is one slight complication. When groups are matched by having pairs of people who are similar on a measure or measures this is also a related design. In unrelated designs, each person is measured just once on each variable and no matching is attempted. Some designs are mixed related and unrelated designs (e.g. see

as efficient as it could be. This is a key matter of psychological methodology and does not involve statistics as such but your understanding of research designs.

So, there we are, statistics is a challenge for most students but it should be less of a challenge than it first appears to be. If we take the analogy that learning statistics has a lot in common with learning a foreign language then a few things become more clear. We do not expect to learn a foreign language well in just a few lessons. However, we do expect that we can do some basic communication very quickly. We also may think that we recognise some of the words in the foreign language which is statistics but we should be careful as their meaning may not be the same as in our everyday language. We will not learn a foreign language unless we use it as much as possible – so do not be shy about talking about your statistical analyses to other people. When we know something of a foreign language then we can understand a lot more than we can actually speak. In statistics, we can understand the elements of new techniques even though they are very advanced. This may be enough for most psychologists in most circumstances.

1.9   A few words about SPSS

SPSS is a statistical package which is very familiar to psychologists worldwide. It is not the only package but it does most things that you are likely to need. So it is generally good news about SPSS and students. The Windows system of drop-down menus, etc. is instantly recognisable. Most students are well used to using computers without needing detailed instruction manuals. If you get it wrong then no harm is done and you can quickly try alternatives to see what button pressing works and what does not. For this reason, we could encourage everyone to adopt an exploratory approach to computing statistics with SPSS. Competence will quickly build up and you will automatically know what button does what. Although we have provided step-by-step instructions for many statistical procedures along with a number of screenshots, we have kept these down to a reasonable and manageable number. Explore to see what SPSS has available and where to find it. There are numerous drop-down menus which give you many options. Choose a different option just to see what happens. Of course, there are times when you need to be pointed in the right direction. Sometimes it is not obvious where a particular procedure is to be found on SPSS. So step-by-step instructions save a lot of frustration on occasion. But mechanically following step-by-step instructions all of the time slows down becoming a skilled user of SPSS and understanding what its output means yourself. At some stage the tightrope walker needs to abandon the safety net. As a psychology student, you will use only a fraction of what is available on SPSS.

All statistics teaching in psychology involves the use of SPSS or some other statistical package. SPSS is very widely available in universities and many other places. Yet it does have some weak points and does not always provide the statistics that you need. Even then, often SPSS provides the important steps which you just substitute into a formula. Since this book is about learning a practical working knowledge of statistics, the statistical technique is the primary thing for us. So we include some procedures that are not available on SPSS. Sometimes there is alternative software available from the web and other times you will find websites which will do the calculation for you. Use your favourite search engine to track these down – for example, try *t*-test calculator and see what you come up with. We found lots.

The major downside of statistics programs like SPSS is that although they have almost eliminated the labour and frustration of hand-calculations, they have raised the stakes in terms of the demands on the statistical analysis. They have made it possible for almost anyone to use statistical techniques which were scarcely considered by researchers in the past. So the researcher has to understand a wider range of statistical techniques and ideas than ever. As a consequence, students have more to learn about. This does mean facing up to one's statistics demons, though these probably will not be too scary if you only just try.

1.10   Quick guide to the book's procedures and statistical tests

Table 1.1 provides you with an overview of procedures and statistical tests covered in this book should you want to skip to the chapter or chapters that you think are most relevant to your needs or interests.

Table 1.1	Major types of analysis and suggested SPSS procedures		
Type/purpose of analysis	**Suggested procedures**	**Chapter**	**SPSS options**
1. Descriptive statistics			
Displaying data for a single variable in tables and diagrams	Frequency table	3, pp. 34–35	Analyze, Descriptive Statistics, Frequencies. . . , pp. 42–43
	Pie chart, bar chart, histogram	3, pp. 36–41	
Displaying data for two or more variables in tables and diagrams	Crosstabulation or contingency table	7, pp. 92–98	Analyze, Tables, Custom Tables. . . , pp. 99–101
	Graph, compound clustered and stacked bar chart and histogram		Graphs, Chart Builder. . . or Legacy Dialogs, pp. 99–101
	Scattergram	8, pp. 103–111	Graphs, Chart Builder. . . , pp. 120–121
Displaying distribution shape of scores	Frequency and histogram distributions	5, pp. 63–71	Analyze, Descriptive Statistics, Frequencies. . . , pp. 73–74
			Graphs, Chart Builder. . . or Legacy Dialogs, pp. 73–74
Determining central tendency and dispersion	Means, medians, mode, range, interquartile range, variance	4, pp. 48–58	Analyze, Descriptive Statistics, Frequencies. . . , pp. 60–61
Determining standard deviation	Standard deviation of score variable	6, pp. 76–80	Analyze, Descriptive Statistics, Descriptives. . . , pp. 88–89
Determining standard error	Standard error of score variable	12, pp. 154–163	Analyze, Descriptive Statistics, Descriptives. . . , pp. 164–165
Standardising scores	Standardised or z-scores	6, pp. 80–86	Analyze, Descriptive Statistics, Descriptives. . . , pp. 88–89
2. Frequency variables			
Comparing frequencies for one unrelated categorical variable	One-way chi-square	18, pp. 237–238	Analyze, Nonparametric Tests, Legacy Dialogs, Chi-square. . . , pp. 241–243
Comparing frequencies for two unrelated categorical variables	Chi-square	18, pp. 226–235	Analyze, Descriptive Statistics, Crosstabs. . . , pp. 241–243
Comparing frequencies for two unrelated categorical variables with some low expected frequencies	Fisher test	18, pp. 236–238	Analyze, Descriptive Statistics, Crosstabs. . . , pp. 241–243
Comparing frequencies for two related categorical variables	McNemar chi-square test	18, pp. 239	Analyze, Nonparametric Tests, Legacy Dialogs, 2 Related Samples. . . , pp. 241–243
Comparing frequencies for three or more unrelated categorical variables	Loglinear analysis	40, pp. 584–604	Analyze, Loglinear, Model Selection. . . , pp. 606–607
Finding predictors for a category variable with two categories	Binomial logistic regression	42, pp. 627–639	Analyze, Regression, Binary Logistic. . . , pp. 641–642
Finding predictors for a category variable with more than two categories	Multinomial logistic regression	41, pp. 610–623	Analyze, Regression, Multinomial Logistic. . . , pp. 624–625
3. Score variables			
3.1.1 Determining agreement among two or more raters	Kappa coefficient	37, pp. 529–533	Analyze, Descriptive Statistics, Crosstabs. . . , pp. 534–535

Type/purpose of analysis	Suggested procedures	Chapter	SPSS options
3.1.2 Determining the internal reliability of a measure:			
of all components of a measure	Cronbach's alpha reliability	37, pp. 526–528	Analyze, Scale, Reliability Analysis…, pp. 534–535
of all components when split into two halves	Split-half reliability	37, pp. 525–526	Analyze, Scale, Reliability Analysis…, pp. 534–535
3.1.3 Determining the factorial structure or dimensionality of a measure	Principal components analysis	32, pp. 445–462	Analyze, Dimension Reduction, Factor…, pp. 464–465
3.2. Correlating score and/or dichotomous variables			
Assessing the linear relationship between two score variable, one score variable and one binary variables or two binary variables	Pearson correlation coefficient	8, pp. 104–113 11, pp. 145–155	Analyze, Correlate, Bivariate…, pp. 118–119; 156–157
Assessing the linear relationship between two ranked score variables	Spearman correlation coefficient	8, pp. 113–116 11, pp. 145–155	Analyze, Correlate, Bivariate…, pp. 118–119; 156–157
Eliminating one or more variables from a Pearson correlation coefficient	Partial correlation	32, pp. 432–440	Analyze, Correlate, Partial…, pp. 441–443
3.3. Predicting one score from another score	Simple regression	9, pp. 123–132	Analyze, Regression, Linear…, pp. 133–134
3.4. Determining variance in one score variable accounted for by two or more predictor variables			
Finding the smallest number of predictors which best predict a score variable	Stepwise multiple regression	34, pp. 475–479	Analyze, Regression, Linear…, pp. 481–483
Finding which of a number of predictors best predict a score variable	Standard or simultaneous multiple regression	34, pp. 468–474	Analyze, Regression, Linear…, pp. 481–483
Finding if one predictor mediates the relation between one predictor and a score variable	Standard or simultaneous multiple regression	34, pp. 468–474	Analyze, Regression, Linear…, pp. 481–483
Finding whether the prediction of the score variable is affected by the order in which the predictors are placed	Hierarchical multiple regression	34, p. 472	Analyze, Regression, Linear…, pp. 497–498
Testing interaction or moderator effects for continuous predictors of a score variable	Hierarchical multiple regression	38, pp. 541–551	Analyze, Regression, Linear…, pp. 556–557
3.5. Determining differences in one score variable between two groups			
Comparing non-normally distributed data for two unrelated groups	Mann–Whitney *U*-test	21, pp. 264–266	Analyze, Nonparametric Tests, Legacy Dialogs, 2 Independent Samples…, pp. 268–270
Comparing non-normally distributed data for two related groups	Sign test	21, pp. 260–261	Analyze, Nonparametric Tests, Legacy Dialogs, 2 Related Samples…, pp. 268–270
	Wilcoxon matched pairs test	21, pp. 262–264	Analyze, Nonparametric Tests, Legacy Dialogs, 2 Related Samples…, pp. 268–270
Comparing two unrelated sets of scores for differences	Unrelated *t*-test	14, pp. 181–192	Analyze, Compare Means, Independent-Samples T Test…, pp. 194–196
Comparing two related sets of scores for differences	Related *t*-test	13, pp. 167–176	Analyze, Compare Means, Paired-Samples T Test…, pp. 178–179
Comparing two variances	*F*-ratio test	22, pp. 274–278	Analyze, Compare Means, Means…, pp. 280–281

Type/purpose of analysis	Suggested procedures	Chapter	SPSS options
3.6. Determining differences in one score variable between two or more groups			
Comparing non-normally distributed data for three or more unrelated groups	Kruskal–Wallis	Appendix B2, pp. 658–660	Analyze, Nonparametric Tests, Legacy Dialogs, K Independent Samples. . . , pp. 662–663
Comparing non-normally distributed data for three or more related groups	Friedman's test	Appendix B2, pp. 660–661	Analyze, Nonparametric Tests, Legacy Dialogs, K Related Samples. . . , pp. 662–663
Comparing one dependent variable in three or more unrelated groups	Unrelated one-way analysis of variance (ANOVA)	23, pp. 283–296	Analyze, Compare Means, One-Way ANOVA. . . , pp. 297–299
Comparing means of two unrelated groups when more than two groups	Multiple comparisons	26, pp. 343–348	Analyze, General Linear Model and Univariate. . . , pp. 350–352
Comparing one dependent variable in three or more related groups	Related one-way analysis of variance (ANOVA) or repeated measures	24, pp. 301–311	Analyze, General Linear Model, Repeated Measures. . . , pp. 313–314
Comparing one dependent variable in two or more unrelated variables	Unrelated two-way analysis of variance (ANOVA)	25, pp. 316–337	Analyze, General Linear Model, Univariate. . . , pp. 339–341
Comparing one dependent variable in one related and one unrelated variable	Mixed two-way analysis of variance (ANOVA)	27, pp. 354–366	Analyze, General Linear Model, Repeated Measures. . . , pp. 376–378
Comparing one dependent variable in one or more unrelated variables while controlling for one or more related variables	One-way analysis of covariance (ANCOVA)	28, pp. 371–381	Analyze, General Linear Model, Univariate. . . , pp. 383–385
3.7. Determining differences in two or more score variables between two or more groups			
Comparing two or more dependent variables on two or more independent variables	Multivariate analysis of variance (MANOVA)	29, pp. 387–397	Analyze, General Linear Model, Multivariate. . . , pp. 399–401
Determining variables best discriminating two or more groups	Discriminant function analysis	30, pp. 403–412	Analyze, Classify, Discriminant. . . , pp. 413–414
4. Determining sample size	Power analysis	39, pp. 558–580	
5. Averaging effect sizes	Meta-analysis	36, pp. 503–521	
6. Recoding groups for multiple comparison tests		31	File, New, Syntax, p. 426–427
7. Recoding values	Recoding old values into new values	3, pp. 38–40	Transform, Recode into Different Variables. . . , pp. 44–45
8. Selecting subsamples	Selecting if	31	Data, Select Cases. . . , pp. 424–425
9. Selecting a random sample		10, pp. 138–141	Data, Select Cases. . . , pp. 142–143

Key points

- Statistics is a difficult topic for most students but an essential part of psychological research.

- The difficulties in learning statistics are more to do with attitudes towards the subject and beliefs about one's own mathematical abilities than actual ability levels. So a basic understanding of the positive contribution that statistics makes to psychological research is helpful as is a realistically low expectation of the mathematical demands that learning statistics imposes.

• A sound working knowledge of statistics involves a basic understanding of the workings of the statistical technique in question together with the computational skills needed to execute this technique. Ignoring the first of these components will not help you to become competent in statistics.

COMPUTER ANALYSIS

SPSS Analyze, Graphs and Transform drop-down menus

Options for conducting statistics are initially selected from the 'Analyze' drop-down menu (Screenshot 1.1). The first option on this menu is 'Reports' and the last option is 'Spatial and Temporal Modeling. . . '. The right-pointing arrowheads on the right of options indicate further options on sub-menus. So, for 'Compare Means' the first option on the sub-menu is 'Means. . . ' and the last one is 'One-Way ANOVA. . . ' (Screenshot 1.1). Options for graphs are at first selected from the 'Graphs' drop-down menu (Screenshot 1.2). The first option on this list is 'Chart Builder. . . ' and the last one is 'Legacy Dialogs' (see Chapters 8 and 5, respectively). Options for changing or transforming data are firstly selected from the 'Transform' drop-down menu (Screenshot 1.3). The first option on this list is 'Compute Variable. . . ' and the last option is 'Random Number Generators. . . '. The options you are most likely to use on this menu are 'Compute Variable. . . ' and 'Recode into Different Variables. . . ' (see Chapter 3).

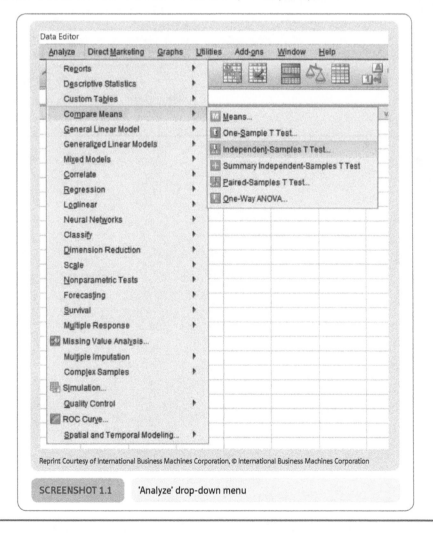

Reprint Courtesy of International Business Machines Corporation, © International Business Machines Corporation

SCREENSHOT 1.1   'Analyze' drop-down menu

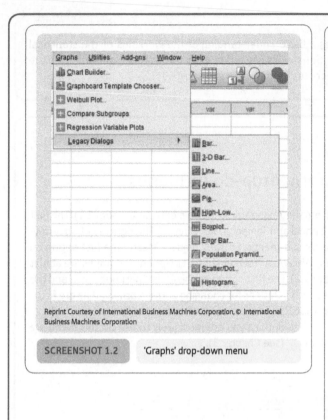

Reprint Courtesy of International Business Machines Corporation, © International Business Machines Corporation

SCREENSHOT 1.2   'Graphs' drop-down menu

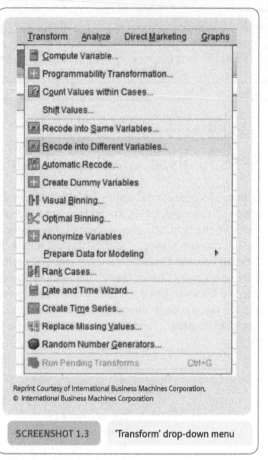

Reprint Courtesy of International Business Machines Corporation, © International Business Machines Corporation

SCREENSHOT 1.3   'Transform' drop-down menu

PART 1

Descriptive statistics

CHAPTER 2

Some basics

Variability and measurement

Overview

- Statistics can be used to describe our data but also assess what reliance can be placed on information based on samples.

- A variable is any concept that we can measure which varies between individuals or cases.

- Classify variables as score (also known as numerical) variables or nominal (also known as category, categorical and qualitative) variables.

- Nominal variables consist of named categories whereas score variables are measured in the form of a numerical scale which indicates the quantity of the variable.

- Formal measurement theory identifies more variable types – nominal, ordinal, interval and ratio. But ordinal, interval and ratio measurements are practically impossible categories to apply.

2.1 Introduction

Imagine a world where everything is the same: people are identical in all respects. They wear identical clothes; they eat the same meals; they are all the same height from birth; they all go to the same school with identical teachers, identical lessons and identical facilities; they all go on holiday in the same month; they all do the same job; they all live in identical houses; and the sun shines every day. There are no sexes so everyone self-reproduces at the age of 30; their gardens have the same plants and the soil is exactly the same no matter whose garden; they all die on their 85th birthdays and are all buried in the same wooden boxes in identical plots of land. They are all equally clever and they all have identical personalities. Their genetic make-up never varies. Mathematically speaking all of these characteristics are constants. If this world seems less than realistic then have we got news for you – you need statistics! Only in a world of standardisation would you not need statistics – in a richly varying world statistics is essential.

If nothing varies, then everything that is to be known about people could be based on a single person. No problems would arise in generalising since what is true of Tracy Green is true of everyone else – they're all called Tracy Green after all. Fortunately, variability is an essential characteristic of life and the social world in which we exist. The sheer quantity of variability has to be tamed when trying to make statements about the real world. Statistics is largely about making sense of variability.

Statistical techniques perform four main functions:

1. They provide ways of summarising the information that we collect from a multitude of sources. Statistics is partly about tabulating your research information or data as clearly and effectively as possible. As such, it merely describes the information collected. This is achieved using tables and diagrams and simple formulae which turn fairly complex data into simple numerical indexes (such as the average) describing numerically the data's main features. This branch of statistics is called descriptive statistics for very obvious reasons. The first few chapters of this book are largely devoted to descriptive statistics.

2. Another branch of statistics is far less familiar to most of us: *inferential statistics*. This branch of statistics is really about economy of effort in research. There was a time when in order to find out about people, for example, everyone in the country would be contacted in order to collect information. This is done today when the government conducts a *census* of everyone in order to find out about the population of the country at a particular time. This is an enormous, time-consuming operation and so infrequent. Everyone now is familiar with relatively small *samples* being used to estimate the information coming from studying everyone. This is common in public-opinion surveying where the answers of a sample of 1000 or so people may be used, say, to predict the outcome of a national election. Although samples can sometimes mislead, the principle of sampling is universally accepted important. *Inferential statistics* is about the confidence with which we can generalise from a sample to the entire population (see Photo 2.1).

3. The amount of data that a researcher can collect is potentially massive. Some statistical techniques enable the researcher to clarify trends in vast quantities of data using a number of powerful methods. Data simplification, data exploration and data reduction are among the names given to the process. Whatever the name, the objective is the same – to make sense of large amounts of data that otherwise would be much too confusing. These *data exploration techniques* are mainly dealt with in the later chapters of this book.

4. The advent of the digital age has resulted in incredible quantities of data being generated on a daily basis. For example, Facebook and Twitter produce information in great quantities which is pertinent to issues such as public opinion and social interaction.

PHOTO 2.1   People vary in very obvious ways but they also vary in terms of their psychological characteristics. Just what would a small sample of people such as this tell us about the bigger crowd? (Photo: HishamIbrahim/Stockbyte/Getty Images)

statistical techniques which can cope better than traditional approaches. This sort of data is known as *big data* and the appropriate analytic methods as *data mining*. We briefly introduce these in Chapter 43.

2.2   Variables and measurement

The concept of a *variable* is basic but vitally important in statistics. It is also as easy as pie. *A variable is anything that varies and can be measured.* These measurements need *not* correspond very well with everyday notions of measurement such as weight, distance and temperature. So the gender of a person is a variable since it can be measured as either male or female, for example – and gender varies among people. Similarly, eye colour is a variable because a set of people will include some with brown eyes, some with blue eyes and some with green eyes. Thus measurement can merely involve categorisation. Clinical psychologists might use different diagnostic categories such as schizophrenia, bipolar disorder and anxiety in research. These diagnostic categories constitute a variable since they are different mental and emotional states to which people can be allocated. Such categorisation techniques are an important type of measurement in statistics.

Another type of measurement in statistics is more directly akin to everyday concepts of

to variables such as weight, length, distance, temperature and the like – for example, 10 kilometres or 30 degrees. These numerical values are often called *scores*. In psychological research many variables are measured and *quantified* in much the same way. Good examples include many tests and scales used to assess intelligence, personality, attitudes and mental abilities. In most of these, people are assigned a number (or score) in order to describe, for example, how neurotic or how extraverted they are. Psychologists will speak of a person having an IQ of 112 or 93, for example, or they will say an individual has a low score of 6 on a measure of psychoticism. Often these numbers are used more-or-less as any other form of measurement such as weight or length. For example, we can make statements such as that a person has a weight of 60 kilograms or is 1.3 metres tall. But this is not necessarily the case.

2.3   Major types of measurement

Traditionally, statistics textbooks for psychologists emphasise different types of measurement – usually using the phrase *scales of measurement*. However, for *virtually all practical purposes there are just two different types of measurement in statistics*. These have already been mentioned, but to stress the point:

1. *Score/numerical measurement* This is the assignment of a *numerical* value to a measurement. This includes most physical and psychological measures. In psychological jargon, these numerical measurements are called *scores*. We could record the IQ scores of five people as in Table 2.1. Each of the numerical values in the table indicates the named individual's *score* on the variable IQ. It is a simple point, but note that the numbers contain information that someone with an IQ of 150 has a higher intelligence than someone with an IQ of 80. In other words, the numbers *quantify* the variable.

2. *Nominal/categorical/category measurement* This is deciding to which category of a variable a particular case belongs. It is also appropriate to refer to it as a *qualitative measure* since it measures the qualities of the variable rather than the quantity on the variable. So, if we were measuring a person's job or occupation, we would have to decide whether or not he or she was a lorry driver, a professor of sociology, a debt collector and so forth. This is called *nominal* measurement since usually the categories are described in words and, especially, given names. Thus the category 'lorry driver' is a name or verbal description of what sort of case should be placed in that category.

Notice that there are no numbers involved in the process of categorisation as such. A person is either a lorry driver or not. *However, you need to be warned of a possible confusion that can occur.* If you have 100 people whose occupations are known, you might wish to count how many are lorry drivers, how many are professors of sociology and so forth. These counts could be entered into a data table like Table 2.2. Notice that the

Table 2.1	IQ scores of five named individuals	
Individual		**IQ score**
Jack		80
Chloe		130
Mohammed		150
Sophie		145
Oliver		105

Table 2.2	Frequencies of different occupations
Occupational category	**Number or frequency in set**
Lorry drivers	27
Sociology professors	10
Debt collectors	15
Other occupations	48

numbers this time correspond to a count of the *frequency* or number of cases falling into each of the four occupational categories. *They are not scores,* but frequencies. The numbers do not correspond to a single measurement but are the aggregate of many separate (nominal) measurements. There is more about the concept of frequency in Box 2.1.

Box 2.1   Key concepts

Frequency

The concept of frequency tends to be taken a little for granted in statistics textbooks although it can cause some confusion in practice. A frequency is simply a count of how often a particular something occurs in your data. So counting the number of people with red hair in your sample gives you the frequency of red-haired people. Quite obviously, therefore, frequency and frequent are not the same – a frequency of 1 cannot usually be described as frequent. In some disciplines, frequency is defined as how often something occurs in a given period of time, such as in the frequency of sound waves. However, in psychology, this usage is not so common and frequency simply means the number of times something occurs in your data. You will find the word count used instead of frequency especially in statistical analysis computer program output.

Frequency is the main statistical procedure which can be used with nominal category data. The analysis of nominal category data is largely in terms of counting the frequency of occurrence of each of the categories of nominal category variables. This is straightforward enough. Things risk getting confused when frequencies are used in relation to score data. So, as we have seen, we can count the frequency of any sort of characteristic in our data such as the frequency of children with dyslexia in a school class. But, equally, we can count the frequency of participants in a research study with an IQ of 140. That is, dyslexia and 140 are both categories (different values) in our data and

so their frequencies can be counted. Dyslexia may have a frequency of 15 and the IQ of 140 may have a frequency of 23 or whatever. It is in the idea that the IQ of 140 has the frequency of 23 that the confusion may emerge. Surely 140 and 23 are both numbers just as 15 is a number? Indeed they are all numbers, but 140 is a score on the variable IQ and 23 is its frequency. What this boils down to is as follows:

- Frequency refers to the number of times that a particular category (or value) of a variable appears in the data. It is irrelevant whether these categories are given a name (e.g. dyslexia) or a number (e.g. 140).

- Scores refer to the amount or extent or quantity of a variable. So a number can be a frequency or a score. Consequently, it is important to carefully distinguish between the two since both are numbers.

There is another potential confusion in relation to scores. Sometimes, a researcher will count how often a participant does something and use this as a score. So, for example, a researcher might be interested in people's abilities to write text messages. A measure of skill at texting might be the number of errors that a person makes while texting for one minute. In this case, each person's frequency of making errors is being used as a score on the variable 'texting errors', for example.

Make a habit of mentally labelling variables as numerical scores or nominal categories. Doing so is a big step forward in thinking statistically. This is all you really need to know but you should be aware that a more complex system has been used in psychology for many years and that SPSS employs a variation on that. Read the following section to learn more about scales of measurement.

Formal measurement theory

Many psychologists speak of four different scales of measurement. Conceptually they are distinct. Nevertheless, for most practical situations in psychologists' use of statistics the nominal category versus numerical scores distinction discussed above is sufficient.

The four 'theoretical' scales of measurement are as follows. The scales numbered 2, 3 and 4 are different types of *numerical* scores.

1. *Nominal categorisation* This is the placing of cases into *named* categories – nominal clearly refers to names. It is exactly the same as our nominal measurement or categorisation process. This sort of data is often referred to as categorical data as well as nominal data.

2. *Ordinal (or rank) measurement* The assumption here is that the values of the numerical scores tell us little else other than which is the smallest, the next smallest and so forth up to the largest. In other words, we can place the scores in order (hence ordinal) from the smallest to the largest. It is sometimes called rank measurement since we can assign ranks to the first, second, third, fourth, fifth, etc. in order from the smallest to the largest numerical value. These ranks have the numerical value 1, 2, 3, 4, 5, etc. You will see examples of this later in the book, especially in Chapters 8 and 21. However, few psychologists collect data directly as ranks.

3. *Interval or equal-interval measurement* The basic idea here is that in some cases the intervals between numbers on a numerical scale are equal in size. Thus, if we measure distance on a scale of centimetres then the distance between 0 and 1 centimetre on our scale is exactly the same as the difference between 4 and 5 centimetres or between 11 and 12 centimetres on that scale. This is obvious for some standard physical measurements such as temperature.

4. *Ratio measurement* This is exactly the same as interval scale measurement with one additional requirement. A ratio scale of measurement has an absolute zero point that is measured as 0. Most physical measurements such as distance and weight have zero points that are absolute. Thus zero on a tape measure is the smallest distance one can have – there is no distance between two coinciding points. With this sort of scale of measurement, it is possible to work out ratios between measures. So, for example, a town that is 20 kilometres away is twice as far away as a town that is only 10 kilometres away. A building that is 15 metres high is half the height of a building that is 30 metres high. (Not all physical measures have a zero that is absolute zero – this applies particularly to several measures of temperature. Temperatures measured in degrees Celsius or Fahrenheit have points that are labelled as zero. However, these zero points do not correspond to the lowest possible temperature you can have. It is then meaningless to say, for example, that it is twice as hot if the temperature is 20 degrees Celsius than if it were 10 degrees Celsius.)

These different scales of measurement are illustrated in Figure 2.1 which includes additional examples. Nominal or categorical measurement is to be found in a distinct, blue box because it is very different from the other three types of measurement. Nominal measurement is about categorisation and involves qualities   quantification. The types of measurement in the green sections are similar to each other as they involve quantities.

Nominal categories

a) Involves putting a variable into a small number of categories
b) The categories do not correspond to numerical values
c) So the categories might be the Australian Team, the British Team, the French Team, and the Canadian Team

Ordinal measurement or ranks

a) The scores can be ordered from smallest to largest
b) Only a rank order is implied – e.g. 1st, 2nd, 3rd etc.
c) Rather like 1st, 2nd, 3rd etc. in a race. Knowing that someone came 2nd does not indicate how far or how many seconds they were behind the winner

Different scales of measurement

Interval measurement

a) The size of the difference between scores is an indication of magnitude
b) So if Bill was 5 seconds behind the winner, Fred was 7 seconds behind the winner etc. then these times are based on an equal interval scale of measurement – that is an interval of 1 second
c) However, unless you have other information, it is not possible to say how long the winner, Bill and Fred took running the race

Ratio measurement

a) Like interval measurement but allows ratios to be calculated between scores meaningfully
b) So if Tom took 50 seconds and Bill took 100 seconds then it can be said that Tom took half the time that Bill did – or that Tom is twice as fast as Bill
c) There has to be a meaningful zero to the measurement

FIGURE 2.1   Different scales of measurement and their characteristics

In practice, it is hard to separate them in terms of their applicability to psychological data. Thus it is usually very difficult to distinguish between ordinal, interval and ratio scales of measurement. Most psychological scores do not have any directly observable physical basis which makes it impossible to decide whether they consist of equal intervals or have an absolute zero. It is noteworthy that the most convincing examples of these three different types of measurement come from the physical world, such as temperature, length and weight – it is virtually impossible to think of examples from psychology itself. Time perhaps is a rare example as in reaction time.

For many years this problem caused great controversy and confusion among psychologists. For the most part, much current usage of statistics in psychology ignores the distinctions between the three different types of numerical scores. This has the support of many statisticians. On the other hand, some psychologists prefer to emphasise that some data are best regarded as rankable and lack the qualities which are characteristic of interval/ratio data (see Figure 2.2). They are more likely to use the statistical techniques to be found in Chapter 21 and the ranking correlation coefficient (Chapter 8) than others. In other words, for precisely the same data, different psychologists will adopt different statistical techniques. Usually this will make little difference to the outcomes of their statistical analyses – the results. In general, it will cause you few, if any, problems if you ignore the three subdivisions of numerical score measurement in your practical use of statistics. The exceptions to this are discussed in Chapters 8 and 21. Since psychologists rarely if ever collect data in the form of ranks, Chapters 3 to 7 are largely unaffected by such considerations.

What system does SPSS use? Well the terms nominal and ordinal are used as described above. However, interval and ratio levels of measurement are combined by SPSS under the name 'scale'. In 'Variable View' (see SPSS instructions at the end of this chapter) on SPSS you can specify the nature of each variable using these three categories of nominal, ordinal and scale. Mostly SPSS works fine if you do not do this but you may at some stage find that it demands you do so for a particular procedure. Use the drop-down menu in the column headed 'Measure'. It may say 'unknown' if no information has been given.

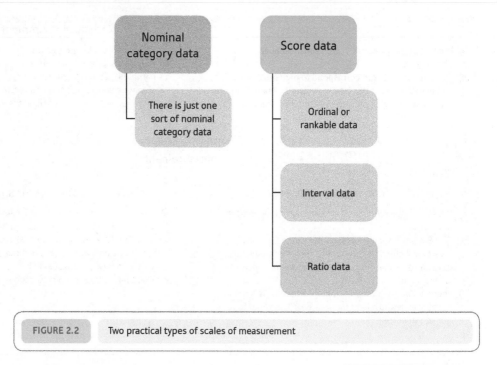

FIGURE 2.2   Two practical types of scales of measurement

Key points

● Always ask yourself what sort of measurement it is you are considering – is it a numerical score on a variable or is it putting individuals into categories?

● Never assume that a number is necessarily a numerical score. Without checking, it could be a *frequency* of observations in a named category.

● Clarity of thinking is a virtue in statistics – you will rarely be expected to demonstrate great creativity in your statistical work. Understanding precisely the meaning of terms is an advantage in statistics.

COMPUTER ANALYSIS

Some basics of data entry using SPSS

Nominal (category/categorical) data are usually analysed differently from data based on scores (including ordinal, interval and ratio data) in statistics. Generally nominal data are entered in the form of an arbitrary numerical code (e.g. 1 = females, 2 = males) which stands for verbal descriptions and, of course, scores are entered as numbers too. The data are entered in the spreadsheet called 'Data View' (Screenshot 2.2). You specify details of each variable in 'Variable View' (Screenshot 2.1). Switch between the two using the tab at the bottom of the screen. You may wish to indicate the type of measurement each variable is in 'Variable View' by using the drop-down menu under 'Measure' six columns to the right of 'Decimals'. Usually it does not matter but some SPSS analyses require it. Overwhelmingly, psychological data is collected in the form of scores.

SCORE DATA
- Make sure that you are in 'Variable View' by clicking on the tab if necessary.
- Name your variable at the beginning of the row. Meaningful names are the sensible way to go (Screenshot 2.1).

SCORE DATA
- Make selections etc. for any of the characteristics you wish. It usually is a good idea to have no decimal places where the scores are whole numbers as this keeps the data looking simple.
- Exploring the options is a good way of learning fast.

SCORE DATA
- Make the 'Type' column entry 'Numeric' using the drop down list.
- Change to 'Data View' by clicking the 'Data View' tab (Screenshot 2.2).

SCORE DATA
- Click on the appropriate cell to highlight it and type in the score for that participant on that variable.
- Move to other cells using 'Return' or by clicking on them with the cursor.

SCORE DATA
- Corrections are easily made by highlighting a cell, deleting and replacing the entry.
- Whole rows or columns can be deleted by clicking on the first cell and dragging up or down to highlight the cells, then deleting.

NOMINAL DATA
- This is similar to entering score variables.
- One difference is that the entry in the 'Type' column should be selected to be 'Nominal'.

NOMINAL DATA
- Another important difference is that the various different categories (values) may be given a verbal description. If you include these, then it is far easier to understand the computer output because recognisable names will be given rather than numbers (Screenshots 2.3 and 2.4).

NOMINAL DATA
- If you prefer to see these verbal labels rather than their numerical codes, in 'Data View' click 'View' then 'Value' labels. Where appropriate, the numbers will change to the fuller label.

| FIGURE 2.3 | Entering score and nominal data into SPSS |

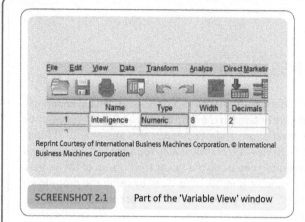

Reprint Courtesy of International Business Machines Corporation, © International Business Machines Corporation

SCREENSHOT 2.1   Part of the 'Variable View' window

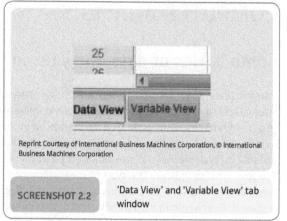

Reprint Courtesy of International Business Machines Corporation, © International Business Machines Corporation

SCREENSHOT 2.2   'Data View' and 'Variable View' tab window

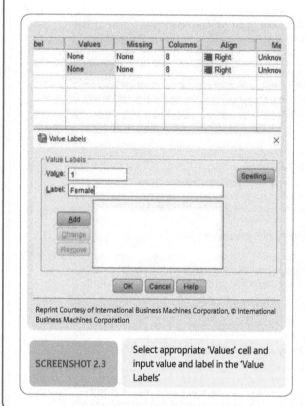

Reprint Courtesy of International Business Machines Corporation, © International Business Machines Corporation

SCREENSHOT 2.3   Select appropriate 'Values' cell and input value and label in the 'Value Labels'

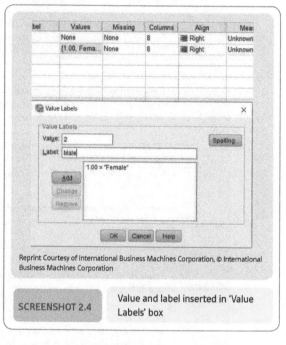

Reprint Courtesy of International Business Machines Corporation, © International Business Machines Corporation

SCREENSHOT 2.4   Value and label inserted in 'Value Labels' box

CHAPTER 3

Describing variables

Tables and diagrams

Overview

- Tables and diagrams are important descriptive statistics (the description of the major features of the data). Examining data in detail is an essential stage of any statistical analysis. At most, a very small number of important tables and diagrams will be included in your report as they consume a lot of space.

- This chapter describes how to create and present tables and diagrams for individual variables.

- Statistical tables and diagrams should effectively communicate information about your data. Beware of unnecessary complexity.

- The type of data (nominal versus score) largely determines what an appropriate table and diagram will be.

- If the data are nominal, then simple frequency tables, bar charts or pie charts are most appropriate. The frequencies indicate the numbers of cases in each of the separate categories.

- If the data are scores, then frequency tables or histograms are appropriate. However, to keep the presentation uncluttered and to help clarify trends, it is often best to put the data into bands (or ranges) of adjacent scores.

Preparation

Remind yourself what a variable is from Chapter 2. Similarly, if you are still not sure of the nominal (categorisation) form of measurement and the use of numerical scores in measurement then revise these too.

3.1   Introduction

You probably know a lot more about statistics than you think. Statistical tables and diagrams are fairly common in newspapers and magazines and on television; children become familiar with statistical tables and diagrams at school. Skill in constructing tables and diagrams is essential because researchers collect large amounts of data from numerous people (see Box 3.1). If we asked 100 people their age, gender, marital status (divorced, married, single, etc.), their number of children and their occupation this would yield 500 separate pieces of information. Although this is small fry compared with much research, it is not very helpful to present these 500 measurements in your research report. Such unprocessed information is called *raw data*. Statistical analysis has to be more than describing the raw ingredients. It requires the data to be structured in ways that effectively communicate the major trends or characteristics of your data. If you fail to do this properly, you may as well just give the reader copies of your questionnaires or observation schedules to interpret themselves.

There are very few rules regarding how to produce tables and diagrams in statistics so long as they are clear to the reader and concise; they need to communicate quickly the important trends in the data. There is absolutely no point in using tables and diagrams that do not ease the task of communication. Probably the best way of deciding whether your tables and diagrams do their job well is to ask other people to decipher what they mean. Tables which are unclear to other people are generally useless. Of course, if you don't understand your own tables and diagrams then it is unlikely that other people will.

Descriptive statistics are, by and large, relatively simple visual and numerical techniques for describing your data's major features. Data analysis begins with a thorough examination of the statistical characteristics of each variable. The researcher may spot problems at this stage but, more importantly, they become aware of the nature of their data. What is the frequency of people in each category of a variable? What is the average score on another variable? Never regard descriptive statistical analysis as an unnecessary

Box 3.1   Focus on

Multiple responses

One easily avoidable mistake in research is to allow participants to give more than one answer to a single question. So, for example, if you ask people to name their favourite television programme and allow each person more than one answer, you will find that the resulting data is not easy to analyse. Take our word for it for now: statistics in general do not handle multiple responses very well. Certainly it is possible to draw up tables and diagrams, but some of the more advanced statistical procedures become difficult to apply. You will sometimes read comments in research reports to the effect that the totals in a table exceed the number of participants in the research. This is usually because the researcher has allowed multiple responses to a single variable. So only allow the participants in your research to give one piece of data for each variable you are measuring to avoid digging a pit for yourself. If you plan your data analysis in detail before you collect your data, you should be able to anticipate any difficulties.

It is possible to do something about data which allow multiple responses. This is to use dummy coding, which is discussed later (Chapter 41). Essentially what one does is to take every possible response as a separate new variable and code each person's data for the presence or absence of each of these new variables. Of course, if there are a lot of different responses then this involves creating a lot of new variables.

Box 3.2	Key concepts

Descriptive statistics

The basic idea of descriptive statistics is very clear. Descriptive statistics consist of the various techniques which give us a picture of what is happening in our data. They include tables which give averages, frequencies and the like and diagrams which represent very much the same things but in a more graphic, pictorial form. Descriptive statistics can involve the examination of one variable on its own or the relationships between two or more variables. We were all taught at least some of them at school. One consequence of this is that we tend to overlook their vital role in our research. This is a mistake as descriptive statistical techniques provide what is essential to understanding our data – they are a window through which we can begin to appreciate what is going on in our data. They are the bedrock on which other more complex statistical techniques are built. To be sure, there are more demanding techniques to learn about in statistics than tables and diagrams. This book and others are full of seemingly complex and, sometimes, difficult new things to learn. The danger is that we neglect descriptive statistics in favour of these. Indeed, there are some popular statistics textbooks which almost entirely overlook how to construct good tables and diagrams. Using descriptive statistics effectively allows us to see the trends, patterns, quirks, bumps and irregularities in our data. Keep sight of what descriptive statistics say about your data as

this helps you anticipate problems in the data analysis. They are an important part of understanding the 'fancier' stuff that comes later.

Qualitative researchers in psychology spend considerable amounts of time and a great deal of effort in familiarising themselves with their data. So why should quantitative researchers not do the same? Try not to think of tables and diagrams as merely something to adorn your practical reports and dissertations. You will not have space to include all of the tables, diagrams and other descriptive statistics which you create in the early part of your analysis. Descriptive statistics are best seen as a tool in the analysis process rather than merely parts of the final product – your research report. Use descriptive techniques to explore your data thoroughly, knowing that you may need to modify your initial attempts in the light of experience. Data analysis is a sort of trial-and-error process of finding out what works for you and for your data. Statistics programs allow you to generate numerous tables and diagrams, some of which are useful and illuminating, although others verge on the useless. The not-so-good stuff is easily deleted from your computer. Be prepared to devote quite some time to this stage of your analysis. It will pay dividends in the long run and bring you close to the data from your study early on.

or trivial stage in research. It is probably more informative than any other aspect of data analysis. Box 3.2 explains the crucial role of descriptive statistics in research further.

The distinction between nominal (category) data and numerical scores discussed in the previous chapter is important in terms of the appropriate tables and diagrams to use. Some only work for nominal data and some only work for score data.

3.2   Choosing tables and diagrams

So long as you are able to decide whether your data are either numerical scores or nominal (category) data, there are few other choices to be made since the available tables and diagrams are essentially dependent upon this distinction. Figure 3.1 gives some of the key steps when considering tables and diagrams.

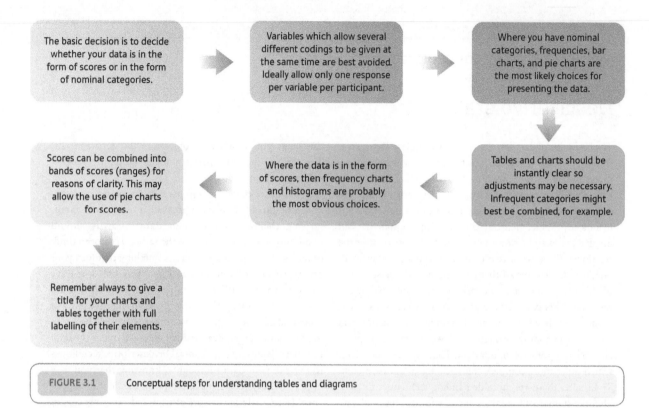

The basic decision is to decide whether your data is in the form of scores or in the form of nominal categories.	
Variables which allow several different codings to be given at the same time are best avoided. Ideally allow only one response per variable per participant.	
Where you have nominal categories, frequencies, bar charts, and pie charts are the most likely choices for presenting the data.	

Scores can be combined into bands of scores (ranges) for reasons of clarity. This may allow the use of pie charts for scores.

Where the data is in the form of scores, then frequency charts and histograms are probably the most obvious choices.

Tables and charts should be instantly clear so adjustments may be necessary. Infrequent categories might best be combined, for example.

Remember always to give a title for your charts and tables together with full labelling of their elements.

FIGURE 3.1 Conceptual steps for understanding tables and diagrams

Tables and diagrams for nominal (category) data

One of the main characteristics of tables and diagrams for nominal (category) data is that they have to show the *frequencies* of cases in each category used. While there may be as many categories as you wish, it is *not* the function of statistical analysis to communicate all of the data's detail; the task is to identify the major trends or features. For example, imagine you are researching the public's attitudes towards private health care. If you ask participants in your research their occupations then you might find that they mention tens if not hundreds of different job titles – newsagents, homemakers, company executives and so forth. Simply counting the frequencies with which different job titles are mentioned results in a vast number of categories. You need to think of relevant and meaningful ways of reducing this unmanageable number into a few broader categories that might reveal important trends. For example, since the research is about a health issue you might wish to form a category made up of those involved in health work – some might be dentists, some nurses, some doctors, some paramedics and so forth. Instead of keeping these as different categories, they might be combined into a category 'health worker'. There are no hard-and-fast rules about combining to form broader categories. It depends on the purpose of your research and the detail of the data as much as anything – plus your own judgement. The following suggestions might prove helpful:

● Keep your number of categories low, especially when you have only small numbers of participants in your research.

● Try to make your 'combined' categories meaningful and sensible in the light of the purposes of your research. It would be nonsense, for example, to categorise jobs by the letter of the alphabet with which they start – nurses, nuns, nursery teachers and national footballers. All of these have jobs beginning with the same letter, but it is very difficult

Table 3.1	Occupational status of participants in the research expressed as frequencies and percentage frequencies	
Occupation	Frequency	Percentage frequency
Nuns	17	21.25
Nursery teachers	3	3.75
Television presenters	23	28.75
Students	20	25.00
Other	17	21.25

In terms of drawing tables, all we do is list the categories we have chosen and give the frequency of cases that fall into each of the categories (Table 3.1). The frequencies are presented in two ways in this table – *simple* frequencies and *percentage* frequencies. A percentage frequency is the frequency expressed as a percentage of the total of the frequencies (or total number of cases, usually).

Notice also that one of the categories is called 'other'. This consists of those cases which do not fit into any of the main categories. It is, in other words, a 'rag bag' category or miscellany. Generally it is best to have a small number of cases in the 'other' category.

Explaining statistics 3.1

How percentage frequencies work

Throughout this book you will find sections headed 'Explaining statistics'. Although most of the statistics discussed in this book may be calculated using SPSS or other computer programs, not everyone is satisfied by simply pressing a few computer keys. They like to know a bit more about how the statistical analysis is carried out. Some may prefer simply to go to the instructions for doing the analysis on the computer and ignore the following. However, most people will learn better by knowing something about what is involved in the calculation that the computer does. We will show you how to do the calculation by hand – not because we think that this is the best way to do the calculation, because it is not. By working through the calculation, you should get some idea though of the mechanics of the statistical technique and understand some things which a computer analysis alone will never clarify. We are not suggesting that the computer does things exactly this way but that this will approximate what the computer does.

Many readers will not need this, but if you are a little rusty with simple maths, it might be helpful. The percentage frequency for a particular category, say for students, is the frequency in that category expressed as a percentage of the total frequencies in the data table.

Step 1   What is the category frequency? For students in Table 3.1:

$$\text{category frequency}_{[students]} = 20$$

Step 2   Add up all of the frequencies in Table 3.1

$$\text{total frequencies} = \text{nuns} + \text{nursery teachers} + \text{TV presenters} + \text{students} + \text{other}$$
$$= 17 + 3 + 23 + 20 + 17$$
$$= 80$$

Step 3 $$\text{Percentage frequency}_{[students]} = \frac{\text{category frequency}_{[students]} \times 100}{\text{total frequencies}}$$

$$\frac{20 \times 100}{} \quad \frac{2000}{}$$

One advantage of using computers is that they enable experimentation with different schemes of categorising data in order to decide the best for your purposes. In this case, you would use initially narrow categories for coding your data. Then you can tell the computer which of these to combine into broader categories. This process is generally termed recoding and simply means putting a category into a new category or putting several categories into a new combined category. Recode is a procedure in SPSS. You will find it under 'Transform' which gives you the choice of recoding the same variable or creating a new variable for the recoded data (see Computer Analysis at the end of this chapter and Chapter 31). Recode into a new variable as this preserves the original variables.

Sometimes it is preferable to turn frequency tables into diagrams. Good diagrams are quickly understood and add variety to the presentation. The main types of diagram for nominal (category) data are *pie diagrams* and *bar charts*. A pie diagram is a very familiar form of presentation – it simply expresses each category as a slice of a pie which represents all cases (see Figure 3.2).

Notice that the *number* of slices is small – a multitude of slices can be confusing. Each slice is clearly marked with its category name, and the percentage frequency in each category also appears.

In Table 3.1, 25.00% of cases were students. In order to turn this into the correct angle for the slice of the pie, you simply need to multiply 25.00 by 3.6 to give an angle of 90 degrees.

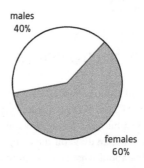

| FIGURE 3.2 | Simple pie diagram |

How pie diagrams work

There is nothing difficult in constructing a pie diagram though most of the time we would use a computer program. Our recommendation is that you turn each of your frequencies into a percentage frequency. Since there are 360 degrees in a circle, if you multiply each percentage frequency by 3.6 you will obtain the angle (in degrees) of the slice of the pie which you need to mark out. In order to create the diagram by hand, you will require a protractor to measure the angles. However, computer graph packages are standard at any university or college and do an impressive job – SPSS included.

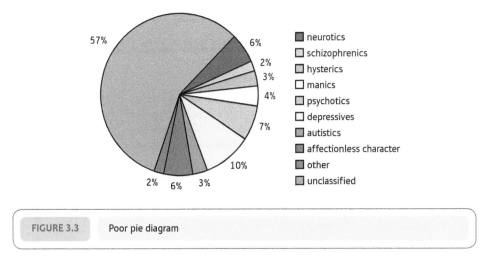

Figure 3.3 shows a bad example of a pie diagram for purposes of comparison. There are several problems with it:

● There are too many small slices identified by different shading patterns and the legend takes time to decode.

● It is not easy to see what each slice represents, and the relative sizes of the slices are difficult to judge. We have the size of the slices around the figure and a separate legend or key to identify the components to help cope with the overcrowding problem. In other words, too many categories have resulted in a diagram which is far from easy to read – a cardinal sin in any statistical diagram. A simple table of the frequencies might be more effective in this case.

Another very familiar form of statistical diagram for nominal (category) data is the *bar chart*. Again these charts are very common in the media. Basically they are diagrams in which bars represent the size of each category. An example is shown in Figure 3.4.

The relative lengths (or heights) of the bars quickly reveal the main trends in the data. With a bar chart, there is very little to remember other than that the bars have a standard space separating them. The spaces indicate that the categories are not in a numerical order; they are frequencies of categories, *not* scores.

It is hard to go wrong with a bar chart (that is not a challenge!) so long as you remember the following:

● The heights of the bars represent frequencies (number of cases) in a category.

● Each bar should be clearly labelled as to the category it represents.

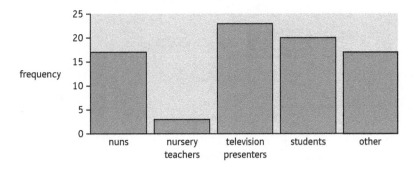

FIGURE 3.4   Bar chart showing occupational categories in Table 3.1

- Too many bars make bar charts hard to follow.

- Avoid having *many* empty or near-empty categories which represent very few cases. Generally, the information about substantial categories is the most important. (Small categories can be combined together as an 'other' category.)

- Nevertheless, if *important* categories have very few entries then this needs to be shown clearly. So, for example, a researcher who is particularly interested in opportunities for women surveys people in top management and finds very few women employed in such jobs. This is easily shown in a simple bar chart comparing the frequencies of men and women in top jobs. There is little point in a bar chart which shows the occupations of a sample of women in general as their scarcity in top management jobs will be obscured by all of the other categories. The chart will not have made its point strongly. Once again, there are no hard-and-fast rules to guide you – common sense will take you a long way.

- Make sure that the vertical axis (the heights of the bars) is clearly marked as being frequencies or percentage frequencies.

- The bars should be of equal width.

In newspapers and on television you are likely to come across a variant of the bar chart called the *pictogram*. In this, the bars of the bar chart are replaced by varying sized drawings of something eye-catching to do with your categories. Thus, pictures of men or women of varying heights, for example, replace the bars. Pictograms are rarely used in professional presentations. The main reason is that pictures of things get wider as well as taller as they increase in size. This can misrepresent the relative sizes of the categories, given that readers easily forget that it is only the height of the picture that counts.

Tables and diagrams for numerical score data

One crucial consideration when deciding what tables and diagrams to use for score data is the number of separate scores recorded for the variable in question. This can vary markedly. So, for example, age in the general population can range from newly born to over 100 years of age. If we merely recorded ages to the nearest whole year then a table or diagram may have entries for 100 different ages. Such a table or diagram would look horrendous. If we recorded age to the nearest month, then we could multiply this number of ages by 12! Such scores can be grouped into bands or ranges of scores to allow effective tabulation (Table 3.2). This sort of grouping into bands involves the recoding procedure when using SPSS.

Many psychological variables have a much smaller range of numerical values. So, for example, it is fairly common to use questions which pre-specify just a few response

Table 3.2	Ages expressed as age bands	
Age range		**Frequency**
0–9 years		19
10–19 years		33
20–29 years		17
30–39 years		22
40–49 years		17
50 years and over		3

alternatives. The so-called Likert-type questionnaire item is a good case in point. Typically this looks something like this:

Statistics is my favourite university subject:
Strongly agree   Agree   Neither agree nor disagree   Disagree   Strongly disagree

Participants completing this questionnaire circle the option that best fits their personal opinion. Conventionally, these different response alternatives are coded on a five-point scale from one to five. Thus strongly agree might be coded 1, neither agree nor disagree 3, and strongly disagree 5. This scale therefore has only five possible values. Because of this small number of possible answers, a table based on this question will be relatively simple. Indeed, if students are not too keen on statistics, you may well find that they select only the disagree and strongly disagree categories.

Tabulating such data is straightforward: simply report the numbers or frequencies of replies for each of the different categories or scores as in Table 3.3. A *histogram* might be the best form of statistical diagram to represent these data. At first sight, histograms look very much like bar charts but without gaps between the bars. This is because the histogram does not represent distinct unrelated categories but different points on a *numerical* measurement scale. So a histogram of the above data might look like Figure 3.5.

But what if your data have numerous different possible values of the variable in question? One common difficulty for most psychological research is that the number of respondents tends to be small. The large number of possible different scores on the variable is therefore shared among very few respondents. Tables and diagrams should present major features of your data in a simple and easily assimilated form. So, sometimes you will have to use *bands of scores* rather than individual score values, just as you did for Table 3.2. So, if we asked 100 people their ages we could categorise their replies into bands such as

Table 3.3	Distribution of students' attitudes towards statistics		
Response category		**Value**	**Frequency**
Strongly agree		1	17
Agree		2	14
Neither agree nor disagree		3	6
Disagree		4	2
Strongly disagree		5	1

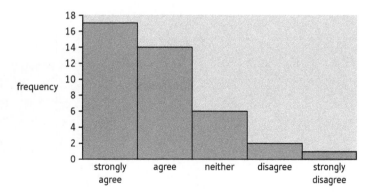

| FIGURE 3.5 | Histogram of students' attitudes towards statistics |

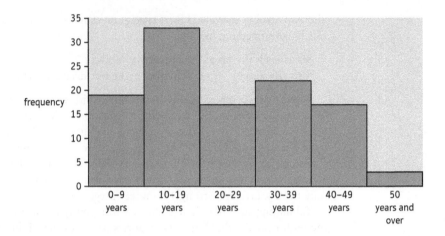

FIGURE 3.6   Use of bands of scores to enable simple presentation

0–9 years, 10–19 years, 30–39 years, 40–49 years and a final category of those 50 years and over. By using bands we reduce the risk of empty parts of the table and allow any trends to become clear (Figure 3.6). This does not mean that you have to use these bands for additional statistical analyses – the point is that tables and diagrams need to show things clearly and if this needs the use of bands or ranges of scores then so be it.

How one chooses the bands to use is an important question. The answer is a bit of luck and judgement, and a lot of trial and error. It is very time-consuming to rejig the ranges of the bands when one is analysing the data by hand. One big advantage of computers is that they will recode your scores into bands repeatedly until you have tables which seem to do the job as well as possible. The criterion of success remains whether the table communicates information effectively.

The one rule is that the bands ought to be of the same size – that is cover, for example, equal ranges of scores. Generally this is easy except at the upper and lower ends of the distribution. Perhaps you wish to use 'over 70' as your upper range. This, in modern practice, can be done as a bar of the same width as the others, but must be very carefully marked. (Strictly speaking, the width of the band should represent the range of scores involved and the height reduced in the light of this. However, this is rarely done in modern psychological statistics.) One might redefine the bands of scores and generate another histogram based on identical data but a different set of bands (Figure 3.7).

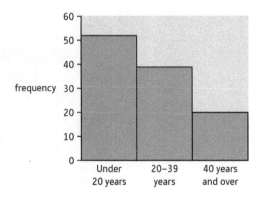

FIGURE 3.7   Histogram showing 'collapsed' categories

It requires some thought to decide which of the diagrams is best for a particular purpose and the style of chart which would be best. You will find many different sorts of charts in SPSS in 'Legacy Dialogs' (Screenshot 5.5) or 'Chart Builder . . . ' (Screenshot 8.7) on the 'Graphs' drop-down menu. There are far too many to discuss here but SPSS does illustrate the range that it can draw. The SPSS instructions at the end of this chapter and Chapter 8 will get you started.

3.3 Errors to avoid

There are a couple of mistakes that you can make in drawing up tables and diagrams:

- *Do not* forget to head the table or diagram with a succinct description of what it concerns. We have done our best throughout this chapter to supply each table and diagram with a clear title.

- Label everything on the table or diagram as clearly as possible. What this means is that you have to mark your bar charts and histograms in a way that tells the reader what each bar means. Then you must indicate what the height of the bar refers to – probably either frequency or percentage frequency.

Note that this chapter has concentrated on describing a *single* variable as clearly as possible. This is known as a *univariate* analysis. In Chapter 8, methods of making tables and diagrams showing the relationships between two or more variables are described.

Research examples

Using graphs and tables

The extent of the use of tables and diagrams varies markedly in psychology. Some subfields use diagrams to a greater extent than others. While it is usually impossible to incorporate every diagram used in data analysis in the final report, diagrams can be very persuasive. So they should be considered for inclusion when they tell an interesting 'story'.

Rothbard and Wilk (2011) examined how a person's mood at the start of the workday primes how they see events at work later in the day in relation to the worker's job performance in a call centre. Graphical methods were used to show such things as the variation in mood at the start of day over time. Start of day mood affected the call centre employees' perceptions of how the customer was feeling emotionally during the telephone conversation and the employees' response to the calls.

Skinner (e.g. 1948) developed operant conditioning which had a big influence on behaviourist psychology. He had a strong preference for the use of graphical methods rather than statistics in his work on animal conditioning. His research findings were usually presented in graph form and he had little time for the sort of inferential statistics which dominates modern psychological research.

Smith-Bell, Burhans and Schreurs (2012) explored animal models of post-traumatic stress disorder. Such models assume that fear conditioning can result in responses to innocuous cues the same as to the traumatic event. The researchers employed classical conditioning methods. Their data were analysed to a substantial extent using graphs. Data from research using rabbits suggested that 25% exhibited a conditioned specific reflex modification similar to the response to innocuous cues that is characteristic of post-traumatic stress disorder.

Key points

- Try to make your tables and diagrams useful. It is not usually their purpose to record the data as you collected it in your research. Of course you can list your data in the appendix of projects that you carry out or include it on a disk, but this is not useful as a way of illustrating trends. It is part of a researcher's job to make the data accessible to the reader in a structured form that is easily understood by the reader.

- Especially when using computers, it is very easy to generate useless tables and diagrams. Computer analysis discourages you from examining your raw data in any detail. Always regard your first analyses as tentative and merely a step towards something better.

- If your table is not clear to you, it is unlikely to be any clearer to anyone else.

- Check each table and diagram for informativeness and full labelling of each part. Especially, check that frequencies are clearly marked as such.

- Check that every table and diagram has a clear, helpful title.

COMPUTER ANALYSIS

Tables, diagrams and recoding using SPSS

Data
- In 'Variable View' of the 'Data Editor', 'name' the variable, 'label' each of its values and select 'Nominal' as the 'Measure' (Screenshots 3.1 and 3.2).
- In 'Data View' of the 'Data Editor', enter the value of the category for each case.

Analysis
- For a frequency table, select 'Analyze', 'Descriptive Statistics' and 'Frequencies...' (Screenshot 3.3).
- Move variables names to the right hand box for the analysis.

2
- For a graph, select 'Graphs', 'Chart Builder...', 'OK' and move type of graph into box above.

Output
- For frequency tables, the percentage of cases for each category is given for the whole sample first including any missing data and second excluding missing data. If there is no missing data, these percentages will be the same (Screenshot 3.4).

2
- Charts may be edited in the 'Chart Editor'.

FIGURE 3.8   SPSS steps for producing tables and diagrams to describe a nominal category variable

Interpreting and reporting the output

- Tables and similar diagrams are primarily part of the initial analysis of your data and can help you to identify significant features of the data – such as unusual distributions of variables and so forth. It would be usual to generate many more charts and tables than you include in your report.

- One therefore has to be selective about what charts and tables one includes in one's report. They are space consuming and often can be summarised in a few words – and so might not need to be included. Charts and tables included in your report should be very clear, fully labelled and as informative as possible.

- See Computer Analysis in Chapter 4 for the analysis of score data.

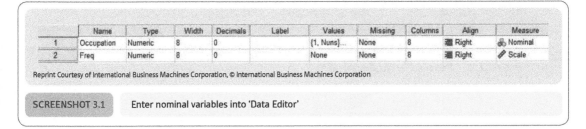

	Name	Type	Width	Decimals	Label	Values	Missing	Columns	Align	Measure
1	Occupation	Numeric	8	0		{1, Nuns}...	None	8	Right	Nominal
2	Freq	Numeric	8	0		None	None	8	Right	Scale

Reprint Courtesy of International Business Machines Corporation, © International Business Machines Corporation

SCREENSHOT 3.1   Enter nominal variables into 'Data Editor'

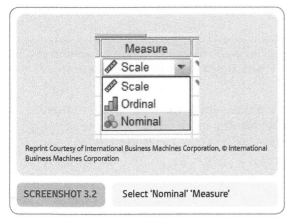

Reprint Courtesy of International Business Machines Corporation, © International Business Machines Corporation

SCREENSHOT 3.2   Select 'Nominal' 'Measure'

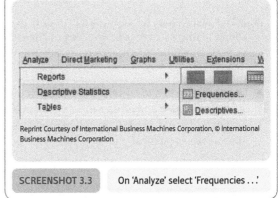

Reprint Courtesy of International Business Machines Corporation, © International Business Machines Corporation

SCREENSHOT 3.3   On 'Analyze' select 'Frequencies . . .'

Occupation

		Frequency	Percent	Valid Percent	Cumulative Percent
Valid	Nuns	17	21.3	21.3	21.3
	Nursery Teachers	3	3.8	3.8	25.0
	Television Presenters	23	28.8	28.8	53.8
	Students	20	25.0	25.0	78.8
	Other	17	21.3	21.3	100.0
	Total	80	100.0	100.0	

Reprint Courtesy of International Business Machines Corporation, © International Business Machines Corporation

See Computer Analysis in Chapter 4 for the analysis of score data.

Data
- Select 'Transform' and 'Recode into Different Variables. . .' (Screenshot 3.5).
- Select variable and the ▶ button to put variable into the 'Numeric Variable -> Output Variable:' box (Screenshot 3.6).

- Type in the name of the new variable in the 'Name:' box (Screenshot 3.6).
- Select 'Change' to add this new name to the 'Numeric Variable -> Output Variable:' box (Screenshot 3.6).

- Select 'Old and New Values. . .' (Screenshot 3.6).
- Type in 'Old Value' and then 'New Value' (Screenshot 3.7).
- Select 'Add' (Screenshot 3.7).

FIGURE 3.9   SPSS steps for recoding values

Interpreting and reporting the output

- Tables and similar diagrams are primarily part of the initial analysis of your data and can help you to identify significant features of the data – such as unusual distributions of variables and so forth. It would be usual to generate many more charts and tables than you include in your report.

- One therefore has to be selective about what charts and tables one includes in one's report. They are space consuming and often can be summarised in a few words – and so might not need to be included. Charts and tables included in your report should be very clear, fully labelled and as informative as possible.

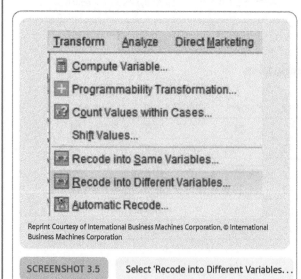

Reprint Courtesy of International Business Machines Corporation, © International Business Machines Corporation

SCREENSHOT 3.5   Select 'Recode into Different Variables. . .'

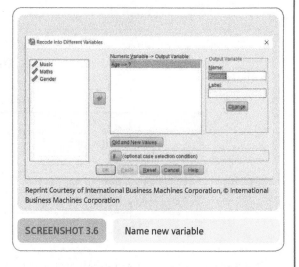

Reprint Courtesy of International Business Machines Corporation, © International Business Machines Corporation

SCREENSHOT 3.6   Name new variable

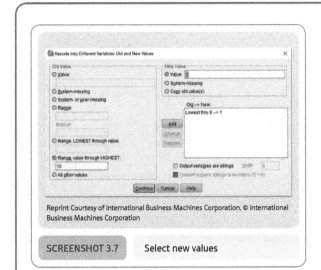

Reprint Courtesy of International Business Machines Corporation, © International Business Machines Corporation

SCREENSHOT 3.7   Select new values

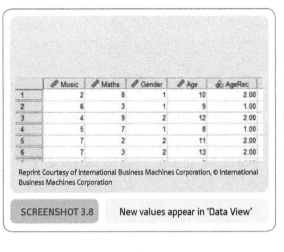

Reprint Courtesy of International Business Machines Corporation, © International Business Machines Corporation

SCREENSHOT 3.8   New values appear in 'Data View'

CHAPTER 4

Describing variables numerically

Averages, variation and spread

Overview

- Scores can be described or summarised numerically – for example the average of a sample of scores can be given.

- There are several measures of central tendency – the most typical or most likely score or value.

- The mean score is simply the average score calculated by the total of the scores divided by the number of scores.

- The mode is the numerical value of the most frequently occurring score.

- The median is the score in the middle if the scores are ordered from smallest to largest.

- The spread of scores can be expressed as the range (which is the difference between the largest and the smallest score).

- Variance (an indicator of variability around the average) indicates the spread of scores in the data. Unlike the range, variance takes into account all of the scores. It is a ubiquitous statistical concept.

- Nominal data can only be described in terms of the numbers of cases falling in each category. The mode is the only measure of central tendency that can be applied to nominal (categorical) data.

- Outliers are unusually large or small values in your data which are very atypical of your data. They can create the impression of trends in your analysis which are not really present. Identifying such outliers and dealing with them effectively can have an important impact on the quality of your analysis.

Preparation

Revise the meaning of nominal (category) data and numerical score data.

4.1   Introduction

Tables and diagrams take up a lot of space. It can be more efficient to use numerical indexes to describe the distributions of variables. For this reason, relatively few pie charts and the like appear in published research. However, many charts may have been produced during the course of the analysis. One numerical index is familiar to everyone – the numerical average (i.e. arithmetic mean). Large amounts of data can be described or summarised adequately using just a few different numerical indexes.

What are the major features of data that we might attempt to summarise in this way? Look at the two different sets of scores in Table 4.1. The major differences between these two sets of data are:

● The sets of scores differ substantially in terms of their typical value – in one case the scores are relatively large (variable *B*); in the other case the scores are much smaller (variable *A*).

● The sets of scores differ in their spread or variability – one set (variable *B*) seems to have more spread or a greater variability than the other.

● If we plot these two sets of scores as histograms then we also find that the shapes of the distributions differ markedly. Variable *A* is much steeper and less spread out than variable *B*.

Each of these different features of a set of scores can be described using various indexes. They do not generally apply to nominal (category) variables. Figure 4.1 describes some of the key steps you need to consider when describing your data numerically.

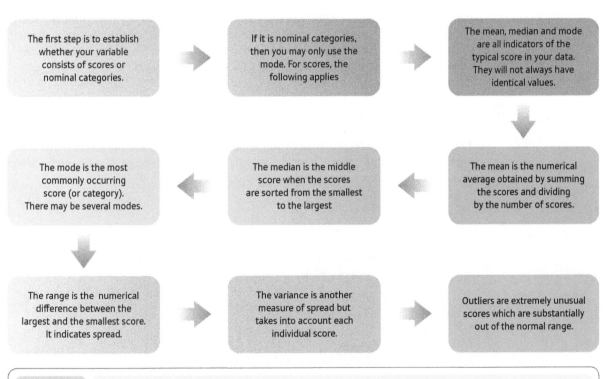

The first step is to establish whether your variable consists of scores or nominal categories.

If it is nominal categories, then you may only use the mode. For scores, the following applies

The mean, median and mode are all indicators of the typical score in your data. They will not always have identical values.

The mode is the most commonly occurring score (or category). There may be several modes.

The median is the middle score when the scores are sorted from the smallest to the largest

The mean is the numerical average obtained by summing the scores and dividing by the number of scores.

The range is the numerical difference between the largest and the smallest score. It indicates spread.

The variance is another measure of spread but takes into account each individual score.

Outliers are extremely unusual scores which are substantially out of the normal range.

FIGURE 4.1   Conceptual steps for understanding how to describe your variables numerically

Table 4.1	Two different sets of scores
Variable A scores	**Variable B scores**
2	27
2	29
3	35
3	40
3	41
4	42
4	45
4	45
4	49
4	49
5	49
5	
5	

4.2   Typical scores: mean, median and mode

Researchers sometimes write about the central tendency of a set of scores. By this is meant the most typical and likely scores in the distribution of measurements. There are three main measures of the central tendency used in statistical analyses: the arithmetic mean, the median and the mode. These are quite distinct concepts but generally simple enough in themselves. Statisticians have other types of average which psychologists would rarely come across except disguised somewhere in a statistical formula.

■ Arithmetic mean

The arithmetic mean is calculated by summing all of the scores in a distribution and dividing by the number of scores. This is the everyday concept of average. In statistical notation we can express this mean as follows:

$$\overline{X}_{\text{mean}} = \frac{\sum X_{[\text{scores}]}}{N_{[\text{number of scores}]}}$$

As this is the first statistical formula we have presented, you should take very careful note of what each symbol means:

X is the statistical symbol for a score
Σ is the summation or sigma sign
ΣX means add up all of the scores X
N is the number of scores
$\overline{X}$ is the statistical symbol for the arithmetic mean of a set of scores

We have added a few comments in small square brackets [just like this]. Although mathematicians may not like them very much, you might find they help you to interpret a formula a little faster. Calculating the average of a set of scores such as 7, 5, 4, 7, 7 and

5 is more quickly done than explained. In statistical notation, a score is usually given the symbol X and subscripts identify different ones. So $X_1 = 7$, $X_2 = 5$, $X_3 = 4$, $X_4 = 7$, $X_5 = 7$ and $X_6 = 5$ for this set of six scores. You will find that this sort of use of subscripts is common in journal articles so it is useful to be familiar with it. The formula for the mean follows together with the calculation for our six scores:

$$\overline{X}_{\text{mean}} = \frac{\sum X_{[\text{scores}]}}{N_{[\text{number of scores}]}}$$

$$= \frac{X_1 + X_2 + X_3 + X_4 + X_5 + X_6}{N}$$

$$= \frac{7 + 5 + 4 + 7 + 7 + 5}{6} = \frac{35}{6} = 5.83$$

■ Median

The median is the middle score of a set if the scores are organised from the smallest to the largest. Thus the set of scores 7, 5, 4, 7, 7, 5, 3, 4, 6, 8, 5 becomes 3, 4, 4, 5, 5, 5, 6, 7, 7, 7, 8 when put in order from the smallest to the largest. Since there are 11 scores and the median is the middle score from the smallest to the largest, the median has to be the sixth score, i.e. 5.

With odd numbers of scores all of which are different, the median is easily calculated since there is a single score that corresponds to the middle score in the set of scores. However, if there is an even number of all different scores in the set then the mid-point will not be a single score but two scores. So if you have 12 different scores placed in order from smallest to largest, the median will be somewhere between the sixth and seventh score from smallest. There is no such score, of course, by definition – the 6.5th score just does not exist. What we could do in these circumstances is to take the average of the sixth and seventh scores to give us an estimate of the median.

For the distribution of 40 scores shown in Table 4.2, the middle score from the smallest is somewhere between the 20th and 21st scores. Thus the median is somewhere between score 5 (the 20th score) and score 6 (the 21st score). One could give the average of these two as the median score – that is, the median is 5.5. For most purposes this is good enough.

Table 4.2	Frequency distribution of 40 scores	
Score		**Frequency (f)**
1		1
2		2
3		4
4		6
5		7
6		8
7		5
8		3
9		2
10		1
11		0
12		1

You may find that computer programs give different values from this. The computer program is making adjustments since there may be several identical scores near the median, but you need only a fraction of them to reach your mid-point score. So, in the above example the 21st score comes in score category 6 although there are actually eight scores in that category. So in order to get that extra score we need take only one-eighth of score category 6. One-eighth equals 0.125 so the estimated median equals 5.125. To be frank, it is difficult to think of many circumstances in which this level of precision about the value of the median is required in psychological statistics. If you follow our advice to use a computer program to do your calculations wherever possible you will always have a precise, adjusted value for the median.

◼ Mode

The mode is the most frequently occurring category of score. It is merely the most common value. In other words, you can apply the mode to any category of data and not just scores. In the above example for arithmetic mean where the scores were 7, 5, 4, 7, 7, 5 we could represent the scores in terms of their frequencies of occurrence (Table 4.3).

Frequencies are often given the symbol f in statistics. It is very easy to see in this example that the most frequently occurring score is 7 with a frequency of 3. So the mode of this distribution is 7.

If we take the slightly different set of scores 7, 5, 4, 7, 7, 5, 3, 4, 6, 8, 5, the frequency distribution of these scores is shown in Table 4.4. Here there is no single mode since scores 5 and 7 jointly have the highest frequency of 3. This sort of distribution is called bimodal and the two modes are 5 and 7. The general term multimodal implies that a frequency distribution has several modes.

The mode is the only measure in this chapter that applies to nominal (category/categorical) data as well as numerical score data.

Table 4.3	Frequencies of scores
Score	**Frequency (f)**
4	1
5	2
6	0
7	3

Table 4.4	Bimodal frequency distribution
Score	**Frequency (f)**
3	1
4	2
5	3
6	1
7	3
8	1

4.3   Comparison of mean, median and mode

Usually the mean, median and mode give different values of the central tendency when applied to the same set of scores. It is only when a distribution is perfectly symmetrical and the distribution peaks in the middle that they coincide completely. Regard big differences between the mean, median and mode as a sign that your distribution of scores is rather asymmetrical or lopsided.

Distributions of scores do not have to be perfectly symmetrical for statistical analysis, but symmetry tends to make some calculations a little more accurate. It is difficult to say how much asymmetry there can be without it becoming a serious problem as it depends on circumstances. There is more about this later, especially in Chapter 21 and Appendix A, which make some suggestions about how to test for asymmetry. SPSS includes skewness in 'Frequencies . . .' (Screenshot 4.5), 'Explore . . .' (Screenshot 4.3) and 'Statistics . . .', and 'Descriptive Statistics' (Screenshot 12.2) and 'Options . . .' (Screenshot 12.4) if you request it. Measures of skewness are rarely included in research reports in our experience. They are not very useful if you have only a small sample size.

4.4   Spread of scores: range and interquartile range

The concept of variability is essential in statistics. Variability is a non-technical term and is related to (but is not identical with) another statistical term, variance. Range and interquartile range are easily understood indicators of the spread of scores on a variable. However, they only involve the extremes of your scores. Variance, which we will deal with in the next section, is a statistical formula indicating spread which involves all of the scores in its calculation.

Table 4.5 gives a set of ages of 12 university students and can be used to illustrate some different ways of measuring data variability. These 12 students vary in age from 18 to 33 years. In other words, the range covers a 15-year period. The interval from youngest to oldest (or tallest to shortest, or fattest to thinnest) is called the range – a useful statistical concept. As a statistical concept, correctly range is always expressed as a single number such as 20 centimetres and not as an interval, say, from 15 to 25 centimetres. SPSS will give you the range if you select 'Frequencies . . .' (Screenshot 4.5), 'Explore . . .' and 'Statistics . . .', or 'Descriptive Statistics' (Screenshot 12.2) and 'Options . . .' (Screenshot 12.4).

One problem with range is that it can be heavily influenced by extreme cases (or outliers) (see Box 4.1). Thus the 33-year-old student in Table 4.5 is having a big influence on the range of ages because they are much older than most of the students. For this reason, the interquartile range might be preferred as this basically ignores the extreme quarters of the distribution. So the interquartile range is the range of the middle 50% of the scores put in order from smallest to largest. To calculate the interquartile range, we split the age distribution into quarters (quartiles) and take the range of the middle two quarters (or

Table 4.5	Ages of a sample of 12 students				
18 years	21 years	23 years	18 years	19 years	19 years
19 years	33 years	18 years	19 years	19 years	20 years

Box 4.1	Key concepts

Outliers and identifying them statistically

Outliers, potentially, put your analysis at risk of erroneous conclusions. This is because they are scores which are so atypical of your data in general that they distort any trend there is simply because they are unusually large or small. In other words, outliers are odd cases which are out of step with the rest of the data. They can mislead an unwary researcher. It is important to eliminate outliers which would lead to wrong conclusions. Routinely, good researchers examine their data for possible outliers simply by inspecting tables of frequencies or scatterplots, for example. This is often sufficient but does involve an element of judgement which is probably best avoided. Fortunately, there are objective ways of identifying outliers to avoid this subjectivity. One method is simply to trim off the extreme 5%, say, of scores from the variable which ought to eliminate any outliers.

Another way of identifying outliers is based on the interquartile range. It defines possible outliers in terms of a number of interquartile ranges outside of the interquartile range. The calculation of interquartile range is given in the main text for this chapter (Section 4.4) so we will not repeat it here. Outliers, which by definition are unusually large or small scores, cannot affect the interquartile range since they will be in the top or bottom extremes and thus not part of the interquartile range. Possible moderate outliers are defined in terms of being more than $1.5 \times$ the interquartile range outside of the interquartile range. Identifying extreme outliers would involve $3 \times$ the interquartile range outside of the interquartile range.

Imagine that we had the following scores for the IQs (Intelligence Quotients) from a sample of 12 people:

120 115 65 140 122 142 125 135 122 136 144 118

We can rearrange these in order:

65 115 118 120 122 122 125 135 136 140 142 144

Common sense would suggest that the score of 65 is uncharacteristic of the general run of the data so it is potentially an outlier (or possibly a data entry error – maybe it should have been 165).

If you wish to use SPSS to calculate percentiles, select 'Frequencies . . .' (Screenshot 4.3), the variable and 'Statistics . . .' (Screenshot 4.4), 'Percentile(s)' and enter or add the percentile points you want (Screenshot 4.5). The 25th (118.5) and

75th (139) percentiles can be read from the Percentiles table. For the interquartile range (20.5), select 'Explore . . .' (Screenshot 4.3), the variable and 'Statistics . . .', and 'Percentile(s)'. The values for the 25th and 75th percentiles have been added in brackets in bold type. They indicate the (boundaries of the) interquartile range

65 115 118 (**118.5**) 120 122 122 125 135 136 (**139**) 140 142 144

The next step is to multiply the interquartile range by 1.5 (if we wish to eliminate moderate outliers or by 3 for extreme outliers). This gives us $1.5 \times 20.5 = 30.75$. Outliers among the low scores are defined as any score which is smaller than the low boundary of the interquartile range minus this figure of 30.75. SPSS has given the lower boundary of the interquartile range as 118.5. So we need to calculate $118.5 - 30.75 = 87.75$. Any score lower than 87.75 is regarded as an outlier. Outliers among the high scores are defined as any score which is bigger than the high boundary of the interquartile range plus 30.75. We have obtained the value of 139 for the upper boundary from SPSS. So the upper cut-off point for outliers is $139 + 30.75 = 169.75$. Any score bigger than 169.75 is considered to be an outlier. There is only one potential outlier in the data which is the IQ of 65 because it is not between 87.75 and 169.75. No potential outliers are present in the high scores since none of them is above 169.75. Here are the data again with the addition of the cut-off points for outliers also added in square brackets in bold type:

65 [**87.75**] 115 118 (**118.5**) 120 122 122 125 135 136 (**139**) 140 142 144 [**169.75**]

On the assumption that the scores are normally distributed, then less than 1% of scores would be defined as outliers by this method. Remember that for extreme outliers the calculation uses $3 \times$ the interquartile range rather than 1.5.

When you have small amounts of data, it is easy enough to spot potential outliers. However, it is difficult when you have a large sample. So you need help with this:

● Produce a histogram of the scores on the variable in question using SPSS (see Computer Analysis in Chapter 5). You will easily spot any extreme scores which are separated from the main part of the distribution by this procedure.

- You may find it helpful to use the Extreme Values procedure on SPSS. All this does is produce a list of the high and low extremes of the distribution. This is helpful when you have a lot of cases. You have to decide if you have an outlier. The steps are: 'Explore . . .' (Screenshot 4.3), the variable and 'Statistics' and 'Outliers'. The information you need is found in the 'Extreme Values' table.

- It would be usual practice to delete outliers from your data. On SPSS, you could simply click on the appropriate row number and clear the row of data. It is best if you do this on a copy of your original data file.

Or you might define the value of the outlier as a discrete missing value in 'Variable View'. You do this in the 'Missing' column by clicking on the row for the variable in question. When you do your analysis you would probably opt for the listwise omission of missing values. You might also wish to compare the outcome of your analysis using the complete data and with the outliers excluded. In this way, you can see the extent of the outliers' influence. However, it is important to mention what you have done in any report about your research.

middle 50%), ignoring the extreme quarters. The interquartile range is the range between the *boundaries* cutting off this middle 50% of scores from the 25% below and the 25% above. Take the following 9 scores:

5 7 2 8 3 8 9 7 5

We then put them in order, which gives:

2 3 5 5 7 7 8 8 9

The median score is 7, which we have isolated from the other scores for easy identification. The median is referred to as the second quartile. The first quartile (the point cutting off the lowest 25%) could be found by finding the median of 2, 3, 5 and 5. That is we are simply looking for the middle score of the lower half of the scores. You will have spotted the problem. There is no middle score. So we have to 'interpolate' to find a value somewhere between 3 and 5. One procedure, which we mentioned before in connection with the median, is simply to average the two scores to give 4 as the median or the boundary between the lowest quarter and the middle 50% of the distribution. For the quartile (the third quartile) at the high end of the scores the median is somewhere between 8 and 8 = 8. The scores are given again below. The boundaries between the middle 50% and the upper and lower quartiles are each marked with an up arrow (↑). Thus the boundaries for the interquartile range are 4 and 8:

2 3 ↑ 5 5 7 7 8 ↑ 8 9

The interquartile range is therefore 8 − 4 = 4.

A word of warning is needed here. Calculating the interquartile range is not as straightforward as it looks. There are many ways of doing 'interpolation' when calculating the interquartile range. We have described one of the easier ones. Different statistical packages calculate the interquartile range differently and sometimes the same program gives you a variety of different ways of doing the calculation though SPSS does not. Generally statistics textbook authors point out that these differences are of little practical importance. Naughty textbook writers sometimes just give an example which works out fine because there is no 'interpolation' to do. SPSS will give you a perfectly good value for the interquartile range and the one that many researchers would use.

You may find the Box Plot or Box and Whisker Plot useful where medians and interquartile ranges are being studied. To obtain the boxplot shown in Figure 4.2, select

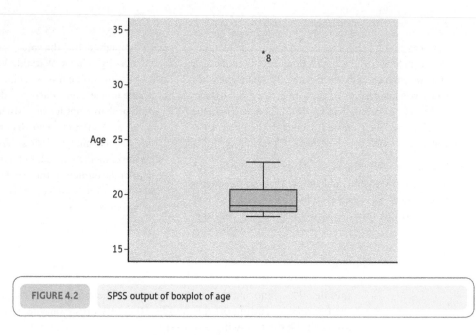

FIGURE 4.2   SPSS output of boxplot of age

Box 4.2   Focus on

Using negative (−) values

Although psychologists rarely collect data that involve negative signs, some statistical techniques can generate them. Negative values occur in statistical analyses because working out differences is common. The mean is often taken away from scores, for example, or one score is subtracted from another. Generally speaking, negative values are not a problem since either the computer or the calculator will do them for you. A positive value is one which is bigger than zero. Often the + sign is omitted as it is taken for granted.

A negative value (or minus value or − value) is a number which is smaller than (less than) zero. The negative sign is never omitted. A value of −20 is a smaller number than −3 (whereas a value of +20 is a bigger number than +3).

Negative values should cause few problems in terms of calculations – the calculator or computer has no difficulties with them. With a calculator you will need to enter that a number is a negative. A key labelled + / − is often used to do this. On a computer, the number must be entered with a − sign.

Probably, the following are the only things you need to know to be able to understand negative numbers in statistics:

- If a negative number is multiplied by another negative number the outcome is a positive number. So $-2 \times -3 = +6$. This is also the case when a number

is squared – squaring is when a number is multiplied by itself. Thus $-3^2 = +9$. You need this information to understand how the standard deviation and variance formulae work, for example.

- Psychologists often speak of negative correlations and negative regression weights. This needs care because the negative in this case indicates that there is a reverse relationship between two sets of scores. That is, for example, the more intelligent a person is, the less time they will take to complete a crossword puzzle.

- If you have got negative values for your scores, it is often advantageous to add a number of sufficient size to make all of the scores positive. This normally makes absolutely no difference to the outcome of your statistical analysis. For example, the variance and standard deviation of −2, −5 and −6 are exactly the same if we add 6 to each of them. That is, calculate the variance and standard deviation of +4, +1 and 0 and you will find them to be identical to those for −2, −5 and −6. It is important that the same number is added to all of your scores. Doing this is helpful since many of us experience anxiety about negative values and prefer it if they are not there.

'Frequencies . . .' (Screenshot 4.3), or 'Legacy Dialogs' (Screenshot 5.5) or 'Chart Builder . . .' (Screenshot 8.9) on the 'Graphs' dropdown menu. The box plot gives the extreme values of your scores and the quartiles including the median.

4.5 Spread of scores: variance

Useful as the range is, a lot of information is ignored when calculating the range. It merely is based on the two extreme scores at each end of the distribution. Other measures of spread or variability involve the extent to which every score differs from the mean score.

One such measure is the mean deviation. To calculate this we have to work out the mean of the set of scores and then how much each score in the set differs from that mean. These deviations are then added up, ignoring the positive and negative signs, to give the total of deviations from the mean. Finally, we can divide by the number of scores to give the average or mean deviation from the mean of the set of scores. If we take the ages of the students listed above, we find that the total of the ages is $18 + 21 + 23 + 18 + 19 + 19 + 19 + 33 + 18 + 19 + 19 + 20 = 246$. Divide this total by 12 and we get the average age in the set to be 20.5 years. Note that this is the same value as given by SPSS in Screenshot 4.6. Now if we subtract 20.5 years from each of the student's ages we get the figures in Table 4.6.

So the average amount of deviation from the mean (ignoring the sign) is known as the mean deviation (for the deviations in Table 4.6 this would give a value of 2.6 years). The mean deviation is not used in research. However, there is a very closely related concept, variance, which is much more useful and has widespread and extensive applications. Actually it is crucial to many statistical techniques. Variance is calculated in an almost identical way to mean deviation but for one thing. When we draw up a table to calculate the variance, we square each deviation from the mean before summing the total of these squared deviations as shown in Table 4.7.

Table 4.6	Deviations from the mean	
Score − mean		**Deviation from mean**
18 − 20.5		−2.5
21 − 20.5		0.5
23 − 20.5		2.5
18 − 20.5		−2.5
19 − 20.5		−1.5
19 − 20.5		−1.5
19 − 20.5		−1.5
33 − 20.5		12.5
18 − 20.5		−2.5
19 − 20.5		−1.5
19 − 20.5		−1.5
20 − 20.5		−0.5

Table 4.7	Squared deviations from the mean	
Score − mean	**Deviation from mean**	**Square of deviation from mean**
18 − 20.5	−2.5	6.25
21 − 20.5	0.5	0.25
23 − 20.5	2.5	6.25
18 − 20.5	−2.5	6.25
19 − 20.5	−1.5	2.25
19 − 20.5	−1.5	2.25
19 − 20.5	−1.5	2.25
33 − 20.5	12.5	156.25
18 − 20.5	−2.5	6.25
19 − 20.5	−1.5	2.25
19 − 20.5	−1.5	2.25
20 − 20.5	−0.5	0.25
	Total = 0	Total = 193

The total of the squared deviations from the mean is 193. If we divide this by the number of scores (12), it gives us the value of the variance, which equals 16.08 in this case. Expressing the concept as a formula:

$$\text{variance} = \frac{\sum (X - \overline{X})^2}{N}$$

The statistical symbol for variance is σ^2.

The formula above says what variance is – it is the definition of the term. Variance is a statistical concept and so is defined mathematically. It is a technical concept and does not correspond exactly to more everyday or common-sense ideas. In statistics there are often quicker ways of doing calculations than using the defining formula. These quicker methods involve computational formulae as described in Box 4.3 though these are largely outmoded given computers. We include them for the reason that aspects of computational formula sometimes make an appearance in other contexts such as the analysis of variance (see Box 4.4).

Box 4.3	Focus on

Computational formulae in statistics

Before there were computers, psychologists would compute statistical formula by hand. This is time consuming and risks errors so we recommend that you avoid doing it. One way of easing the computational chore in the past was to use what are known as computational formulae.

These are little used now statistical analysis is almost always computerised. They occasionally pop-up in a slightly disguised form in some statistical techniques – especially the analysis of variance (Chapters 23 to 29). You may never need to use these computational formulae but being aware of them can help you understand some statistics better. In the light of all of this one computational formula is worth mentioning here – the formula for computing variance:

$$\text{variance}_{[\text{computational formula}]} = \frac{\sum X^2 - \frac{(\sum X)^2}{N}}{N}$$

Take care with elements of this formula:

X = the general symbol for each member of a set of scores
Σ = sigma or the summation sign, i.e. add up all the things which follow
$\sum X^2$ = the sum of the square of each of the scores
$(\sum X)^2$ = sum all the scores and square that total
N = the number of scores

This formula for variance is quicker to calculate by hand because it saves a lot of subtraction steps. If you understand the formula then fine but, if not, the important thing is simply to remember that there are quick formulae for doing calculations which are now outmoded but which appear in the explanation of some statistics. Using the scores $18 + 21 + 23 + 18 + 19 + 19 + 19 + 33 + 18 + 19 + 19 + 20$ again, and the computational formulae gives us the same value for the variance as before (i.e. 16.08):

$$\text{variance}_{(\text{computational formula})} = \frac{\sum X^2 - \frac{(\sum X)^2}{N}}{N}$$

$$= \frac{5236 - \frac{246^2}{12}}{12}$$

$$= \frac{5236 - \frac{60\,516}{12}}{12}$$

$$= \frac{5236 - 5043}{12} = \frac{193}{12}$$

$$= 16.08$$

There are some correlation coefficients (Chapter 8) such as Spearman's rho and phi which are nothing other than computational formula for special applications of the Pearson correlation coefficient.

| Box 4.4 | Key concepts |

Variance estimate

There is a concept called the *variance estimate* (or estimated variance) which is closely related to variance. The difference is that the variance estimate is your best guess as to the variance of a population of scores *if* you only have the data from a small set of scores from that population on which to base your estimate. The variance estimate is described in detail in Chapter 22. It involves a slight amendment to the variance formula in that instead of dividing by N one divides by $N - 1$.

The formula for the estimated population variance is:

$$\text{estimated variance} = \frac{\sum (X - \overline{X})^2}{N - 1}$$

Although not strictly speaking correct, it is common practice to refer to the variance estimate simply as variance. So if you calculate variance on SPSS you will not get the same value as elsewhere in this chapter but the one based on the formula above. Since virtually all statistical analyses in psychology are based on samples from which we wish to generalise, the variance estimate is likely to be used in most if not all practical situations. Hence it is reasonable to use the estimated variance as the general formula for variance. The drawback to this is that if we are merely describing the data, this practice is theoretically imprecise. As everyone else refers to the variance estimate as the variance, you will be in good company if you follow suit.

If we calculate the estimated variance using the data in Table 4.5, we need to divide 193 by 11 instead of the 12 that we did earlier. 193 divided by 11 is 17.545 or 17.55. This is the value you will get using SPSS as we describe in the Computer Analysis at the end of this chapter. This is shown in Screenshot 4.6 and confirms that SPSS is calculating the variance estimate.

■ Interpreting the results

Variance is difficult to interpret in isolation because of its mathematical abstractness. You need more information about the data since variance is dependent on the measurement in question. Measures which are based on a wide numerical scale for the scores will tend to have higher variance than measures based on a narrow scale. Thus if the range of scores is only 10 then the variance is likely to be less than if the range of scores is 100. The variance of age for the general population is greater than for university students. Interpreting variance is easier when comparing the variances of two different groups (see Chapter 22) than looking at the variance of one group in isolation.

■ Reporting the results

Usually variance is routinely reported in tables which summarise a variable or a number of variables along with other statistics such as the mean and range. This is shown in Table 4.8. *Standard deviation (see Chapter 6) is computationally very closely related to variance. Indeed, textbooks often describe them at the same time. It is better to maintain their distinctiveness.*

Table 4.8	Illustrating the table for descriptive statistics			
Variable	N	Mean	Variance	Range
Age	12	20.50 years	16.08	15 years

Research examples

Averages, variation and spread

It is difficult to imagine quantitative research studies in psychology which do NOT give details of averages and variation in some form. Typically very little space is devoted to this and highly stylised and structured ways of presenting such information are used. So you could open virtually any psychology journal describing an empirical study and you are almost certain to find them reported. Although variance is the basic measure of variation it is not so often reported. Modern psychologists seem to prefer to use standard deviation (SD) instead (standard deviation is the square root of variance). However, variance, standard deviation and standard error can be used virtually interchangeably as they are closely related and any researcher worth their salt knows the relationship between the three. Here are just a few examples.

Cetinkalp (2012) provides some basic information on those taking part in his study of achievement goals in sport in the following way: 'Participants comprised 208 adolescent athletes of whom 120 were female ($M \pm SD = 16.33 \pm 0.47$)) and 88 male ($M \pm SD = 16.38 \pm 0.49$) with a mean of age of 16.35 ± 0.48 years. Participants, who took part in handball and volleyball competition at a regional level in Adana, Turkey, reported that their sport experience was 4.00 ± 2.41 years, and they trained for 3.59 ± 1.75 days per week.' (pp. 467–8).

Otgaar and colleagues (2012) reported the characteristics of the participants of their study of correct and incorrect reports of being touched as: 'Eighty 4/5-year-olds (40 girls; mean age 4.66 years (56 months), $SD = 0.53$ (6.36 months)) and 80 9/10-year-olds (36 girls; mean age 9.50 (114 months), $SD = 0.64$ (7.68 months)) obtained parental consent for their participation. These children were recruited from different primary schools in the Netherlands.' (p. 643).

Van Schaik and Ling (2012) write of their study: 'One hundred and fourteen undergraduate psychology students (91 female, 23 male), with a mean age of 22.66 years ($SD = 6.03$) took part in the experiment. There were 30 participants in the condition of low artifact complexity/low task complexity, 29 in the low/high condition, 28 in the high/low condition, and 27 in the high/high condition. All participants had used the Web. Mean experience using the Web was 9.68 years ($SD = 3.03$), mean time per week spent using the Web was 17.25 hr ($SD = 16.73$) and mean frequency of Web use per week was 14.76 ($SD = 9.87$).' (p. 209).

Key points

- Because they are routine ways of summarising the typical score and the spread of a set of scores, it is important always to report the following information for each of your variables:

  - mean, median and mode

  - range and variance (or more commonly) standard deviation

  - number of scores in the set of scores.

- ***The above does not apply to nominal categories.*** For these, the mode and the frequency of cases in each category exhausts the main possibilities.

- It is worth trying to memorise the definitional and computational formulae for variance. You will be surprised how often these formulae appear in statistics.

- When using a computer, look carefully for variables that have zero variance. They can cause problems and generally ought to be omitted from your analyses. Normally the computer will not compute the calculations you ask for in these circumstances. The difficulty is that if all the scores of a variable are the same, it is impossible to calculate many statistical formulae. It is not surprising that a computer won't calculate variance if there is no variance in the data!

COMPUTER ANALYSIS

Descriptive statistics using SPSS

Data	• Name variables in 'Variable View' of the 'Data Editor'. In the example, the only variable is termed 'Age' but you could have several variables (Screenshot 4.1).
2	• Move to the 'Data View' by clicking on the tab at the bottom of your screen.
3	• Enter the data under the appropriate variable names. So the data in our example have been entered under 'age'. The 12 scores listed are the ones given in Table 4.5 (also Screenshot 4.2).
Analysis	• Select 'Analyze', 'Descriptive Statistics' and 'Frequencies...'. You can see the selections highlighted in Screenshot 4.3.
2	• Move the variables to be analysed to the right hand box by clicking on your choice and using the arrow button at the middle of the screen (Screenshot 4.4).
3	• Select 'Statistics...', 'Mean', 'Median', 'Mode', 'Variance' and 'Range' or whichever ones you require (Screenshot 4.5). We have included standard deviation to show how easy it is to compute statistics which we haven't even discussed yet.
Output	• These statistics are presented in a single table (Screenshot 4.6).
2	• Notice that the calculation for variance is not the same as we calculated in this chapter. This is because SPSS gives the variance estimate rather than the variance. It also gives the estimated standard deviation rather than the standard deviation.
3	• It is best to be precise and call the estimated variance and estimated standard deviation just that. However, given this, there is no problem in reporting these estimated values rather than variance and standard deviation. It is common to do so.

FIGURE 4.3	SPSS steps for descriptive statistics when dealing with scores

Interpreting and reporting the output

● In the example calculated, we can see that the mean, median and mode are relatively similar. The variance is 17.55 to two decimal places. These are the basic facts. It is difficult to say much more without having additional variables for comparison.

● One could write 'The ages of the sample had a mean of 20.50 years with a median of 19.00 and a mode of 19. These are fairly close and perhaps indicate that the distribution is fairly symmetrical. The estimated variance was large at 17.55 reflecting the large value of the range (15).'

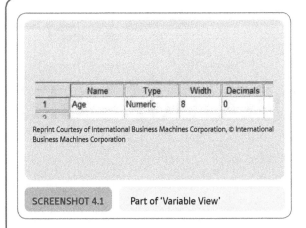

	Name	Type	Width	Decimals
1	Age	Numeric	8	0

Reprint Courtesy of International Business Machines Corporation, © International Business Machines Corporation

SCREENSHOT 4.1   Part of 'Variable View'

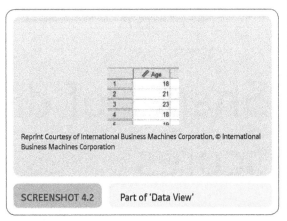

Reprint Courtesy of International Business Machines Corporation, © International Business Machines Corporation

SCREENSHOT 4.2   Part of 'Data View'

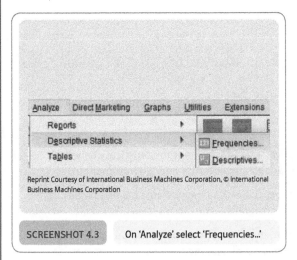

Reprint Courtesy of International Business Machines Corporation, © International Business Machines Corporation

SCREENSHOT 4.3   On 'Analyze' select 'Frequencies...'

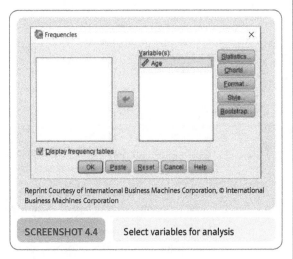

Reprint Courtesy of International Business Machines Corporation, © International Business Machines Corporation

SCREENSHOT 4.4   Select variables for analysis

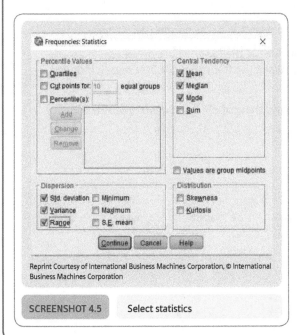

Reprint Courtesy of International Business Machines Corporation, © International Business Machines Corporation

SCREENSHOT 4.5   Select statistics

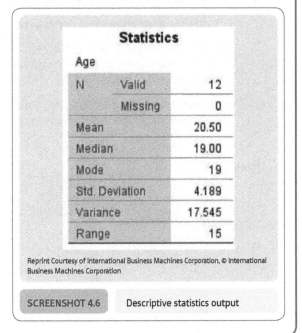

Statistics

Age

N	Valid	12
	Missing	0
Mean		20.50
Median		19.00
Mode		19
Std. Deviation		4.189
Variance		17.545
Range		15

Reprint Courtesy of International Business Machines Corporation, © International Business Machines Corporation

SCREENSHOT 4.6   Descriptive statistics output

CHAPTER 5

Shapes of distributions of scores

Overview

- The shape of the distribution of scores on a variable is important in statistical analysis. A histogram of the frequencies of scores on a variable provides the needed information.

- The normal distribution forms part of the theory underlying many statistical techniques. It is best remembered as a bell-shaped frequency diagram.

- The normal distribution is symmetrical. That is, it can be folded perfectly on itself at the mean. Such symmetry is another 'ideal' in many statistical techniques. Non-symmetrical distributions are called skewed distributions.

- Kurtosis indicates how steep or flat a curve is compared with the normal (bell-shaped) curve.

- Cumulative frequencies are ones which include all of the lower values on an accumulating basis. So the highest score will always have a cumulative frequency of 100% since it includes all of the smaller scores.

- Percentiles are the numerical values of the score that cut off the lowest 10%, 30%, 95% or what have you of the distribution of scores.

Preparation

Be clear about numerical scores and how they can be classified into ranges of scores (Chapter 3).

5.1 Introduction

The final important characteristic of scores on a variable is their frequency distribution's particular shape. Obviously virtually any shape of distribution is possible given the multitude of potential variables. However, there are a few shapes which are particularly important in statistics. We shall discuss these. The key steps when planning to discuss the shapes of data distributions are given in Figure 5.1.

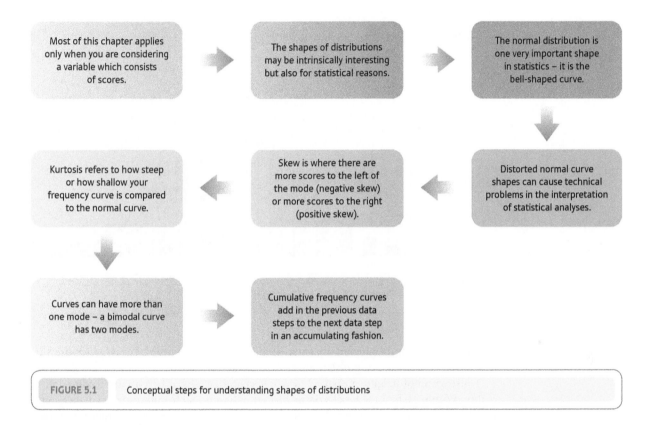

Most of this chapter applies only when you are considering a variable which consists of scores.	The shapes of distributions may be intrinsically interesting but also for statistical reasons.	The normal distribution is one very important shape in statistics – it is the bell-shaped curve.
Kurtosis refers to how steep or how shallow your frequency curve is compared to the normal curve.	Skew is where there are more scores to the left of the mode (negative skew) or more scores to the right (positive skew).	Distorted normal curve shapes can cause technical problems in the interpretation of statistical analyses.
Curves can have more than one mode – a bimodal curve has two modes.	Cumulative frequency curves add in the previous data steps to the next data step in an accumulating fashion.	

FIGURE 5.1   Conceptual steps for understanding shapes of distributions

5.2 Histograms and frequency curves

Most of us have very little difficulty in understanding histograms; we know that they are plots of the frequency of scores (the vertical dimension) against a numerical scale (the horizontal dimension). Figure 5.2 is an example of a histogram based on a relatively small set of scores. This histogram is quite angular and not a smooth shape at all going from bar to bar. Partly this is because the horizontal numerical scale moves along in discrete steps, so resulting in this pattern. Things would be different if we measured on a *continuous scale* on which every possible score could be represented to the smallest fraction. For example, we might decide to measure people's heights in centimetres to the nearest whole centimetre. But we know that heights do not really conform to this set of discrete steps or points; people who measure 120 centimetres actually differ in height by up to a centimetre from each other. Height can be measured in fractions of centimetres, not just whole centimetres. In other words, height is a continuous

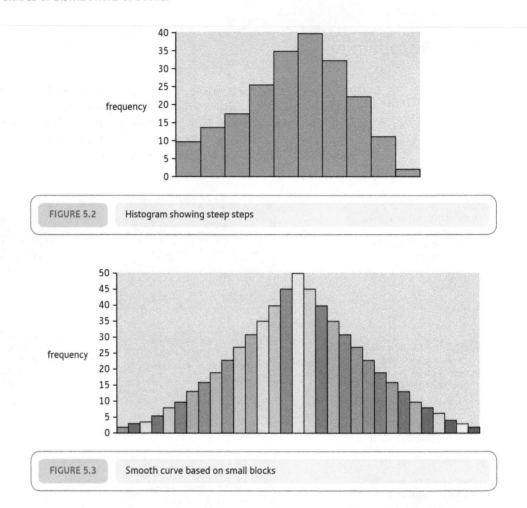

FIGURE 5.2   Histogram showing steep steps

FIGURE 5.3   Smooth curve based on small blocks

measurement with infinitesimally small steps between measures so long as we use sufficiently precise measuring instruments.

A histogram of heights measured in whole centimetres is at best an approximation to reality. Within each of the blocks of the histogram is a possible multitude of smaller steps. For this reason, it is conventional when drawing frequency curves for theoretical purposes to smooth out the blocks to form a continuous curve. In essence, this is like taking much finer and more precise measurements and redrawing the histogram. Instead of doing this literally we approximate it by drawing a smooth curve through imaginary sets of extremely small steps. In this way, our histogram is 'miraculously' turned into a continuous unstepped curve (try doing this with Figure 5.3 compared to Figure 5.2).

A frequency curve can, of course, be of virtually any shape but one shape in particular is of concern in psychological statistics – the normal curve.

5.3   Normal curve

The normal curve describes a particular shape of the frequency curve. Although this shape is defined by a formula and so can be described mathematically, for most purposes regard it as a symmetrical bell-shape (Figure 5.4). Actually, to be pedantic, two normal curves can look very different from each other because a normal curve is defined by a mathematical

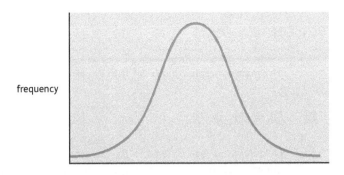

frequency

FIGURE 5.4   Normal (bell-shaped) frequency curve

formula, not a precise shape (Huck, 2009). Ultra-pedantically, the bell-shape does not apply to all normal curves but is good enough a description for most purposes.

Once it was believed that distributions in the natural world corresponded to the 'normal' shape, hence the name. Even though the perfect normal curve is uncommon, nevertheless many distributions are roughly this shape – at least sufficiently so for most practical purposes. The crucial reason the normal curve is important is that theoreticians developed many statistical techniques assuming that the distributions of scores had this particular bell-shape. However, this assumption has relatively little bearing on the day-to-day application of these statistical techniques. That is, the distributions need only be roughly bell-shaped for the statistic to work effectively enough. Substantial violations of normality make little difference to the outcome of the statistical test. Of course, the more your data correspond to the normal curve the more precise your statistical test will be. Perhaps psychologists have worried too much in the past about non-normality. As a rule of thumb, it has been suggested that for practical purposes, you can disregard deviations from the ideal distribution, especially when dealing with about 30 or more scores. Unfortunately, all of this involves a degree of subjective judgement since there are no useful ways of assessing what is an acceptable amount of deviation from the ideal when faced with the small amounts of data that student projects often involve. If you wish you can use statistics which do not involve the normal curve (Chapter 21). Some of these are known as nonparametric or distribution-free methods. Furthermore, it is possible to use bootstrapping (see Box 21.1) with many statistical techniques which usually are based on the normal distribution. In bootstrapping the theoretical normal distribution is replaced by the distribution of randomly drawn samples based on the available data. So there are alternative versions of many statistical tests which avoid the issue of normality. As yet, bootstrapping is underutilised by psychologists. Bootstrapping methods are often easy on SPSS. Exceptions will be mentioned as appropriate in later chapters.

Don't forget that for the perfectly symmetrical, bell-shaped (normal) curve the values of the mean, median and mode are identical. Disparities between the three are indications that you have an asymmetrical curve.

5.4   Distorted curves

The main concepts which deal with distortions in the normal curve are *skewness* and *kurtosis*.

■ Skewness

Despite what was written in the previous section, always consider the shape of the frequency distributions for all of your variables. Gross skewness is the exception to our rule of thumb that non-normality of data has little influence on statistical analyses. By skewness we mean the extent to which your frequency curve is lopsided rather than symmetrical. A mid-point of a frequency curve may be skewed either to the left or to the right of the range of scores (Figures 5.5 and 5.6).

There are special terms for left-handed and right-handed skew:

- *Negative skew:*
  - more scores are to the left of the mode than to the right
  - the mean and median are smaller than the mode.

- *Positive skew:*
  - more scores are to the right of the mode than to the left
  - the mean and median are bigger than the mode.

There is also an index of the amount of skew shown in your set of scores. Looking at the frequency curve for the variable in question will give you a good idea of whether there

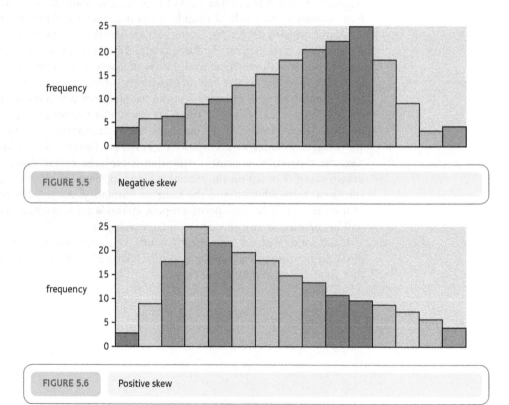

FIGURE 5.5   Negative skew

FIGURE 5.6   Positive skew

is skewness. The index of skewness is positive for a positive skew and negative for a negative skew. Appendix A explains how to test for skewness in your data. SPSS includes skewness in 'Frequencies . . .' (Screenshot 4.5), 'Explore . . .' (Screenshot 4.3) and 'Statistics . . .', and 'Descriptive Statistics' (Screenshot 12.2) and 'Options . . .' (Screenshot 12.4) if you request it. For a perfect normal distribution the value of skewness would be 0.

Kurtosis (or steepness/shallowness)

Some symmetrical curves may look rather like the normal bell-shaped curve except that they are excessively steep or excessively flat compared to the mathematically defined normal bell-shaped curve (Figures 5.7 and 5.8).

Kurtosis is the term used to identify the degree of steepness or shallowness of a distribution. There are technical words for different types of curve:

- a steep curve is called *leptokurtic*

- a normal curve is called *mesokurtic*

- a flat curve is called *platykurtic*.

These are terms beloved of statistics book writers. However, since the terms mean nothing more than steep, middling and flat there is probably good reason to avoid these Greek words in favour of clear descriptions in everyday English.

It is possible to obtain indexes of the amount of shallowness or steepness of your distribution compared with the mathematically defined normal distribution. An inspection of the frequency curve of your data will give you a good enough idea for most

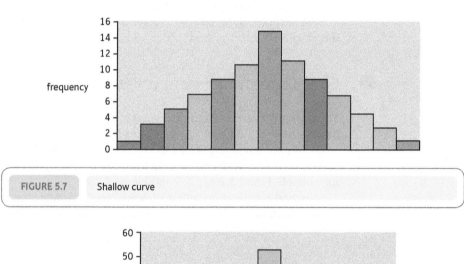

| FIGURE 5.7 | Shallow curve |

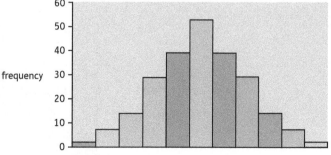

| FIGURE 5.8 | Steep curve |

purposes. Knowing what the index means should help you cope with computer output; quite simply:

- a positive value of kurtosis means that the curve is steep compared to the normal curve
- a zero value of kurtosis means that the curve is middling – just like the normal curve
- a negative value of kurtosis means that the curve is flatter compared to the normal curve.

SPSS includes kurtosis in 'Frequencies . . .' (Screenshot 4.5), 'Explore . . .' (Screenshot 4.3) and 'Statistics . . .', and 'Descriptive Statistics' (Screenshot 12.2) and 'Options . . .' (Screenshot 12.4) if you request it. A value of 0 means no kurtosis, a negative value indicates a flat curve, and a positive value indicates a steep curve.

Steepness and shallowness have little or no bearing on the statistical techniques you use to analyse your data, quite unlike skewness.

5.5 Other frequency curves

■ Bimodal and multimodal frequency distributions

There is no rule that says that frequency curves have to peak in the middle and tail off to the left and right. As we have already explained, it is perfectly possible to have a frequency distribution with twin peaks (or even multiple peaks). Such twin-peaked distributions are called *bimodal* since they have two modes – most frequently occurring scores. Such a frequency curve might look like Figure 5.9.

SPSS includes the mode in 'Frequencies . . .' (Screenshot 4.3), 'Variable' (Screenshot 4.4), 'Statistics . . .' and 'Mode' (Screenshot 4.5), and output (Screenshot 4.6).

■ Cumulative frequency curves

There are any number of different ways of presenting a single set of data. Take, for example, the 50 scores in Table 5.1 for a measure of extraversion obtained from airline pilots.

One way of tabulating these extraversion scores is simply to count the number of pilots scoring at each value of extraversion from 1 to 5. This could be presented in several forms, for example Tables 5.2 and 5.3 and Figure 5.10.

Exactly the same distribution of scores could be represented using a *cumulative* frequency distribution. A simple frequency distribution merely indicates the number of

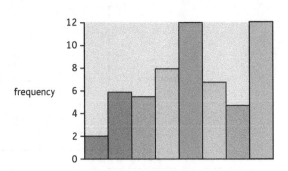

| FIGURE 5.9 | Bimodal frequency histogram |

Table 5.1	Extraversion scores of 50 airline pilots								
3	5	5	4	4	5	5	3	5	2
1	2	5	3	2	1	2	3	3	3
4	2	5	5	4	2	4	5	1	5
5	3	3	4	1	4	2	5	1	2
3	2	5	4	2	1	2	3	4	1

Table 5.2	Frequency table based on data in Table 5.1
Number scoring 1	7
Number scoring 2	11
Number scoring 3	10
Number scoring 4	9
Number scoring 5	13

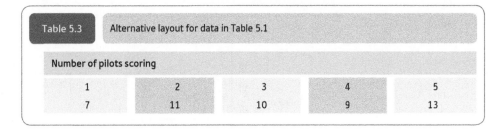

Table 5.3	Alternative layout for data in Table 5.1

Number of pilots scoring

1	2	3	4	5
7	11	10	9	13

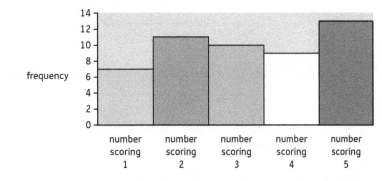

FIGURE 5.10	Histogram of Table 5.1

people who achieved any particular score. A cumulative frequency distribution gives the number scoring, say, one, two or less, three or less, four or less, and five or less. In other words, the frequencies accumulate. Examples of cumulative frequency distributions are given in Tables 5.4 and 5.5 and Figure 5.11. Cumulative frequencies can be given also as cumulative percentage frequencies in which the frequencies are expressed as percentages and these percentages accumulated. This is shown in Table 5.4.

There is nothing difficult about cumulative frequencies. However, you must label such tables and diagrams clearly – simply by using the word cumulative wherever appropriate –

Table 5.4	Cumulative frequency distribution of pilots' extraversion scores from Table 5.1	
Score range	**Cumulative frequency**	**Cumulative percentage frequency**
1	7	14%
2 or less	18	36%
3 or less	28	56%
4 or less	37	74%
5 or less	50	100%

Table 5.5	Alternative style of cumulative frequency distribution of pilots' extraversion scores from Table 5.1			
Number of pilots scoring				
1	2 or less	3 or less	4 or less	5 or less
7	18	28	37	50

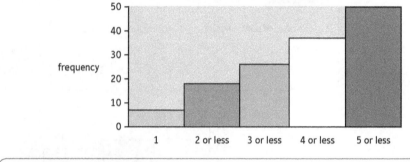

FIGURE 5.11   Cumulative histogram of the frequencies of pilots' extraversion scores from Table 5.1

To compute a frequency distribution in SPSS see the Computer Analysis at the end of this chapter.

Percentiles

Percentiles are merely a form of cumulative frequency distribution, but instead of being expressed in terms of accumulating scores from lowest to highest, the categorisation is in terms of whole numbers of percentages of people. In other words, the percentile is the score which a given percentage of scores equals or is less than. You do not necessarily have to report every percentage point and units of 10 might suffice for some purposes. Such a distribution would look something like Table 5.6. The table shows that 10% of scores are equal to 7 or less and 80% of scores are equal to 61 or less. Note that the 50th percentile corresponds to the median score (but not necessarily the mean or mode). Quartiles which we discussed in the previous chapter in connection with the interquartile range are merely the 25th percentile, the 50th percentile which is also the median, and

Table 5.6	Example of percentiles

Percentile	Score
10th	7
20th	9
30th	14
40th	20
50th	39
60th	45
70th	50
80th	61
90th	70
100th	78

Percentiles are commonly used in standardisation tables of psychological tests and measures. That is, tables which present information on the distribution of test scores based on large samples of people. For these it is often very useful to be able to describe a person's standing compared with the set of individuals on which the test or measure was initially researched. Thus if a particular person's neuroticism score is described as being at the 90th percentile it means that they are more neurotic than about 90% of people. In other words, percentiles are a quick method of expressing a person's score relative to those of others. Not using percentiles can result in rather clumsy and convoluted explanations.

In order to calculate the percentiles for any data, first produce a table of cumulative percentage frequencies. This table is then examined to find the score which cuts off, for example, the bottom 10%, the bottom 20%, the bottom 30%, etc. of scores. It should be obvious that calculating percentiles in this way is actually easier if there are a large number of scores so that the cut-off points can be found precisely.

To compute percentiles on SPSS, select 'Frequencies . . .' (Screenshot 4.3), the 'Variable' and 'Statistics . . .' (Screenshot 4.4), 'Percentile(s)' and enter or add the percentile points you want (Screenshot 4.5).

Research examples

Kurtosis, skew, etc.

Brasel and Gips (2011) were interested in people's use of what the researchers term the media landscape, which includes television and the internet. Just what happens when people use either of these media? Using a laboratory-based design, individuals were studied when they 'multitasked' (i.e. used a computer and television simultaneously). One of the findings was the strongly skewed nature of people's gaze at the screen. People gazed longer at the computer than the television. Nevertheless, the conclusion was that the distribution of gaze is strongly skewed – short duration gazes of only a few seconds dominate. One of the intriguing findings was that people were very poor at estimating the extent of their gaze-switching behaviour compared with the objective reality as measured by the researchers.

→

Peters and Durding (1978) were interested in the relationship between laterality (right versus left-handedness) and the differences between performance on a simple tapping task for the left and right hand. Of course, obvious preference for the use of one hand to perform tasks will tend to emphasise that laterality has a biased distribution (many people are right-handed, some are left-handed, and a few have no clear preference). However, handedness in task performances not allowing such a preference is different and some have regarded it as a continuous variable. The tapping task involved in this study had children tapping with the index finger as fast as possible over a series of timed trials using the different index fingers. Laterality preference was assessed by having the child show the researcher how to do things like hammering in a nail, combing hair and brushing teeth. The hand chosen was recorded as the preferred hand. An index of laterality was calculated for a range of this sort of task. There was a linear relationship between the left/right speed of finger tapping and the child's laterality as measured by the preference test for activities. Furthermore, the distribution of the tapping task differences was symmetrical about the mean and it was unimodal rather than, say, bimodal which would indicate discontinuities in handedness. This was not at all the case for the preference task. However, the distribution for finger tapping differences was more peaked than the normal distribution, indicating a degree of kurtosis which was significant. Overall, the research provided some support for the idea that laterality in performance is a continuous variable.

Wickham, Morris and Fritz (2000) addressed the question of the distinctiveness of faces. One conventional assumption is that there are many relatively typical faces but rather few that are distinctive. This would indicate a highly skewed distribution in terms of facial distinctiveness. The researchers went about testing this using three separate but related studies which used different ways of estimating distinctiveness. For example, traditional ratings of distinctiveness produced normal distributions but ratings that emphasised the amount of deviation from the typical face were very skewed. In their first study, however, they used traditional ratings of distinctiveness of faces. They used the distance on a physical scale such that 0 equalled extremely typical and 9 would be extremely distinctive. The mean rating was found to be 3.7 cm with a skewness of 0.25 and kurtosis of -0.91. A bar chart for these data looks relatively flat and there is a long tail towards the distinctiveness end of the continuum.

Key points

- The most important concept in this chapter is that of the normal curve or normal distribution. It is worth extra effort to memorise the idea that the normal curve is a bell-shaped symmetrical curve.

- Be a little wary if you find that your scores on a variable are very *skewed* since this can lose precision in certain statistical analyses.

COMPUTER ANALYSIS

Frequencies using SPSS

Data	• Name the variables in 'Variable View' of the 'Data Editor'. • Enter the data under the appropriate variables names in 'Data View' of the 'Data Editor' (Screenshot 5.1).
Analysis	• For frequency tables, select 'Analyze', 'Descriptive Statistics' and 'Frequencies...' (Screenshot 5.2). • Move variables to be analysed to right hand side box (Screenshot 5.3).
2	• For histograms, select 'Graphs', and then either 'Chart Builder...' or 'Legacy Dialogs' (Screenshot 5.5).
Output	• The frequency table shows the frequency as well as the percentage of the frequency for each value (Screenshot 5.4). • If needed, use the 'Chart Editor' to edit the histogram (Screenshot 5.6).

FIGURE 5.12   SPSS steps for frequency tables and histograms

Interpreting and reporting the output

- The frequency table and histogram should be studied to identify their most characteristic features. Since tables and histograms are basically descriptive methods then their features may simply be reported and little or nothing by way of interpretation may be necessary.

- Although frequency tables and histograms may be presented in your report, be careful to ensure that what appears is clear and effective. Too many tables and histograms can be distracting if not confusing. Perhaps you should find ways of reducing their number without changing effectiveness. Make sure that any that you use are properly labelled and mentioned in the text. In our experience, SPSS tables and histograms can always be improved by careful reflection and using the chart editor, etc. It is easy to create a bad impression by including tables and diagrams which add nothing or even confuse the reader.

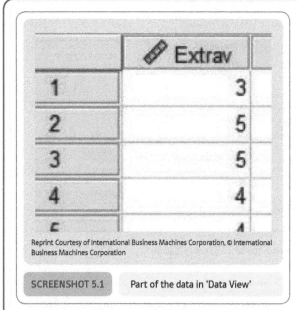

Reprint Courtesy of International Business Machines Corporation, © International Business Machines Corporation

SCREENSHOT 5.1 Part of the data in 'Data View'

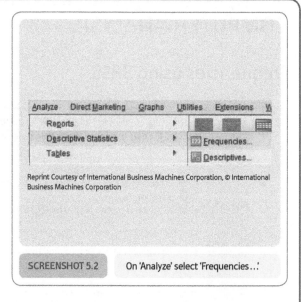

Reprint Courtesy of International Business Machines Corporation, © International Business Machines Corporation

SCREENSHOT 5.2 On 'Analyze' select 'Frequencies…'

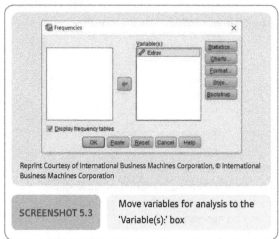

Reprint Courtesy of International Business Machines Corporation, © International Business Machines Corporation

SCREENSHOT 5.3 Move variables for analysis to the 'Variable(s):' box

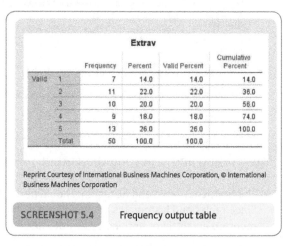

Extrav

		Frequency	Percent	Valid Percent	Cumulative Percent
Valid	1	7	14.0	14.0	14.0
	2	11	22.0	22.0	36.0
	3	10	20.0	20.0	56.0
	4	9	18.0	18.0	74.0
	5	13	26.0	26.0	100.0
	Total	50	100.0	100.0	

Reprint Courtesy of International Business Machines Corporation, © International Business Machines Corporation

SCREENSHOT 5.4 Frequency output table

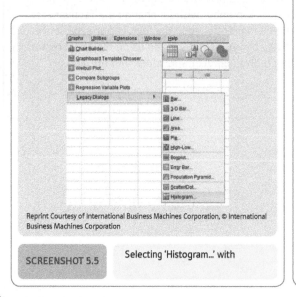

Reprint Courtesy of International Business Machines Corporation, © International Business Machines Corporation

SCREENSHOT 5.5 Selecting 'Histogram…' with

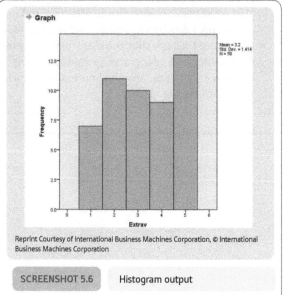

Reprint Courtesy of International Business Machines Corporation, © International Business Machines Corporation

SCREENSHOT 5.6 Histogram output

CHAPTER 6

Standard deviation and z-scores

Standard unit of measurement in statistics

Overview

- Standard deviation computationally is the square root of variance (Chapter 4).

- Think of standard deviation as a unit of distance along a frequency distribution of scores.

- The estimated standard deviation is calculated by SPSS and other packages. Nevertheless, it is almost universally referred to as the standard deviation. If you are using a sample to estimate the characteristics of a population then the estimated standard deviation should be used. Almost invariably, this is what psychologists are doing. But knowing about both makes the explanation more understandable.

- Because the normal (bell-shaped) curve is a standard shape, it is possible to give the distribution as percentages of cases which lie between any two points on the frequency distribution. Tables are available to do this easily if necessary.

- It is common to express scores as z-scores. A z-score for a particular score is simply the number of standard deviations that the score lies from the mean of the distribution. (A negative sign is used to indicate that the score lies below the mean.) Z-scores are also referred to as standardised scores or standard scores.

Preparation

Make sure you know the meaning of variables, scores, Σ and scales of measurement – especially nominal, interval and ratio (Chapter 2).

6.1   Introduction

Measurement ideally uses standard or universal units. It would be really stupid if, when we ask people how far it is to the nearest railway station, one person says 347 cow's lengths, another says 150 poodle jumps and a third person says three times the distance between my doctor's house and my dentist's surgery. If you ask us how hot it was on midsummer's day you would be pretty annoyed if one of us said 27 degrees Howitt and the other said 530 degrees Cramer. We measure in standard units such as centimetres, degrees Celsius, kilograms and so forth. The advantages of doing so are obvious: standard units of measurement allow us to communicate easily, precisely and effectively with other researchers.

It is much the same in statistics but there is a difficulty. Statistics is applied to data of all sorts and in all sorts of disciplines. So how is it possible for the same statistical methods to be applied to things measured in kilograms and to more abstract things in psychology such as acquiescence tendency? Although it would be nice if statisticians had a standard unit of measurement, it is not intuitively obvious what this should be.

6.2   Theoretical background

Imagine a 30 centimetre rule – it will be marked in 1 centimetre units from 0 centimetres to 30 centimetres (Figure 6.1). The standard unit of measurement here is the centimetre. But you could have a different sort of rule in which instead of the scale being from 0 to 30 centimetres, the mid-point of the scale is 0 and the scale is marked as $-15, -14, -13,$ $\ldots, -1, 0, +1, \ldots, +13, +14, +15$ centimetres. This rule is in essence marked in deviation units (Figure 6.2).

The two rules use the same unit of measurement (the centimetre) but the deviation rule is marked with 0 in the middle, not at the left-hand side. In other words, the mid-point of the scale is marked as 0 deviation (from the mid-point). The standard deviation is similar to this rule in so far as it is based on *distances or deviations* from the average or mid-point.

One of the odd things about the standard deviation is that its value is dependent on the variability of the scores. So the standard deviation might be 5 or it might be 7 of the

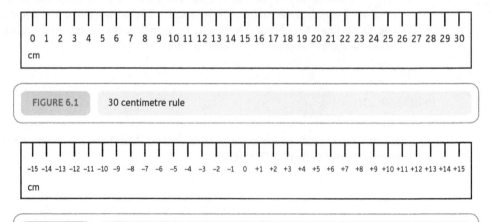

FIGURE 6.1   30 centimetre rule

FIGURE 6.2   30 centimetre rule using deviation units

units in which the scores were measured. For example, it could be 5 inches or 2 IQ points and so forth. But we can talk about the number of standard deviations a score is away from the mean. In this way, we can ignore the units of measurement. So the number of standard deviations a score is away from the mean is a sort of standard measurement unit. That is, although the standard deviation itself depends on the data involved, the number of standard deviations frees us from the measurement scale. Standard deviation is a key concept in statistics; it is nearly universal in quantitative analyses. So it is worth spending time getting to terms with it. It allows the standardisation of variables and makes comparisons between very different measures possible.

Some statisticians would have apoplexy but we think that the best way of understanding standard deviation is that it is a *measure of the amount by which scores differ from the mean or average score*. Of course, each score will differ by a different amount from the mean and some scores will differ in a positive direction and other scores will differ in a negative direction. So a particular score may be described as being 1.5 standard deviations from the mean. It is quite an odd idea to base a standard unit of measurement on the variability in the data rather than some absolute standard. And we need to be a little cautious about suggesting that the standard deviation is the average deviation from the mean – this might cause more statisticians apoplexy. The standard deviation is not calculated in the way that one might expect. The obvious way would be as follows and it is wrong. Imagine that the scores were 4, 6, 3 and 7 then the mean is 20 divided by 4 (the number of scores), or 5. Each of the four scores deviates from the average by a certain amount – for example, 7 deviates from the mean of 5 by just 2. The sum of the deviations of our four scores from the mean of 5 is $1 + 1 + 2 + 2$ which equals 6. Surely, then, the standard deviation is 6 divided by 4, which equals 1.5?

But this is *not* how statisticians work out the average deviation for their standard unit. Such an approach might seem logical, but it turns out to be not very useful in practice. Instead *standard deviation uses a different type of average which most mortals would not even recognise as an average.*

The big difference is that standard deviation is calculated as the average *squared* deviation. Instead of taking our four deviation scores $(1 + 1 + 2 + 2)$ we square each of them $(1^2 + 1^2 + 2^2 + 2^2)$ which gives $1 + 1 + 4 + 4 = 10$. If we divide this total deviation of 10 by the number of scores (4), this gives a value of 2.5. However, this is still not quite the end of the story since *we then have to calculate the square root of this peculiar average deviation from the mean*. Thus we take the 2.5 and work out its square root – that is, 1.58. In words, *the standard deviation is the square root of the average squared deviation from the mean.*

And that really is it – honest. It is a pity that one of the most important concepts in statistics is less than intuitively obvious, but there we are. To summarise:

- The standard deviation is the standard unit of measurement in statistics.

- The standard deviation is simply the 'average' amount that the scores on a variable deviate (or differ) from the mean of the set of scores. In essence, the standard deviation is the average deviation from the mean. Think of it like this since most of us will have little difficulty grasping it in these terms. Its peculiarities can be safely ignored for most purposes. Of course, this being statistics, standard deviation is defined as a formula. Putting it into understandable words can only approximate what it is.

- Although the standard deviation is an average, it is not the sort of average which most of us are used to. However, it is of greater use in statistical applications than any other way of calculating the average deviation from the mean.

It should be stressed that the *standard deviation is not a unit-free measure*. If we measured a set of people's heights in centimetres, the standard deviation of their heights would also be a certain number of   If we measured 50 people's intelligences using an intelligence test, the standard deviation would be a certain number of IQ points. It might help you to remember this, although most people would say or write things like 'the standard deviation of height was 4.5' without mentioning the units of measurement. Figure 6.3 gives the key steps in relation to using standard deviation.

The standard deviation gives greater numerical emphasis to scores which depart by larger amounts from the mean. The reason is that it involves squared deviations from the mean which give disproportionately more emphasis to larger deviations.

The standard deviation is important for many reasons. It is often used in preference to variance as an indicator of the amount of variability there is in the scores. This makes sense because variance is simply the square of the standard deviation. The more spread in the scores the bigger will be the standard deviation and the variance.

The standard deviation and the estimated standard deviation are slightly different. The estimated standard deviation is used when you are generalising from a sample to the population from which the sample was taken. However, the distinction between the two has become blurred and invariably researchers give the estimated standard deviation though they refer to it as the standard deviation. One good reason for this is that researchers overwhelmingly are trying to say something about the population on the basis of the sample data. When you use SPSS to calculate standard deviation it gives you the estimated standard deviation. The calculation of the estimated standard deviation involves dividing by the sample size minus one $(N - 1)$ instead of the sample size. Another way of saying this, as we shall see, is that we divide by the degrees of freedom rather than the sample size. You will frequently come across degrees of freedom in psychological statistics.

The calculation of the estimated standard deviation using SPSS is described at the end of this chapter.

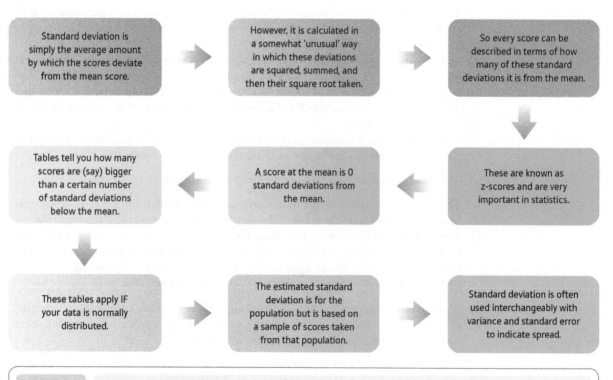

| FIGURE 6.3 | Conceptual steps for understanding standard deviation |

Explaining statistics 6.1

How standard deviation works

The defining formula for standard deviation is as follows:

$$\text{standard deviation} = \sqrt{\frac{\sum(X - \overline{X})^2}{N}}$$

or the computationally quicker formula is:

$$\text{standard deviation} = \sqrt{\frac{\sum X^2 - \frac{(\sum X)^2}{N}}{N}}$$

Table 6.1 lists the ages of nine students (N = number of scores = 9) and shows steps in calculating the standard deviation. Substituting these values in the standard deviation formula:

Table 6.1	Steps in the calculation of the standard deviation
Scores (X) (age in years)	**Scores squared (X^2)**
20	400
25	625
19	361
35	1225
19	361
17	289
15	225
30	900
27	729
$\sum X = 207$	$\sum X^2 = 5115$

$$\text{standard deviation} = \sqrt{\frac{\sum X^2 - \frac{(\sum X)^2}{N}}{N}} = \sqrt{\frac{5115 - \frac{(207)^2}{9}}{9}}$$

$$= \sqrt{\frac{5115 - 4761}{9}}$$

$$= \sqrt{\frac{354}{9}} = \sqrt{39.333} = 6.27$$

(You may have spotted that the standard deviation is simply the square root of the variance.)

Interpreting the results

Like variance, standard deviation is difficult to interpret without other information about the data. Standard deviation is just a sort of average deviation from the mean. Its size will depend on the scale of the measurement in question. The bigger the units of the scale, the bigger the standard deviation is likely to be.

Reporting the results

Usually standard deviation is routinely reported in tables which summarise a variable or a number of variables along with other statistics such as the mean and range. This is shown in Table 6.2.

Table 6.2	Illustrating the table for descriptive statistics			
Variable	**N**	**Mean**	**Range**	**Standard deviation**
Age	9	23.00 years	20.00 years	6.27 years

Box 6.1	Key concepts

Estimated standard deviation

In this chapter the standard deviation is discussed as a descriptive statistic; that is, it is used like the mean and median, for example, to characterise important features of a set of scores. Be careful to distinguish this from the estimated standard deviation which is discussed in more detail in Chapter 12. Estimated standard deviation is your best guess as to the standard deviation of a population of scores based on information known about only a small subset or sample of scores from that population. Estimated standard deviation involves a modification to the standard deviation formula so that the estimate is better – the formula is modified to read $N - 1$ instead of just N.

The formula for the estimated standard deviation is:

If you wish, this formula can be used in all of your calculations of standard deviation. Some textbooks and some computer programs give you calculations based on the above formula in all circumstances. Since virtually all statistical analyses in psychology are based on samples and we normally wish to generalise from these samples to all cases then there is good justification for this practice. The downside is that if we are describing the data rather than generalising from them to the population then the formula is theoretically a little imprecise. If we did this calculation we would obtain a value of 6.65. This is the value that SPSS calls the standard deviation, as shown in Screenshot 6.4 though this is a bit of a misnomer. The distinction between the two standard deviations has been lost.

$$\text{estimated standard deviation} = \sqrt{\frac{\Sigma X^2 - \dfrac{(\Sigma X)^2}{N}}{N - 1}}$$

6.3 Measuring the number of standard deviations – the z-score

Given that one of the aims of statisticians is to make life as simple as possible for themselves, they try to use the minimum number of concepts possible. Expressing standard statistical units in terms of standard deviations is just one step towards trying to express many measures in a consistent way. Another way of achieving consistency is to express all scores in terms of a *number* of standard deviations. That is, we can abandon the original units of measurements almost entirely if all scores are re-expressed as a number of standard deviations.

It is a bit like calculating all weights in terms of kilograms or all distances in terms of metres. So, for example, since there are 2.2 pounds in a kilogram, something that weighs 10 pounds converts to 4.5 kilograms. We simply divide the number of pounds weight by the number of pounds in a kilogram in order to express our weight in pounds in terms of our standard unit of weight, the kilogram.

Similar things are done in statistics. If we know that the size of the standard deviation is, say, 7, we know that a score which is 21 above the mean score is $21 \div 7$ or three standard deviations above the mean. A score which is 14 below the mean is $14 \div 7$ or two standard deviations below the mean. So, once the size of the standard deviation is known (and the value of the mean score), all scores can be re-expressed in terms of the *number of standard deviations they are from the mean.* One big advantage of this is that, unlike other standard units of measurement such as distance and weight, the *number* of standard deviations applies no matter what the variable being measured is. Thus it is equally applicable if we are measuring time, anxiety, depression, height or any other variable. So *the number of standard deviations is a universal scale* of measurement. But note the stress on the *number* of standard deviations.

Despite sounding a bit space-age and ultra-modern, the *z*-score is nothing other than the *number* of standard deviations a particular score lies above or below the mean of the set of scores – precisely the concept just discussed. So in order to work out the *z*-score for a particular score (X) on a variable we also need to know the mean of the set of scores on that variable and the value of the standard deviation of that set of scores. Sometimes it is referred to as the *standard score* since it allows all scores to be expressed in a standard form.

The standard deviation in this case is technically the standard deviation of the population if it is known. Usually we do not know it as we only have information from a sample from that population. So we use the estimated standard deviation which involves the division by $N - 1$. There are rare occasions when we are dealing with the population. For example, if your university published its student profile based on its records of all of the students there then we do not have a sample but a population. In this case, arguably the correct thing to do would be to use the first version of standard deviation not the estimated standard deviation. When SPSS calculates the *z*-scores for you it uses the estimated standard deviation formula invariably.

Explaining statistics 6.2

How z-scores work

To convert the age of a 32-year-old to a *z*-score, given that the mean of the set of ages is 40 years and the standard deviation of age is 6 years, just apply the following formula:

$$z\text{-score} = \frac{X - \overline{X}}{SD}$$

where X stands for a particular score, $\overline{X}$ is the mean of the set of scores and SD stands for standard deviation.

The *z*-score of any age (e.g. 32) can be obtained as follows:

$$z\text{-score}_{[\text{of a 32-year-old}]} = \frac{32 - 40}{6} = \frac{-8}{6} = -1.33$$

The value of -1.33 means that:

- a 32-year-old is 1.33 standard deviations from the mean age of 40 for this set of age scores

- the minus sign simply means that the 32-year-old is younger (lower) than the mean age for the set of age scores. A plus sign (or no sign) would mean that the person is older (higher) than the mean age of 40 years.

➔

Interpreting the results

There is little to be added about interpreting the z-score since it is defined by the formula as the number of standard deviations a score is from the mean score. Generally speaking, the larger the z-score (either positive or negative) the more atypical a score is of the typical score in the data. Z-scores of about 2 or more are fairly rare.

Reporting the results

As z-scores are scores they can be presented as you would any other score using tables or diagrams. Usually there is no point in reporting the mean of a set of z-scores since this will be 0.00 if calculated for all of the cases.

6.4   Use of z-scores

Z-scores, at first sight, deter a lot of students. They are an odd, abstract idea which needs a little time to master. So what is the point of a z-score? Well they are important to know about because z-scores and related concepts appear in many of the more advanced statistical techniques to be found later in this book. You will come across values for z often in the output from SPSS. So if you grasp the idea now then things will be easier later on.

So the z-score is a score expressed in terms of the *number* of standard statistical units of measurement (standard deviations) it is from the mean of the set of scores. One big advantage of using these standard units of measurement is that variables measured using different units of measurement can be compared with each other and even combined.

A good example of this comes from a student project (Szostak, 1995). The researcher was interested in the amount of anxiety that child tennis players exhibited and its effect on their performance (serving faults) in competitive situations as compared with practice. One consideration was the amount of commitment that parents demonstrated to their children's tennis. Rather than base this simply on the extent to which parents claimed to be involved, she asked parents the amount of money they spent on their child's tennis, the amount of time they spent on their child's tennis and so forth:

1. How much money do you spend *per week* on your child's *tennis coaching?*

2. How much money do you spend *per year* on your child's *tennis equipment?*

3. How much money do you spend *per year* on your child's *tennis clothing?*

4. How many *miles per week* on average do you spend travelling to *tennis events?*

5. How many *hours per week* on average do you spend watching your child *play tennis?*

6. How many *LTA tournaments* does your child participate in *per year?*

This is quite straightforward information to collect, but it causes difficulties for the analysis. The reason is that there are six different measures of parental commitment which would make the report cumbersome if each was to be discussed separately. The student wanted to combine these six different measures to give an overall commitment score for each parent. However, the six items are based on radically different units of measurement – time, money and so forth. Her solution was to firstly turn each parent's score on each of the questionnaire items into a z-score. SPSS will do this for you. These six z-scores were then added together (including the + or − signs) to give a total score on the amount of commitment by each parent, which could be a positive or negative value
-scores can be   since they are relative to the mean.

This was an excellent strategy since this measure of parental commitment was the best predictor of a child performing poorly in competitive situations; the more parental commitment the worse the child does in real matches compared with practice.

6.5   Standard normal distribution

There is a remaining important use of standard deviation. Although it should now be obvious that there are some advantages in converting scores into standard units of measurement, you might get the impression that, in the end, the scores themselves on a variable contain extra information which the z-score does not fully capture. In particular, if one looks at a distribution of the original scores, it is possible to have a good idea of how a particular individual scores relative to other people. So, for example, if you know the distribution of weights in a set of people, it should be possible to say something about the weight of a particular person relative to other people. A histogram giving the weights of 38 children in a school class allows us to compare a child with a weight of, say, 42 kilograms with the rest of the class (Figure 6.4).

We can see that a child of 42 kilograms is in the top four of the distribution – that is, in about the top 10% of the weight distribution. Counting the frequencies in the histogram tells us the percentage of the part of the distribution the child falls in. We can also work out that 34 out of 38 (about 90%) of the class are lighter than this particular child.

Surely this cannot be done if we work with standard deviations? Actually it is relatively straightforward to do this. There are ready-made tables to tell us precisely how a particular score (expressed as a z-score or number of standard deviations from the mean) compares with other scores. This table is based on the frequency distribution of the normal (bell-shaped) curve. This table is known as either the standard normal distribution or the z-distribution. These tables can be complicated but we have opted for a relatively simple and useful version. Tables like this are generally called *significance* tables for reasons which will become more apparent later on.

Significance Table 6.1 gives the percentage number of scores which will be higher than a score with a given z-score. Basically this means that the table gives the proportion of the frequency distribution of z-scores which lie in the shaded portions in the example shown in Figure 6.5. The table assumes that the distribution of scores is normal or bell-shaped. The table usually works sufficiently well even if the distribution departs somewhat from the normal shape. Of course, since the area of the entire curve is 100% then it is quite easy to work out other characteristics of the curve. So if you know, for example, that 15.87% of scores will be above 1 standard deviation above the mean, it is a quick calculation to say that $100\% - 15.87\% = 84.13\%$ will be below 1 standard deviation above the mean.

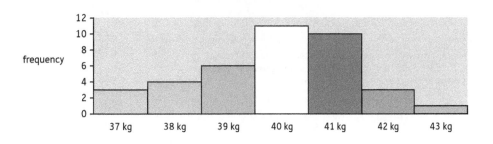

FIGURE 6.4   Distribution of weights in a set of children

Explaining statistics 6.3

How the table of the standard normal distribution works

Significance Table 6.1 is easy to use. Imagine that you have the IQs of a set of 250 people. The mean $\overline{X}$ of these IQs is 100 and you calculate that the standard deviation (SD) is 15. You could use this information to calculate the z-score of Darren Jones who scored 90 on the test:

$$z\text{-score} = \frac{X - \overline{X}}{SD} = \frac{90 - 100}{15}$$

$$= \frac{-10}{15} = -0.67 = -0.7 \ (\text{to 1 decimal place})$$

Taking a z-score of -0.7, Significance Table 6.1 tells us that 75.80% of people in the set would have IQs equal to or greater than Darren's. In other words, he is not particularly intelligent. If the z-score of Natalie Smith is $+2.0$ then this would mean that only 2.28% of scores are equal to or higher than Natalie's – she's very bright.

Of course, you could use the table to calculate the proportion of people with lower IQs than Darren and Natalie. Since the total amount of scores is 100%, we can calculate that, for Darren, there are 100% − 75.80% = 24.20% of people with IQs equal to or smaller than his. For Natalie, there are 100% − 2.28% = 97.72% of scores equal to or lower than hers.

Significance Table 6.1	Standard normal z-distribution: this gives the percentage of z-scores which are higher than the tabled values		
z-score	**Percentage of scores higher than this particular z-score**	**z-score**	**Percentage of scores higher than this particular z-score**
−4.00	99.997%	−1.70	95.54%
−3.00	99.87%	−1.64	95.00%
−2.90	99.81%	*z-scores above this point are in the extreme 5% below the mean*	
−2.80	99.74%		
−2.70	99.65%	−1.60	94.52%
−2.60	99.53%	−1.50	93.32%
−2.50	99.38%	−1.40	91.92%
−2.40	99.18%	−1.30	90.32%
−2.30	98.93%	−1.20	88.49%
−2.20	98.61%	−1.10	86.43%
−2.10	98.21%	−1.00	84.13%
−2.00	97.72%	−0.90	81.59%
−1.96	97.50%	−0.80	78.81%
z-scores above this point are in the extreme 5% of scores in either direction from the mean (i.e. the extreme 2.5% below the mean)		−0.70	75.80%
		−0.60	72.57%
		−0.50	69.15%
−1.90	97.13%	−0.40	65.54%
−1.80	96.41%	−0.30	61.79%

z-score	Percentage of scores higher than this particular z-score	z-score	Percentage of scores higher than this particular z-score
−0.20	57.93%	*z-scores below this point are in the extreme 5% above the mean*	
−0.10	53.98%		
0.00	50.00%	+1.64	5.00%
0.00	50.00%	+1.70	4.46%
+0.10	46.02%	+1.80	3.59%
+0.20	42.07%	+1.90	2.87%
+0.30	38.21%	*z-scores below this point are in the extreme 5% of scores in either direction from the mean (i.e. the extreme 2.5% above the mean)*	
+0.40	34.46%		
+0.50	30.85%	+1.96	2.50%
+0.60	27.43%	+2.00	2.28%
+0.70	24.20%	+2.10	1.79%
+0.80	21.19%	+2.20	1.39%
+0.90	18.41%	+2.30	1.07%
+1.00	15.87%	+2.40	0.82%
+1.10	13.57%	+2.50	0.62%
+1.20	11.51%	+2.60	0.47%
+1.30	9.68%	+2.70	0.35%
+1.40	8.08%	+2.80	0.26%
+1.50	6.68%	+2.90	0.19%
+1.60	5.48%	+3.00	0.13%
		+4.00	0.0003%

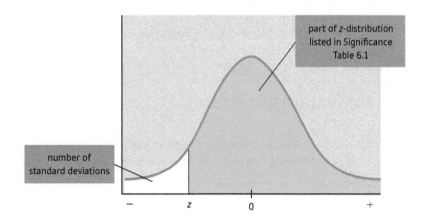

FIGURE 6.5   Part of the z-distribution which is listed in Significance Table 6.1

| Box 6.2 | Focus on |

Negative signs

One thing which can cause confusion is when psychologists talk about plus two standard deviations or minus one standard deviation. The first thing to say is that a standard deviation can never itself have a negative value – a standard deviation is positive. The reason why psychologists talk about minus standard deviations is because they are saying how many standard deviations a score is below the mean.

Thus a plus indicates that a score is so many standard deviations above the mean and a minus means that the score is so many standard deviations below the mean. Really, what they should be saying is that a score has a *z*-score of +2 or a *z*-score of −1 since this is where the pluses and minuses come from and nobody would get confused.

■ More about Significance Table 6.1

Significance Table 6.1 is just about as simple as we could make it. It is not quite the same as similar tables in other books:

● We have given negative as well as positive values of *z*-scores.

● We have only given *z*-scores in intervals of 0.1 with a few exceptions.

● We have given percentages – many other versions of the table give *proportions* out of 1. In order to convert the values in Significance Table 6.1 into proportions, simply divide the percentage by 100 and delete the % sign.

● We have introduced a number of 'cut-off points' or zones into the table. These basically isolate extreme parts of the distribution of *z*-scores and identify those *z*-scores which come into the extreme 5% of the distribution. If you like, these are the exceptionally high and exceptionally low *z*-scores. The importance of this might not be obvious right now but will be clearer later on. The cut off points are related to the concept of statistical significance which we deal with later in the book. We have indicated the extreme 5% in either direction (that is, the extreme 2.5% above and below the mean) as well as the extreme 5% in a particular direction.

6.6　Important feature of *z*-scores

By using *z*-scores the researcher is able to say an enormous amount about a distribution of scores extremely succinctly. If we present the following information:

● the mean of a distribution

● the standard deviation of the distribution

● that the distribution is more or less bell-shaped or normal

then we can use this information to make very clear statements about the relative position of any score on the variable in question. In other words, rather than present an entire frequency distribution, these three pieces of information are virtually all that is required.

Research examples

Standard deviation and *z*-scores

Contador and colleagues (2010) used *z*-scores to define the level of memory scores which they describe as impaired: 'To find the proportion of the subjects whose performance fell outside of the normal range, scores were converted to *z*-scores. Patients were considered to be impaired if their *z*-scores were lower than −1.5. Considering that −2 *SD* are also often used as a cut off for such purposes, we computed additionally the proportion of patients whose *z*-scores fell lower than −2 *SD*.' (p. 255).

Di Filippo and colleagues (2006) were interested in the lexicality (readability) of words in relation to word length in a sample of dyslexic Italian children and a sample of age-matched controls. They analysed their data twice: once using the raw scores on reaction times to the words and again using *z*-score transformations. The raw reaction time data demonstrated that reaction times to non-words were bigger than for real words and bigger for long words than for short words in dyslexics than proficient readers. But things changed when the data had been transformed into *z*-scores. The lexicality effect disappeared although the length of word effect remained. The researchers put this down to what they call the 'overadditivity' effect in the raw data. The authors explain this in the following way: 'However, overall performance changes can directly influence the size of the interaction (so-called overadditivity effect . . .) when response time is considered, one can expect that the effect due to any experimental manipulation will be smaller for a subject with relatively fast responses than a subject with slower responses. As a consequence, a "spurious" interaction may be produced.' (p. 142). Faust and colleagues (1999) proposed transformations (*z*-scores) to control for this overadditivity effect.

Tremont and Alosco (2011) investigated the correlates of lack of awareness of their condition in Alzheimer's sufferers. Such lack of insight into one's condition is known as anosognosia. It is common in Alzheimer's disease but its role in cognitive performance has not been extensively researched. The participants were 65 Alzheimer's sufferers who took part in an extensive neuropsychological evaluation using a range of different measures. About half were aware and about half were unaware of their condition. This classification was done using the ratings of a clinical interview which also included a family member as informant. In order to compare their cognitive functioning based on a wide variety of measures, the researchers chose to convert each measure to a *z*-score by subtracting the sample mean from each individual's score and dividing by the standard deviation of that measure. The *z*-scores for each individual could be added up and averaged. This gave a measure of cognitive performance based on each measure contributing equally. Although there were no significant differences between the aware and non-aware groups in terms of age, gender, education level, the unaware group did significantly worse on cognitive tasks which involved learning. Despite this, generally, the groups performed similarly on cognitive tasks.

Key points

- Do not despair if you have problems in understanding standard deviation; it is one of the most abstract ideas in statistics, but so fundamental that it cannot be avoided. It can take some time to absorb completely.

- Remember that the standard deviation is a sort of average deviation from the mean and you will not go far wrong.

● Remember that using z-scores is simply a way of putting variables on a standard unit of measurement irrespective of special characteristics of that variable. Standardised values are common in the more advanced statistical techniques so it is good to master them at an early stage.

● Remember that virtually any numerical score variable can be summarised using the standard deviation and that virtually any measurement can be expressed as a z-score. The main exception to its use is measurements which are in *nominal* categories like occupation or eye colour. Certainly if a score is *interval or ratio* in nature, standard deviation and z-scores are appropriate.

COMPUTER ANALYSIS

Standard deviation and z-scores using SPSS

Data
● Name the variables in 'Variable View' of the 'Data Editor'.
● Enter the data under the appropriate variable names in 'Data View' of the 'Data Editor' (Screenshot 6.1).

Analysis
● Select 'Analyze', 'Descriptive Statistics' and 'Descriptives . . . ' (Screenshot 6.2).
● Move the variables to be analysed to the right-hand box (Screenshot 6.3).
● The output is shown in Screenshot 6.4.

2
● Select 'Save standardized values as variables' (Screenshot 6.5).

Output
● The standardised values are presented in the next free column of 'Data View' in the 'Data Editor' with the name of the original variable following the letter Z (Screenshot 6.6).

| FIGURE 6.6 | SPSS steps for standard deviation and z-scores |

Interpreting and reporting the output

● The standard deviation of just one variable is readily mentioned in the text of your report: 'The standard deviation of age was 6.65 years ($N = 9$).' However, if you have a lot of variables, a table giving basic descriptive statistics for several variables may be more effective. Remember that SPSS gives the estimated standard deviation so the value here is the one we calculated in Box 6.1 – the estimated standard deviation.

● It is not usual to report standard scores as this would be somewhat like reporting the raw scores for each individual. However, you need to understand standard scores as these can be meaningfully added, etc. because they have been standardised to be on the same scale of measurement.

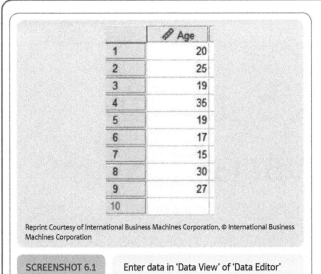

Reprint Courtesy of International Business Machines Corporation, © International Business Machines Corporation

SCREENSHOT 6.1   Enter data in 'Data View' of 'Data Editor'

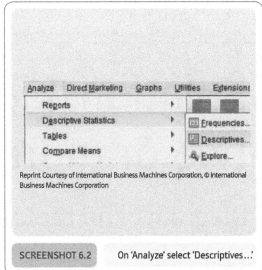

Reprint Courtesy of International Business Machines Corporation, © International Business Machines Corporation

SCREENSHOT 6.2   On 'Analyze' select 'Descriptives…'

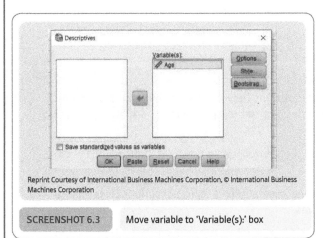

Reprint Courtesy of International Business Machines Corporation, © International Business Machines Corporation

SCREENSHOT 6.3   Move variable to 'Variable(s):' box

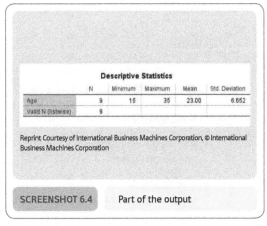

Descriptive Statistics

	N	Minimum	Maximum	Mean	Std. Deviation
Age	9	15	35	23.00	6.652
Valid N (listwise)	9				

Reprint Courtesy of International Business Machines Corporation, © International Business Machines Corporation

SCREENSHOT 6.4   Part of the output

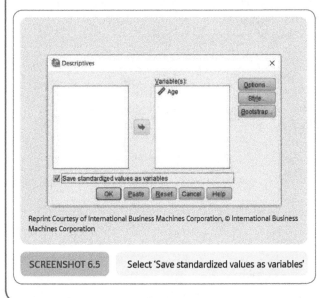

Reprint Courtesy of International Business Machines Corporation, © International Business Machines Corporation

SCREENSHOT 6.5   Select 'Save standardized values as variables'

	Age	ZAge
1	20	-.45099
2	25	.30066
3	19	-.60132
4	35	1.80395
5	19	-.60132
6	17	-.90198
7	15	-1.20263
8	30	1.05230
9	27	.60132
10		

Reprint Courtesy of International Business Machines Corporation, © International Business Machines Corporation

SCREENSHOT 6.6   z-scores appear in 'Data View'

CHAPTER 7

Relationships between two or more variables

Diagrams and tables

Overview

- Most psychological research involves relationships between two or more sets of scores. Relationships between two variables can be represented pictorially as a scattergram (or scatterplot).

- Alternatively, a crosstabulation table with the scores broken down into ranges (or bands) can be effective.

- If both variables are nominal (category) then compound bar charts of various sorts may be used or, alternatively, crosstabulation tables.

- If there is one score variable and one nominal (category) variable then often tables of means of the score variable tabulated against the nominal (category) variable will be adequate. It is possible, alternatively, to employ a compound histogram.

Preparation

You should be aware of the meaning of variables, scores and the different scales of measurement, especially the difference between nominal (category) measurement and numerical scores.

7.1   Introduction

Relationships between variables form the bedrock of virtually all psychological research. It is rare in psychology to have research questions which require data from only one variable at a time. Studies involving *interrelationships* between variables are more typical. Public opinion polling is the most common use of single-variable statistics that most of us come across. Opinion pollsters ask a whole series of questions about political leaders and voting intentions which are generally reported separately – 57% of people support the Prime Minister, for example. Nevertheless, pollsters could look at two variables together. To ask how men compare with women in their voting intentions, whether there is a relationship (or correlation or association) between gender and voting intentions, and whether men and women differ in their voting intentions are the same thing and all involve two variables. If one asks whether the popularity of the President of the USA changed over time, this really implies that there may be a relationship between the variable 'time' and the variable 'popularity of the President'. Questions like these seem common sense ones to ask. Statistics gives us ways of quantifying and illustrating relationships.

Much of psychology concerns explanations of why things happen – what causes what – which clearly is about relationships between variables. This chapter describes some of the main graphical and tabular methods for showing relationships between variables. Usually graphs and tables are simply alternative ways of doing this. Importantly, graphs and tables are not simply ways of smartening up a report or dissertation. They are the basis for any statistical analysis. Looking at many published research reports, graphs, in particular, are rather uncommon. Do not assume, as a consequence, that graphs were irrelevant to the statistical analysis. A good researcher will generate numerous graphs and tables in the analysis process though few will appear in the report. At the start of the analysis, graphs and tables allow the researcher to understand a great deal of what is happening in the data. It is hard to do the same simply by looking at a data spreadsheet since they are usually far too large to allow this. Histograms, bar charts, means, and so forth for each variable are usually the starting point. Histograms and bar charts will quickly show you the distribution of each variable. You may see problems such as a very skewed distribution or bunching and clustering around particular data points. Outliers may be spotted and removed, as appropriate. Then you can move on to graphs and tables of the sort described in this chapter which show you the relationships between pairs of variables. You may see the first evidence that your expectations are supported by the data – or not. Or you may find that the relationships are much more complex than you had expected. You may need to adjust your plans for the later stages of the statistical analysis on the basis of what you see.

Graphs and tables may seem very basic compared with the riches of more advanced statistical techniques. A wise researcher will avoid launching into advanced techniques without first exploring their data using simple descriptive statistics. Numerous charts and tables can quickly be produced on a computer. A researcher may get as much from these as from the more fancy statistical techniques to be found later in this book. Figure 7.1 gives the key steps to consider when describing relationships between two variables in diagram and table form.

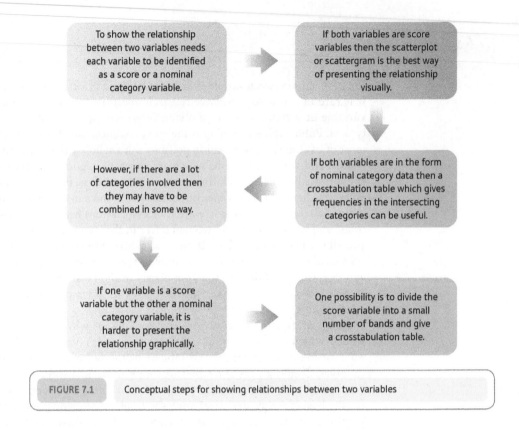

FIGURE 7.1   Conceptual steps for showing relationships between two variables

7.2   Principles of diagrammatic and tabular presentation

Some students have difficulty deciding what tables and graphs they should use for their data. An easy way of choosing appropriate techniques to show relationships requires an understanding of the difference between nominal category data and numerical score data. You need to be able to classify each variable as one or other of these. If we are considering the interrelationships between *two* variables (X and Y) then Table 7.1 classifies relationships on the basis of the types of variables involved. Once you have decided to which category your pair of variables belongs, it is easy to suggest appropriate descriptive statistics. We have classified different situations as type A, type B and type C. Thus type B has both variables measured on the nominal category scale of measurement.

Table 7.1   Types of relationships based on nominal categories and numerical scores

	Variable X = numerical scores	Variable X = nominal categories
Variable y = numerical scores	type A	type C
Variable y = nominal categories	type C	type B

7.3 Type A: both variables numerical scores

Where both variables take the form of numerical scores, generally the best form of graphical presentation is the *scattergram* or scatterplot. This is a sort of graph in which the values on one variable are plotted against the values on the other variable. The most familiar form of graph is one that plots a variable against time. These are very familiar from newspapers, especially the financial sections (see Figure 7.2).

Time is no different, statistically speaking, from a wide range of other numerical scores. Figure 7.3 is an example of a scattergram from a psychological study. You will see that the essential features remain the same. In Figure 7.3, the point marked with an arrow represents a case (person) whose score on the X-variable is 8 and whose score on the Y-variable is 120. It is sometimes possible to see that the points of a scattergram fall more or less on a straight line. This line through the points of a scattergram is called the *regression line*. It is the best-fitting straight line to the data points. Figure 7.3 includes the regression line for the points of the scattergram.

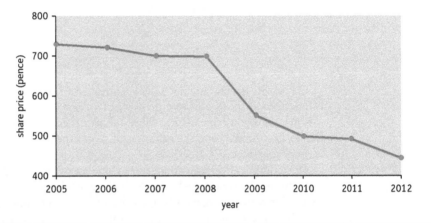

| FIGURE 7.2 | Dramatic fall in share price in the Timeshare Office Company |

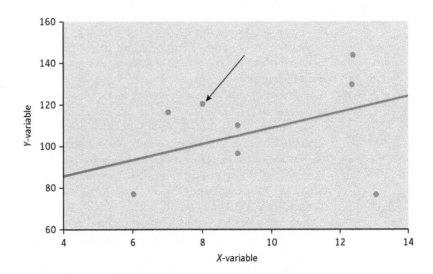

| FIGURE 7.3 | Scattergram showing the relationship between two variables |

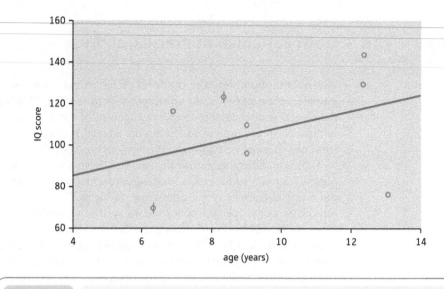

FIGURE 7.4 Scattergram with the x- and y-axes labelled and overlapping points illustrated

In line with general mathematical notation, the horizontal axis or horizontal dimension is described as the X-axis and the vertical axis or vertical dimension is called the Y-axis. It is helpful if you remember to label one set of scores the X scores since these belong on the horizontal axis, and the other set of scores the Y scores because these belong on the vertical axis (Figure 7.4).

One complication you sometimes come across is where several points on the scattergram overlap completely. In these circumstances you may well see a number next to a point which corresponds to the number of overlapping points at that position on the scattergram. In Figure 7.4, overlapping points are marked not with a number but with lines around the point on the scattergram. These are called 'sunflowers' – the number of 'petals' indicates the number of cases overlapping at the same point. Another way of indicating overlaps is simply to put the *number* of overlaps next to the scattergram point. SPSS has a system by which the size of the data point will get bigger the more cases overlap on a particular data point. You find it in 'Chart Editor' (Screenshot 8.10) under 'Options' and then 'Bin Element', which opens up 'Binning' (Screenshot 8.11). You will find instructions for obtaining scattergrams on SPSS at the end of Chapter 8.

Apart from cumbersomely listing all of your pairs of scores, it is often difficult to think of a manageable method for presenting data from pairs of numerical scores in tabular form. This is because there are often many different score values involved. The main possibility is to categorise each of your score variables into 'bands' of scores and express the data in terms of *frequencies* of occurrence in these bands; a table like Table 7.2 might be appropriate. Just to remind you, on SPSS it is possible to recode ranges of scores into bands. Select 'Transform' then 'Recode into Different Variables...' (Screenshot 3.5).

Such tables are known as 'crosstabulation' or 'contingency' tables. In Table 7.2 there does seem to be a relationship between variable X and variable Y. People with low scores on variable X also tend to get low scores on variable Y. High scorers on variable X also tend to score highly on variable Y. However, the trend in the table is less easily discerned than in the equivalent scattergram. You will find the SPSS steps for creating a contingency or crosstabulation table at the end of this chapter.

Table 7.2	Use of bands of scores to tabulate the relationship between two numerical score variables				
Variable X	Variable Y				
	1–5	6–10	11–15	16–20	21–25
0–9	15	7	6	3	4
10–19	7	12	3	5	4
20–29	4	9	19	8	4
30–39	1	3	2	22	3
40–49	3	2	3	19	25

7.4   Type B: both variables nominal categories

Where both variables are in nominal categories, it is necessary to report the frequencies in all of the possible groupings of the variables. If you have more than a few nominal categories, the tables or diagrams can be too big and cumbersome.

Take the imaginary data shown in Table 7.3 on the relationship between a person's gender and whether they have been hospitalised at any time in their life for a psychiatric reason. These data are ideal for certain sorts of tables and diagrams because *there are few categories of each variable.* Thus a suitable crosstabulation or contingency table for summarising these data might look like Table 7.4.

The numbers (frequencies) in each category are instantly obvious from this table. You might prefer to express the table in percentages rather than frequencies, but some thought needs to go into the choice of percentages. For example, you could express the frequencies as percentages of the total of males and females (Table 7.5).

You probably think that Table 7.5 is not much of an improvement in clarity. An alternative is to express the frequencies as percentages of males *and* percentages of females (Table 7.6). By presenting the percentages based on males and females separately, it is

Table 7.3	Gender and whether previously hospitalised for a set of 89 people	
Person	Gender	Previously hospitalised
1	male	yes
2	male	no
3	male	no
4	male	yes
5	male	no
...	...	...
85	female	yes
86	female	yes
87	female	no
88	female	no
89	female	yes

Table 7.4	Crosstabulation table of gender against hospitalisation	
	Male	**Female**
Previously hospitalised	$f = 20$	$f = 25$
Not previously hospitalised	$f = 30$	$f = 14$

Table 7.5	Crosstabulation table with all frequencies expressed as a percentage of the total number of frequencies	
	Male	**Female**
Previously hospitalised	22.5%	28.1%
Not previously hospitalised	33.7%	15.7%

Table 7.6	Crosstabulation table with hospitalisation expressed as a percentage of the male and female frequencies taken separately	
	Male	**Female**
Previously hospitalised	40.0%	64.1%
Not previously hospitalised	60.0%	35.9%

easier to see the trend for females to have had a previous psychiatric history relatively more frequently than males. Remember, the instructions for creating a contingency or crosstabulation table are at the end of this chapter.

The same data can be expressed as a *compound bar chart*. In a compound bar chart information is given about the subcategories based on a pair of variables. Figure 7.5 shows one example in which the proportions are expressed as percentages of the males and females separately.

The golden rule for such data is to ensure that the number of categories is manageable. In particular, avoid having too many empty or near-empty categories. The compound bar

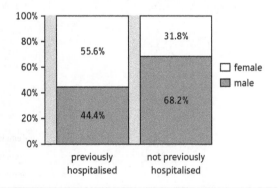

| FIGURE 7.5 | Compound percentage bar chart showing gender trends in previous hospitalisation |

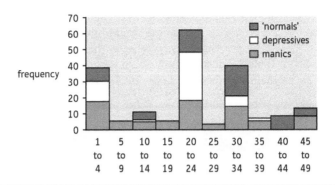

FIGURE 7.6   How not to do a compound bar chart

chart shown in Figure 7.6 is a particularly bad example and is *not to be copied*. This chart fails any reasonable clarity test and is too complex to decipher quickly. Your chart should be a model of clarity if you are to impress others with your thoughtful approach to statistical analysis. SPSS instructions for compound bar charts are at the end of this chapter.

7.5 Type C: one variable nominal categories, the other numerical scores

This final type of situation offers a wide variety of ways of presenting the relationships between variables. We have examined the compound bar chart so it is not surprising to find that there is also a *compound histogram*. To be effective, a compound histogram needs to consist of:

● a small number of categories for the nominal category variable

● a few *ranges* for the numerical scores.

So, for example, if we wish to plot the relationship between managers' anxiety scores and whether they are managers in a high-tech or a low-tech industry, we might create a compound histogram like Figure 7.7 in which there are only two values of the nominal variable (high-tech and low-tech) and four bands of anxiety score (low anxiety, medium

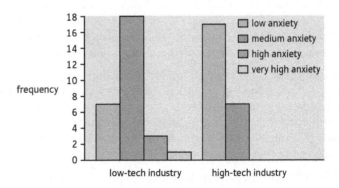

FIGURE 7.7   Compound histogram

anxiety, high anxiety and very high anxiety). The SPSS steps to make compound histograms are described at the end of this chapter in the Computer Analysis section.

An alternative way of presenting such data is to use a crosstabulation table as in Table 7.7. Instead, however, it is almost as easy to draw up a table (Table 7.8) which gives the mean, median, mode, etc. for the anxiety scores of the two different groups.

Table 7.7	Crosstabulation table of anxiety against type of industry			
	Frequency of anxiety score			
	0–3	4–7	8–11	12–15
Low-tech industry	7	18	3	1
High-tech industry	17	7	0	0

Table 7.8	Comparison of the statistical characteristics of anxiety in two different types of industry				
	Mean	Median	Mode	Interquartile range	Variance
High-tech industry	3.5	3.9	3	1.9	2.2
Low-tech industry	5.3	4.7	6	2.4	3.2

Research examples

Crosstabulation and charts

Deary and his colleagues (1991) looked at the relation between intelligence and deciding which of two vertical lines was the longer. They used three groups of different people. They presented the relation between intelligence and the time to do the task as a correlation and as a scattergram for the three groups combined. The correlation was negative with lower intelligence scores associated with longer inspection times.

Meeten and Davey (2012) manipulated five moods by showing participants one of five films. The five moods were sad, happy, anxious, angry and neutral. Participants rated how they felt in these five conditions in terms of four scales of sadness, happiness, anxiety and anger. The mean scores and their standard deviations were presented in a crosstabulation with the five conditions represented by five columns and the four moods by four rows. They used a compound histogram to show the mean number of instances of exaggerating negative consequences using one of two rules in the five mood conditions.

Sierra, Livianos and Rojo (2005) employed a bar chart to show the differences in means on eight subscale scores of a measure of quality of life between patients with bipolar depression and a sample from the general population.

Key points

- Never assume that your tables and diagrams are good enough at the first attempt. They could probably be improved with a little care and adjustment.

- Do not forget that tables and diagrams are there to present clearly the major trends in your data (or lack of them). There is not much point in having tables and diagrams that do not clarify your data.

- Your tables and diagrams are not means of tabulating your unprocessed data. If you need to present your data in full then most of the methods to be found in this chapter will not help you much.

- Labelling tables and diagrams clearly and succinctly is an important part of the task – without clear titling and labelling you are probably wasting your time.

COMPUTER ANALYSIS

Crosstabulation and compound bar charts using SPSS

Data
- Name and label the values of the variables in 'Variable View' of the 'Data Editor'.
- Enter the data under the appropriate variable names in 'Data View' of the 'Data Editor' (Screenshot 7.1).

Analysis
- For a contingency table, select 'Analyze', 'Table' and 'Custom Tables. . .' (Screenshot 7.2).

2
- Select 'OK' and move the appropriate variables to the column and row boxes (Screenshot 7.3).

3
- For compound bar charts, select 'Graphs', 'Chart Builder. . .' or 'Legacy Dialog' and appropriate graph (Screenshot 1.2). For clustered bar chart, select 'Bar. . .', 'Clustered' and 'Define' (Screenshot 7.4).

Output
- Check tables (Screenshot 7.4) and charts (Screenshot 7.6) are correct.

FIGURE 7.8   SPSS steps for contingency (crosstabulation) tables and compound charts

Interpreting and reporting the output

- You should have a good idea of what you want your tables and charts or diagrams to tell you. If you find the chart difficult to understand then you cannot expect anyone reading your report to understand it any better. You might wish to start again. Basically in order to interpret the chart or table you are looking for evidence for a relationship between the two variables.

- Always think carefully about whether to present tables and diagrams in reports. They may be very important to the researcher when they are analysing their data but less important in the light of this analysis in terms of their inclusion in the report. If you do choose to include a table or diagram, always refer to it in the main text of your report – never leave it to the reader to interpret what it indicates. As always, make sure that the labelling, etc. of the chart is as good as you can make it.

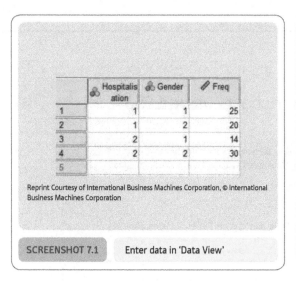

Reprint Courtesy of International Business Machines Corporation, © International Business Machines Corporation

SCREENSHOT 7.1 Enter data in 'Data View'

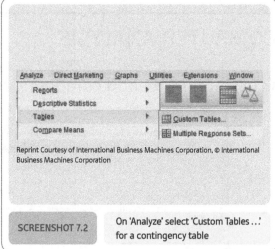

Reprint Courtesy of International Business Machines Corporation, © International Business Machines Corporation

SCREENSHOT 7.2 On 'Analyze' select 'Custom Tables …' for a contingency table

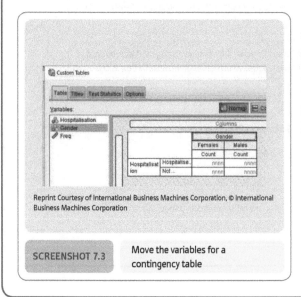

Reprint Courtesy of International Business Machines Corporation, © International Business Machines Corporation

SCREENSHOT 7.3 Move the variables for a contingency table

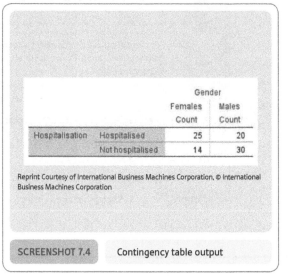

Reprint Courtesy of International Business Machines Corporation, © International Business Machines Corporation

SCREENSHOT 7.4 Contingency table output

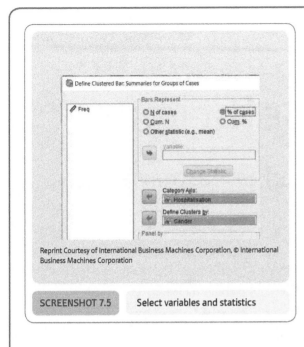

Define Clustered Bar: Summaries for Groups of Cases

Reprint Courtesy of International Business Machines Corporation, © International Business Machines Corporation

SCREENSHOT 7.5   Select variables and statistics

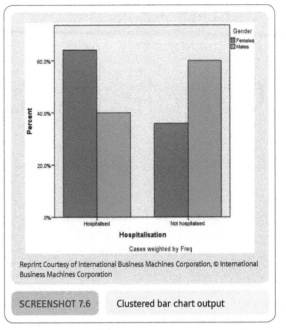

Reprint Courtesy of International Business Machines Corporation, © International Business Machines Corporation

SCREENSHOT 7.6   Clustered bar chart output

CHAPTER 8

Correlation coefficients

Pearson's correlation and Spearman's rho

Overview

- Correlation coefficients are numerical indexes of the relationship between two variables. They are the bedrock of much statistical analysis.

- The correlation coefficient may be positive or negative depending on whether both sets of scores increase together (positive correlation) or whether one set increases as the other decreases (negative correlation).

- The numerical size of the correlation coefficient ranges from 0 (no relationship) to 1 (a perfect relationship). Intermediate values indicate different amounts of spread around the best-fitting straight line through the points (i.e. the spread around the regression line). If the points on the scattergram do not lie close to the regression line then the correlation is poor.

- The Pearson correlation is primarily used for score variables (though it can be used where one or both variables are nominal variables with just two categories).

- Spearman's correlation works differently in that it is a correlation between scores which are ranked from smallest to largest. It is used sometimes when the scores are not normally distributed. It is a special case of the Pearson correlation coefficient formula.

- Great care should be taken to inspect the scattergram between the two variables in question in order to make sure that the best-fitting line is a straight line rather than a curve.

- The statistical significance of correlation coefficients is dealt with in detail in Chapter 11.

Preparation

Revise variance (Chapter 4) and the use of the scattergram to show the relationship between two variables (Chapter 7).

8.1 Introduction

Although the scattergram is an important statistical tool for examining relationships between two variables, it is space consuming. The correlation coefficient is a numerical index which summarises some of the main features of a scattergram. By far the most commonly used correlation coefficient is the *Pearson correlation,* also known more grandly and obscurely as the Pearson product–moment correlation. It includes two pieces of information:

- The closeness of the fit of the points of a scattergram to the best-fitting straight line through those points.

- Information about whether the slope of the scattergram is positive or negative.

The cost is that other information which is in a scattergram is omitted such as the measurement scales of the two variables and information about individual cases.

Correlation coefficients, then, summarise aspects of the information found in scattergrams thus saving a great deal of space. They most certainly do not replace using

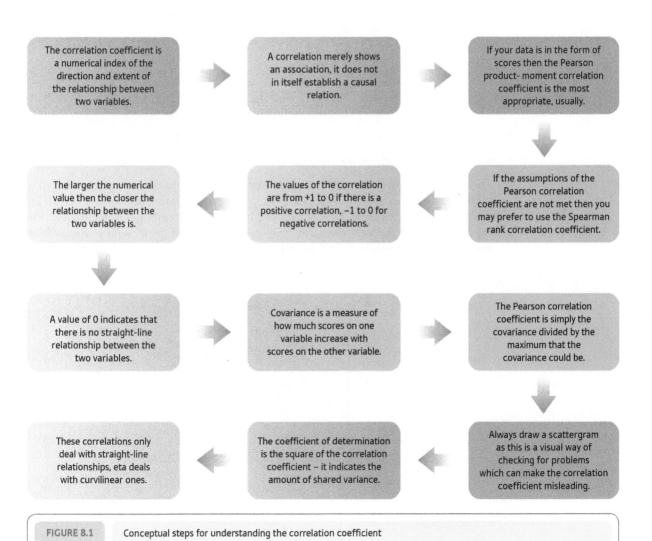

FIGURE 8.1   Conceptual steps for understanding the correlation coefficient

scattergrams as you begin to analyse your data. As far as possible, you should produce a scattergram for every correlation since this is the only way that you can see exactly what the relationships between pairs of variables are. Failing to do so means that you will probably be unaware of outliers, curvilinear relationships, and other challenges to interpreting your data.

Although the correlation coefficient is a basic descriptive statistic, it can be extended in sophisticated ways such as partial correlation, multiple correlation and factor analysis, which are some of the more advanced statistics to be found later in this book. Correlation is of paramount importance in many forms of research, especially survey, questionnaire and similar kinds of investigation. Figure 8.1 gives the key steps to consider when using the correlation coefficient.

8.2   Principles of the correlation coefficient

The Pearson correlation coefficient basically takes the following form:

$$r_{[\text{correlation coefficient}]} = +1.00$$
$$\text{or} \quad .00$$
$$\text{or} \quad -1.00$$
$$\text{or} \quad 0.30$$
$$\text{or} \quad -0.72 \text{ etc.}$$

So a correlation coefficient consists of two parts:

- a positive or negative sign (although for positive values the sign is normally omitted)

- any numerical value in the range of .00 to 1.00.

The $+$ or $-$ sign tells us something important about the slope of the regression line (i.e. the best-fitting straight line through the points on the scattergram). A positive value means that the slope is *from the bottom left to the top right* of the scattergram (Figure 8.2). On the other hand, if the sign is negative ($-$) then the slope of the straight line goes from *upper left to lower right* on the scattergram (Figure 8.3).

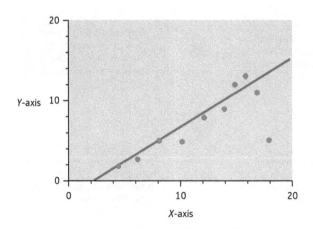

| FIGURE 8.2 | Positive correlation between two variables |

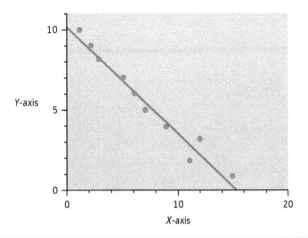

FIGURE 8.3   Negative correlation between two variables

The numerical value of the correlation coefficient (.50, .42, etc.) is an index of how close the points on the scattergram fit the best-fitting straight line through them. A value of 1.00 means that the points of the scattergram all lie exactly on the best-fitting straight line (Figure 8.4), unless that line is perfectly vertical or perfectly horizontal, in which case it means that there is no variation in the scores on one of the variables and so no correlation can be calculated.

A value of .00 means that the points of the scattergram are randomly scattered around the straight line. It is purely a matter of luck if any of them actually touch the straight line (Figure 8.5). In this case, the best-fitting straight line for the scattergram could be virtually any line you arbitrarily decide to draw through the points. Conventionally it is drawn as a horizontal line, but any other angle of slope would do just as well since there is no discernible trend in the relationship between the two variables on the scattergram.

A value of .50 would mean that although the points on the scattergram are generally close to the best-fitting straight line, there is considerable spread of these points around

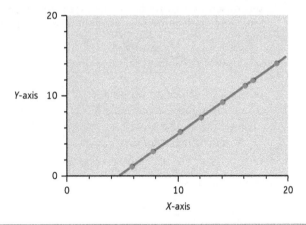

FIGURE 8.4   Perfect correlation between two variables

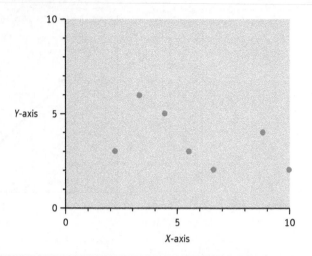

| FIGURE 8.5 | Near-zero correlation between two variables |

that straight line. If you would like verbal labels for different sizes of the Pearson correlation coefficient then this is the commonly described scheme:

● A small correlation is .10 or larger.

● A medium correlation is .30 or larger.

● A large correlation is .50 or larger.

To summarise, the components of the correlation coefficient are the sign ($+$ or $-$), which indicates the direction of the slope, and a numerical value which indicates how much variation there is around the best-fitting straight line through the points (i.e. the higher the numerical value the closer the fit).

■ Covariance

The calculation of the correlation coefficient involves something called the covariance which is compared to the maximum value it could take based on the variances of the two sets of scores. Covariance is the extent to which two variables vary together and its calculation is little more than an elaboration of the formula for variance:

$$\text{variance} = \frac{\sum (X - \overline{X})^2}{N}$$

where X = scores on variable X
$\overline{X}$ = mean score on variable X
N = number of scores
$\sum$ = sum of what follows

If you wished (you will see why in a moment), the formula for variance could be re-expressed as:

$$\text{variance} = \frac{\sum (X - \overline{X})(X - \overline{X})}{N}$$

All we have done is to expand the formula so as not to use the square sign. (A square is simply a number multiplied by itself.)

The formula for *covariance* is almost exactly the same as this formula for variance, but instead of multiplying scores by themselves we multiply the score on one variable (X) by the score on the second variable (Y) having subtracted the relevant mean:

$$\text{covariance}_{[\text{of variable } X \text{ with variable } Y]} = \frac{\sum(X - \overline{X})(Y - \overline{Y})}{N}$$

where X = scores on variable X
$\overline{X}$ = mean score on variable X
Y = scores on variable Y
$\overline{Y}$ = mean score on variable Y
N = number of pairs of scores
$\sum$ = sum of what follows

We get a large positive value of covariance if there is a strong positive relationship between the two variables, and a big negative value if there is a strong negative relationship between the two variables. If there is no relationship between the variables then the covariance is zero. Notice that, unlike variance, the covariance can take positive or negative values.

However, the size of the covariance is affected by the size of the variances of the two variables involved. The larger the variances, the larger is the covariance, potentially. This makes comparisons difficult. So the covariance is adjusted by dividing by the square root of the product of the variances of the two separate variables. Because N, the number of pairs of scores, in the variance and covariance formulae can be cancelled out in the correlation formula, the usual formula includes no division by the number of scores. Once this adjustment is made, we have the formula for the correlation coefficient:

$$r_{[\text{correlation coefficient}]} = \frac{\sum(X - \overline{X})(Y - \overline{Y})}{\sqrt{\sum(X - \overline{X})^2}\sqrt{\sum(Y - \overline{Y})^2}}$$

The lower part of the formula gives the largest possible value of the covariance of the two variables – that is, the theoretical covariance if the two variables lay perfectly on the straight line through the scattergram. Dividing the covariance by the maximum value it could take (if there were no spread of points away from the straight line through the scattergram) ensures that the correlation coefficient can never be greater than 1.00. The covariance formula also gives the necessary sign to indicate the slope of the relationship.

A slightly quicker computational formula which does not involve the calculation of the mean scores directly is as follows, though we will not illustrate its use here as we assume that you will prefer to do calculations on a computer:

$$r_{[\text{correlation coefficient}]} = \frac{\sum XY - \dfrac{\sum X \sum Y}{N}}{\sqrt{\left(\sum X^2 - \dfrac{(\sum X)^2}{N}\right)\left(\sum Y^2 - \dfrac{(\sum Y)^2}{N}\right)}}$$

The resemblance of parts of this formula to the computational formula for variance should be fairly obvious. This is not surprising as the correlation coefficient is a measure of the *lack* of variation around the straight line through the scattergram (see also Box 8.1).

Explaining statistics 8.1

How the Pearson correlation works

Our data for this calculation come from scores on the relationship between mathematical ability and musical ability for a group of 10 children (Table 8.1). It cannot be stressed enough that it is always good practice to draw the scattergram for any correlation coefficient you are calculating. For these data, the scattergram will be like Figure 8.6. Notice that the slope of the scattergram is negative, as one could have deduced from the tendency for those who score highly on mathematical ability to have low scores on musical ability. You can also see not only that a straight line is a pretty good way of describing the trends in the points on the scattergram but that the points fit the straight line reasonably well. Thus we should expect a fairly high negative correlation from the correlation coefficient.

Table 8.1	Scores on musical and mathematical ability for 10 children	
Individual	**Music score**	**Mathematics score**
Jessica	2	8
Joshua	6	3
Tyler	4	9
Daniel	5	7
Emily	7	2
Brittany	7	3
Samantha	2	9
Alexis	3	8
Ryan	5	6
Nicola	4	7

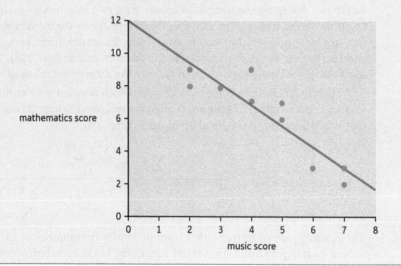

FIGURE 8.6   Scattergram for Table 8.1

Step 1 Set the scores out in a table (Table 8.2) and follow the calculations as shown. Here N is the number of pairs of scores, i.e. 10.

Step 2 Substitute the appropriate values from Table 8.2 in the formula:

$$r_{[\text{correlation coefficient}]} = \frac{\sum (X - \bar{X})(Y - \bar{Y})}{\sqrt{\sum (X - \bar{X})^2}\sqrt{\sum (Y - \bar{Y})^2}}$$

$$= \frac{-39}{\sqrt{30.5 \times 61.6}}$$

$$= \frac{-39}{43.35}$$

$$= -0.90$$

Note this is the same value as given by SPSS in Screenshot 8.6.

Interpreting the results

So the value obtained for the correlation coefficient equals $-.90$. This value is in line with what we suggested about the scattergram which serves as a rough check on our calculation. There is a very high negative relationship between mathematical and musical ability. In other words, the good mathematicians tended to be the poor musicians and vice versa. It is not claimed that they are good at music *because* they are poor at mathematics but merely that there is an inverse association between the two.

Reporting the results

When reporting the size of a correlation coefficient it is usual to report its statistical significance as well. Statistical significance is such an important concept that it needs to be discussed in some depth as it is so easily misunderstood. We briefly

Table 8.2	Essential steps in the calculation of the correlation coefficient					
X score (music)	Y score (maths)	$X - \bar{X}$	$(X + \bar{X})^2$	$Y + \bar{Y}$	$(Y - \bar{Y})^2$	$(X - \bar{X})(Y - \bar{Y})$
2	8	2 − 4.5 = −2.5	6.25	8 − 6.2 = 1.8	3.24	−2.5 × 1.8 = −4.5
6	3	6 − 4.5 = 1.5	2.25	3 − 6.2 = −3.2	10.24	1.5 × −3.2 = −4.8
4	9	4 − 4.5 = −0.5	0.25	9 − 6.2 = 2.8	7.84	−0.5 × 2.8 = −1.4
5	7	5 − 4.5 = 0.5	0.25	7 − 6.2 = 0.8	0.64	0.5 × 0.8 = 0.4
7	2	7 − 4.5 = 2.5	6.25	2 − 6.2 = −4.2	17.64	2.5 × −4.2 = −10.5
7	3	7 − 4.5 = 2.5	6.25	3 − 6.2 = −3.2	10.24	2.5 × −3.2 = −8.0
2	9	2 − 4.5 = −2.5	6.25	9 − 6.2 = 2.8	7.84	−2.5 × 2.8 = −7.0
3	8	3 − 4.5 = −1.5	2.25	8 − 6.2 = 1.8	3.24	−1.5 × 1.8 = −2.7
5	6	5 − 4.5 = 0.5	0.25	6 − 6.2 = −0.2	0.04	0.5 × −0.2 = −0.1
4	7	4 − 4.5 = −0.5	0.25	7 − 6.2 = 0.8	0.64	−0.5 × 0.8 = −0.4
$\sum X = 45$	$\sum Y = 62$		$\sum (X - X)^2 =$ 30.50		$\sum (X - X)^2 =$ −61.6	$\sum (X - \bar{X})(Y - \bar{Y}) =$ −39
Mean $\bar{X} = 4.5$	Mean $\bar{Y} = 6.2$					

→

introduced the concept in Chapter 1 (Section 1.5) and devote a chapter (Chapter 11) to explaining it. Statistical significance indicates that your correlation, etc. is unlikely to be a fortuitous or fluke finding. That is, the correlation is large enough that it is unlikely to come from a population in which there is really a zero correlation. So you assume that your finding reflects a relationship that truly exists. If it is unlikely that your correlation is a fluke then the correlation is said to be statistically significant. This probability is usually set at .05 (i.e. 5%) or lower. However, the important point for now is to remember that statistical significance is invariably given with the value of the correlation coefficient.

We would write something like: 'It was found that musical ability was inversely related to mathematical ability. The Pearson correlation coefficient was −.90 which is statistically significant at the 5% level with a sample size of 10.' The statement about statistical significance will become clearer after you have studied Chapter 11.

If we follow the advice of the 2010 Publication Manual of the American Psychological Association (APA) we could write: 'Musical ability was significantly inversely related to mathematical ability, $r(8) = -.90, p < .05$.' The number in brackets after r is the sample size minus 2. This number is called the degrees of freedom and is explained in detail in Section 23.4. It is more usual in a statistical analysis to report degrees of freedom rather than sample size. Statistical significance is usually reported as a proportion rather than a percentage. Computer packages like SPSS give the exact significance level. The APA Publication Manual recommends that researchers give this exact significance rather than simply to indicate significance at the 5% or .05 level.

Box 8.1	Key concepts

Covariance

Many of the basic concepts taught in introductory statistics are relevant even at the advanced level. The concept of covariance is one of these. As we have seen, covariance is based on the deviation from the mean for the variable X multiplied by the deviation of the variable Y for each pair of scores. In other words, it is the top part of the Pearson correlation formula. The correlation coefficient is simply the ratio of the covariance over the largest value that the covariance could take for a particular pair of variables. That makes the correlation coefficient a standardised measure of covariance. But the term covariance crops up throughout this book in a number of different contexts. It is involved in ANOVA (especially the analysis of covariance) and regression, for example – lots of places, some of them unexpected.

One phrase that might cause some consternation when you first come across it is that of the 'variance–covariance' matrix. This is simply a table (matrix) which includes the variances of each variable in the diagonal and their covariances off the diagonal. This is illustrated for variables X, Y and Z in Table 8.3. The diagonal contains the variances but the other numbers are the covariances – each of these is presented twice because the covariance of X with Z is the same as the covariance of Z with X.

Similar matrices are produced for correlation coefficients. However, in this case the diagonal consists of 1.00s (the correlation of a variable with itself is always 1) and the off-diagonals have the correlation coefficients of each variable with the other variables.

Table 8.3	Variance–covariance matrix for three variables		
	Variable X	**Variable Y**	**Variable Z**
Variable X	2.400	1.533	1.244
Variable Y	1.533	4.933	3.733
Variable Z	1.244	3.733	5.156

8.3   Some rules to check out

- You should make sure that a straight line is the best fit to the scattergram points. If the best-fitting line is a *curve* such as in Figure 8.7 then you should not use the Pearson correlation coefficient. The reason for this is that the Pearson correlation assumes a straight line which is a gross distortion if you have a curved (curvilinear) relationship.

- Make sure that your scattergram does not contain a few extreme cases which are unduly influencing the correlation coefficient (Figure 8.8). In this diagram you can see that the points at the top left of the scattergram are responsible for the apparent negative correlation between the two variables. Your eyes probably suggest that for virtually all the points on the scattergram there is no relationship at all. You could in these circumstances eliminate the 'outliers' (i.e. extreme, highly influential points) and recalculate the correlation coefficient based on the remaining, more typical group of scores. If the correlation remains significant with the same sign as before then your interpretation of your data is likely to remain broadly unchanged. However, there needs to be good reason for deleting the 'outliers'; this should not be done simply because the data as they stand do not support your ideas. It may be that something unusual had happened – perhaps an outlier arose from the responses of a slightly deaf person who could not hear the researcher's instructions, for example.

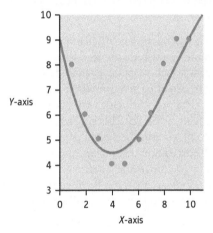

FIGURE 8.7   Curved relationship between two variables

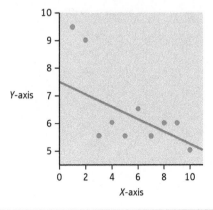

FIGURE 8.8   Influence of outliers on a correlation

Box 8.2   Key concepts

Correlation and causality

It is typically argued that a correlation does not prove causality. Just because two variables are related to each other is not sufficient reason to say anything other than that they are related. Statistical analysis is basically incapable of showing that one variable influenced the other variable directly one way or the other. It is your research design which allows you to infer causality or not. Your particular statistical analysis is irrelevant. Psychologists use laboratory experiments (or randomised trials) to address the issue

of causality. In experimental designs, variables can be systematically manipulated by the researcher and participants randomly assigned to the various experimental conditions. As a consequence, it is possible to infer causality.

Be careful when you read phrases such as 'the effect of Variable *A* on Variable *B*' in psychological writings. This can be misleading as it does not always mean causal effect. Instead, sometimes it merely refers to a relationship, causal or otherwise.

8.4   Coefficient of determination

The correlation coefficient is an index of how much variance two variables have in common. However, you need to square the correlation coefficient in order to know precisely how much variance is shared. The squared correlation coefficient is also known as the *coefficient of determination*.

The proportion of variance shared by two variables whose correlation coefficient is .5 equals $.5^2$ or .25. This is a proportion out of 1 so as a percentage it is $.25 \times 100\% = 25\%$. A correlation coefficient of .8 means that $.8^2 \times 100\%$ or 64% of the variance is shared. A correlation coefficient of 1.00 means that $1.00^2 \times 100\% = 100\%$ of the variance is shared. Since the coefficient of determination is based on *squaring* the correlation coefficient, it should be obvious that the amount of variance shared by the two variables declines increasingly rapidly as the correlation coefficient gets smaller (Table 8.4).

Table 8.4	Variance shared by two variables
Correlation coefficient	**Variance the two variables share**
1.00	100%
.90	81%
.80	64%
.70	49%
.60	36%
.50	25%
.40	16%
.30	9%
.20	4%
.10	1%
.00	0%

8.5   Significance testing

Some readers who have previously studied statistics a little will be familiar with the notion of significance testing and might be wondering why this has not been dealt with for the correlation coefficient. We mention it briefly in this chapter when explaining how to interpret and report your data largely so it does not get omitted when you report a study that you have carried out. It is a crucial statistical concept but easily misunderstood. Consequently we devote two chapters (Chapters 10 and 11) to explaining it. It is important when you are trying to make generalisations from your sample. The present chapter presents the correlation coefficient as a descriptive statistic or index which numerically summarises a scattergram between two variables. Nevertheless, researchers would always give significance levels for a correlation coefficient. Significance levels are easily obtained from SPSS output. We show you how to do this in the Computer Analysis section at the end of this chapter.

8.6   Spearman's rho – another correlation coefficient

Spearman's rho is often written as r_s. We have not used this symbol in the following discussion although it is common in textbooks. Just why do we need another variety of correlation coefficient? The answer is that every statistical procedure is developed by statisticians who make assumptions about the characteristics of the data to which they apply. One of the assumptions underlying the Pearson correlation is that the variables are normally distributed and so, roughly speaking, correspond to the bell-shaped frequency curve. If this assumption is not met then the outcome becomes more and more inaccurate. Spearman's rho does not make this assumption about the normality of the variables. So it may be used when the data are not normally distributed. Nonparametric is the term used for statistical techniques which do not assume that each variable is normally distributed. They were often used in the past before personal computers because they were easy to calculate especially when sample sizes are small.

Actually, the Pearson correlation remains acceptably accurate even with quite a lot of non-normality so it can be used even when its assumptions are violated. Nevertheless, some researchers will opt for distribution-free or nonparametric techniques when the normality assumption is not met (see Chapter 21 for other nonparametric and ranking tests). It is not possible to argue that they are wrong to do so. There are many different opinions in statistics. Generally speaking, however, we would suggest that you use the Pearson correlation coefficient unless there is a good reason not to. You could try comparing both coefficients to see whether it makes much difference. The Pearson correlation is used in many advanced statistical techniques which is not the case with Spearman's rho.

Spearman's rho is a version of the Pearson correlation coefficient. Instead of using the scores from your data, in Spearman's rho the scores on each variable are ranked from smallest to largest. That is, the smallest score on variable X is given rank 1, the second smallest score on variable X is given rank 2 and so forth. The smallest score on variable Y is given rank 1, the second smallest score on variable Y is given rank 2, etc. (Saying that an athlete was fifth in a race is to give their performance a rank.) In Spearman's rho, it is these two sets of ranks which are correlated and not the scores. To get the value of Spearman's rho you could simply calculate the Pearson correlation between these two sets of ranks. The Spearman's rho formula is merely a quick method of doing this calculation. You have to bear in mind that these correlation coefficients were originated at the beginning of the 20th century – long before computers. The quick method used simpler steps and saved labour.

Table 8.5	Ranking of a set of scores when tied (equal) scores are involved								
Scores	4	5	5	6	7	8	9	9	9	10
Ranks	1	2.5	2.5	4	5	6	8	8	8	10

Statistical methods involving ranks have a problem. What do you do when ranks are tied? This is when there are two or more identical scores on a variable. There might be two people who scored 7 on variable *X*, for example. Then we pretend that the two scores are minutely different and allocate the appropriate ranks to these scores. But they are exactly the same scores so we give each of the tied scores the average of these ranks. Table 8.5 shows a set of ten scores and their corresponding ranks. The two scores of 5 are each given the rank 2.5 because if they were slightly different they would have been given ranks 2 and 3, respectively. But they cannot be separated and so we average the ranks as follows:

$$\frac{2 + 3}{2} = 2.5$$

This average of the two ranks corresponds to what was entered into Table 8.5.

There are three scores of 9 which would have been allocated the ranks 7, 8 and 9 if the scores had been slightly different from each other. These three ranks are averaged to give an average rank of 8 which is entered as the rank for each of the three tied scores in Table 8.5.

So Spearman's rho is a special computational formula (see Box 4.3 for an explanation of computational formula) which is equivalent to the Pearson correlation formula when you have ranked scores. This computational formula becomes a little inaccurate when you have tied ranks. As tied ranks are not uncommon in psychological data, using the computational formula has its limitations.

Although Spearman's rho can be calculated using the Pearson correlation formula, they are not the same thing. One is based on the scores and the other on the ranks of scores so one should expect them to be different. They have different theoretical distributions. The practical consequence of this is in terms of statistical significance. So what you find is that for any given value of the correlation coefficient (say .6) the statistical significances of the Pearson correlation for the scores and Spearman's rho for the ranked scores will be different.

Explaining statistics 8.2

How Spearman's rho works

If you calculate the Pearson correlation coefficient between the ranks of the scores in Table 8.1 the correlation coefficient is −.89. In other words, the Spearman rho is −.89. This is a little different from the value of −.90 that we obtained earlier when we correlated the scores for the Pearson correlation (Explaining statistics 8.1). We will use the same data to show how the computational formula for Spearman's rho works and illustrate ranking. The calculation steps are given in Table 8.6. You will see that the scores on the two variables have been ranked separately from smallest

Table 8.6	Steps in the calculation of Spearman's rho correlation coefficient using the speedy formula					
Person	Maths score X_{score}	Music score Y_{Score}	Maths rank X_r	Music rank Y_r	Maths rank – music rank D (difference)	Square of previous column D^2
1	8	2	7.5	1.5	6.0	36.00
2	3	6	2.5	8	−5.5	30.25
3	9	4	9.5	4.5	5	25.00
4	7	5	5.5	6.5	−1.0	1.00
5	2	7	1	9.5	−8.5	72.25
6	3	7	2.5	9.5	−7.0	49.00
7	9	2	9.5	1.5	8.0	64.00
8	8	3	7.5	3	4.5	20.25
9	6	5	4	6.5	−2.5	6.25
10	7	4	5.5	4.5	1.0	1.00
						$\sum D^2 = 305$

to largest in the table. Since the sample size is ten the ranks go from 1 to 10. You will also notice that there are quite a few scores which tie and have been given the average of the ranks which would have been given were the scores slightly different. For example, there are two mathematics scores which are 7 both of which receive the average of the ranks 5 and 6, which is 5.5.

Following the columns of ranks there is another column which consists of the difference (D) between the two sets of ranks. So the music column ranks have been subtracted from the mathematics column ranks. If there is a perfect correlation between the two variables then all of the differences would be zero. The differences between the two sets of ranks will be larger the lower the correlation between the two variables. The final column consists of these differences squared. At the bottom of this column you will find the sum of these squared differences, which is 305. This is $\sum D^2$. The sample size (N) is 10.

All that needs to be done now is to substitute these two values into the formula below and work through the computation:

$$p_{[Spearman's\ rho]} = 1 - \frac{6\sum D^2}{N(N^2 - 1)}$$

$$= 1 - \frac{6 \times 305}{10(10^2 - 1)}$$

$$= 1 - \frac{1830}{10(100 - 1)}$$

$$= 1 - \frac{1830}{10 \times 99}$$

$$= 1 - \frac{1830}{990}$$

$$= 1 - 1.848$$

$$= -.848$$

$$= -.85 \text{ to 2 decimal places}$$

Interpreting the results

It should be noted that this value of Spearman's rho is a little different from its correct value (−.89) that we calculated using the Pearson correlation formula. Had we not got tied ranks in the data, the calculations would have given exactly the same values. In other words, this computational formula for Spearman's rho is slightly inaccurate where there are tied ranks – another good reason for not doing the computation by hand. Although the difference is not major, it is best to avoid the inaccuracy. The easy way of doing this is to use SPSS to do the calculation for you. Otherwise the interpretation of the negative correlation is the same as we have previously discussed.

Reporting the results

As with the Pearson correlation (Explaining statistics 8.1), when reporting the Spearman's rho correlation coefficient we would report the statistical significance of the coefficient.

We would write up the results something along the lines of the following: 'It was found that musical ability was inversely related to mathematical ability. The value of Spearman's rho correlation coefficient was −.85 which is statistically significant at the 5% level with a sample size of 10.' The last sentence may not mean much until Chapters 10 and 11 have been studied. The statistical significance of the Spearman rho correlation coefficient may be obtained from Appendix D when doing this calculation by hand. However, it is preferable to let SPSS do the calculation for you.

8.7   Example from the literature

Pearson correlation coefficients are extremely common in published research. They can be found in a variety of contexts so choosing a typical example is virtually meaningless. The correlation coefficient is sometimes used as an indicator of the validity of a psychological test. So it might be used to indicate the relationship between a test of intelligence and children's performance in school. The test is a valid predictor of school performance if there is a substantial correlation between the test score and school performance.

The correlation coefficient is also very useful as an indicator of the reliability of a psychological test. This might mean the extent to which people's scores on the test are consistent over time. You can use the correlation coefficient to indicate whether those who perform well now on the test also performed well a year ago. For example, Gillis (1980) in the manual accompanying the Child Anxiety Scale indicates that he retested 127 US schoolchildren in the first to third grades immediately after the initial testing. The reliability coefficients (test–retest reliability) or the correlation coefficients between the two testings were:

Grade 1 = .82
Grade 2 = .85
Grade 3 = .92

A sample of children retested after a week had a retest reliability coefficient of .81. It is clear from this that the reliability of the measure is good. This means that the children scoring the most highly one week also tend to get the highest scores the next week. It does not mean that the scores are identical from week to week – only that the relative scores are the same. Practically all reliability and validity coefficients used in psychological testing are variants on much the same theme and are rarely much more complex than the correlation coefficient itself.

Research examples

Pearson correlation and Spearman's rho

Blom, van Middendorp and Geenen (2012) proposed that embitterment is the consequence of childhood attachment problems such as anxious attachment. Embitterment involves the overall feeling of being invalidated by others such as having persistent feelings that one has been let down, or one is a loser, or that one needs revenge but is helpless to do so. Attachment was measured using the Attachment Styles Questionnaire which measures 1) fearful attachment, 2) preoccupied attachment, 3) dismissive attachment and 4) secure attachment. Embitterment was measured using the Bern Embitterment Inventory. Some of the subscales of the embitterment inventory had very skewed distributions which led the researchers to choose Spearman's rank correlation coefficient to assess associations. Embitterment correlated .39 with fearful attachment and .44 with preoccupied attachment. These two scales are the ones measuring anxious attachment.

Carlson, Vazire and Oltmanns (2011) investigated narcissistic personalities, asking such questions as whether such individuals understand the negative aspects of their personalities and reputations. Various measures of narcissism were used including clinical ones. Their meta-perceptions of others concerning themselves were also measured. The research suggested that narcissistic individuals did have a degree of self-insight into how others see them. However, using Pearson correlation coefficients, it was shown that individuals scoring higher on narcissism also saw themselves more positively on such traits as being funny ($r = .25$), being extravert ($r = .43$) and intelligence ($r = .31$).

Teissedre and Chabrol (2004) examined depression in 299 French women using the Edinburgh Postnatal Depression Scale. They completed the measure at two to three days following giving birth and four to six weeks after giving birth. They decided to use the Spearman rho correlation coefficient because of the non-normality of the distribution of the Edinburgh Postnatal Depression Scale. The Spearman rank correlation or rho was fairly high at .61 which was significant at the .0001 level.

Key points

Most of the major points have been covered already. But they bear repetition:

- Check the scattergram for your correlation coefficient for signs of a nonlinear relationship – if you find one you should not be using the Pearson correlation coefficient. In these circumstances you should use coefficient eta (η) which is designed for curvilinear relationships. However, eta is a relatively obscure statistic. It is mentioned again in Chapter 17.

- Check the scattergram for outliers which may spuriously be producing a correlation when overwhelmingly the scattergram says that there is a poor relationship.

- Examine the scattergram to see whether there is a positive or negative slope to the scatter and form a general impression of whether the correlation is good (the points fit the straight line well) or poor (the points are very widely scattered around the straight line). Obviously you will become more skilled at this with experience, but it is useful as a rough computational check among other things.

- Before concluding your analysis, look at Chapter 10 to decide whether or not to generalise from your set of data.

COMPUTER ANALYSIS

Correlation coefficients using SPSS

Data
- In 'Data View' of the 'Data Editor', the data are entered as different variables in different columns – each row equals a person (Screenshot 8.1).
- Name each variable in 'Variable View' of the 'Data Editor'.

Analysis
- Select 'Analyze' (Screenshot 8.2).
- Select 'Correlate' and 'Bivariate'.

2
- Move variables to be correlated to right-hand side box (Screenshot 8.3).
- Select 'Pearson' or 'Spearman' according to what is appropriate.
- Select 'Options' to give additional choices (Screenshot 8.4).

Output
- Screenshot 8.5 shows the additional descriptive statistics.
- Screenshot 8.6 is the ouput for the correlation matrix.
- The matrix includes the correlation of each variable with itself and does not provide a significance level for this, of course.

FIGURE 8.9	SPSS steps for correlation coefficient

Interpreting and reporting the output

- Interpretation of the output is complicated by the fact that SPSS intercorrelates each of the variables with itself and with the other variables. The correlation of a variable with itself is always 1. No significance level is given for this. The table also includes the correlation between the variables with the other variables twice. So you have the correlation of Variable X with Variable Y and the correlation of Variable Y with Variable X. These are, of course, the same. The output gives the correlation $(-.900)$, the statistical significance $(.000)$ and the sample size (10).

- It would be good to report the significance level as being less than .001 and something known as the degrees of freedom which for the correlation coefficient is $N - 2$ or 8 in this case. Significance is discussed in Chapter 11 and degrees of freedom in Chapter 23.

- In a report, we could write 'There is a significant negative correlation between musical ability and mathematical ability, $r(8) = .90, p \leq .001$. Children with more musical ability have lower mathematical ability.'

Reprint Courtesy of International Business Machines Corporation, © International Business Machines Corporation

SCREENSHOT 8.1 Data in 'Data View' of the 'Data Editor'

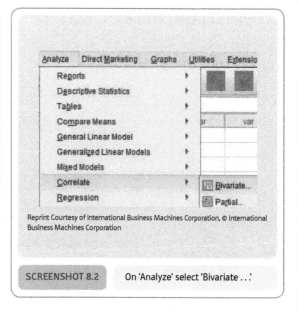

Reprint Courtesy of International Business Machines Corporation, © International Business Machines Corporation

SCREENSHOT 8.2 On 'Analyze' select 'Bivariate . . .'

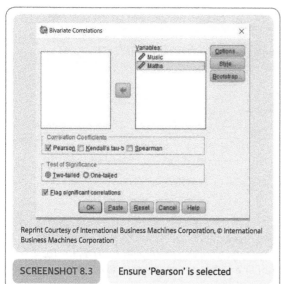

Reprint Courtesy of International Business Machines Corporation, © International Business Machines Corporation

SCREENSHOT 8.3 Ensure 'Pearson' is selected

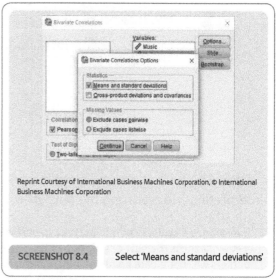

Reprint Courtesy of International Business Machines Corporation, © International Business Machines Corporation

SCREENSHOT 8.4 Select 'Means and standard deviations'

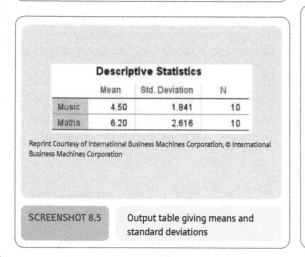

Descriptive Statistics

	Mean	Std. Deviation	N
Music	4.50	1.841	10
Maths	6.20	2.616	10

Reprint Courtesy of International Business Machines Corporation, © International Business Machines Corporation

SCREENSHOT 8.5 Output table giving means and standard deviations

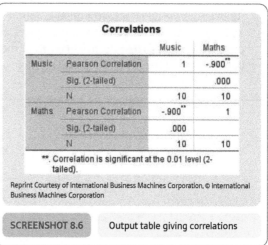

Correlations

		Music	Maths
Music	Pearson Correlation	1	-.900**
	Sig. (2-tailed)		.000
	N	10	10
Maths	Pearson Correlation	-.900**	1
	Sig. (2-tailed)	.000	
	N	10	10

**. Correlation is significant at the 0.01 level (2-tailed).

Reprint Courtesy of International Business Machines Corporation, © International Business Machines Corporation

SCREENSHOT 8.6 Output table giving correlations

COMPUTER ANALYSIS

Scattergram using SPSS

Data
- Data have already been entered for the correlation coefficient (Screenshot 8.1).

Analysis
- Select 'Graphs', 'Chart Builder. . .' or 'Legacy Dialogs' (Screenshot 8.7).
- Select 'OK' if your variables are defined (Screenshot 8.8).

2
- Move appropriate variables names to the vertical and horizontal axes (Screenshot 8.9).

Output
- A regression line can be fitted by double clicking anywhere on the scattergram to bring up the 'Chart Editor'.
- Select 'Elements' and 'Fit Line at Total' (Screenshot 8.10).
- The number of points with the same values can be indicated by clicking on 'Marker Size' (Screenshot 8.11).
- The scatterplot may be further edited (Screenshot 8.12).

FIGURE 8.10   SPSS steps for scattergrams

Interpreting and reporting the output

- Interpreting a scatterplot is important. In particular, the researcher should look to make sure that a straight line is the best description of the pattern of points. Also, the researcher should look for outliers which are data points which are radically out of line with most of the data. Both of these mean that the Pearson correlation coefficient should not be used.

- By all means include the scattergram in your report especially if it reveals something of importance about your data. Make sure that it is properly labelled. Too many scattergrams can make your report too cumbersome so be selective in terms of the ones that you use. Comment on the linearity of the data points and the presence of outliers, if any.

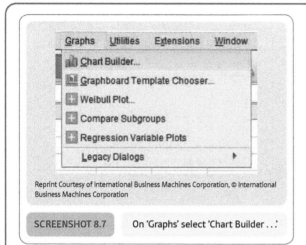

Reprint Courtesy of International Business Machines Corporation, © International Business Machines Corporation

SCREENSHOT 8.7   On 'Graphs' select 'Chart Builder . . .'

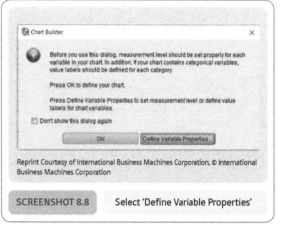

Reprint Courtesy of International Business Machines Corporation, © International Business Machines Corporation

SCREENSHOT 8.8   Select 'Define Variable Properties'

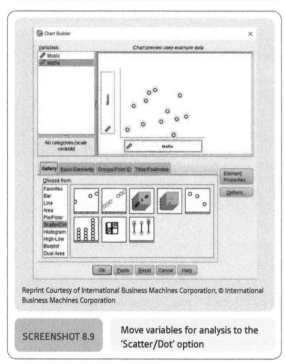

Reprint Courtesy of International Business Machines Corporation, © International Business Machines Corporation

SCREENSHOT 8.9   Move variables for analysis to the 'Scatter/Dot' option

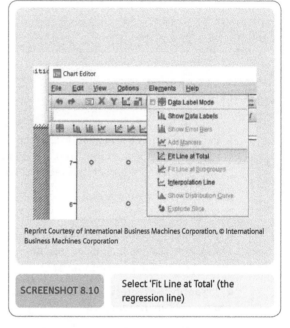

Reprint Courtesy of International Business Machines Corporation, © International Business Machines Corporation

SCREENSHOT 8.10   Select 'Fit Line at Total' (the regression line)

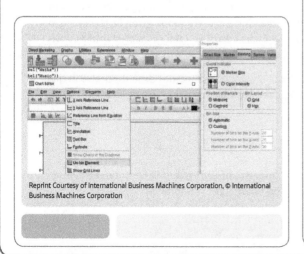

Reprint Courtesy of International Business Machines Corporation, © International Business Machines Corporation

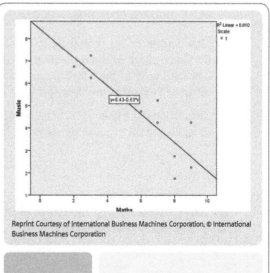

Reprint Courtesy of International Business Machines Corporation, © International Business Machines Corporation

CHAPTER 9

Regression

Prediction with precision

Overview

- Regression finds the regression line (the best-fitting straight line) for a scatterplot between two variables. (By this token, the correlation coefficient can be seen as an index of the spread of the data points around this regression line.)

- Variable X is the horizontal axis of the scatterplot and variable Y is the vertical axis of the scatterplot.

- Sometimes (somewhat misleadingly) the X variable is named the independent variable and Y variable the dependent variable. Alternatively, the X variable is the predictor variable and the Y variable the criterion variable.

- To specify the regression line, its slope and the point where it touches the vertical axis (the intercept) are needed.

- Using this information, it is possible to estimate the most likely score on the variable Y for any given score on variable X. Sometimes this is referred to as making predictions.

- Standard error is a term used to describe the likely variability of any statistical estimate including those of the regression calculation. So there is a standard error of the slope, a standard error of the intercept and so forth. Standard error is analogous to standard deviation and indicates the likely spread of any of the estimates.

- Regression is the foundation of many of the more advanced techniques described later in this book. So the better you understand the concept at this stage, the easier will be your later work.

Preparation

You should have a working knowledge of the scattergram, of the relationship between two variables (Chapter 7) and understand the correlation coefficient (Chapter 8).

9.1   Introduction

Regression, like the correlation coefficient, numerically describes important features of a scattergram relating two variables. However, it does it in a different way. Among its important uses is allowing researchers to make predictions (for example, when choosing the best applicant for a job on the basis of an aptitude or ability test).

Assume that research has shown that a simple test of manual dexterity is capable of distinguishing between the better and not-so-good assembly workers in a precision components factory. Manual dexterity is a *predictor* variable and job performance the *criterion* variable. So it should be possible to predict which applicants are likely to be the more productive employees from scores on the test of manual dexterity. Using the test might be a lot cheaper than employing and training employees who fail to make the grade in the factory. Imaginary data for such a study are shown in Table 9.1.

The scattergram (Figure 9.1) shows the relationship between scores on the manual dexterity test and the number of units per hour the employee produces in the components factory. Notice that we have made scores on the manual dexterity test the horizontal dimension (X-axis) and the number of units produced per hour the vertical dimension (Y-axis). This is because we eventually want to predict work productivity from scores on the manual dexterity test.

In regression in order to keep the number of formulae to the minimum, the horizontal dimension (X-axis) should always be used to represent the variable from which the prediction is being made, and the vertical dimension (Y-axis) should always represent what is being predicted. It requires a different formula to predict the X values from the Y values and this is not commonly available. Furthermore, statistical packages such as SPSS require that you enter the predictor and criterion variables in this standard way.

It is clear from the scattergram that the number of units produced by workers is fairly closely related to scores on the manual dexterity test. If we draw a straight line as best we can through the points on the scattergram, this line could be used as a basis for making predictions about the most likely score on work productivity from the aptitude test score for manual dexterity. This line through the points on a scattergram is called the *regression line*. In order to predict the likeliest number of units per hour corresponding to a score of 70 on the manual dexterity test, we simply draw a right angle from the score 70 on the horizontal axis (manual dexterity test score) to the regression line, and then a right angle

Table 9.1	Manual dexterity and number of units produced per hour	
Manual dexterity score		**Number of units produced per hour**
56		17
19		6
78		23
92		22
16		9
23		10
29		13
60		20
50		16
35		19

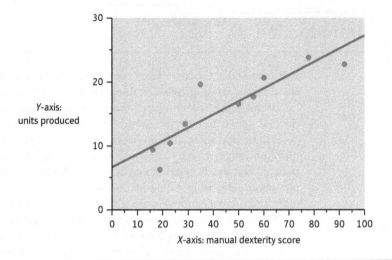

FIGURE 9.1   Scattergram of the relationship between manual dexterity and productivity

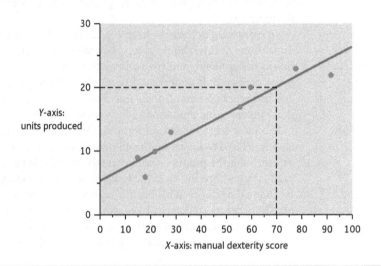

FIGURE 9.2   Using a regression line to make approximate predictions

from the vertical axis to meet this point. In this way we can find the productivity score which best corresponds to a particular manual dexterity score (Figure 9.2). Estimating from this scattergram and regression line, it appears that the best prediction from a manual dexterity score of 70 is a productivity rate of about 19 or 20.

There is only one major problem with this procedure – the prediction depends on the particular line drawn through the points on the scattergram. You might draw a somewhat different line from the one we did. Subjective factors such as these are not desirable in statistical analyses and it would be better to have a method which was not affected in this way. So mathematical ways of determining the best regression line have been developed. Fortunately, the computations involved are generally straightforward and SPSS and other computer programs do all of the hard work for you.

Regression is a component of many of the more advanced statistical techniques which

advanced work easier. See Box 9.1 for a discussion of the General Linear Model which underlies a great deal of the statistical analyses used by psychologists. Figure 9.3 describes the key steps when using regression.

Box 9.1   Key concepts

General Linear Model

GLM, the General Linear Model, is the basis of many of the statistical techniques discussed in this book. It is quite simple – it is the assumption that the effects of variables on other variables are additive. In other words, an increase of 1 unit on variable A is associated with an increase of x on variable B. This is assumed to be the case irrespective of where the increase of 1 unit is on variable A (i.e. at the top, middle or bottom of the distribution, etc.). The basis of the General Linear Model is the formula that you can see in Explaining statistics 9.1 which is used to predict values on one variable from values on another. The formula only needs slight modification to give the relationship between one set of data Y and another set of data X:

$$Y_{\text{data set}} = a_{\text{constant}} + (b_{\text{regression weight}} \times X_{\text{scores}}) + e_{\text{error}}$$

All that we have done is to add in e for error. That is, there is not a perfect relationship between the Y data and the X data. The imperfection is the result of error in the measurements. (Error is really just variation which is unaccounted for in the rest of the equation.)

The General Linear Model is actually more general than this basic formula implies. The reason is that there may be several Y variables (as in multivariate ANOVA – Chapter 29), several X variables (as in multiple regression – Chapter 34), several intercept values for each X variable and several regression coefficients also for each X variable. But the basic regression equation is the simplest version of the General Linear Model.

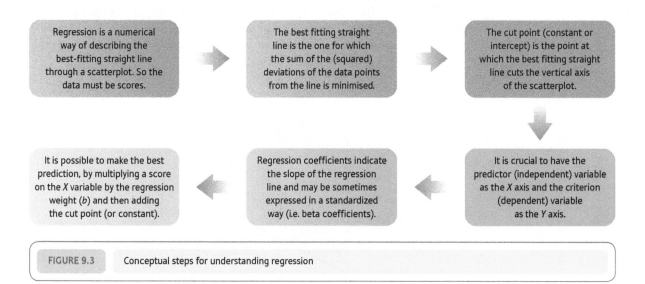

| FIGURE 9.3 | Conceptual steps for understanding regression |

9.2   Theoretical background and regression equations

The straight line through a set of points on a scattergram is called the regression line. In order to establish an objective criterion, the regression line is chosen which gives the closest fit to the points on the scattergram. In other words, the procedure minimises the total distances between the regression line and the points in the scattergram. In theory, then, one could keep trying different possible regression lines until one is found which has the minimum deviation of the points from it.

The best regression line is the one which has the smallest sum of deviations from it with one proviso. This taken literally would mean that the sum of the deviations from the regression line is used (Σd), which is not the case. Actually, the precise criterion is the sum of the squared deviations from the regression line. The line is chosen which minimises the sum of these squared deviations, so this is known as the least squares solution. It would be a thankless task to draw every possible regression line and calculate the sum of the squared deviations for each of these looking for the smallest. Fortunately things are not done like that and trial and error is not involved. The formulae for regression do all of that work. SPSS makes it even easier.

In order to specify the regression line for any scattergram, you quantify two things:

1. The point at which the regression line cuts the vertical axis at $X = 0$ – this is a number of units of measurement from the zero point of the vertical axis. It can take a positive or negative value, according to whether the vertical axis is cut above or below its zero point. It is normally denoted in regression as point a or the *intercept*.
2. The *slope* of the regression line or, in other words, the gradient of the best-fitting line through the points on the scattergram. Just as with the correlation coefficient, this slope may be positive in the sense that it goes up from bottom left to top right or it can be negative in that it goes downwards from top left to bottom right. The slope is normally denoted by the letter b.

The intercept and slope are both shown in Figure 9.4. To work out the slope, we have drawn a horizontal dashed line from $X = 30$ to $X = 50$ (i.e. its length is 20) and a vertical dashed line up to the regression line (length about 4) up the Y-axis.

The slope b is the increase (+) or decrease (−) of the units produced (in this case +4) divided by the increase in the manual dexterity score (in this case 20), i.e. +0.2.

The slope is simply the number of units that the regression line moves up the vertical axis for each unit it moves along the horizontal axis. In other words, you mark a single step along the horizontal axis and work out how much increase this represents on the

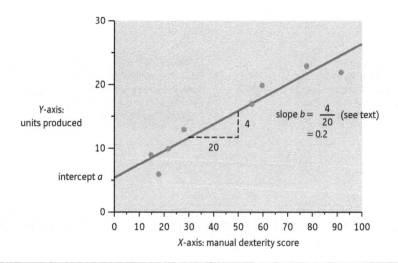

FIGURE 9.4   Slope b and intercept a of a regression line

vertical axis. (It does not matter which single step you choose along the horizontal axis as we are dealing with a straight regression line.) So, for example, if you read that the slope of a scattergram is 2.00, this means that for every increase of 1.00 on the horizontal axis (X-axis) there is an increase of 2.00 on the vertical axis (Y-axis). If there is a slope of -0.5 then this means that for every increase of 1 on the horizontal axis (X-axis) there is a decrease of 0.5 on the vertical axis (Y-axis).

In our example, for every increase of 1 in the manual dexterity score, there is an increase of 0.2 (more accurately, 0.21) in the job performance measure (units produced per hour). We have estimated this value from the scattergram – it may not be exactly the answer that we would have obtained had we used mathematically more precise methods or a computer program. This increase defines the slope. (Note that you do not work with angles, merely distances on the vertical and horizontal axes.)

Fortunately, the application of only two relatively simple formulae (see Explaining statistics 9.1) will give us the slope and the intercept. A third formula is used to make our predictions from the horizontal axis to the vertical axis.

The major differences between correlation and regression are as follows:

- Regression retains the original units of measurement so direct comparisons between regression analyses based on different variables are difficult. Correlation coefficients can readily be compared as they are essentially on a standardised measurement scale and free of the original units of measurement.

- The correlation coefficient does *not* specify the slope of a scattergram. Correlation indicates the amount of spread or variability of the points around the regression line in the scattergram.

In other words, correlation and regression have somewhat different functions despite their close similarities. See more about regression in Box 9.2.

| Box 9.2 | Focus on |

Regression lines

One of the things which can cause difficulty when using regression is the question of what variable should go on the horizontal axis and what variable should go on the vertical axis. Get them the wrong way around and your calculation will be incorrect. There are, in reality, always two regression lines between two variables: that from which variable Y is predicted from variable X, and that from which variable X is predicted from variable Y. They almost always have different slopes. But you probably will never come across these two different formulae. The reason is that life is made simpler if we always have the predictor on the horizontal axis and the criterion to be predicted on the vertical axis. You need to be careful what you are trying to predict and from what. Make sure that you put your predictor on the horizontal axis. If you are using regression weights to calculate actual scores on the dependent variable then it is sensible to produce a scattergram for your data. From this you should be able to estimate what the correct answer should be. If this is very different from what your calculation says, then one possibility is that you have got the axes the wrong way round.

Explaining statistics 9.1

How regression works

To facilitate comparison, we will take the data used in the computation of the correlation coefficient (Chapter 8). The data concern the relationship between mathematical and musical ability for a group of 10 individuals. The 10 scores need to be set out in a table like Table 9.2 and the various intermediate calculations carried out. However, it is important with

Table 9.2	Important steps in calculating the regression equation				
Person	Maths score X score	Music score Y score	X^2	Y^2	XY
1	8	2	64	4	16
2	3	6	9	36	18
3	9	4	81	16	36
4	7	5	49	25	35
5	2	7	4	49	14
6	3	7	9	49	21
7	9	2	81	4	18
8	8	3	64	9	24
9	6	5	36	25	30
10	7	4	49	16	28
	$\Sigma X = 62$	$\Sigma Y = 45$	$\Sigma X^2 = 446$	$\Sigma Y^2 = 233$	$\Sigma XY = 240$

regression to make the X scores the predictor variable; the Y scores are the criterion variable. N is the number of pairs of scores, i.e. 10. (Strictly speaking the Y^2 and $\sum Y^2$ calculations are not necessary for regression but are included here because they highlight the similarities between the correlation and regression calculations.)

The slope b of the regression line is given by the following formula:

$$b = \frac{\sum XY - \left(\frac{\sum X \sum Y}{N}\right)}{\sum X^2 - \frac{(\sum X)^2}{N}}$$

Thus, substituting the values from the table in the above formula:

$$b_{[slope]} = \frac{240 - \left(\frac{62 \times 45}{10}\right)}{446 - \frac{(62)^2}{10}}$$

$$= \frac{240 - \frac{2790}{10}}{446 - \frac{3844}{10}}$$

$$= \frac{240 - 279}{446 - 384.4}$$

$$= \frac{-39}{61.6}$$

$$= -.63$$

Note that this is the same value as given by SPSS in Screenshot 9.5.

The negative sign in the value of the slope tells us that the slope of the regression line is negative – it moves downwards from top left to bottom right. Furthermore, for every unit one moves along the horizontal axis, the regression line moves 0.63 units down the vertical axis since in this case it is a negative slope.

We can now substitute in the following formula to get the cut-off point or intercept a of the regression line on the vertical axis:

$$a_{[\text{intercept on vertical axis}]} = \frac{\Sigma Y - b\Sigma X}{N}$$

$$= \frac{45 - (-0.63 \times 62)}{10}$$

$$= \frac{45 - (-39.06)}{10}$$

$$= \frac{84.06}{10}$$

$$= 8.41$$

This value for a is the point on the vertical axis (musical ability) cut by the regression line. Note that this value is similar to that produced by SPSS in Screenshot 9.5 given rounding error in our hand calculation.

If one wishes to predict the most likely score on the vertical axis from a particular score on the horizontal axis, one simply substitutes the appropriate values in the following formula:

$$Y_{[\text{predicted score}]} = a_{[\text{intercept}]} + (b_{[\text{slope}]} \times X_{[\text{known score}]})$$

Thus if we wished to predict musical ability for a score of 8 on mathematical ability, given that we know the slope b is -0.63 and the intercept is 8.41, we simply substitute these values in the formula:

$$Y_{[\text{predicted score}]} = a_{[\text{intercept}]} + (b_{[\text{slope}]} \times X_{[\text{known score}]})$$

$$= 8.41 + (-0.63 \times 8)$$

$$= 8.41 + (-5.04)$$

$$= 3.37$$

This is the *best* prediction – it does not mean that people with a score of 8 on mathematical ability inevitably get a score of 3.37 on musical ability. It is just our most intelligent estimate.

Interpreting the results

The proper interpretation of the regression equations depends on the scattergram between the two variables showing a more or less linear (i.e. straight line) trend. If it does not show this, then the interpretation of the regression calculations for the slope and intercept will be misleading since the method assumes a straight line. Curvilinear relationships (see Chapter 8) are difficult to handle mathematically.

If the scattergram reveals a linear relationship, then the interpretation of the regression equations is simple as the formulae merely describe the scattergram mathematically.

→

Reporting the results

This regression analysis could be reported as follows: 'Because of the negative correlation between mathematical and musical abilities, it was possible to carry out a regression analysis to predict musical ability from mathematical ability. The slope of the regression of mathematical ability on musical ability b is -0.63 and the intercept a is 8.41.'

Box 9.3	Focus on

Problems interpreting regression

The use of regression in prediction is a fraught issue not because of the statistical methods but because of the characteristics of the data used. In particular, note that our predictions about job performance are based on data from the people already in the job. So, for example, those with the best manual dexterity might have developed these skills on the job rather than having them when they were interviewed. Thus it may not be that manual dexterity determines job performance but that they are both influenced by other (unknown) factors. Similarly, if we found that age was a negative predictor of how quickly people get promoted in a banking corporation, this may simply reflect a bias against older people in the profession rather than greater ability of younger people.

9.3   Confidence intervals and standard error: how accurate are the predicted score and the regression equations?

You may prefer to leave studying the following material until you have had the opportunity to study Chapter 12.

The accuracy of the predicted score on the criterion is dependent on the closeness of the scattergram points to the regression line; if there is a strong correlation between the variables there is little error in the prediction. Examining the scattergram between two variables will give you an idea of the variability around the regression line and hence the precision of the estimated or predicted scores. See Box 9.3 for more on interpreting regression.

Statisticians prefer to calculate what they call the standard error to indicate how certain one can be about aspects of regression such as the prediction of the intercept or cut-off points, and the slope. A standard error is much the same as the standard deviation except it applies to the variability of samples rather than individual scores. So the standard error of something is the average deviation of samples from the population value. Don't worry too much if you don't quite understand the concept yet, since we come back to it (in Chapters 11 and 12). *Just regard standard error of an estimate as the average amount by which an estimate is likely to be wrong.* As you might expect, since this is statistics, the average is calculated in an unexpected way, as it was for the standard deviation which is not dissimilar.

Although the formulae for calculating the standard errors of the various aspects of the regression line are readily available, they add considerably to the computational labour involved in regression, so we recommend that you use a computer to relieve you of this computational chore.

The main standard errors involved in regression are:

- the one for your predicted (or estimated) value on the criterion (this is known as the standard error of the estimate of y)

- the one for the slope of the regression line b

- the one for the intercept on the vertical axis a.

Don't forget that the formulae for calculating these standard errors merely give you the 'average' amount by which your estimate is wrong. OK, what we mean by 'average' is a little bit convoluted but it might help you get a grasp on the concept.

It might be more useful to estimate the likely range within which the true value of the prediction, slope or intercept is likely to fall. In other words, to be able to say that, for example, the predicted score on the criterion variable is likely to be between 2.7 and 3.3. In statistics, this likely range of the true value is known as the *confidence interval* (CI). Actually there are several confidence intervals depending on how confident you wish to be that you have included the true value – the interval is obviously going to be wider if you wish to be *very* confident rather than just confident. In statistics one would routinely use the 95% confidence interval. This 95% confidence interval indicates the range of values within which the true value will fall 95% of the time. That is, our confidence interval will not contain the true value only in 5% of times.

The following is a rule of thumb which is accurate enough for your purposes for now. Multiply the standard error by 2. This gives you approximately the amount which you need to *add and subtract* from the estimated value to cut off the middle 95% of the possible values – that is the 95% confidence interval. In other words, if the estimated value of the criterion (Y-variable) is 6.00 and the standard error of this estimate is 0.26, then the 95% confidence interval is $6.00 \pm (2 \times 0.26)$ which is 6.00 ± 0.52. This gives us a 95% confidence interval of 5.48 to 6.52. Thus it is highly likely that the person's score will actually fall in the range of 5.48 to 6.52 although the most likely value is 6.00.

Exactly the same applies to the other aspects of regression. If the slope is 2.00 with a standard error of 0.10, then the 95% confidence interval is $2.00 \pm (2 \times 0.10)$, which gives a confidence interval of 1.80 to 2.20.

The use of confidence intervals is not as common as it ought to be despite the fact that it gives us a realistic assessment of the precision of our estimates. If you look at Screenshot 9.5 it shows the output from SPSS for simple regression. The 95% confidence intervals are given both for the constant (intercept) and for the regression weight for Maths. For the regression weight of Maths the confidence interval is $-.883$ to $-.383$. Confidence intervals are generally provided on SPSS so there is little to stop you reporting them. Given that the use of confidence intervals is being advocated by many experts and increasingly insisted upon by journal editors, there is every reason to include them.

The above calculations of confidence intervals are approximate if you have fewer than about 30 pairs of scores. If you have between 16 and 29 pairs of scores the calculation will be more accurate if you multiply by 2.1 rather than 2.0. If you have between 12 and 15 pairs of scores then multiplying by 2.2 would improve the accuracy of the calculation. With fewer than 12 pairs the method gets a little more inaccurate. When you have become more knowledgeable about statistics, you could obtain precise confidence intervals by multiplying your standard error by the appropriate value of t from Significance Table 13.1.

The appropriate value is in the row headed 'Degrees of freedom', corresponding to your number of pairs of scores minus 2 under the column for the 5% significance level (i.e. if you have 10 pairs of scores then you would multiply by 2.31).

Research examples

Simple regression

Examples of the use of simple regression in the modern psychological research literature are not common. One likely reason is the general ease of adding in more predictor variables into a study than one. So regard our discussion of simple regression as primarily preparing you to understand multiple regression. Of course, anytime that you use Pearson correlation then it would be appropriate to include the statistics from the equivalent simple regression.

Ang and Huan (2006) tested whether depression mediated the relation between academic stress and thoughts of killing oneself (suicidal ideation) in adolescents. As a first step, they carried out simple regressions of academic stress with depression and suicidal ideation. Both depression and suicidal ideation were positively related to academic stress. Greater academic stress was predictable from greater depression and suicidal ideation.

Fayed and colleagues (2011) were interested in the sorts of factors which predict optimism in the parents of children who are suffering from cancer. They obtained a sample of such parents whose children were actively undergoing treatment. Their measure of optimism was the Life Orientation Test and they included another 26 predictor variables based on stress process theory expectations. They included a number of measures of positive intrapsychic traits which they found to be more predictive of optimism than factors to do with the child's cancer such as the prognosis. They chose to analyse each of their predictors of optimism separately in order to find the predictors which explained substantial amounts of variation. On the basis of their choices made in this way, the initial simple regressions were followed up with multiple regression analysis.

Gallagher and his colleagues (2013) investigated the relation between patients' weight and a number of other variables such as their confidence in exercising and following a cholesterol-lowering diet. Before carrying out a multiple regression, they conducted simple regressions. They found a number of significant regressions such as greater weight being associated with less confidence in exercising and with following a cholesterol-lowering diet.

Key points

- Drawing the scattergram will invariably illuminate the trends in your data and strongly hint at the broad features of the regression calculations. It will also provide a visual check on your computations.

- These regression procedures assume that the best-fitting regression line is a straight line. If it looks as if the regression line ought to be curved or curvilinear, do not apply these numerical methods. Of course, even if a relationship is curvilinear you could use the curved-line scattergram to make graphically based predictions.

- It may be that you have more than one predictor variable that you wish to use – if so, look at Chapter 34 on multiple regression.

COMPUTER ANALYSIS

Simple regression using SPSS

Data
- Like for the correlation coefficient, the data are entered as different variables in different columns in 'Data View' of the 'Data Editor' – each row equals a person (Screenshot 9.1).
- Name each variable in 'Variable View' of the 'Data Editor'.

Analysis
- Select 'Analyze', 'Regression' and 'Linear' (Screenshot 9.2).

2
- Select the dependent variable and move to 'Dependent' box (Screenshot 9.3).
- Select the independent variable and move to the 'Independent(s)' box. Only use one independent variable.

3
- Select 'Statistics' and then 'Confidence Intervals' or any other option you wish (Screenshot 9.4).
- Select 'Continue' and 'OK'.

Output
- The output gives the regression weight as well as its statistical significance (Screenshot 9.5).
- The confidence intervals are presented as a range – take care as it is also given for the constant.

Extras
- If you want the scattergram, follow the instructions as found in Chapter 8 for the correlation coefficient.

FIGURE 9.5   SPSS steps for performing simple regression

Interpreting and reporting the output

- The most important part of the regression output is the *b*-weight (SPSS output uses capital B for this) and its sign as this tells you about the direction of the relationship in the scattergram. The significance level is also important, of course. You can largely ignore the row for the constant as this generally is not involved in the interpretation. Remember that there is always a direction to the prediction and that one variable will be the predictor variable and the other the predicted variable.

- One way of reporting this regression analysis following APA recommendations (see Section 15.2) would be: 'Because of the negative correlation between mathematical and musical abilities, it was possible to carry out a regression analysis to predict musical ability from mathematical ability. The slope of the regression of mathematical ability on musical ability $b = -0.63, p < .001$, 95% CI $[-.88, -.38]$ and the intercept $a = 8.41, p < .001$, 95% CI $[6.75, 10.10]$.' Probability or significance levels (p) are explained in Chapter 11 and confidence intervals (CIs) in Chapter 16.

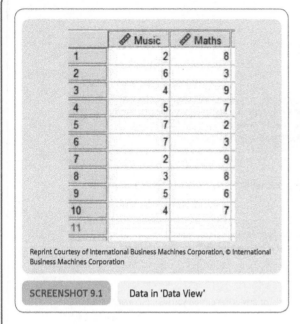

Reprint Courtesy of International Business Machines Corporation, © International Business Machines Corporation

SCREENSHOT 9.1   Data in 'Data View'

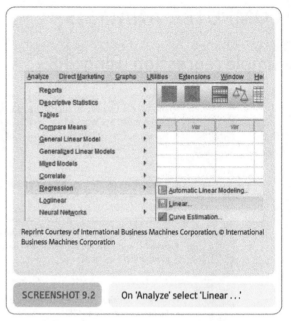

Reprint Courtesy of International Business Machines Corporation, © International Business Machines Corporation

SCREENSHOT 9.2   On 'Analyze' select 'Linear . . .'

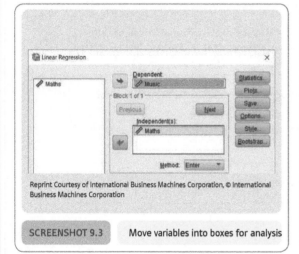

Reprint Courtesy of International Business Machines Corporation, © International Business Machines Corporation

SCREENSHOT 9.3   Move variables into boxes for analysis

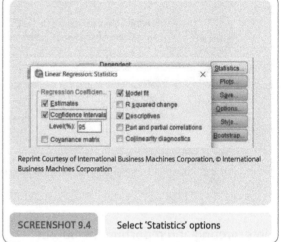

Reprint Courtesy of International Business Machines Corporation, © International Business Machines Corporation

SCREENSHOT 9.4   Select 'Statistics' options

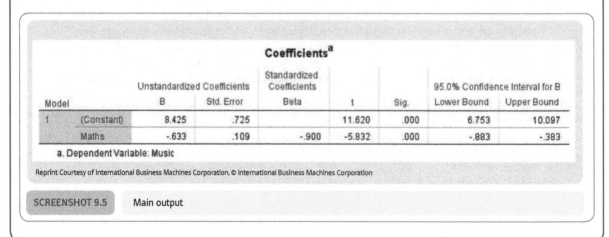

Coefficients[a]

Model		Unstandardized Coefficients		Standardized Coefficients	t	Sig.	95.0% Confidence Interval for B	
		B	Std. Error	Beta			Lower Bound	Upper Bound
1	(Constant)	8.425	.725		11.620	.000	6.753	10.097
	Maths	-.633	.109	-.900	-5.832	.000	-.883	-.383

a. Dependent Variable: Music

Reprint Courtesy of International Business Machines Corporation, © International Business Machines Corporation

SCREENSHOT 9.5   Main output

PART 2

Significance testing

CHAPTER 10

Samples from populations

Overview

- Samples characterise modern research. Inferential statistical techniques are required to analyse data from samples.

- A population in statistics is all of the scores on a particular variable and a sample is a smaller set of these scores.

- Random samples are systematically drawn samples in which each score in the population has an equal likelihood of being selected.

- Random samples tend to be like the population from which they are drawn in terms of their mean, variability, and so forth.

- Standard error is the variation in the means of samples drawn from a population. It is essentially the standard deviation of the sample means.

Preparation

This chapter introduces some important new ideas. They can be understood by anyone with a general familiarity with Chapters 2–9.

10.1   Introduction

Most research in psychology relies on just a small sample of data from which general statements are made. The terms *sample* and *population* are familiar to most of us, although the fine detail may be a little obscure. So far we have mainly discussed *sets* of data. This was deliberate since *most things we have discussed in previous chapters are applicable to either samples or populations*. The next stage is to understand how we can use a sample of scores to make general statements or draw general conclusions that apply beyond that sample. This is a branch of statistics called *inferential* statistics because it is about drawing inferences about the population from just a sample. But first of all we need to understand what happens when we randomly sample from a population.

10.2   Theoretical considerations

We need to be careful when defining our terms. A *sample* is fairly obvious – it is just a small number of scores selected from the entirety of scores. A *population* is the entire set of scores. In other words, a sample is a small set, or a subset, taken from the full set or population of scores. In this chapter we concentrate on a known (rather small) population of scores.

Notice the terminology that has been used. We referred to a population of *scores* and a sample of *scores*. In other words, population and sample refer to scores on a variable. Populations in statistics are not people as such. So, in statistical terms, all of the people living in Scotland do not constitute a population. Similarly, all of the people working in clothing factories in France or all of the goats on the Isle of Capri are not *statistical* populations. They may be populations for geographers or for everyday purposes, but they are not what we are talking about in statistics when we refer to populations. A statistical population is *all* of the scores on a particular variable and in research we study samples of scores.

In some cases, all of the scores are potentially obtainable, for example the ages of students entering psychology degree courses in a particular year. However, often the population of scores is infinite and otherwise impossible to specify. An example of this might be the amount of time people take to react to an auditory signal in a laboratory. The number of possible measures of reaction time in these circumstances is bounded only by time and resources. No one could actually find out the population of scores other than by taking measurement after measurement – and then there is always another measurement to be taken. The notion of population in statistics is much more of a conceptual tool than something objective. Normally a psychologist will only have a few scores (his or her sample) and no direct knowledge of what the population of scores is. But it is the population that we really are trying to say something about.

Can we generalise from samples? What can we possibly say about the population based on our knowledge of a sample? The answer is quite a lot if we are prepared to infer information from our sample. And we have little choice other than to do that since our sample is all that we know about.

If we know nothing about the population other than the characteristics of a sample drawn from that population of scores, our best estimate or inference about the characteristics of the population is the characteristics of the sample from that population. It does not necessarily have to be particularly precise since an informed guess has to be better than nothing. So, in general, if we know nothing else, our best guess as to the mean of the population is the mean of the sample, our best guess as to the mode of the population is the mode of the sample, and our best guess as to the variance of the population is the

In statistical inference, it is generally assumed that samples are drawn *at random* from the population. Such samples are called *random samples* from the population. The concept of randomness is sometimes misunderstood. Randomness is not the same as arbitrariness, informality, haphazardness or any other term that suggests a casual approach to drawing samples. A random sample of scores from a population entails selecting scores in such a way that each score in the population has an equal chance of being selected. In other words, a random sample favours the selection of no particular scores in the population. Although it is not difficult to draw a random sample, it does require a systematic approach. Any old sample you choose because you like the look of it is not a random sample.

There are a number of ways of drawing a random sample. Here are just a couple:

- Put the information about each member of the population on a slip of paper, put all of the slips into a hat, close your eyes, give the slips a long stir with your hand and finally bring one slip out of the hat. This slip is the first member of the sample; repeat the process to get the second, third and subsequent members of the sample. *Technically the slip of paper should be returned to the container after being selected so it may be selected again. However, this is not done, largely because with a large population it would make little difference to the outcome.*

- Number each member of the population. Then press the appropriate randomisation button on your scientific calculator to generate a random number. If it is not one of the numbers in your population, ignore it and press the button again. The member of the population corresponding to this number becomes a member of the sample. Apps to generate random numbers are downloadable for your PC, tablet, or mobile to do the same thing.

Low-tech researchers might use the random number tables that can be found in books of statistical tables. Essentially what you do is choose a random starting point in the table (closing your eyes and using a pin is recommended) and then choose numbers using a predetermined formula. For example, you could take the first three numbers after the pin, then a gap of seven numbers and then the three numbers following this, then a gap of seven numbers and then the three numbers following this, etc. Do not laugh at these procedures – they are all valid and convenient ways of choosing random samples. However, they are a little labour intensive given that there are available computer programs and apps on your smartphone and the Internet which will generate a random sequence of numbers for you. These are clearly preferable but less intuitive than the above approaches. Figure 10.1 gives the basics facts about random samples.

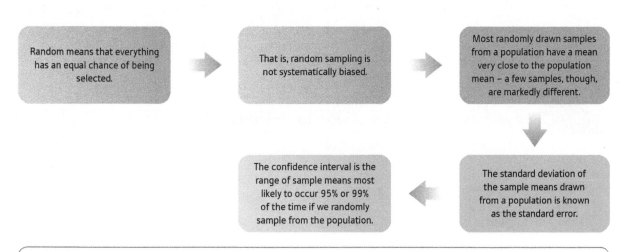

FIGURE 10.1   Conceptual steps for understanding significance testing

10.3   Characteristics of random samples

In Table 10.1 there is a population of 100 scores – the mode is 2, the median is 6.00 and the mean is 5.52. Have a go at drawing random samples of, say, five scores from this population. Repeat the process until you have a lot of sets (or samples) of scores. For each sample calculate any of the statistics just mentioned – the mean is a particularly useful statistic.

We drew 40 samples from this population at random using a computer. The means of each of the 40 samples are shown in Table 10.2. It is noticeable that these means vary quite considerably. However, if we plotted them graphically we would find that sample means that are close to the population mean of 5.52 are relatively common. The average of the sample means is 5.20 which is close to the population mean. The minimum sample mean is 2.00 and the maximum is 8.80; these contrast with minimum and maximum values of 0 and 12 in the population. Sample means that are very different from this population mean become increasingly uncommon the further away they are from the population mean.

We can calculate the (estimated) standard deviation of these 40 sample means on SPSS which gives us a value of 1.6. The standard deviation of sample means has a technical name, although the basic concept differs only in that it deals with means of samples and not scores. The special term is *standard error*. So, in general, it would seem that sample means are a pretty good estimate of population means although not absolutely necessarily

Table 10.1	Population of 100 scores								
7	5	11	3	4	3	5	8	9	1
9	4	0	2	2	2	9	11	7	12
4	8	2	9	7	0	8	0	8	10
10	7	4	6	6	2	2	1	12	2
2	5	6	7	10	6	6	2	1	9
3	4	2	4	9	7	5	1	6	4
5	7	12	2	8	8	3	4	6	5
9	2	6	0	7	7	5	9	10	8
6	1	7	12	3	5	2	7	2	7
2	2	8	11	4	5	8	6	4	6

Table 10.2	Means of 40 samples each of five scores taken at random from the population in Table 10.1						
2.20	5.60	4.80	5.00	8.40	6.80	4.60	6.60
4.00	3.00	5.00	5.60	8.80	5.60	4.60	6.80
3.00	8.20	8.20	3.80	5.40	6.00	4.80	5.20
3.20	5.20	3.00	5.00	5.40	4.80	6.00	7.40
5.00	2.00	3.60	4.60	5.60	4.60	4.40	6.00

Table 10.3	Means of 40 samples each of size 20 taken at random from the population in Table 10.1						
4.50	5.70	5.90	5.15	4.25	5.25	5.60	5.00
5.35	5.90	6.85	5.55	5.30	5.60	5.70	4.55
6.35	6.30	4.40	5.25	4.65	5.30	4.80	5.65
4.85	5.35	5.70	4.35	5.25	5.10	6.45	5.05
5.50	6.15	5.65	5.05	5.15	5.10	4.65	4.95

so. All of this was based on samples of size 5. Table 10.3 shows the results of exactly the same exercise with samples of size 20. Much the same trends appear with these larger samples but for the following:

- The spread of the sample means is reduced somewhat and they appear to cluster closer to the population mean. The minimum value is 4.25 and the maximum value is 6.85. The overall mean of these samples is 5.33, close to the population mean of 5.52.

- The standard deviation of these means (i.e. the standard error) of larger samples is smaller. For Table 10.3 the standard deviation is 0.60.

- The distribution of sample means is a steeper curve than for the smaller samples.

The conclusion to be drawn from all of this is that the larger sample size produces better estimates of the mean of the population. For statistics, this verges on common sense.

10.4 Confidence intervals

There is another idea that is fundamental to some branches of statistics – *confidence interval of the mean*. In public opinion surveys you often read of the margin of error being a certain percentage. The smaller the margin of error the more confident we should be in the estimate of the population based on the sample. Confidence intervals (CIs) are similar in that they tell us the range of means (and other things) which is likely to contain the actual population mean 95% of the time. That is, if we repeatedly draw random samples from a population, the confidence interval is the range of means likely to contain the actual population mean 95% of the time. The smaller the confidence interval the more confidence that we should have that the sample mean accurately estimates the population mean. The definition of confidence intervals is a little technical. Mostly students find it easiest to think of the confidence interval as the range of values which is 95% likely to include the population value. This is more or less the same as when public opinion pollsters give a margin of error – it indicates that the pollster thinks that the true value is likely to be within a certain range as a consequence of sampling variation. The confidence interval includes the margin of error in both directions.

Finally, a little more jargon. The correct term for characteristics of samples such as their means, standard deviations, ranges and so forth is *statistics*. The same characteristics of populations are called *parameters*. In other words, you use the statistics from samples to estimate or infer the parameters of the population from which the sample came.

Key points

● The material in this chapter is not immediately applicable to research. Regard it as a conceptual basis for the understanding of inferential statistics.

● You need to be a little patient since the implications of this chapter will not be appreciated until later.

COMPUTER ANALYSIS

Selecting a random sample using SPSS

Data
● If you have the data you wish to use on file then select that file – otherwise enter the data and name your variable (Screenshot 10.1).

Analysis
● Select 'Data' and 'Select Cases. . .' (Screenshot 10.2).

2
● Select 'Random sample of cases' and 'Sample' (Screenshot 10.3).

3
● Enter 10 next to 'Approximately' to obtain about 10% of cases for instance (Screenshot 10.4).
● Alternatively, select 'Exactly' and give number of cases required out of whatever number of cases you enter in the next box.

Output
● The cases not selected for inclusion in your sample are struck out in the very first column of the data spreadsheet and a 'filter_$' column is added to indicate inclusion (1) or exclusion (0) (Screenshot 10.5).

Extras
● You may carry out any procedure you wish using 'Analyze', etc.

FIGURE 10.2   SPSS steps for selecting a random sample of cases

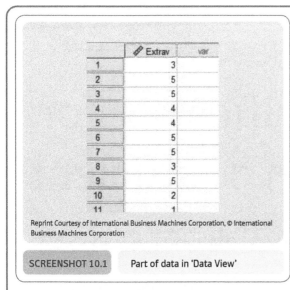

Reprint Courtesy of International Business Machines Corporation, © International Business Machines Corporation

SCREENSHOT 10.1   Part of data in 'Data View'

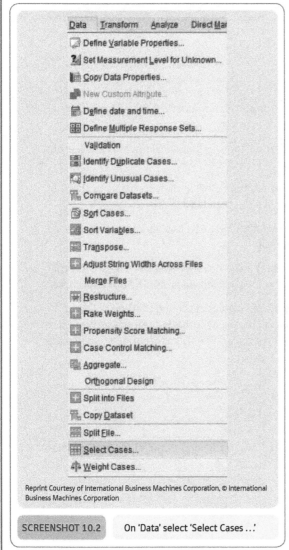

Reprint Courtesy of International Business Machines Corporation, © International Business Machines Corporation

SCREENSHOT 10.2   On 'Data' select 'Select Cases …'

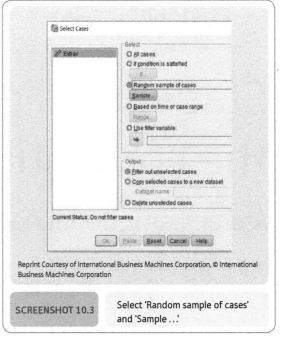

Reprint Courtesy of International Business Machines Corporation, © International Business Machines Corporation

SCREENSHOT 10.3   Select 'Random sample of cases' and 'Sample …'

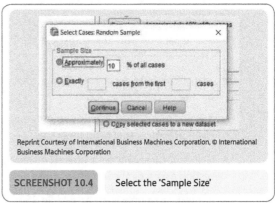

Reprint Courtesy of International Business Machines Corporation, © International Business Machines Corporation

SCREENSHOT 10.4   Select the 'Sample Size'

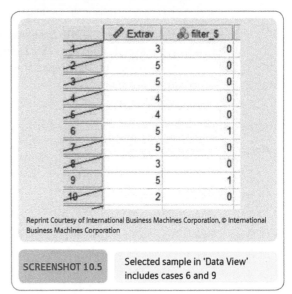

Reprint Courtesy of International Business Machines Corporation, © International Business Machines Corporation

SCREENSHOT 10.5   Selected sample in 'Data View' includes cases 6 and 9

CHAPTER 11

Statistical significance for the correlation coefficient

A practical introduction to statistical inference

Overview

- It is usual to report the statistical significance of correlation coefficients and many other statistical techniques.

- Statistical significance merely indicates whether or not your statistical findings are likely to be due to chance.

- Samples drawn randomly from a population usually have similar characteristics to those of the population. However, some samples are unlike the population.

- Null hypothesis always states that there is no relation between two variables. Significance testing assesses the validity of the null hypothesis.

- If our data sample is in the middle 95% of samples if the null hypothesis is true, we say that our findings are not statistically significant at the 5% level and we prefer the null hypothesis.

- However, if our data sample is in the extreme 5% of samples assuming that the null hypothesis is true, our sample does not seem to support the null hypothesis. In this case, we prefer the alternative hypothesis and reject the null hypothesis. We also say that our findings are statistically significant.

Preparation

You must be familiar with correlation coefficients (Chapter 8) and populations and samples (Chapter 10).

11.1 Introduction

Researchers have correlated two variables for a sample of 20 people. They obtained a correlation coefficient of .56. The problem is that they wish to generalise beyond this sample and make statements about the trends in the data which apply more widely. However, their analyses are based on just a small sample which might not be characteristic of the trends in the population. What do they do?

11.2 Theoretical considerations

We can all sympathise with these researchers. The reason why they are concerned is straightforward. Imagine that Table 11.1 contains the *population* of pairs of scores. Overall, the correlation between the two variables in this population is .0. That is, there is absolutely no relationship between variable X and variable Y in the population.

What happens, though, if we draw many samples of, say, eight pairs of scores at random from this population and calculate the correlation coefficients for *each* sample? Some of the correlation coefficients are indeed more-or-less zero, but a few are substantially

Table 11.1	Imaginary population of 60 pairs of scores with zero correlation between the pairs						
Pair	**Variable**		**Pair**	**Variable**		**Pair**	**Variable**	
	X	Y		X	Y		X	Y
01	14	12	02	5	11	03	12	5
04	3	13	05	14	9	06	10	14
07	5	12	08	17	17	09	4	8
10	15	5	11	3	3	12	19	12
13	16	7	14	14	9	15	12	13
16	13	8	17	15	11	18	15	7
19	12	17	20	11	14	21	5	13
22	12	11	23	11	9	24	15	14
25	5	12	26	15	9	27	12	13
28	6	13	29	14	7	30	18	13
31	12	1	32	19	12	33	12	19
34	11	14	35	12	17	36	13	9
37	14	12	38	15	5	39	18	13
40	17	11	41	3	12	42	16	9
43	16	12	44	11	9	45	18	2
46	12	14	47	12	14	48	15	11
49	16	12	50	12	14	51	8	14
52	5	11	53	7	8	54	16	8
55	13	13	56	12	15	57	18	2
58	3	1	59	7	8	60	11	6

different from zero, as we can see from Table 11.2. Plotted on a histogram, the distribution of these correlation coefficients looks like Figure 11.1. It is more or less a normal distribution with a mean correlation of about zero and most of the correlations being close to that zero point. However, some of the correlation coefficients are substantially different from .0. So even where there is zero relationship in the population, random samples can have correlations which depart from .0. In the table correlations are ones as large as .81 which would delight most researchers – though this correlation is really due to chance and, in truth, there is no correlation in the population.

Table 11.2	Two hundred correlation coefficients obtained by repeatedly random sampling eight pairs of scores from Table 11.1								
−.56	−.30	.36	.54	−.27	.05	−.33	−.19	.54	.18
−.54	.11	.25	−.15	−.57	−.31	−.24	.17	−.69	−.19
−.53	.68	−.22	−.22	−.26	−.42	.08	−.30	−.41	.29
−.45	−.09	−.06	−.30	−.72	−.53	.04	−.66	.65	−.53
−.39	−.21	.07	−.80	−.68	.08	.13	.76	−.04	.18
−.36	−.19	.29	.24	.38	−.55	−.40	.50	−.09	−.30
−.30	−.56	.68	−.14	.35	−.28	.56	−.38	−.16	.15
−.29	−.23	−.42	−.27	.01	.43	.01	−.33	−.20	.49
−.26	−.41	−.09	.00	.54	.17	.34	.52	−.11	.67
−.26	−.16	−.70	.00	−.17	.40	.03	−.02	.35	−.01
−.23	.03	.30	−.52	−.05	−.26	−.32	−.37	−.51	.18
−.20	−.17	−.43	−.39	.37	.23	−.10	.32	.02	.52
−.18	.38	.45	−.50	−.58	.28	−.34	−.28	.24	.53
−.17	−.02	−.34	−.23	−.54	.25	−.71	.72	.03	−.13
−.08	−.30	−.06	−.10	−.65	.27	−.04	.32	−.52	−.42
−.04	.59	−.29	−.31	.48	−.48	.02	−.30	.81	−.23
.10	−.12	−.51	−.19	.08	.18	−.27	−.67	−.69	.50
.15	−.54	−.15	.05	.01	.52	.19	.19	.07	.27
.34	−.44	−.11	−.21	−.02	−.07	.17	−.30	−.06	−.49
.57	−.10	−.23	.01	−.09	−.27	.22	−.28	.43	−.34

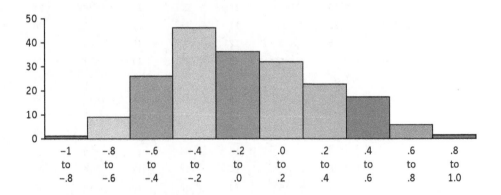

| FIGURE 11.1 | Distribution of correlation coefficients presented in Table 11.2 |

Just about anything is possible in samples although only certain things are likely. Consequently, we try to stipulate which are the *likely* correlations in samples of a given size and which are the *unlikely* ones (if the population correlation is zero). Actually all we say is that correlations in the *middle* 95% of the distribution of samples are likely if the population correlation is zero. Correlations in the extreme 5% (usually the extreme 2.5% in each direction) are unlikely in these circumstances. These are arbitrary cut-off points, but they are conventional in statistics and have long antecedents. It is also a reasonable cut-off for most purposes to suggest that if a sample has only a 1 in 20 chance of occurring then it is unlikely to represent the population value.

If a correlation is in the extreme 5% of the distribution of samples from a population where the correlation is zero, it is deemed statistically significant. We should be sitting up and taking notice if this happens. In other words, statistical significance merely signals the statistically unusual or unlikely. In the above example, by examining Table 11.2 we find that the correlations .81, .76, .72, .68 and .68 and −.80, −.72, −.71, −.70 and −.69 are in the extreme 5% of correlations away from zero. This extreme 5% is usually made up of the extreme 2.5% positive correlations and the extreme 2.5% negative correlations. Therefore, a correlation of between .68 and 1.00 or −.69 and −1.00 is in the extreme 5% of correlations in our example. This range we describe as statistically significant. Statistical significance simply means that our sample falls in the relatively extreme part of the distribution of samples obtained if the null hypothesis (see the next section) of no relationship between the two variables is true.

These ranges of significant correlations mentioned above only apply to samples of size eight. A different size of sample from the same population results in a different spread of correlations obtained from repeated sampling. The spread is bigger if the samples are smaller and less if the samples are larger. In other words, there is more variation in the distribution of samples with small sample sizes than with larger ones.

On the face of things, all of this is merely a theoretical meandering of little value. We know that the population correlation is zero – actually we made it zero. A major difficulty is that we are normally unaware of the population correlation since our information is based solely on a sample which may or may not represent the population very well. However, it is not quite the futile exercise it appears to be. Some information provided by a sample can be used to infer or estimate the characteristics of the population. For one thing, information about the variability or variance of the scores in the sample is used *to estimate the variability of scores in the population.*

11.3   Back to the real world: null hypothesis

There is another vitally important concept in statistics – the hypothesis. Hypotheses in psychological statistics are usually presented as antithetical pairs – the *null hypothesis* and its corresponding *alternative hypothesis*. The *null hypothesis* is essentially a statement that there is no relationship between two variables. The following are all examples of null hypotheses:

- There is no relationship between brain size and intelligence.

- There is no relationship between gender and income.

- There is no relationship between baldness and virility.

- There is no relationship between children's self-esteem and that of their parent of the same sex.

- There is no relationship between ageing and memory loss.

- There is no relationship between the amount of carrots eaten and ability to see in the dark.

The *alternative hypothesis* simply states that there is a relationship between two variables. In its simplest forms the alternative hypothesis says things like:

- There is a relationship between the number of years of education people have and their income.

- There is a relationship between people's gender and how much they talk about their emotional problems.

- There is a relationship between people's mental instability and their artistic creativity.

- There is a relationship between abuse in childhood and later psychological problems.

- There is a relationship between birth order and social dominance.

- There is a relationship between the degree of similarity of couples and their sexual attraction for each other.

So the difference between null and alternative hypotheses is merely the word 'no'. Of course, sometimes psychologists dress their hypotheses up in fancier language than this but the basic principle is unchanged. (Actually there is a complication – directional hypotheses – but these are dealt with in Chapter 20.)

The statistical reason for using the null hypothesis and alternative hypothesis is that they *clarify* the populations in statistical analyses. *In statistics, inferences are based on the characteristics of the population as defined by the null hypothesis.* Invariably the populations defined by the null hypothesis are ones in which there is no relation between a pair of variables. Thus, the population defined by the null hypothesis is one where the correlation between the two variables under consideration is .00. The characteristics of a sample can be used to assess whether it is likely that the correlation for the sample comes from a population in which the correlation is zero.

So the basic trick is to use certain of the characteristics of a sample together with the notion of the null hypothesis to define the characteristics of a population. Other characteristics of the sample are then used to estimate the likelihood that this sample comes from this particular population. To repeat and summarise:

- The null hypothesis is used to define a population in which there is no relationship between two variables.

- Other characteristics, especially the variability of this population, are estimated or inferred from the known sample.

It is then possible to decide whether or not it is likely that the sample comes from this population defined by the null hypothesis. If it is *unlikely* that the sample comes from the null hypothesis-based population, the possibility that the null hypothesis is true is rejected. Instead the view that the alternative hypothesis is true is accepted. That is, the alternative hypothesis that there really is a relationship is preferred (we never say proven). This is the same thing as saying that we can safely generalise from our sample because we think that there is a real trend. It is conventional to regard correlations in the extreme 5% of correlations as being statistically significant. That is, we prefer the hypothesis that there is a correlation to the null hypothesis that there is no correlation. Correlations which are not in the extreme 5% are described as being not significant. That is, we cannot reject the null hypothesis.

Box 11.1 explains how to test whether two correlations are significantly different from each other.

Box 11.1	Focus on

Do correlations differ?

Notice that throughout this chapter we are comparing a particular correlation coefficient obtained from our data with the correlation coefficient that we would expect to obtain if there were no relationship between the two variables at all. In other words, we are calculating the likelihood of obtaining the correlation coefficient based on our sample of data if, in fact, the correlation between these two variables in the population from which the sample was taken is actually .0. However, there are circumstances in which the researcher might wish to assess whether two correlations obtained in their research are significantly different from each other. Imagine, for example, that the researcher is investigating the relationship between satisfaction with one's marriage and the length of time that

individuals have been married. The researcher notes that the correlation between satisfaction and length of marriage is .25 for male participants but .53 for female participants. There is clearly a difference here, but is it a statistically significant one? So essentially the researcher needs to know whether a correlation of .53 is significantly different from a correlation of .25 (the researcher has probably already tested the significance of each of these correlations separately but, of course, this does not answer the question of whether the two correlation coefficients differ from each other). It is a relatively simple matter to do this calculation. It has to be done by hand, unfortunately. The procedure for doing this is described in Section 36.7 Comparing a study with a previous study.

11.4 Pearson's correlation coefficient again

Computer programs such as SPSS give exact significance levels for your correlation coefficient. Nevertheless, originally one would have used tables of the distribution of the correlation coefficient to find the significance level. Occasionally you still might need to consult such a table:

- For example, imagine that you are reviewing the research literature and find that one old study reports a correlation of .66 between two variables but fails to give the significance level, then what do you do? This sort of situation can occasionally happen since not every research paper is exemplary in its statistical analysis. Or you wish to check that there is not a typographical error for the given significance level then what do you do? SPSS will not be of help in these situations.

- What if you wanted to know the size of correlation which would be statistically significant for a given sample size? If, for example, you are expecting a small correlation of say .2 then how big a sample would be needed for this to be statistically significant? The only way to find out is to consult tables.

Since SPSS does not help here, in this section we will explain how significance levels may be obtained from tables. But you need to know the size of the correlation coefficient and the sample size (or in some tables the degrees of freedom) involved.

The null hypothesis for research involving the correlation coefficient is that there is *no* relationship between the two variables. In other words, the null hypothesis states that the correlation coefficient between the two variables is .00 in the population (defined by the null hypothesis). So what if, in a sample of 10 pairs of scores, the correlation is .94 as for the data in Table 11.3? Do we accept or reject the null hypothesis?

Table 11.3	Sample of 10 pairs of scores	
Pair number	X score	Y score
1	5	4
2	2	1
3	7	8
4	5	6
5	0	2
6	1	0
7	4	3
8	2	2
9	8	9
10	6	7

Is it likely that such a correlation would occur in a sample if it actually came from a population where the true correlation is zero? We need to know the distribution of correlations based on samples of ten assuming the null hypothesis. This is not a simple task but was done at the time the correlation coefficient was developed many decades ago. Mere mortals like us can use significance tables for the correlation coefficient calculated way back then. Actually all we really need to know is the minimum value which puts a correlation into the extreme 5% of correlation coefficients. This tells us whether or not our correlation coefficient is statistically significant.

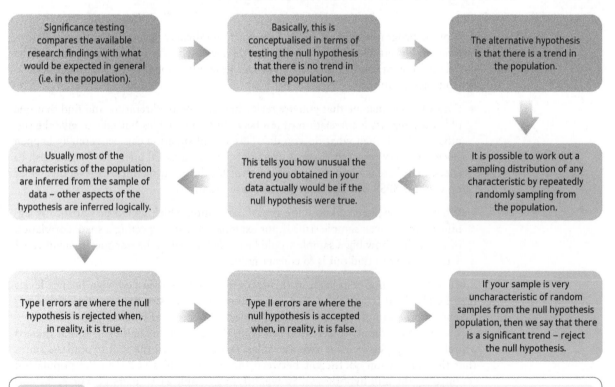

FIGURE 11.2   Conceptual steps for understanding statistical significance testing

For any given size of sample (or number of degrees of freedom), the table gives us the minimum size of a correlation coefficient required to be statistically significant. These cut-off points are usually called *critical values*.

If the sample's correlation is smaller than the critical value required then we accept the null hypothesis that there is no relationship between the two variables. By accept, we mean that in the absence of any other information or considerations, the null hypothesis cannot be rejected. So correlations which are smaller than the critical value are described as being statistically non-significant.

However, if the correlation is equal to or larger than the critical value then it is in the extreme 5% of correlations. In this case the alternative hypothesis is accepted (that there is a relationship between the two variables). Correlations equal to or larger than the critical value are described as being statistically significant. That is, we accept the alternative hypothesis that there is a correlation between the two variables.

Significance Table 11.1 indicates that for a sample size of 10, a correlation has to be between −.63 and −1.00 *or* between .63 and 1.00 to be sufficiently large as to be in the extreme 5% of correlations which support the alternative hypothesis. Correlations closer to .00 than these come in the middle 95%, which supports the null hypothesis. So our correlation of .94 based on a sample of 10 is clearly statistically significant. Figure 11.2 gives the key steps in testing statistical significance. See Box 11.2 for a discussion of the two types of error in hypothesis testing.

Explaining statistics 11.1

Statistical significance of a Pearson correlation coefficient

Given that you know the value of the Pearson correlation coefficient, whether or not this is significant or not may be found from Significance Table 11.1. You need either the sample size or the degrees of freedom to do this. The degrees of freedom (*df*) for a correlation coefficient is the sample size minus 2 so it is easy to convert degrees of freedom to sample sizes simply by adding 2 to the degrees of freedom. In the example in Chapter 8 (Explaining statistics 8.1), the correlation between mathematical scores and musical scores was found to be −.90 with a sample size of 10. If this correlation is in the range of correlations listed as being in the extreme 5% of correlations for this sample size, the correlation is described as being statistically significant at the 5% level of significance.

Interpreting the results

In this case, since our obtained value of the correlation coefficient is in the significant range of the correlation coefficient (−.63 to −1.00 and .63 to 1.00), we reject the null hypothesis in favour of the alternative hypothesis that there is a relationship between mathematical and musical scores.

Reporting the results

In our report of the study we would conclude by writing something to the following effect: 'There is a negative correlation of −.90 between mathematical and musical scores which is statistically significant at the 5% level with a sample size of 10.' Alternatively, following the recommendations of the APA (2010) Publication Manual we could say something like 'Mathematical scores were significantly negatively correlated with musical scores, $r(8) = -.90, p < .05$.' This gives the degrees of freedom in the brackets. The size of the sample itself for the correlation would not be given in modern research publications. The value of the degrees of freedom will be the sample size minus 2 for the Pearson correlation. If you use SPSS to obtain the significance level, then it is given as .000 in the output. You would in this case give the probability as being $p < .001$ and not as $p = .00$. But if the probability level given by SPSS is, say, .002 then it is correct to give it as $p = .002$.

→

Significance Table 11.1	5% significance values of the Pearson correlation coefficient (two-tailed test). An extended and conventional version of this table is given in Appendix C						
Sample size	**Significant at 5% level** **Accept hypothesis**						
5	−.88	to	−1.00	or	+.88	to	+1.00
6	−.81	to	−1.00	or	+.81	to	+1.00
7	−.75	to	−1.00	or	+.75	to	+1.00
8	−.71	to	−1.00	or	+.71	to	+1.00
9	−.67	to	−1.00	or	+.67	to	+1.00
10	−.63	to	−1.00	or	+.63	to	+1.00
11	−.60	to	−1.00	or	+.60	to	+1.00
12	−.58	to	−1.00	or	+.58	to	+1.00
13	−.55	to	−1.00	or	+.55	to	+1.00
14	−.53	to	−1.00	or	+.53	to	+1.00
15	−.51	to	−1.00	or	+.51	to	+1.00
16	−.50	to	−1.00	or	+.50	to	+1.00
17	−.48	to	−1.00	or	+.48	to	+1.00
18	−.47	to	−1.00	or	+.47	to	+1.00
19	−.46	to	−1.00	or	+.46	to	+1.00
20	−.44	to	−1.00	or	+.44	to	+1.00
25	−.40	to	−1.00	or	+.40	to	+1.00
30	−.36	to	−1.00	or	+.36	to	+1.00
40	−.31	to	−1.00	or	+.31	to	+1.00
50	−.28	to	−1.00	or	+.28	to	+1.00
60	−.25	to	−1.00	or	+.25	to	+1.00
100	−.20	to	−1.00	or	+.20	to	+1.00

Your value must be in the listed ranges for your sample size to be significant at the 5% level (i.e. to accept the hypothesis). If your required sample size is not listed, then take the nearest smaller sample size. Alternatively, extrapolate from listed values.

Box 11.2　Key concepts

Type I and Type II errors

The terms Type I error and Type II error frequently appear in statistics textbooks although they are relatively uncommon in reports and other publications. They refer to the risk that no matter what decision you make in research based on your statistical analysis there is always a chance that you have made the wrong decision. There are two types of wrong decision – one involves deciding that there is a trend when there is in reality no trend; the other involves deciding that there is not a trend when in reality there is:

● a Type I error is deciding that the null hypothesis is false when it is actually true

● a Type II error is deciding that the null hypothesis is true when it is actually false. Powerful statistical tests are those in which there is less chance of a Type II error.

Figure 11.3 shows the process by which correct decisions are made and the processes by which Type I errors and Type II errors are made. Of course, these are not errors which it is easy to do anything about since the researcher simply does not know what is truly the case in general (i.e. in the population) as they only have information from the sample of data that they have collected. So these are rather abstract concepts rather than concrete situations. You may have also noticed that if the researcher does something to minimise the risk of a Type I error then the risk of a Type II error increases. So to avoid a Type I error then the researcher could set a more stringent level of significance than the 5% level – say the 1% level – but this would reduce the risk of a Type I error at the cost of increasing the risk of a Type II error. The main issue in succeeding chapters is significance testing and the Type I error. However, Chapter 39 discusses statistical power in which the Type II error is just as important.

Unfortunately, the terms are not particularly useful in the everyday application of statistics where it is hard enough making a decision let alone worrying about the chance that you have made the wrong decision. Given that statistics deals with probabilities and not certainties, it is important to remember that there is always a chance that any decision you make is wrong in statistical analysis.

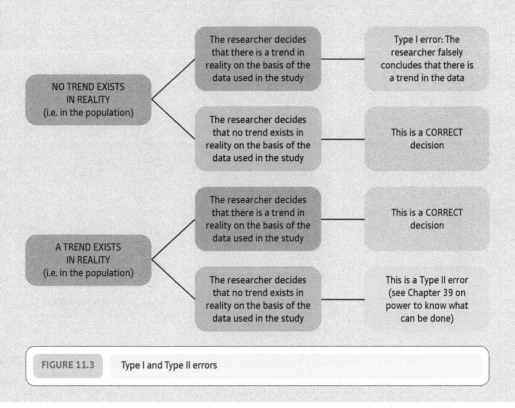

| FIGURE 11.3 | Type I and Type II errors |

11.5   Spearman's rho correlation coefficient

We discussed the Spearman's rho correlation coefficient in Chapter 8 (Explaining statistics 8.2). There are tables for finding the critical values of this statistic which can be used. An example of such a table is Significance Table 11.2. Compare this with the table for the Pearson correlation coefficient (Significance Table 11.1). They are different because the two correlations have different distributions. For a sample size of eight, the Pearson correlation needs to be .72 (or −.72) at least to be statistically significant. However, to be significant with this sample size, the Spearman's rho correlation has to be .74 (or −.74) at least. Generally the differences are quite small and with samples of 100 or so they are indistinguishable. Nevertheless, they are different distributions.

Significance Table 11.2	5% significance values of the significance correlation coefficient (two-tailed test). Extended and conventional version of this table is given in Appendix D							
Sample size	Significant at 5% level Accept hypothesis							
5			−1.00	or	+1.00		
6	−.89	to	−1.00	or	+.89	to	+1.00
7	−.79	to	−1.00	or	+.79	to	+1.00
8	−.74	to	−1.00	or	+.74	to	+1.00
9	−.68	to	−1.00	or	+.68	to	+1.00
10	−.65	to	−1.00	or	+.65	to	+1.00
11	−.62	to	−1.00	or	+.62	to	+1.00
12	−.59	to	−1.00	or	+.59	to	+1.00
13	−.57	to	−1.00	or	+.57	to	+1.00
14	−.55	to	−1.00	or	+.55	to	+1.00
15	−.52	to	−1.00	or	+.52	to	+1.00
16	−.51	to	−1.00	or	+.51	to	+1.00
17	−.49	to	−1.00	or	+.49	to	+1.00
18	−.48	to	−1.00	or	+.48	to	+1.00
19	−.46	to	−1.00	or	+.46	to	+1.00
20	−.45	to	−1.00	or	+.45	to	+1.00
25	−.40	to	−1.00	or	+.40	to	+1.00
30	−.36	to	−1.00	or	+.36	to	+1.00
40	−.31	to	−1.00	or	+.31	to	+1.00
50	−.28	to	−1.00	or	+.28	to	+1.00
60	−.26	to	−1.00	or	+.26	to	+1.00
100	−.20	to	−1.00	or	+.20	to	+1.00

Your value must be in the listed ranges for your sample size to be significant at the 5% level (i.e. to accept the hypothesis).
If your required sample size is not listed, then take the nearest smaller sample size. Alternatively, extrapolate from listed values.

In Chapter 8 we calculated Spearman's rho correlation coefficient between mathematical score and musical score. The correlation was found to be −.89 with a sample size of 10. Significance Table 11.2 reveals that in order to be significant at the 5% level with a sample size of 10, correlations have to be in the range .65 to 1.00 or −.65 to −1.00.

Interpreting the results

Since our obtained value of the Spearman's rho correlation coefficient is in the range of significant correlations we accept the alternative hypothesis that mathematical and musical scores are (inversely) related and reject the null hypothesis.

Reporting the results

We can report a significant correlation: 'There is a negative correlation of −.89 between mathematical and musical scores which is statistically significant at the 5% level with a sample size of 10.' Alternatively, following the APA (2010) Publication Manual recommendations we could write something like 'Mathematical scores were significantly negatively correlated with musical scores, $r_s(8) = -.89, p < .05$'. The APA manual uses the degrees of freedom which are given in brackets. The value of the degrees of freedom will be the sample size minus 2 for Spearman's rho. Using SPSS to do the calculation, you will find that it gives the probability as .00. In this case the procedure is to give it as $p < .001$ as explained earlier for the Pearson correlation.

Research examples

Significance of Pearson's correlation and Spearman's rho

Rohmer and Louvet (2012), in their analysis of stereotyping of people with disability, report some correlations as follows: 'To examine the relationships between the implicit and the explicit measures, separate scores were computed on competence and warmth at both the implicit and the explicit level, by subtracting the scores given to targets with disability from those given to targets without disability. Results indicated that there were no significant correlations for both competence ($r = .08, p = .46$) and warmth ($r = .05, p = .65$).' (p. 738).

Gannon and Barrowcliffe (2012) in their study of firesetters make the comment: 'Overall scores on the Fire Setting Scale and the Fire Proclivity Scale were not significantly related to impression management scores across the whole sample ($r = -.12$ and $-.01$, respectively). However, when these correlations were computed for firesetters and nonfiresetters separately, scores on the Fire Setting Scale were significantly negatively related to impression management scores for the firesetters ($r = -.64; p = .01$).' (p. 9).

Vallat-Azouvi, Pradat-Diehl and Azouvi (2012) report on the Working Memory Questionnaire which measures aspects of working memory including short-term storage, executive control and attention. As part of this, they investigated the validity of this scale by reference to the Cognitive Failure Questionnaire (CFQ) and the Rating Scale of Attentional Behaviour (RSAB). They write: 'Concurrent validity was assessed by computing Spearman rank order correlation coefficients between the total score of the scale on the one hand and the CFQ and the RSAB on the other hand ... Both correlations were significant (rho $= .90, p < .0001$ with the CFQ, and rho $= .81, p < .0001$ with the RSAB).' (pp. 623–4).

Key points

- There is nothing complex in the calculation of statistical significance for the correlation coefficients which SPSS routinely does to a precise level. Statistical tables normally do not include every sample size. When a particular sample size is missing you can simply use the nearest (lower) tabulated value. Alternatively you could extrapolate from the nearest tabulated value above and the nearest tabulated value below your actual sample size.

- It is a bad mistake to report a correlation without indicating whether it is statistically significant.

- Chapter 15 explains how to report your significance levels in a more succinct form. Try to employ this sort of style as it eases the writing of research reports and looks professional.

- Beware that some statistical textbooks provide significance tables for the correlation coefficient which are distributed by degrees of freedom rather than sample size. For any given sample size, the degrees of freedom are *two* less. Thus, for a sample size of 10, the degrees of freedom are $10 - 2$, or 8.

COMPUTER ANALYSIS

Correlation coefficients using SPSS

Data
- In 'Data View' of the 'Data Editor', the data are entered as different variables in different columns – each row equals a person (Screenshot 11.1).
- Name each variable in 'Variable View' of the 'Data Editor'.

Analysis
- Select 'Analyze' (Screenshot 11.2).
- Select 'Correlate' and 'Bivariate...'.

2
- Move variables to be correlated to right-hand side box (Screenshot 11.3).
- Select 'Pearson' or 'Spearman' according to what is appropriate.
- Select 'Options' to give additional choices (Screenshot 11.4).

Output
- Screenshot 11.5 shows the additional descriptive statistics.
- Screenshot 11.6 is the ouput for the correlation matrix.
- The matrix includes the correlation of each variable with itself and does not provide a significance level for this, of course.

FIGURE 11.4   SPSS steps for the significance of the correlation coefficient

Interpreting and reporting the output

- Interpretation of the output is complicated by the fact that SPSS intercorrelates each of the variables with itself and with the other variables. The correlation of a variable with itself is always 1. No significance level is given for this. The table also includes the correlation between the variables with the other variables twice, so you have the correlation of Variable X with Variable Y AND the correlation of Variable Y with Variable X. These are, of course, the same. The output gives the correlation ($-.900$), the statistical significance (.000) and the sample size (10).

- It would be good to report the significance level as being less than .001 and something known as the degrees of freedom which for the correlation coefficient is $N - 2$ or 8 in this case. Statistical significance is discussed further in Chapter 20 and degrees of freedom in Chapter 23.

- In a report, we could write 'There is a significant negative correlation between musical ability and mathematical ability, $r(8) = .90, p < = .001$. Children with more musical ability have lower mathematical ability.'

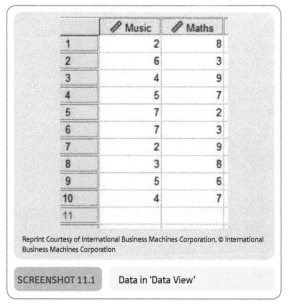

Reprint Courtesy of International Business Machines Corporation, © International Business Machines Corporation

SCREENSHOT 11.1   Data in 'Data View'

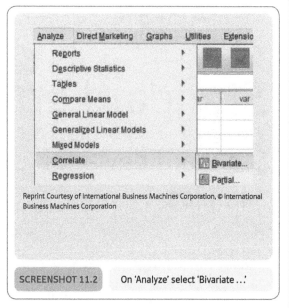

Reprint Courtesy of International Business Machines Corporation, © International Business Machines Corporation

SCREENSHOT 11.2   On 'Analyze' select 'Bivariate ...'

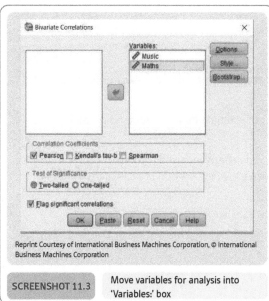

Reprint Courtesy of International Business Machines Corporation, © International Business Machines Corporation

SCREENSHOT 11.3   Move variables for analysis into 'Variables:' box

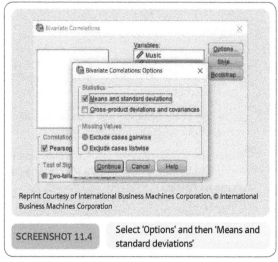

Reprint Courtesy of International Business Machines Corporation, © International Business Machines Corporation

SCREENSHOT 11.4   Select 'Options' and then 'Means and standard deviations'

Descriptive Statistics

	Mean	Std. Deviation	N
Music	4.50	1.841	10
Maths	6.20	2.616	10

Reprint Courtesy of International Business Machines Corporation, © International Business Machines Corporation

SCREENSHOT 11.5   Output table giving means and standard deviations

Correlations

		Music	Maths
Music	Pearson Correlation	1	-.900**
	Sig. (2-tailed)		.000
	N	10	10
Maths	Pearson Correlation	-.900**	1
	Sig. (2-tailed)	.000	
	N	10	10

**. Correlation is significant at the 0.01 level (2-tailed).

Reprint Courtesy of International Business Machines Corporation, © International Business Machines Corporation

SCREENSHOT 11.6   Output table giving correlations

CHAPTER 12

Standard error

Standard deviation of the means of samples

Overview

- Standard error is the term for the standard deviation of sample means. It is important theoretically.

- We never calculate the standard error directly but estimate its value from the characteristics of our sample of data.

- The standard error is simply estimated by dividing the standard deviation of scores in the population by the square root of the sample size for which we need to calculate the standard error.

- We use the estimated standard deviation when calculating the standard error.

Preparation

Review z-scores and standard deviation (Chapter 6) and sampling from populations (Chapter 10).

12.1 Introduction

Most psychological research involves the use of samples drawn from a population. How much do such samples differ from the population? Some samples will be very similar to the population from which they were drawn, a smaller number will be somewhat different from the population and others will be very different from the population. So sometimes we expect to find a sample very atypical of the population. Since normally the distribution of the population is unknown, we cannot be certain whether our research sample is like the population or not. However, we can estimate the likelihood that our sample comes from a particular population by using the sample's characteristics. For illustrative purposes we will use a known population of scores to make things a little more concrete.

This chapter explains the concept of standard error. The standard error can be thought of as a summary index of the diversity in sample means drawn from a population. It is employed in many different contexts in statistics though not always reported in the research report. There are many types of standard error but we will concentrate on the standard error of the mean for now. The importance of the standard error will become clearer in the next two chapters. Master the concept now and things will be easier later on. Figure 12.1 illustrates the key steps in understanding standard error.

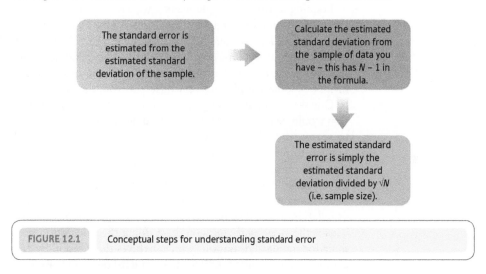

FIGURE 12.1   Conceptual steps for understanding standard error

12.2 Theoretical considerations

The first thing we need is a population from which samples are drawn. For learning purposes, Table 12.1 gives all the scores for a population. Of course, populations are not

Table 12.1	Population of 25 scores			
5	7	9	4	6
2	6	3	2	7
1	7	5	4	3
3	6	1	2	4
2	5	3	3	4

Table 12.2	Means of 20 samples each of four scores taken at random from the population of 25 scores in Table 12.1		
3.75	6.00	4.00	4.25
3.00	3.75	4.50	3.50
4.50	3.00	4.25	2.50
3.50	5.00	3.00	4.25
4.00	3.00	4.50	5.75

small like this and mostly they are potentially infinitely large. The population consists of 25 scores. The mean of the population is 4.20. What pattern of means do we get if we select a lot of samples at random from this population? We will use samples of four scores. Using a random procedure, we take 20 samples of four from the population. The decision to take 20 samples of four is an arbitrary one and other values could have been used. For each of these 20 samples the mean has been calculated, giving 20 separate sample means. They are shown in Table 12.2. The distribution of the sample means is an example of a sampling distribution.

Looking at the 20 sample means, we can see that they vary and that they vary from our population mean of 4.16. The largest and smallest sample means are 6.00 and 2.50, respectively. (The average of the 20 sample means is 4.00, which suggests that sample means cluster around the population mean.) The outcome of our little exercise in sampling from a known population is that samples tend to have similar means to the population mean but some samples are very different from the population.

One way of summarising the variation in the means of samples drawn from a population would be to work out the standard deviation of the means. Standard deviation refers to scores, though, and a different name is given to the standard deviation when it is applied to means. It is called the *standard error*. So there is not much new about the standard error that we have not seen before. Consequently, the standard error is simply the average deviation of sample means from the mean of the sample means. If we had taken many more samples, then the mean of the sample means would be the same as the population mean. The (estimated) standard deviation of these 20 sample means is 0.91. This is the value that you would get doing the calculation on SPSS. Using the basic formula for standard deviation (which involves the division by N and not $N − 1$) we would get the smaller value of 0.89 for the standard deviation (see Explaining statistics 6.1). (To stress, usually we would work out the standard error around the population mean. In our example, only a small number of samples were taken. If we had taken a very large number of samples, the mean of the sample means would get to be much closer to or identical with the population mean.)

If we sampled from the population of scores in Table 12.1 using a different sample size, say samples of 12, we would get a rather different sampling distribution. In general, all other things being equal, the standard error of the means of bigger samples is less than that of smaller sized samples. This is just a slightly convoluted way of supporting the common-sense belief that larger samples are more precise estimates of the characteristics of populations than are smaller samples. This is why we tend to be more convinced by studies with larger samples than smaller samples.

A frequency curve of the means of samples drawn from a population will get taller and narrower as the sample size increases. It will also tend to show a normal (bell-shaped) frequency curve. The more normal the population of scores, the more normal the frequency curve of the sample means.

12.3 Estimated standard deviation and standard error

Usually in research we know nothing directly about the characteristics of the population. We only know about the characteristics of the data we have collected, our sample. At first sight, this seems to suggest that we never can calculate the standard error in practice. The solution is simple though the underlying mathematics is hard. We use the variability of scores in the sample to work out the standard error. This is possible because there is a simple relationship between the standard deviation of a sample of scores and the standard error of sample means taken from the population.

The first step is to estimate the standard deviation of the population of scores from the scores in our sample. One quick formula for doing this is as follows:

$$\text{estimated standard deviation} = \sqrt{\frac{\sum X^2 - \frac{(\sum X)^2}{N}}{N - 1}}$$

We talked a little before about the difference between the standard deviation and the estimated standard deviation. The formulae for the two are almost exactly the same except that for the standard deviation we divide by the sample size N and for the estimated standard deviation we divide by $N - 1$ as above. Since we are estimating the population standard deviation from a sample of scores, we use the estimated standard deviation formula. If we were merely describing a set of scores, then the standard deviation formula would be more appropriate. The estimated standard deviation formula corrects for a systematic bias that would otherwise occur. That is to say, if we used the basic standard deviation formula as our estimate of the population standard deviation then we would systematically underestimate the population standard deviation. So we divide by $N - 1$ to correct for this bias. With large sample sizes the correction for bias makes very little difference. The distinction between the standard deviation and the estimated standard deviation is generally overlooked in modern statistics, though it is part of statistical theory. The probable reason is that almost always in research we are trying to generalise from a sample to the population. These are the circumstances where the adjustment is necessary. So invariably you will find the estimated standard deviation given when standard deviation is calculated. SPSS does exactly this.

The second step is to use the estimated standard deviation from a sample of *scores* to calculate the standard error of sample *means*. It is not obvious how to do this. Fortunately, mathematically it can be shown that there is a simple relationship between the standard deviation and the standard error. The standard error is obtained by dividing the population standard deviation by the *square root* of the size of the sample. That is, we divide the standard deviation by $\sqrt{N}$. So the standard error for large samples will be smaller than the standard error for small samples.

$$(\text{estimated}) \text{ standard error} = \frac{(\text{estimated}) \text{ standard deviation of population}}{\sqrt{N}}$$

Obviously it is possible to combine the (estimated) standard deviation and the (estimated) standard error formulae:

$$(\text{estimated}) \text{ standard error} = \frac{\sqrt{\frac{\sum X^2 - \frac{(\sum X)^2}{N}}{N - 1}}}{\sqrt{N}}$$

> ### Explaining statistics 12.1

How the estimated standard error works

Table 12.3 is a sample of six scores taken at random from the population: 5, 7, 3, 6, 4, 5.

Table 12.3	Steps in calculating the standard error	
X (scores)		**X^2 (squared scores)**
5		25
7		49
3		9
6		36
4		16
5		25
$\sum X = 30$		$\sum X^2 = 160$

Step 1 Using this information we can estimate the standard error of samples of size 6 taken from the same population. Taking our six scores (X), we need to produce Table 12.3, where $N = 6$.

Step 2 Substitute these values in the standard error formula:

$$(\text{estimated}) \text{ standard error} = \frac{\sqrt{\dfrac{\sum X^2 - \dfrac{(\sum X)^2}{N}}{N - 1}}}{\sqrt{N}} = \frac{\sqrt{\dfrac{160 - \dfrac{30^2}{6}}{6 - 1}}}{\sqrt{6}} = \frac{\sqrt{\dfrac{160 - \dfrac{900}{6}}{5}}}{2.449}$$

$$= \frac{\sqrt{\dfrac{160 - 150}{5}}}{2.449} = \frac{\sqrt{\dfrac{10}{5}}}{2.449}$$

$$= \frac{\sqrt{2}}{2.449} = \frac{1.414}{2.449} = 0.58$$

Note that this is the same value as that given by SPSS in Screenshot 12.5.

Interpreting the results

The standard error is 0.58. This is a measure of deviation of sample means from the population mean. It is a difficult concept to make concrete. Very roughly speaking, we could say that the standard deviation is the typical amount by which sample means deviate from the population mean. Some statisticians (e.g. Huck, 2009) dislike this sort of explanation though they offer no easily understood alternative for non-statisticians. It is possible to use a special mathematical distribution, the t-distribution, to indicate the proportions of sample means which lie between the population mean and any number of standard errors away from it. This is discussed in the following two chapters.

Reporting the results

Standard error is not routinely mentioned in research reports. You will almost always find that standard deviation is given. There is a close connection between variance, standard deviation and standard error. So there is no point in reporting all three.

The term standard *error* is a standardised unit indicating by how much your estimate of the population mean is wrong. Like many statistical concepts which are defined mathematically, it is difficult to express its meaning precisely in words.

Research examples

Standard error

Standard error as discussed in this chapter is rarely reported in modern psychological research directly. It is nevertheless extremely important to understand as it occurs in the calculation of the t-tests which are discussed in the following chapters. You will rapidly realise that standard error can mean various things. Standard error can refer to the means of samples of scores but it can also refer to the standard error of the difference between scores. The term is also very common in the context of regression where there are a number of standard errors. There are also circumstances in which the term is used in a sense which is very different from that intended in the present chapter – i.e. in the context of standard error of measurement (SEM).

Bierie (2013) in his study of complaints made by federal prison inmates provides an example of the use of standard error in describing the findings from a regression study. The standard errors of regression coefficients are reported in a table alongside the regression coefficients. He does not discuss the standard errors in the text which is commonly the case.

Mercer and colleagues (2012) provide an example of a use of the term standard error which is very different from that in this chapter. They refer to SEM (which is standard error of measurement). They write: 'Reliability for absolute decisions based on single probes was excellent for both probe sets (HV = .92, LV = .98); however, there were substantial differences in SEM across the probe sets. For absolute decisions based on comparisons of single probes, the SEM was 5.76 on the LV set compared with 12.17 on the HV set. In general, reliability and SEM improved for decisions comparing averages of two probes versus single probes.' (p. 229). Standard error of measurement indicates the amount of uncertainty associated with an individual's score on a particular psychological measurement. It is based on the standard deviation of the measurement adjusted for the unreliability of the measurement. As such it is very different from standard error of sample means. It is a concept from psychological measurement theory.

Key points

- The standard error is often reported in computer output but not in research publications. Very much like standard deviation, it can be used as an indicator of the variability in one's data. Variables with different standard errors essentially have different variances so long as the number of scores is the same.

- Standard error is almost always really the estimated standard error in current usage. However, it is simply referred to as the standard error. This is a pity in the sense that it loses sight of a conceptual distinction.

COMPUTER ANALYSIS

Standard error using SPSS

Data
- In 'Data View' of the 'Data Editor', the data should be in columns, a different column for each variable in that you want the standard errors for (Screenshot 12.1).
- Name each variable in 'Variable View' of the 'Data Editor'.

Analysis
- Select 'Analyze', 'Descriptive statistics' and 'Descriptives...' (Screenshot 12.2).

2
- Select the variables you want the standard errors for and move into right-hand box labelled 'Variable(s):' (Screenshot 12.3).
- Select 'Options'.

3
- Select 'S.E. mean' and any other option you wish (Screenshot 12.4).
- Select 'Continue' and 'OK'.

Output
- The standard error of the mean is given in the output table as 'Std. Error' (Screenshot 12.5).

| FIGURE 12.2 | SPSS steps for standard error in Descriptive Statistics |

Interpreting and reporting the output

- It is difficult to give meaning to standard error since it is the outcome of the application of a statistical formula which is its meaning. It can be thought of as a sort of average amount by which samples are likely to be different from the population mean.

- It would be unusual to use standard error to describe a sample as an indication of the variability in the scores. The standard deviation would almost certainly be used to do this. This does not mean that standard errors are never given. You will find them presented for some techniques such as multiple regression. They can often be seen in SPSS output.

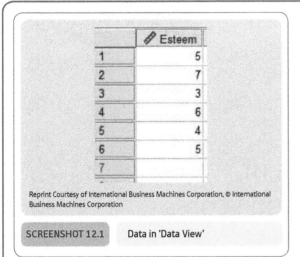

SCREENSHOT 12.1   Data in 'Data View'

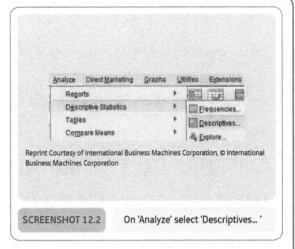

SCREENSHOT 12.2   On 'Analyze' select 'Descriptives...'

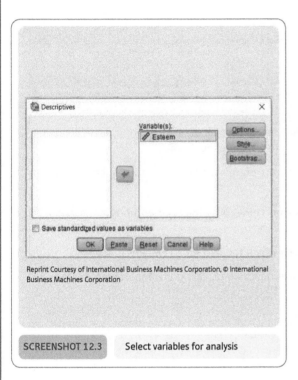

SCREENSHOT 12.3   Select variables for analysis

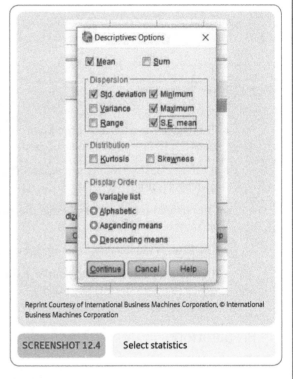

SCREENSHOT 12.4   Select statistics

Descriptive Statistics

	N Statistic	Minimum Statistic	Maximum Statistic	Mean Statistic	Mean Std. Error	Std. Deviation Statistic
Esteem	6	3	7	5.00	.577	1.414
Valid N (listwise)	6					

SCREENSHOT 12.5   Table of 'Descriptive Statistics' output

CHAPTER 13

Related *t*-test

Comparing two samples of related/correlated/paired scores

Overview

- The related *t*-test is mainly used when our data is scores collected under two separate conditions but from a single sample of participants (e.g. change over time).

- It can also be used when the two sets of scores are correlated with each other such as when matching is used.

- The related *t*-test assesses whether the mean of one set of scores is different from the mean of another set of scores.

- The *t*-test is the number of standard errors by which the two sample means differ.

- There are tables of the *t*-distribution for assessing its statistical significance. Computer programs calculate significance exactly.

Preparation

Review *z*-scores and standard deviation (Chapter 6) and standard error (Chapter 12).

13.1 Introduction

Researchers often wish to compare two groups of scores. Conceptually, each of the two groups is from a population of scores. The related (correlated) *t*-test compares the means of two *related* samples of scores to see whether they differ significantly. There are in fact (at least) two versions of the *t*-test – a correlated/related and an uncorrelated/unrelated samples version. The uncorrelated version is more frequently used in psychology simply because unrelated designs are more generally employed. However, the correlated/related *t*-test is substantially simpler to understand and is useful as a learning aid prior to tackling the more difficult unrelated *t*-test (described in Chapter 14). Examples of related samples are illustrated in the following:

- People's scores on a psychological test of creativity are measured at two different points in time to see whether any improvement takes place (see Table 13.1). The people in the sample have been given names in this table to emphasise that each person is measured twice – they are not different individuals in the two conditions. Also, some data have been omitted.

- A group of students' memory test scores are measured in the morning and in the afternoon in order to see whether memory is affected by time of day (Table 13.2).

- The reaction times of participants in an experiment are assessed a) when they have taken the anti-depressant drug 'Nogloom' and b) when they have taken an inert control tablet (placebo) (see Table 13.3).

- The key characteristic of all of these imaginary studies is that a group of people are measured twice on a single variable in slightly different conditions or circumstances

Table 13.1	Creativity scores measured at two different times	
	1 March	**6 months later**
Sam	17	19
Jack	14	17
...	...	...
Karl	12	19
Shahida	19	25
Mandy	10	13
Mean	$\bar{X}_1 = 15.09$	$\bar{X}_2 = 18.36$

Table 13.2	Time of day and memory performance scores	
	Morning	**Afternoon**
Rebecca	9	15
Sharon	16	23
...	...	...
Neil	18	24
Mean	$\bar{X}_1 = 17.3$	$\bar{X}_2 = 22.1$

Table 13.3	Reaction time in seconds for drug and no-drug conditions	
	'Nogloom'	**Placebo**
Jenny	0.27	0.25
David	0.15	0.18
...	...	...
Mean	$\bar{X}_1 = 0.22$	$\bar{X}_2 = 0.16$

(see Boxes 13.1 and 13.2). So in the previous studies, creativity has been measured twice, memory has been measured twice and reaction time has been measured twice. In other words, they are *repeated measures designs* for the obvious reason that each person has been measured more than once on the same variable. Repeated measures designs are also called *related measures designs* and *correlated scores designs*.

The statistical question is whether the mean scores in the two conditions differ sufficiently that the difference is unlikely to be due to chance. If the difference is so big that it is likely to happen by chance in only 5% of pairs of samples, then we should decide that this is a statistically significant finding. That is, we assume that (probably) there truly is a difference.

Box 13.1   Key concepts

Counterbalancing

Repeated measures designs of the sort described in this chapter can be problematic. For example, since the participants in the research are measured under both the experimental and control conditions, it could be that their experiences in the experimental condition affect the way they behave in the control condition. Many of the problems can be overcome by counterbalancing conditions. By this we mean that a random selection of half of the participants in the research are put through the experimental condition first; the other half are put through the control condition first.

Box 13.2   Key concepts

Matching

It is also possible to have a related design if you take pairs of subjects *matched* to be as similar as possible on factors which might be related to their scores on the dependent variable. So pairs of participants might be matched on gender and age so that each member of the pair in question is of the same gender and age group (or as close as possible). One member of the pair would be assigned at *random* to one experimental condition, the other member to the other experimental condition. Using the effect of time of day on the memory research question (Table 13.2), the

Table 13.4	Matched pairs design testing memory score	
Matched pairs	**Morning score**	**Afternoon score**
Both male and under 20	16	17
Both female and under 20	21	25
Both male and over 20	14	20
Both female and over 20	10	14

arrangement for a matched pairs or matched subjects design might be as in Table 13.4. Of course, this is only the basic design – the full design would repeat Table 13.4 several times to get a large enough sample size overall.

The purpose of matching, like using the same person twice, is to reduce the influence of unwanted variables on the comparisons.

13.2 Dependent and independent variables

The scores in Tables 13.1–13.3 are scores on the *dependent variable*. They include the variables creativity, memory and reaction time in the imaginary experiments.

However, there is another variable – the *independent variable*. This refers to the various conditions in which the measurements are being taken. In Table 13.1 measurements are being taken at two different points in time – on 1 March and six months later. The alternative hypothesis is that there *is* a relationship between the independent variable 'time of measurement' and the dependent variable 'creativity score'. Obviously, it is being assumed that creativity scores are *dependent* on the variable time.

13.3 Some basic revision

Many statistical concepts and ideas are closely related. So understanding one thing helps understand another. Some revision of z-scores is appropriate here because z-scores have a lot in common with the related t-test.

A z-score is simply the number of standard deviations a score is away from the mean of the set of scores. The formula is:

$$z\text{-score} = \frac{X - \overline{X}}{SD}$$

where X is a particular score, $\overline{X}$ is the mean of the set of scores and SD is the standard deviation of the set of scores.

Remember, once you have obtained the z-score, it is possible to use the table of the standard normal distribution (z-distribution) (Significance Table 13.1) to identify the relative position of the particular score compared to the rest of the set.

Significance Table 13.1	5% significance values of related t (two-tailed test). Appendix E gives a fuller and conventional version of this table

Degrees of freedom (always $N - 1$ for related *t*-test)	Significant at 5% level Accept hypothesis
3	± 3.18 or more extreme
4	± 2.78 or more extreme
5	± 2.57 or more extreme
6	± 2.45 or more extreme
7	± 2.37 or more extreme
8	± 2.31 or more extreme
9	± 2.26 or more extreme
10	± 2.23 or more extreme
11	± 2.20 or more extreme
12	± 2.18 or more extreme
13	± 2.16 or more extreme
14	± 2.15 or more extreme
15	± 2.13 or more extreme
18	± 2.10 or more extreme
20	± 2.09 or more extreme
25	± 2.06 or more extreme
30	± 2.04 or more extreme
40	± 2.02 or more extreme
60	± 2.00 or more extreme
100	± 1.98 or more extreme
∞	± 1.96 or more extreme

Your value must be in the listed ranges for your degrees of freedom to be significant at the 5% level (i.e. to accept the hypothesis).

If your required degrees of freedom are not listed, then take the nearest smaller listed values. Refer to Appendix E if you need a more precise value of *t*.

'More extreme' means that, for example, values in the ranges of +3.18 to infinity or −3.18 to (minus) infinity are statistically significant with 3 degrees of freedom.

13.4   Theoretical considerations underlying the computer analysis

As we have seen in Chapter 11, the null hypothesis is a crucial concept underlying inferential statistical tests. This states that there is *no* relationship between the two variables. In one of the examples given earlier (Table 13.2), the independent variable is time of day and the dependent variable is memory. The null hypothesis is that there is no relation between the independent variable time and the dependent variable memory. This implies, by definition, that the two samples, according to the null hypothesis, come from the same population. In other words, in the final analysis the overall trend is for pairs of samples drawn from this population to have identical means. However, that is the trend over many pairs of samples. The means of some pairs of samples will differ somewhat from each other simply because samples from even the same population tend to vary. Little differences will be more common than big differences.

Another important concept is that of the *t*-distribution. This is a theoretical statistical distribution which is similar to the *z*-distribution discussed in Chapter 6. There is also a *t*-score which is similar to the *z*-score. The *t*-score is based on analogous logic to the *z*-score. The major difference is that the *t*-score involves standard error and not standard deviation. As we saw in the previous chapter, the standard error is nothing other than the standard deviation of a set of sample means. Using the *z*-distribution, it is possible to work out the standing of any score relative to the rest of the set of scores. Exactly the same applies where one has the standard error of a set of sample means. One can calculate the relative extent to which a particular sample mean differs from the average sample mean. (The average sample mean with many samples will be the same as the mean of the population, so normally the population mean is referred to rather than the average of sample means.) The key formulae are as follows:

$$z = \frac{\text{particular score} - \text{sample mean of scores}}{\text{standard deviation of scores}}$$

$$t = \frac{\text{particular sample mean} - \text{average of sample means}}{\text{standard error of sample means}}$$

or

$$t = \frac{\text{particular sample mean} - \text{population mean}}{\text{standard error of sample means}}$$

As you can see, the form of each of these formulae is identical.

Both *z* and *t* refer to standard distributions which are symmetrical and bell-shaped. The *z*-distribution is a normal distribution – the standard normal distribution. Similarly, the *t*-distribution is also a normal distribution when large sample sizes are involved. In fact *z* and *t* are identical in these circumstances. As the sample size gets smaller, however, the *t*-distribution becomes a decidedly flatter distribution. Significance Table 13.1 is a table of the *t*-distribution which reports the value of the *t*-score needed to put a sample mean outside the middle 95% of sample means and into the extreme 5% of sample means that are held to be unlikely or statistically significant sample means. Notice that the table of the *t*-distribution is structured according to the *degrees of freedom*. Usually this is the sample size minus one if a single sample is used to *estimate* the standard error; otherwise it may be different.

The *t*-test can be applied to the data on the above population. Assume that for a given population, the population mean is 1.0. We have estimated the standard error by taking a known sample of 10 scores, calculating its estimated standard deviation and dividing by the square root of the sample size. All of these stages are combined in the following formula, which was discussed in Chapter 12:

$$(\text{estimated}) \text{ standard error} = \frac{\sqrt{\dfrac{\sum X^2 - \dfrac{(\sum X)^2}{N}}{N - 1}}}{\sqrt{N}}$$

This gives the (estimated) standard error to be 2.5. We can calculate if a sample with a mean of 8.0 ($N = 10$) is statistically unusual. We simply apply the *t*-test formula to the information we have:

$$t = \frac{\text{particular sample mean} - \text{population mean}}{\text{standard error of sample means}}$$

$$= \frac{8.0 - 1.0}{2.5}$$

$$= \frac{7.0}{2.5}$$

$$= 2.8$$

In other words, our sample mean is actually 2.8 standard errors *above* the average sample mean (i.e. population mean) of 1.0.

We can now use Significance Table 13.1. This table is distributed according to the number of degrees of freedom involved in the estimation of the population standard deviation. Since the sample size on which this estimate was based is 10, the degrees of freedom are 1 less than 10, i.e. $N - 1 = 9$ degrees of freedom. Significance Table 13.1 tells us that we need a *t*-score of 2.26 or more to place our particular sample mean in the extreme 5% of sample means drawn from the population. Our obtained *t*-score was 2.8. This tells us that our sample mean is within the extreme 5% of sample means, i.e. that it is statistically significantly different from the average of sample means drawn from this particular population.

Wonderful! But what has this got to do with our research problem which we set out at the beginning of this chapter? The above is simply about a single sample compared with a multitude of samples. What we need to know is whether or not *two* sample means are sufficiently different from each other that we can say that the difference is statistically significant. There is just one remaining trick that statisticians employ in these circumstances. That is, *the two samples of scores are turned into a single sample by subtracting one set of scores from the other.* We calculate the difference between a person's score in one sample and their score in the other sample. This leaves us with a sample of difference scores *D* which constitutes the single sample we need.

The stylised data in Table 13.5 show just what is done. The difference scores in the final column are the single sample of scores which we use in our standard error formula. For this particular sample of difference scores the mean is 4.0. According to the null hypothesis, the general trend should be zero difference between the two samples – that is, the mean of the difference scores would be zero if the sample reflected precisely the null hypothesis. Once again we are reliant on the null hypothesis to tell us what the population characteristics are. Since the null hypothesis has it that there is no difference between the samples, there should be zero difference in the population, that is, the average difference score should be 0. (Since the difference between sample means – under the null hypothesis that the two samples do not differ – is zero by definition, the population mean should be zero. In other words, we can delete the population mean from the formula for *t*-scores.)

Table 13.5	Basic rearrangement of data for the related samples *t*-test		
Person	Sample 1 (X_1)	Sample 2 (X_2)	Difference $X_1 - X_2 = D$
A	9	5	4
B	7	2	5
C	7	3	4
D	11	6	5
E	7	5	2

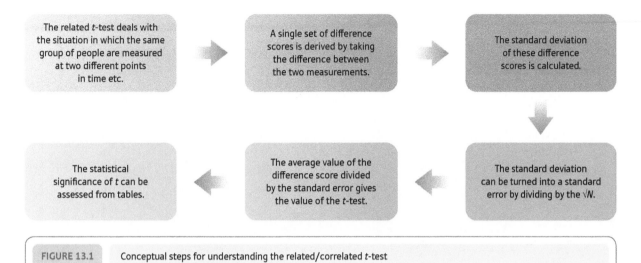

| FIGURE 13.1 | Conceptual steps for understanding the related/correlated *t*-test |

We would of course expect some samples of difference scores to be above or below zero by varying amounts. The question is whether a mean difference of 4.0 is sufficiently different from zero to be statistically significant. If it comes in the middle 95% of the distribution of sample means then we accept the null hypothesis. If it comes in the extreme 5% then we describe it as significant and reject the null hypothesis in favour of the alternative hypothesis. We achieve this by using the *t*-test formula applied to the sample of difference scores. We then test the significance of *t* by comparing it to the values in Significance Table 13.1. For a sample of 4, since the degrees of freedom are $N - 1$ which equals 3, the table tells us that we need a *t*-score of 3.18 at the minimum to put our sample mean in the significant extreme 5% of the distribution of sample means. Figure 13.1 gives the key steps in carrying out a related/correlated samples *t*-test.

Explaining statistics 13.1

How the related *t*-test works

The data are for an imaginary study examining the relationship between an infant's age and the amount of eye contact it makes with its mother. Each infant was tested at six months and nine months of age – age is the independent variable. The dependent variable is the number of one-minute segments during which the infant made any eye contact with its mother during a ten-minute session. The null hypothesis is that there is no relation between age and eye contact. The data are given in Table 13.6, which includes the difference between the six-month and nine-month scores as well as the square of this difference. The number of cases, N, is the number of difference scores, i.e. 8.

Table 13.6 clearly shows that the nine-month-old babies are spending more periods in eye contact with their mothers, on average, than at six months old. The average difference in eye contact scores is 1.5. The question remains, however, whether this difference is statistically significant.

| Step 1 | The formula for the standard error of the difference (D) scores is as follows. It is exactly as for the calculation in Explaining statistics 12.1 except that we have substituted D for X. |

→

| | Table 13.6 | Steps in calculating the related/correlated samples *t*-test (number of one-minute segments with eye contact) | | | |

Subject	6 months X_1	9 months X_2	Difference $D = X_1 - X_2$	Difference^2 D^2
Baby Clara	3	7	−4	16
Baby Martin	5	6	−1	1
Baby Sally	5	3	2	4
Baby Angie	4	8	−4	16
Baby Trevor	3	5	−2	4
Baby Sam	7	9	−2	4
Baby Bobby	8	7	1	1
Baby Sid	7	9	−2	4
Sums of columns	$\sum X_1 = 42$	$\sum X_2 = 54$	$\sum D = -12$	$\sum D^2 = 50$
Means of columns	$\bar{X}_1 = 5.25$	$\bar{X}_2 = 6.75$	$\bar{D} = -1.5$	

$$\text{standard error} = \frac{\sqrt{\dfrac{\sum D^2 - \dfrac{(\sum D)^2}{N}}{N-1}}}{\sqrt{N}}$$

Substituting the values from Table 13.6:

$$= \frac{\sqrt{\dfrac{50 - \dfrac{(-12)^2}{8}}{8-1}}}{\sqrt{8}} = \frac{\sqrt{\dfrac{50 - \dfrac{144}{8}}{7}}}{2.828}$$

$$= \frac{\sqrt{\dfrac{50 - 18}{7}}}{2.828}$$

$$= \frac{\sqrt{\dfrac{32}{7}}}{2.828} = \frac{\sqrt{4.571}}{2.828} = \frac{2.138}{2.828} = 0.756$$

Step 2   We can now enter our previously calculated values in the following formula:

$$t\text{-score} = \frac{\bar{D}}{SE}$$

where $\bar{D}$ is the average difference score and SE is the standard error

$$t\text{-score} = \frac{-1.5}{0.756} = -1.98$$

Note that this value is the same as that given by SPSS in Screenshot 13.5.

Step 3 If we look up this *t*-score in Significance Table 13.1 for $N - 1 = 7$ degrees of freedom, we find that we need a *t*-value of 2.37 or more (or −2.37 or less) to put our sample mean in the extreme 5% of sample means. In other words, our sample mean of −1.5 is in the middle 95% of sample means which are held to be statistically not significant. In these circumstances we prefer to believe that the null hypothesis is true. In other words, there is no significant difference between the babies' scores at six and nine months.

Interpreting the results

Check the mean scores for the two conditions in order to understand which age group has the highest levels of eye contact. Although eye contact was greater at nine months, the *t*-test is not significant, which indicates that the difference between the two ages was not sufficient to allow us to conclude that the two groups truly differ from each other.

Reporting the results

We would write something along the lines of the following in our report: 'Eye contact was slightly higher at nine months ($M = 6.75$) than at six months ($M = 5.25$). However, the difference did not support the hypothesis that eye contact differs in six-month and nine-month-old babies since the obtained value for *t* of −1.98 is not statistically significant at the 5% level.'

Alternatively, following the recommendations of the APA (2010) Publication Manual we could write: 'Eye contact was slightly higher at nine months ($M = 6.75$) than at six months ($M = 5.25$). However, the difference did not support the hypothesis that the amount of eye contact differs significantly at six months and nine months, $t(7) = -1.98$, $p > .05$.'

The material in the last part of the second sentence simply gives the statistic used (the *t*-test), the degrees of freedom (7), its value (−1.98), and the level of significance which is more than that required for the 5% level ($p > .05$). Chapter 15 explains this in greater detail.

Warning *The distribution of the difference scores should not be markedly skewed if the t-test is to be used. Appendix A explains how to test for significant skewness. If the distribution of difference scores is markedly skewed, you might wish to consider the use of the Wilcoxon matched pairs test (Explaining statistics 21.2).*

13.5 Cautionary note

Many psychologists act as if they believe that it is the design of the research which determines whether you should use a related test. Related designs are those, after all, in which people serve in both research conditions. It is assumed that there is a correlation between subjects' scores in the two conditions. What if there is no correlation between the two samples of scores? The standard error becomes relatively large compared to the number of degrees of freedom so your research is less likely to be statistically significant (especially if the samples are small). So while trying to control for unwanted sources of error, if there is no correlation between the scores in the two conditions of the study, the researcher may simply reduce the likelihood of achieving statistical significance. The reason is that the researcher may have obtained non-significant findings simply because a) they have reduced the error degrees of freedom, which therefore b) increases the error estimate, thus c) reducing the significance level perhaps to non-significance. Some computer programs print out the correlation between the two variables as part of the correlated *t*-test output. If this correlation is not significant then you might be wise to think again about your test of significance. This situation is particularly likely to occur where you are using a matching procedure (as opposed to having the same people in both conditions). Unless your matching variables actually do correlate with the dependent variable, the matching can have no effect on reducing the error variance.

In the previous calculation, we found no significant change in eye contact in older babies compared with younger ones. It is worth examining the correlation between the two sets of scores to see if the assumption of correlation is fulfilled. If we calculate the correlation between the two measures, we obtain a value of .42. However, from tables of the significance of Pearson's correlation coefficient (Significance Table 11.1) we find a correlation of .71 or greater to be statistically significant. In other words, the correlated scores do not really correlate – certainly not significantly. Even applying the uncorrelated version of the *t*-test described in the next chapter makes no difference. It still leaves the difference between the two age samples non-significant. We are not suggesting that if a related *t*-test fails to achieve significance you should replace it by an unrelated *t*-test, merely that you risk ignoring trends in your data which may be important. The most practical implication is that matching variables should relate to the dependent variable; otherwise there is no point in matching in the first place.

Research examples

Related/correlated/paired *t*-test

Drees and Mack (2012) argue that mental toughness is critical for achieving athletic success and that it comes with experiences. The researchers wanted to know, among other things, whether the mental toughness ability of high-school wrestlers changes over time (the competitive season). Participants in the study completed MeBTough (the Mental, Emotional and Bodily Toughness Inventory). A related/correlated/paired *t*-test was used to examine the change in mental toughness over the sporting season. No significant change was found.

Jafari and colleagues (2013) examined whether spiritual therapy improved the quality of life of women undergoing radiation therapy for breast cancer. In a randomised control experiment, quality of life was assessed psychometrically. Using the related/correlated/paired *t*-test it was found that for the treated group there was an improvement in quality of life scores from the start of the treatment until after six weeks of the intervention. This was not the case for the control group.

Wilkes and colleagues (2011) studied children with ADHD (attention deficit hyperactivity disorder), who can be deficient in social skills. The study examined the effectiveness of a new intervention. This, in part, involved play sessions incorporating feedback and peer modelling. This was intended to enhance play and social skills in children with ADHD and their playmates. The design was a matched samples one of the sort to which the paired *t*-test can be applied. The pre- and post-measures were the Test of Playfulness. A related samples *t*-test (they call it the dependent samples *t*-test) was used to test for improvement. Separate related *t*-tests showed that both the ADHD and the paired controls improve over the period of the intervention.

Key points

- The related or correlated *t*-test is merely a special case of the one-way analysis of variance for related samples (Chapter 24). Although it is frequently used in psychological research it tells us nothing more than the equivalent analysis of variance would do. Since the analysis of variance is generally a more flexible statistic, allowing any number of groups of scores to be compared, it might be your preferred statistic. However, the common occurrence of the *t*-test in psychological research means that you need to have some idea about what it is.

- The related *t*-test assumes that the distribution of the difference scores is not markedly skewed. If it is then the test may be unacceptably inaccurate. Appendix A explains how to test for skewness.

- If you compare many pairs of samples with each other in the same study using the *t*-test, you should consult Chapter 26 to find out about appropriate significance levels. There are better ways of making multiple comparisons, as they are called, but with appropriate adjustment to the critical values for significance, multiple *t*-tests can be justified.

- If you find that your related *t*-test is not significant, it could be that your two samples of scores are not correlated, thus not meeting the assumptions of the related *t*-test.

- Significance Table 13.1 applies whenever we have estimated the standard error from the characteristics of a sample. However, if we had actually known the population standard deviation and consequently the standard error was the actual standard error and not an estimate, we should not use the *t*-distribution table. In these rare (virtually unknown) circumstances, the distribution of the *t*-score formula is that for the *z*-scores.

- Although the correlated *t*-test can be used to compare any pairs of scores, it does not always make sense to do so. For example, you could use the correlated *t*-test to compare the weights and heights of people to see if the weight mean and the height mean differ. Unfortunately, it is a rather stupid thing to do since the numerical values involved relate to radically different things which are not comparable with each other. It is the comparison which is nonsensical in this case. The statistical test is not to blame. On the other hand, one could compare a sample of people's weights at different points in time quite meaningfully.

COMPUTER ANALYSIS

Related/correlated/paired *t*-test using SPSS

Data
- Name each variable in 'Variable View' of the 'Data Editor' in the usual way. We have named the variables 'Six_mths' and 'Nine_mths'.

2
- In 'Data View' of the 'Data Editor', enter the two related variables as separate columns with the data for each participant in the same row (Screenshot 13.1).

Analysis
- Select 'Analyze', 'Compare Means' and 'Paired-samples T Test...' (Screenshot 13.2).

2
- Select and move the two related variables into the 'Paired Variables:' box using the arrow button at the centre of the screen (Screenshot 13.3).

3
- Select 'OK'.

Output
- The first table for Screenshot 13.4 Includes the means, Ns and standard deviations of both variables. This tells you which average score is the highest.

2
- The second table for Screenshot 13.4 allows you to check that there is a correlation between the two variables – the related/correlated *t* test assumes that there is.

3
- The value of *t*, the degrees of freedom, and the exact significance level is given. Give them in your report (Screenshot 13.5).

FIGURE 13.2   SPSS steps for calculating the related/correlated/paired *t*-test

Interpreting and reporting the output

- In the example calculated, although the mean score at nine months is higher than the mean score at six months, the difference is not statistically significant at the 5% level so there is no reliable increase in scores with age.

- One could write, therefore: 'Eye contact was slightly higher at nine months ($M = 6.75, SD = 2.05$) than at six months ($M = 5.25, SD = 1.91$). However, the difference of -1.50, 95% CI $[-3.29, 0.29]$, was not statistically significant, $t(7) = -1.98, p = .09$.' CI stands for Confidence Interval and is discussed in Chapter 16. The *SD*s and CIs are obtained from Screenshots 13.4 and 13.5, respectively.

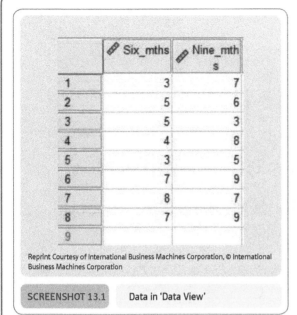

Reprint Courtesy of International Business Machines Corporation, © International Business Machines Corporation

SCREENSHOT 13.1   Data in 'Data View'

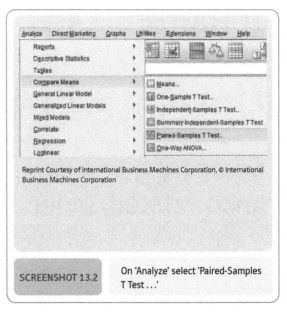

Reprint Courtesy of International Business Machines Corporation, © International Business Machines Corporation

SCREENSHOT 13.2   On 'Analyze' select 'Paired-Samples T Test . . .'

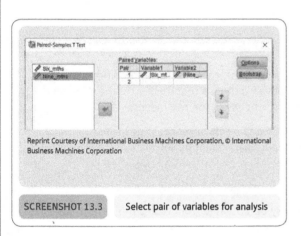

Reprint Courtesy of International Business Machines Corporation, © International Business Machines Corporation

SCREENSHOT 13.3   Select pair of variables for analysis

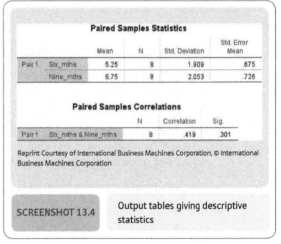

Reprint Courtesy of International Business Machines Corporation, © International Business Machines Corporation

SCREENSHOT 13.4   Output tables giving descriptive statistics

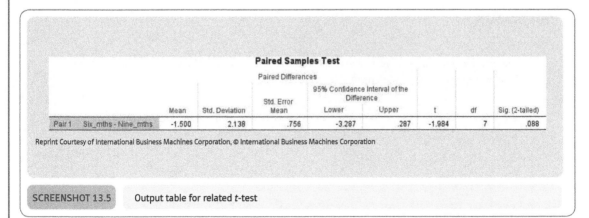

Reprint Courtesy of International Business Machines Corporation, © International Business Machines Corporation

SCREENSHOT 13.5   Output table for related *t*-test

CHAPTER 14

Unrelated *t*-test

Comparing two samples of unrelated/ uncorrelated/independent scores

Overview

- The unrelated *t*-test compares mean scores of two different samples on a single variable.

- It indicates whether the difference between the two means is statistically significant or not: that is, whether you should accept the alternative hypothesis that there is really a difference or the null hypothesis that there is no difference between the two means.

- The unrelated *t*-test combines the variation in the two sets of scores to estimate the standard error. This leads to a rather clumsy and superficially daunting calculation which is easily done using a statistical package in preference.

- The *t*-value is simply the number of standard errors that the two means are apart.

- The statistical significance of this *t*-value may be obtained from tables though computer programs will give you exact significance values.

Preparation

This chapter will be easier if you have mastered the related *t*-test (Chapter 13). Revise dependent and independent variables from that chapter.

14.1 Introduction

The *t*-test described in this chapter has various names. The unrelated *t*-test, the uncorrelated scores *t*-test and the independent samples *t*-test are the most common variants. It is also known as the Student *t*-test after its inventor who used the pen-name Student.

Often researchers compare two groups of scores from two separate groups of individuals to assess whether the average score of one group is higher than that of the other group. The possible research topics involved in such comparisons are limitless:

- One might wish to compare an experimental group with a control group. For example, do volunteers who are randomly assigned to a sexually abstinent condition have more erotic dreams than those in the sexually active control group? The independent variable is sexual activity (which has two levels – sexually abstinent and sexually active) and the dependent variable is the number of erotic dreams in a month (see Table 14.1). The independent variable differentiates the two groups being compared. In the present example, this is the amount of sexual activity (sexually abstinent versus sexually active). The dependent variable is the variable which might be influenced by the independent variable. This variable corresponds to the scores given in the main body of the table (i.e. number of erotic dreams).

- A group of experienced managers may be compared with a group of inexperienced managers in terms of the amount of time which they take to make complex decisions. The independent variable is experience in management (which has two levels – experienced versus inexperienced) and the dependent variable is decision-making time (Table 14.2).

- A researcher might compare the amount of bullying in two schools, one with a strict and punitive policy and the other with a policy of counselling on discipline infringements. A sample of children from each school is interviewed and the number of times they have been bullied in the previous school year obtained. The independent variable is policy on discipline (which has two levels – strict versus counselling); and the

Table 14.1	Number of erotic dreams per month in experimental and control groups	
Experimental group **Sexually abstinent**		**Control group** **Sexually active**
17		10
14		12
16		7

Table 14.2	Decision time (seconds) in experienced and inexperienced managers	
Experienced managers		**Inexperienced managers**
24		167
32		133
27		74

Table 14.3	Number of times bullied in a year in schools with different discipline policies	
Strict policy		**Counselling**
8		12
5		1
2		3

dependent variable is the number of times a child has been bullied in the previous school year (see Table 14.3).

The basic requirements for the unrelated/uncorrelated scores *t*-test are straightforward enough – two groups of scores coming from two distinct groups of people. The scores should be roughly similar in terms of the shapes of their distributions. Ideally both distributions should be bell-shaped and symmetrical. However, even where this ideal cannot be met, the test will remain accurate enough.

So the unrelated *t*-test examines whether two groups of scores have significantly *different* means – in other words, how likely is it that there could be a difference between the two group means as big as the one obtained if there is no difference in reality in the population?

14.2   Theoretical considerations

Figure 14.1 gives the steps in carrying out an unrelated *t*-test. The unrelated *t*-test helps you decide between the null and alternative hypotheses. We explained null hypotheses in Chapter 11. Null hypotheses are statements that there is no relationship between two variables. *This is another way of saying that there is no difference between the*

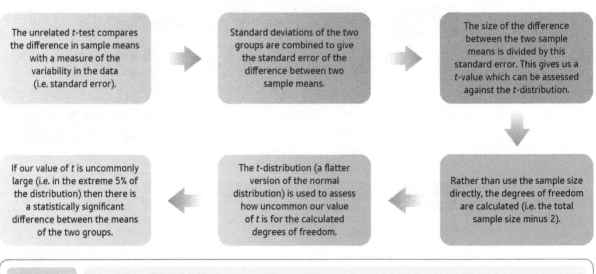

FIGURE 14.1   Conceptual steps for understanding the *t*-test

means of the two groups (i.e. columns) of scores. The two variables in question are the independent and dependent variables. The simplest null hypotheses for the above three studies are:

- There is no relationship between sexual activity and the number of erotic dreams that participants have.

- Managerial experience is not related to speed of complex decision-making.

- The disciplinary style of a school is not associated with the amount of bullying.

The alternative hypotheses to these null hypotheses can be obtained by simply deleting *no* or *not* from each of the above. Notice that the above way of writing the null hypothesis is relatively streamlined compared with what you often read in books and journals. So do not be surprised if you come across null hypotheses expressed in much more clumsy language such as:

- Participants who abstain from sex will have the same number of erotic dreams as participants who are sexually active.

- Erotic dreams do not occur at different frequencies in sexually active and sexually inactive participants.

These two statements tend to obscure the fact that null hypotheses are fundamentally similar irrespective of the type of research under consideration.

The erotic dreams experiment will be used to illustrate the theoretical issues. There are two different samples of scores defined by the independent variable – one for the sexually abstinent group and the other for the sexually active group. The scores in Table 14.4 are the numbers of sexual dreams that each participant in the study has in a seven-day period. On average, the sexually active participants have fewer erotic dreams. Does this reflect a generalisable (significant) difference? The data might be as in Table 14.4. Apart from suggesting that Wendy's fantasy life is wonderful, the table indicates that sexual abstinence leads to an increase in erotic dreams.

The null hypothesis suggests that the scores in the two samples come from the same population since it claims that there is no relationship between the independent and dependent variables. That is, for all intents and purposes, the two samples can be construed as coming from a single population of scores; there is no difference between them due to the independent variable. Any differences between samples drawn from this null-hypothesis-defined population are due to chance factors rather than a true relationship between the independent and

Table 14.4	Possible data from the sexual activity and erotic dreams experiment (dreams per seven days)		
Participant	**Sexually abstinent**	**Participant**	**Sexually active**
Lindsay	6	Janice	2
Claudine	7	Jennifer	5
Sharon	7	Joanne	4
Natalie	8	Anne-Marie	5
Sarah	9	Helen	6
Wendy	10	Amanda	6
Ruth	8	Sophie	5
Angela	9		

Table 14.5	Imaginary population of scores for erotic dreams study			
Experimental group Sexually abstinent			**Sexually active Control group**	
8	3		6	6
7	6		8	4
6	7		7	7
7	7		4	9
5	9		6	8
5	8		9	7
2	7		10	5
4	6		2	7
6	7		3	5
10	8		6	5
9	6		7	7
7	4		8	6
5			7	

dependent variables. Table 14.5 is an imaginary population of scores from this null-hypothesis-defined population on the dependent variable 'number of erotic dreams'. The table also indicates whether the score is that of a sexually abstinent participant or a sexually active one. If the two columns of scores are examined carefully, there are no differences between the two sets of scores. In other words, they have the same average scores. Statistically, all of the scores in Table 14.5 can be regarded as coming from the same population. There is no relationship between sexual activity and the number of erotic dreams.

Given that the two samples (sexually abstinent and sexually active) come from the same population of scores on erotic dreams, in general we would expect no difference between pairs of samples drawn at random from this single population. Of course, sampling always introduces a chance element so some pairs of samples would be different, but mostly the differences will cluster around zero. Overall, numerous pairs of samples will yield an *average* difference of zero. We are assuming that we consistently subtract the sexually active mean from the sexually abstinent mean (or vice versa – it does not matter so long as we always do the same thing) so that positive and negative differences cancel each other out.

Since in this case we know the population of scores under the null hypothesis, we could pick out samples of 10 scores at random from the population to represent the sexually abstinent sample and, say, nine scores from the population to represent the sexually active sample. (Obviously the sample sizes will vary and they do not have to be equal.) Any convenient randomisation procedure could be used to select the samples (e.g. computer-generated, random number tables or numbers drawn from a hat). The two samples selected at random, together with their respective means, are listed in Table 14.6.

Examining Table 14.6, we can clearly see that there is a difference between the two sample means. This difference is $7.0 - 6.7 = 0.3$. This difference between the two sample means has been obtained despite the fact that we know that there is no relationship between the independent variable and the dependent variable in the null-hypothesis-defined population. This is the nature of random sampling.

We can repeat this experiment by drawing more pairs of samples of these sizes from the null-hypothesis-defined population. This is shown for 40 new pairs of variables in

Table 14.6	Random samples of scores from population in Table 14.5 to represent experimental and control conditions

Experimental group Sexually abstinent	Control group Sexually active
4	5
5	5
10	10
7	9
7	7
5	7
7	8
9	6
9	2
	8
$\bar{X}_1 = 7.0$	$\bar{X}_2 = 6.7$

Table 14.7	Forty pairs of random samples from the population in Table 14.5

Experimental group Sexually abstinent $N = 10$	Control group Sexually active $N = 9$	Difference (column 1 – column 2)
6.100	6.444	−0.344
6.300	5.444	0.856
6.000	6.556	−0.556
6.400	6.778	−0.378
6.600	6.111	0.489
5.700	6.111	−0.411
6.700	6.111	0.589
6.300	5.667	0.633
6.400	6.667	−0.267
5.900	5.778	0.122
6.400	6.556	−0.156
6.360	6.444	−0.084
6.400	6.778	−0.378
6.200	6.222	−0.022
5.600	5.889	−0.289
6.100	6.222	−0.122
6.800	6.667	0.133
6.100	6.222	−0.122
6.900	6.000	0.900
7.200	5.889	1.311
5.800	7.333	−1.533
6.700	6.889	−0.189

Experimental group Sexually abstinent $N = 10$	Control group Sexually active $N = 9$	Difference (column 1 – column 2)
6.200	6.000	0.200
6.500	6.444	0.056
5.900	6.444	−0.544
6.000	6.333	−0.333
6.300	6.778	−0.478
6.100	5.778	0.322
6.000	6.000	0.000
6.000	6.667	−0.667
6.556	6.778	−0.222
6.700	5.778	0.922
5.600	7.000	−1.400
6.600	6.222	0.378
5.600	6.667	−1.067
5.900	7.222	−1.322
6.000	6.667	−0.667
7.000	6.556	0.444
6.400	6.556	−0.156
6.900	6.222	0.678

Many of the differences between the pairs of means in Table 14.7 are very close to zero. This is just as we would expect since the independent and dependent variables are not related. Nevertheless, the means of some pairs of samples are somewhat different. In Table 14.7, 95% of the differences between the two means come in the range 0.922 to −1.400. (Given the small number of samples we have used, it is not surprising that this range is not symmetrical. If we had taken large numbers of samples, we would have expected more symmetry. Furthermore, had we used normally distributed scores, the symmetry may have been better.) The middle 95% of the distribution of differences between pairs of sample means are held to support the null hypothesis. The extreme 5% beyond this middle range are held more likely to support the alternative hypothesis.

The standard deviation of the 40 'difference' scores gives the standard error of the differences. Don't forget we are dealing with *sample* means so the term standard error is the correct one. The value of the standard error is 0.63. This is the 'average' amount by which the differences between sample means is likely to deviate from the population mean difference of zero.

14.3   Standard deviation and standard error

The trouble with all of the above is that it is abstract theory. Normally, we know nothing for certain about the populations from which our samples come. Fortunately, quite a lot can be inferred about the population given the null hypothesis and information from the samples:

- Since the null hypothesis states that there is no relationship between the independent and dependent variables in the population, it follows that there should be no systematic

between the two means should be zero over many pairs of samples.

• We can use the scores in a sample to estimate the standard deviation of the scores in the population. However, if we use our usual standard deviation formula the estimate tends to be a little too low. Consequently we have to modify our standard deviation formula (Chapter 6) when estimating the standard deviation of the population. The change is minimal – the N in the bottom half of the formula is changed to $N - 1$:

$$\text{estimated standard deviation} = \sqrt{\frac{\sum X^2 - \frac{(\sum X)^2}{N}}{N - 1}}$$

• The net effect of this adjustment is to increase the estimated standard deviation of the population – the amount of adjustment is greatest if we are working with small sample sizes for which subtracting 1 is a big adjustment. But this only gives us the estimated standard deviation of the *scores* in the population. We really need to know about the standard deviation (i.e. standard error) of sample means taken from that population. Remember, there is a simple formula which converts the estimated standard deviation of the population to the estimated standard error of sample means drawn from that population: we simply divide the estimated standard deviation by the square root of the sample size. It so happens that the computationally most useful way of working out the standard error is as follows:

$$\text{standard error} = \frac{\sqrt{\dfrac{\sum X^2 - \dfrac{(\sum X)^2}{N}}{N - 1}}}{\sqrt{N}}$$

Still we have not finished because this is the estimated standard error of *sample means*; we want the estimated standard error of *differences between pairs of sample means*. It makes intuitive sense that the standard error of differences between pairs of sample means is likely to be the sum of the standard errors of the two samples. After all, the standard error is merely the average amount by which a sample mean differs from the population mean of zero. So the standard error of the differences between pairs of sample means drawn from a population should be the two separate standard errors combined.

Well, that is virtually the procedure. However, the two different standard errors (*SE*) are added together in a funny sort of way:

$$SE_{[\text{of differences between sample means}]} = \sqrt{(SE_1^2 + SE_2^2)}$$

Finally, because the sample sizes used to estimate the two individual standard errors are not always the same, it is necessary to adjust the equation to account for this; otherwise you end up with the wrong answer. The computational formula for the estimated standard error of differences between pairs of sample means is as follows:

Standard error of differences between pairs of sample means

$$= \sqrt{\left(\frac{\sum X_1^2 - \frac{(\sum X_1)^2}{N_1} + \sum X_2^2 - \frac{(\sum X_2)^2}{N_2}}{N_1 + N_2 - 2}\right)\left(\frac{1}{N_1} + \frac{1}{N_2}\right)}$$

Although this looks appallingly complicated, the basic idea is fairly simple. It appears complex because of the adjustment for different sample sizes.

We then use this standard error of differences in the *t*-test formula. The average difference between the pairs of sample means is zero assuming the null hypothesis to be true. The *t* formula is:

$$t = \frac{\text{sample 1 mean} - \text{sample 2 mean} - 0}{\text{standard error of differences between sample means}}$$

or

$$t = \frac{\text{differences between the two sample means} - 0}{\text{standard error of differences between sample means}}$$

Since in the above formula the population mean of difference between pairs of sample means is always zero, we can omit it:

$$t = \frac{\text{sample 1 mean} - \text{sample 2 mean}}{\text{standard error of differences between sample means}}$$

The formula expressed in full looks even more complicated (Explaining statistics 14.1). So *t* is the number of standard errors by which the difference between our two sample means differs from the population mean of zero. The distribution of *t* is rather like the distribution of *z* if you have a large sample – thus it approximates very closely the normal distribution. However, with smaller sample sizes the curve of *t* becomes increasingly flat and more spread out than the normal curve. Consequently we need different *t*-distributions for different sample sizes.

Significance Table 14.1 gives values for the *t*-distributions. Notice that the distribution is dependent on the degrees of freedom which for this *t*-test are the total number of scores in the two samples combined minus 2.

Significance Table 14.1	5% significance values of unrelated *t* (two-tailed test). Appendix E gives a fuller and conventional version of this table
Degrees of freedom (always $N - 2$ for unrelated *t*-test)	**Significant at 5% level** Accept hypothesis
3	± 3.18 or more extreme
4	± 2.78 or more extreme
5	± 2.57 or more extreme
6	± 2.45 or more extreme
7	± 2.37 or more extreme
8	± 2.31 or more extreme
9	± 2.26 or more extreme
10	± 2.23 or more extreme
11	± 2.20 or more extreme
12	± 2.18 or more extreme
13	± 2.16 or more extreme
14	± 2.15 or more extreme
15	± 2.13 or more extreme
18	± 2.10 or more extreme
20	± 2.09 or more extreme

Degrees of freedom (always $N - 2$ for unrelated t-test)	Significant at 5% level Accept hypothesis
25	$\pm$ 2.06 or more extreme
30	$\pm$ 2.04 or more extreme
40	$\pm$ 2.02 or more extreme
60	$\pm$ 2.00 or more extreme
100	$\pm$ 1.98 or more extreme
∞	$\pm$ 1.96 or more extreme

Your value must be in the listed ranges for your degrees of freedom to be significant at the 5% level (i.e. to accept the hypothesis).

If your required degrees of freedom are not listed, then take the nearest smaller listed values. Refer to Appendix E if you need a precise value of t.

'More extreme' means that, for example, values in the ranges of $+3.18$ to infinity or -3.18 to (minus) infinity are statistically significant with 3 degrees of freedom.

Explaining statistics 14.1

How the unrelated t-test works

The calculation of the unrelated t-test uses the following formula:

$$t = \frac{\overline{X}_1 - \overline{X}_2}{\sqrt{\left(\dfrac{\sum X_1^2 - \dfrac{(\sum X_1)^2}{N_1} + \sum X_2^2 - \dfrac{(\sum X_2)^2}{N_2}}{N_1 + N_2 - 2}\right)\left(\dfrac{1}{N_1} + \dfrac{1}{N_2}\right)}}$$

Table 14.8	Emotionality scores in two-parent and lone-parent families

Two-parent family X_1	Lone-parent family X_2
12	6
18	9
14	4
10	13
19	14
8	9
15	8
11	12
10	11
13	9
15	
16	

Horrific, isn't it? It is perhaps the worst formula that you are likely to come across in psychological statistics. However, it contains little that is new. It is probably best to break the formula down into its component calculations and take things step by step. However, if you prefer to try to work directly with the above formula do not let us stand in your way.

The data are from an imaginary study involving the emotionality of children from lone-parent and two-parent families. The independent variable is family type which has two levels – the lone-parent type and the two-parent type. The dependent variable is emotionality on a standard psychological measure – the higher the score on this test, the more emotional is the child. The data are listed in Table 14.8.

A key thing to note is that we have called the scores for the two-parent family condition X_1 and those for the lone-parent family condition X_2.

Step 1 Extend the data table by adding columns of squared scores and column totals as in Table 14.9.

The sample size for $X_1 = N_1 = 12$; the sample size for $X_2 = N_2 = 10$.

$\sum X_1$ = sum of scores for two-parent family sample

$\sum X_1^2$ = sum of squared scores for two-parent family sample

$\sum X_2$ = sum of scores for lone-parent family sample

$\sum X_2^2$ = sum of squared scores for lone-parent family sample

Step 2 Do each of the following calculations.

Calculation of *A*:

$$A = \overline{X}_1 - \overline{X}_2$$

$$= \frac{\sum X_1}{N_1} - \frac{\sum X_2}{N_2}$$

$$= \frac{161}{12} - \frac{95}{10}$$

$$= 13.417 - 9.500 = 3.917$$

Table 14.9	Table 14.8 extended to include steps in the calculation		

Two-parent family X_1	Square previous column X_1^2	Lone-parent family X_2	Square previous column X_2^2
12	144	6	36
18	324	9	81
14	196	4	16
10	100	13	169
19	361	14	196
8	64	9	81
15	225	8	64
11	121	12	144
10	100	11	121
13	169	9	81
15	225		
16	256		
$\sum X_1 = 161$	$\sum X_1^2 = 2285$	$\sum X_2 = 95$	$\sum X_2^2 = 989$

Calculation of B:

$$B = \sum X_1^2 - \frac{\left(\sum X_1\right)^2}{N_1}$$

$$= 2285 - \frac{161^2}{12} = 2285 - \frac{25\,921}{12}$$

$$= 2285 - 2160.0833$$

$$= 124.9167$$

Calculation of C:

$$C = \sum X_2^2 - \frac{\left(\sum X_2\right)^2}{N_2}$$

$$= 989 - \frac{95^2}{10} = 989 - \frac{9025}{10}$$

$$= 989 - 902.5$$

$$= 86.5$$

Calculation of D:

$$D = N_1 + N_2 - 2$$

$$= 12 + 10 - 2$$

$$= 20$$

Calculation of E:

$$E = \frac{1}{N_1} + \frac{1}{N_2} = \frac{1}{12} + \frac{1}{10}$$

$$= 0.0833 + 0.1000 = 0.1833$$

Calculation of F:

$$F = \left(\frac{B + C}{D}\right) \times E$$

$$= \left(\frac{124.9167 + 86.5000}{20}\right) \times 0.1833$$

$$= \left(\frac{211.4167}{20}\right) \times 0.1833$$

$$= 10.57083 \times 0.1833 = 1.938$$

Calculation of G:

$$G = \sqrt{F} = \sqrt{1.938} = 1.392$$

Calculation of t:

$$t = \frac{A}{G} = \frac{3.917}{1.392} = 2.81$$

Note that this is the same value as that produced by SPSS for equal variances assumed in Screenshot 14.5.

➡

Step 3

t is the *t*-score or the number of standard errors our sample data are away from the population mean of zero. We can use Significance Table 14.1 to check the statistical significance of our value of 2.81 by checking against the row for degrees of freedom (i.e. $N_1 + N_2 - 2 = 20$ degrees of freedom). This table tells us that our value of *t* is in the extreme 5% of the distribution because it is larger than 2.09; so we reject the null hypothesis that family structure is unrelated to emotionality. Our study showed that emotionality is significantly greater in the two-parent family structure as opposed to the lone-parent family structure.

Interpreting the results

Remember to check carefully the mean scores for both groups in order to know which of the two groups has the higher scores on the dependent variable. In our example, this shows that the greater emotionality was found in the children from the two-parent families. The significant value of the *t*-test means that we are reasonably safe to conclude that the two groups do differ in terms of their emotionality.

Reporting the results

The statistical analysis could be reported in the following style: 'It was found that emotionality was significantly higher ($t = 2.81$, $df = 20$, $p < .05$) in the two-parent families ($\overline{X} = 13.42$) than in the lone-parent families ($\overline{X} = 9.50$).'

The material in the final brackets simply reports the significance test used (the *t*-test), its value (2.81), the degrees of freedom ($df = 20$) and that the value of *t* is statistically significant ($p < .05$). Chapter 15 explains the approach to reporting the outcomes of statistical analyses in greater detail.

Alternatively, following the recommendations of the APA (2010) Publication Manual, we could write the results as follows: 'It was found that emotionality was significantly higher, $t(20) = 2.81$, $p < .05$, in the two-parent families ($M = 13.42$, $SD = 3.37$) than in the lone-parent families ($M = 9.50$, $SD = 3.10$).'

Box 14.1 explains how to avoid rounding errors.

Box 14.1 Focus on

Avoiding rounding errors

When doing calculations of any sort by hand, there is a risk of inaccuracy if you use too few numbers after the decimal point. These inaccuracies are known as rounding errors. So you risk getting a somewhat different answer from that calculated by the computer. Generally speaking, you need to work to at least three decimal places on your calculator though the actual calculated figures given by the calculator are best and easiest to use. Because of limitations of space and for clarity, the calculations reported in this book have been given to a small number of decimal places – usually three decimal places. When you report the results of the calculation, however, round the figure to no more than two decimal places. Remember to be consistent in the number of decimal places you present in your results.

14.4 Cautionary note

You should not use the *t*-test if your samples are markedly skewed, especially if they are skewed in opposite directions. Appendix A explains how to test for skewness. You might consider using the Mann–Whitney *U*-test in these circumstances (Explaining

Research examples

Unrelated/uncorrelated/independent sample *t*-test

Mutsvunguma and Gwandure (2011) compared the psychological well-being of two groups of South African bank employees – those who handled cash versus those who did not. The measures included a Burnout Inventory and a Life Satisfaction scale. Each of these dependent variables was analysed separately using independent samples *t*-tests. The findings indicated that the two groups differed significantly in terms of the measures of stress and burnout used.

Passmore and Rehman (2012) studied the way in which driving development could be enhanced using a coaching-based paradigm as opposed to an instruction-based approach. Participants were learning to drive large goods vehicles. Their methodology was basically a randomised controlled trial (experiment) though they did supplement this with semi-structured interviews and qualitative analysis, which are not reported here. Participants were randomly allocated to one of the two learning conditions so there were different participants in each group. The first group was taught by instructors who were trained in coaching skills which involved a mixture of coaching and instruction. The second group of participants was taught by driving instructors using exclusively an instruction-based approach much like a driving instructor at a driving school. The coaching approach sought to teach a wider variety of skills and abilities. For example, vehicle control ranges from the basic manual handling of the vehicle through driving in traffic to goals for life and skills for living. The data were analysed with independent samples *t*-tests using a variety of dependent variables. For example, the coaching group spent fewer hours in total in learning to drive ($M = 21.43$) whereas the control group spent 30.12 hours on average ($t = 4.014$, $p < .01$, one-tailed $p = .0005$).

Schulenberg and Yutrzenka (2001) researched whether a conventionally administered and a computerised version of the Beck Depression Inventory-II (BDI-II) produced equivalent results. Their concern was that the then aversion to computers might affect responses to a computerised version of the scale. Although overall their research was a little more complicated than this, one of their primary analyses was to compare the results of those who received the conventional version of the Beck scale first with those who received the computerised version of the Beck scale first using an independent samples *t*-test. The results showed that the two versions were equivalent as with fairly substantial overall samples of 180, the *t*-test was not significant at the 5% level.

Key points

- The *t*-test is commonly used in psychological research, so it is important that you have an idea of what it does. However, it is only a special case of the analysis of variance (Chapter 23) which is a much more flexible statistic. Given the analysis of variance's ability to handle any number of samples, you might prefer to use it instead of the *t*-test in most circumstances. To complicate matters, some use the *t*-test in the analysis of variance.

- The *t*-test assumes that the variances of the two samples are similar so that they can be combined to yield an overall estimate. However, if the variances of the two samples are significantly different from each other, you should not use this version of the *t*-test. The way to see if two variances are dissimilar is to use the variance ratio test described in Chapter 22.

→

● If you wish to use the *t*-test but find that you fall foul of this *F*-ratio requirement, there is a version of the *t*-test which does not assume equal variances. The best way of doing such *t*-tests is to use a computer package which applies both tests to the same data. Unfortunately, the calculation for the degrees of freedom is a little complex (you can have decimals involved in the values) and it goes a little beyond reasonable hand calculations. The calculation details are provided in Blalock (1972).

COMPUTER ANALYSIS

Unrelated/uncorrelated/independent *t*-test using SPSS

Data
- In 'Data View' of the 'Data Editor', the data are entered as two columns – 1) the scores on the dependent variable and 2) a code number to indicate the group that the score comes from, e.g. code 1 for Group 1, code 2 for Group 2 (Screenshot 14.1).
- Name each variable in 'Variable View' of the 'Data Editor'.

Analysis
- Select 'Analyze', 'Compare Means' and 'Independent Samples T Test...' (Screenshot 14.2).

2
- Select the dependent variable and move to the box 'Test Variable(s):' (Screenshot 14.3).
- Select the variable containing the group codes and move it into the box 'Grouping Variable:'.

3
- Select 'Define Groups' to identify the two groups for the *t*-test (Screenshot 14.4).
- Enter 1 to identify scores from the first group, enter 2 to define scores from the second group.

4
- Select 'Continue' and 'OK'. See Screenshot 14.5 for the important output.

Output
- The 'Group Statistics' table gives means, standard deviations and standard errors.

2
- In 'Independent Samples Test' use the first row (Equal variances assumed) unless Levene's Test is significant then use the second row values of *t* etc.

| FIGURE 14.2 | SPSS steps for the unrelated *t*-test |

Interpreting and reporting the output

- The means tell you which group has the highest scores. Normally the highest scores mean a higher amount of the variable. In this example, emotionality was found to be higher for the children of two-parent families. The significance level should be noted as this tells you whether the difference is likely to be the product of chance.

- Reporting the results can following this pattern: 'It was found that emotionality was significantly higher, $t(20) = 2.81, df = 20, p < .05, 95\%\ CI\ [-6.82, -1.01]$, in the two-parent families ($M = 13.42, SD = 3.37$) than in the lone-parent families ($M = 9.50, SD = 3.10$).' CI stands for Confidence Interval and is discussed in Chapter 16.

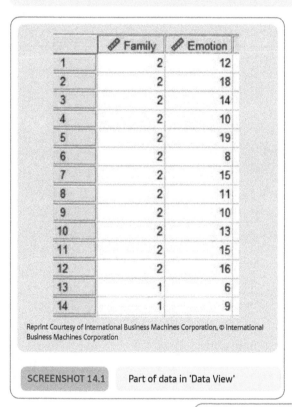

Reprint Courtesy of International Business Machines Corporation, © International Business Machines Corporation

SCREENSHOT 14.1 Part of data in 'Data View'

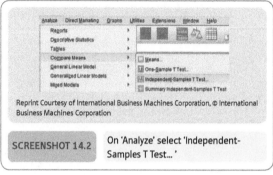

Reprint Courtesy of International Business Machines Corporation, © International Business Machines Corporation

SCREENSHOT 14.2 On 'Analyze' select 'Independent-Samples T Test...'

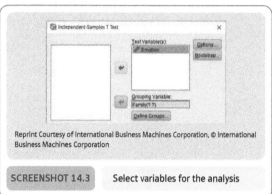

Reprint Courtesy of International Business Machines Corporation, © International Business Machines Corporation

SCREENSHOT 14.3 Select variables for the analysis

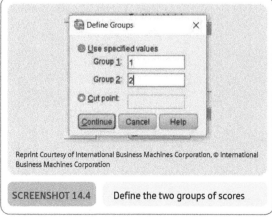

Reprint Courtesy of International Business Machines Corporation, © International Business Machines Corporation

SCREENSHOT 14.4 Define the two groups of scores

Group Statistics

	Family	N	Mean	Std. Deviation	Std. Error Mean
Emotion	1	10	9.50	3.100	.980
	2	12	13.42	3.370	.973

Independent Samples Test

		Levene's Test for Equality of Variances		t-test for Equality of Means					95% Confidence Interval of the Difference	
		F	Sig.	t	df	Sig. (2-tailed)	Mean Difference	Std. Error Difference	Lower	Upper
Emotion	Equal variances assumed	.212	.650	-2.813	20	.011	-3.917	1.392	-6.821	-1.013
	Equal variances not assumed			-2.836	19.768	.010	-3.917	1.381	-6.800	-1.034

SCREENSHOT 14.5   Main output

CHAPTER 15

What you need to write about your statistical analysis

Overview

- A glance at reports in psychology journals shows that the reporting of outcomes of statistical analyses is brief and succinct.

- Things can look complicated because researchers often report (very similar) multiple statistical analyses in the same paper.

- The American Psychological Association recommends reporting the abbreviated name of the statistic you are using, the value of this test statistic, the degrees of freedom or the sample size as appropriate, the significance level, whether a one-tailed test of significance is used, confidence intervals, effect size and statistical power if possible. Many psychology journals including those of the British Psychological Society emulate this style.

- These are recommendations for professional publications but are appropriate for student reports at nearly every stage.

Preparation

You need to know about testing significance, from Chapter 11 onwards.

15.1   Introduction

A glance at any psychology journal shows that precious little space is devoted to reporting tests of significance and their outcomes, also that there are standard ways of reporting statistical analyses. These make it easier for even novice researchers to report their statistical findings in an acceptable fashion. Ways of reporting statistics have changed somewhat over the years and not all research journals use the same style but many do. The major influence on writing up research in psychology is the *Publication Manual of the American Psychological Association* (APA, 2010). Researchers wishing to publish their work in an APA journal, a British Psychological Society (BPS) journal, and in many other places need to conform to its style recommendations. As a student, you should check what is required by your department but it is likely to be APA style or a variant of it.

The current *Publication Manual* stresses the importance of not merely reporting information about the test of significance used but also (a) confidence intervals and (b) effect sizes. These are discussed in detail in Chapters 16 and 17, respectively. They are not particularly difficult ideas to understand and are fairly easily incorporated into your reports. Confidence intervals are given in most of the output of SPSS. Things are a little less satisfactory with effect sizes since SPSS does not provide too many of these though they are generally easily calculated using simple formulae where they cannot be obtained from SPSS.

What is a confidence interval? Briefly, in statistical significance testing the most probable value of the population parameter is given as a single figure based on the information we have from our sample or samples. So if the mean of the sample is 2.51 then we estimate the mean of the population as being 2.51, for example. This is known as a point estimate as it consists of a single value. However, this is only the best estimate and, as such, does not indicate anything about the probable range within which the population mean is likely to fall. We all know that samples usually vary somewhat from the population from which they came. A confidence interval (CI) is a range of scores within which a population parameter (such as the population mean) plausibly could fall. So a confidence interval might be 1.21 to 3.81 in this case. Confidence intervals are usually expressed as a percentage such as the 95% confidence interval. What this means is that the population parameter is likely to be within the stipulated confidence interval 95% of the time. It is possible to have confidence intervals for many of the statistics given in this book and SPSS usually calculates them for you routinely. More on confidence intervals and how they are calculated can be found in Chapter 16.

What is effect size? An effect size is just that – the size of the correlation or difference found in your study. So, in an experiment, the effect size would be the difference between the mean score in the experimental condition and the mean score in the control condition. In another study, it might be the size of the correlation between two variables. When analysing data, among the most important things to look at is the size of the effect. It would seem very obvious to include the effect size in your reports but it can be overlooked if one is too focused on statistical significance testing. So means and standard deviations for, say, the experimental and control groups need to be in the report as should be the size of the correlation coefficients that you have calculated. Without this, the reader will struggle to appreciate the importance of your findings. There is nothing difficult about effect sizes except that sometimes they are reported in standardised form to allow easy comparison between studies. Actually the correlation coefficient is a good measure of effect size in itself but others include Cohen's *d* and many more. The calculation of effect size is discussed in Chapter 17.

These are the basics. This chapter concentrates on reporting the fundamental features of your statistical analysis and mainly concentrates on statistical significance. Confidence intervals and effect size can be added in once you have studied Chapters 16 and 17.

15.2 Reporting statistical significance

At a minimum, the following should be mentioned when reporting statistical significance:

- The size of the effect.

- The statistical distribution used (F, chi-square, r, z, t, etc.).

- The degrees of freedom (df). Alternatively, for some statistical techniques you may report the sample size (N).

- The value of the calculation (e.g. the value of your z-score or your chi-square).

- The probability or significance level. In older journal articles you will find the following used: 'not significant', 'not sig.' or 'ns'. However, statistical calculations are now done almost exclusively on computers and it is most usual now to give the exact probabilities for your significance test. These are provided routinely by SPSS.

- If you have a one-tailed hypothesis then this should be also mentioned. Otherwise a two-tailed hypothesis will be assumed by the reader.

As your statistical skills develop, you might wish to add confidence intervals and standardised measures of effect size.

15.3 Shortened forms

In research reports, comments such as the following are to be found:

- The hypothesis that drunks slur their words was supported ($t = 2.88$, degrees of freedom $= 97$, $p < .01$).

- The null hypothesis that drunks do not slur their words more than sober people was rejected ($t = 2.88$, $df = 97$, $p = .01$).

- The hypothesis that drunks slur their words was accepted, $t(97) = 2.88$, $p = < .003$, 1-tail.

Each of these says more or less the same thing. The symbol t indicates that the t-test was used. The symbol $<$ indicates that your probability level is smaller than the given value. That is, the test is statistically significant at better than the reported level of .01. Sometimes, the degrees of freedom (df) are put in brackets after the symbol for the statistical test used, as in $t(97) = 2.88$. All of the above examples are statistically significant at the .0 or 5% level and so the null hypothesis is rejected.

The following are examples of what might be written if the hypothesis was not supported by your data:

- The hypothesis that drunks slur their words was rejected ($t = 0.56$, degrees of freedom $= 97$, $p > 0.05$).

- Drunks and sober people did not differ in their average rates of slurring their speech ($t = 0.56$, $df = 97$, not significant).

- The hypothesis that drunks slur their words was rejected, $t(97) = 0.13$, $p = .45$, ns, 1-tail.

All of these mean much the same. The symbol $>$ means that your probability is greater than the listed value. Notice that each of these examples in some way states that the finding is not significant ($p > 0.05$, *ns*, and not significant all mean the same).

The significance level determines whether we accept or reject the statistical null hypothesis. The significance level is usually set at .05 or 5% but it is not unusual to see the .01 or 1% levels used. If the probability is equal or less than this then we reject the null hypothesis in favour of the alternative hypothesis. Computers do far more complex calculations than are practicable by hand. In particular, they work out the exact probability for your statistical test. So instead of writing that a difference is significant at the 5% level we can give the exact significance, such as .037. Our significance level for rejecting the null hypothesis still remains at 5%. The current American Psychological Association (APA) style is to report the exact significance. One possible objection to this is that it gives a false sense of precision to the statistical findings. Statistical significance can become a holy grail in statistics, supporting the view 'the smaller the probability the better'. We have seen the variability that is possible in randomly selected data so we should be very cautious about assuming that a significance level of .003 is really better in some sense than a significance level of .006. On the other hand, the 5% is a somewhat arbitrary but traditional criterion questioned by some. It has been suggested that by giving the precise significance it is absolutely clear whether the significance level was, say, .049 or .051. Pedantically, .049 would be statistically significant but .051 would not be, though the difference is miniscule.

Remember, statistical significance is important but the size of the effect is arguably more so. A significant result with a strong trend is the ideal which is not obtained simply by exploring the minutiae of probability. If you are using exact probabilities, then make it clear what significance level you are using to reject the null hypothesis. This significance level is known as alpha so you could write 'Throughout the analysis an alpha level of .05 was used for all statistical tests.' The reader may have assumed this but it is best to be absolutely clear. It would not be common but the alpha criterion could be varied.

15.4   APA (American Psychological Association) style

The *Publication Manual of the American Psychological Association* sets out the ways in which manuscripts should be typed to be considered for publication in the Association's journals. The latest version is the sixth edition and was published in 2010. It is claimed that about 1000 journals worldwide use APA style. The recommendations for reporting statistics seem to be relatively straightforward although there are a lot of them. The main ones are:

● Generally, report numbers to no more than two decimal places.

● Probability or significance values are the exception to this. These may be reported to three decimal places. APA style asks for exact probabilities to be given down to the .001 level of significance. So if your significance level starts with .000 (e.g. 0003) then report this as $p < .001$. (Giving significance levels such as .000 is confusing because it is not the same as zero.)

● Leading zeroes (i.e. zeroes before the decimal point) should not be used for numbers which cannot be more than 1.00 such as correlation coefficients. For example, correlations should not be reported with a leading zero such as 0.671 but as .671.

- It is preferable to report the exact significance level to three decimal places as given by statistics software such as SPSS. For example, it is more informative to report $p = .343$ than $p > .05$ or p ns.

- Means (M) and standard deviations (SD) when reported within sentences should be appropriately abbreviated and reported within round brackets. Details of the results of the inferential test are placed after a comma and are not bracketed. Round bracketing is reserved for the degrees of freedom. The appropriate letter of the statistical test is given first followed by the degrees of freedom in brackets, an $=$ sign, the value of the statistical test to two decimal places, a comma, p, an $=$ sign and the probability level to three decimal places or a $<$ sign and .001.

- The size of the confidence interval should be given followed in square brackets by the size of the lower confidence limit, a comma, and the value of the upper confidence limit. Both values should be placed within square brackets. For example, we could write 'Post-test depression was lower in the treated ($M = 3.52, SD = 1.09, 95\%$ CI [3.42, 3.62]) than in the untreated group ($M = 5.39, SD = 2.13, 95\%$ CI [5.20, 5.68]).' Confidence intervals are discussed further in Chapter 16. Their width indicates the uncertainty that you have about the statistic.

- (Standardised) effect sizes should be reported if these are readily available and you are familiar with them. They are discussed further in Chapter 17. However, always give the size of the effect as it appears in your data in addition. This may be as simple as the difference between the means of the experimental and control conditions.

Of course, it is difficult to absorb this list and apply it, so we would suggest that you use a published journal article as a model or guide to your use of the style. Any paper published by the APA or the BPS in their journals may be suitable especially one on a similar topic to your research. Here are two examples taken from APA journals:

- 'Participants indicated that selfless behaviors are driven more by the internal force, the moral conscience ($M = 4.57, SD = 1.41$), $t(185) = 5.47, p < .001$.' (Critcher & Dunning, 2013, p. 34)

- 'Asian Americans who heard a positive stereotype about their group evaluated their partner more negatively ($M = 3.57, SD = 1.27$) than Asian Americans who did not hear a positive stereotype ($M = 2.69, SD = 0.60$), $t(39) = 2.70, p = .01, d = 0.89$.' (Siy & Cheryan, 2013, p. 90)

Both report the results of a t-test. The main difference is that the second example includes a measure of the effect size 'd' which is Cohen's d. Effect size is discussed further in Chapter 17. Missing from both of these examples are confidence intervals.

You should make sure that your report gives all of the necessary means and standard deviations to understand the extent of trends (differences, etc.) in your data. So give, for example, the means and standard deviations for the experimental and control groups on the dependent variable. Just reporting significance tests is not enough as they tell the reader nothing about the size of the effects. This is basic information but it can be overlooked when faced with the complexities of the statistical analysis and computer output. As your statistical knowledge improves, then try to include standardised effect sizes such as Cohen's d and r (Chapters 17 and 36).

Tables are a good solution if you have a lot of very similar statistical findings to report. If the statistical information is in a table then you do not unnecessarily repeat this information in the text of the results section.

The following is a quick summary of how you would report some of the basic statistical analyses covered in this book using APA style:

- *Percentages* Give percentages in brackets, use the symbol %, and avoid decimal places: 'Over half of the sample (53%) were unemployed at the beginning of the study.'

- *Means and standard deviations* These would generally be reported together using brackets wherever possible as this tends to add clarity: 'The mean number of years since qualifying for the university graduates was 6.37 years ($SD = 1.23$)' or 'The university graduates had been qualified for relatively few years ($M = 6.37, SD = 1.23$).'

- *Correlations* These are reported as follows with the degrees of freedom put in brackets after the value of r: 'Mathematical ability and musical ability were strongly negatively correlated, $r(8) = -.90, p < .001$.'

- *t-tests* For these t is followed by the degrees of freedom in brackets, followed by the value of the t statistic, followed by the significance level: 'The mean emotionality score for the two-parent families ($M = 13.42, SD = 3.37$) was higher than for the lone-parent families ($M = 9.50, SD = 3.37$). The difference was statistically significant, $t(20) = 2.81, p = .01$.'

- *Chi-square* This is different because in the APA system both the degrees of freedom and the sample size are given in brackets. The value of chi-square is then given (13.52) followed by the probability level (.001). Degrees of freedom do not indicate sample size in chi-square. So you could write: 'Preference for the three different types of TV programme differed significantly according to gender, $\chi^2(2, N = 119) = 13.52, p = .001$. As can be seen from the contingency table, males tended to prefer soap operas more than females do, prefer crime drama less than females, and were more likely to report a preference for neither.' Of course, the analysis is likely to test specific trends in the data (as explained in Chapter 18).

- *ANOVA* These use very much the same style as for the t-test with the exception that two values of the degrees of freedom need to be given. These are given in order starting with the between treatment degrees of freedom followed by the within-group (error/residual) degrees of freedom: 'The main effects for both Alcohol and Sleep Deprivation were significant. They were respectively, $F(1, 12) = 31.68, p < .001$, $F(2, 12) = 130.11, p < .001$. However, the interaction of Alcohol and Sleep Deprivation was not significant, $F(2, 12) = 2.71, p = .11$.' You would then probably describe the outcome of a multiple comparisons test (Chapter 26) for the Sleep Deprivation condition as it has more than two levels.

- *Regression* The best way to give the results of a regression analysis is to provide a table. This can be based on the SPSS Coefficients table in the output for multiple regression. Different types of multiple regression vary somewhat in the form of this table. The important part of Screenshot 34.5 could be given as in Table 15.1. This is a small table for a regression but still contains a lot of numbers if they were to be given in the text.

Table 15.1	Regression weights for predictors of academic achievement						
	Unstandardised ß	Standard error	Standardised beta	t	Sig.	95% confidence interval	
Ability	.83	.09	.65	9.56	.0001	.66	1.01
Motivation	.17	.07	.16	2.42	.02	.03	.30

Research examples

Reporting significance succinctly

In the first example, a measure of effect size (d) is given in addition to other basic information (see Chapter 17).

Mitsumatsu (2013) reported part of the statistical analysis of his study concerning the perception of causality as follows: 'In the dual-cause condition, the mean screen locations were 2.0 (1.1) cm right and 0.3 (0.9) cm above when rating the finger; when rating the object, touch locations were 2.0 (0.7) cm right and 0.5 (0.7) cm above. The mean time between space bar release and screen touch was 471 ms ($SD = 95$) in the single-cause condition and 467 ms ($SD = 73$) and 454 ms ($SD = 108$) in blocks of rating the finger and object in the dual-cause conditions, respectively. t-tests showed that no mean finger touch time was significantly different from the time when the effect object started moving, $t(9) = 0.9, p > .3, d = 0.30, t(9) = 1.3, p > .2, d = 0.43, t(9) = 1.3, p > .2, d = 0.42$, respectively. The mean finger touch times did not differ significantly by condition, $F(2, 18) = 0.45, p > .6, d = 0.05$.' (p. 104).

Rowe (2012) wrote of her statistical analysis: 'Child PPVT [Peabody Picture Vocabulary Test] scores varied widely at each age. At child age 30 months, the mean normed score was 96.2 ($SD = 15.2$), compared to 106.2 ($SD = 17.4$) at 42 months and 110.4 ($SD = 18.2$) at 54 months. PPVT scores at each age were positively related to one another ($r_s = .65 - .84, p < .001$). At child ages 30 and 54 months, 2 children did not complete the PPVT and the sample size is 48 for each of those ages. At child age 42 months, all 50 children completed the PPVT.' (p. 1767).

Key points

- Remember that the important pieces of information to report are:
  - the symbol for the statistic (t, T, r, etc.)
  - the value of the statistic for your analysis – two decimal places are enough
  - an indication of the degrees of freedom or the sample size involved ($df = \ldots, N = \ldots$)
  - the probability or significance level
  - whether a one-tailed test was used.

- Sometimes you will see symbols for statistical techniques that you have never heard of. Do not panic since it is usually possible to work out the sense of what is going on. Certainly if you have details of the sort described in this chapter, you know that a test of significance is involved.

- Using the approaches described in this chapter creates a good impression and ensures that you include pertinent information. However, standardise on one of the variants in your report. Eventually, when you submit papers to a journal for consideration, you should check out that journal's method of reporting significance.

- Some statistical tests are regarded as being directionless. That is, their use always implies a two-tailed test. This is true of chi-square and the analysis of variance. These tests can only be one-tailed if the degrees of freedom equal one. Otherwise, the test is two-tailed. Even when the degrees of freedom equal one, only use a one-tailed test if you are satisfied that you have reached the basic requirements of one-tailed testing (see Chapter 20).

CHAPTER 16

Confidence intervals

Overview

- Confidence intervals are an alternative way of conceptualising inferential statistics that stresses the uncertainty of statistical data. Increasingly, they are regarded as essential by some authorities.

- The confidence interval is usually calculated as the 95% confidence interval though using the 99% confidence interval is not uncommon.

- A confidence interval is essentially a range (of means, differences between means, correlations, etc.) within which the population value (based on our sample data) will lie 95% of the time. That is, instead of estimating the population value as a single point value (such as the population mean equals 6.0), the confidence interval approach estimates that the population mean will lie between 4.5 and 7.5 based on the characteristics of the sample, for example.

- The calculation of the confidence interval involves the calculation of the standard error. Since for any given sample size, tables of the t-distribution are available which indicate how many standard errors embrace the middle 95% of values, the 95% confidence interval is easily found. SPSS routinely provides confidence intervals.

Preparation

Read the previous discussions of confidence intervals (Chapter 9). Revise the concepts of sampling distributions and standard error (Chapters 10 and 12, respectively).

16.1 Introduction

Confidence intervals have been briefly introduced in earlier chapters. Although confidence intervals have long been a part of psychological statistics, they took a back seat but now their greater use has been strongly advocated, most notably in the publication manual of the American Psychological Association (APA, 2010). More radically, it has been proposed that confidence intervals should replace null hypothesis statistical significance testing using point estimates. Point estimates are ones which give a single figure rather than the likely range. Whatever the merits of this argument, both confidence intervals and significance testing based on point estimates are informative and likely to coexist in the foreseeable future. This chapter provides some information on the computation of confidence intervals for a variety of statistics discussed at various points in this book together with advice on how to report significance levels when using them. Despite the fact that any measure based on a sample has a confidence interval in theory, methods of calculating confidence intervals for some statistical procedures are not readily available on SPSS. However, the availability of bootstrapping methods (Box 21.1) makes such calculations much easier because with bootstrapping there is no need to develop statistical theory on which to base the confidence intervals for a particular statistic. Instead, purely empirical methods can be used to calculate confidence intervals.

Confidence intervals concern the estimates of population characteristics (parameters) based on a sample or samples taken from that population. Of course, normally in research the population values are known and have to be estimated. The characteristics of samples tend to vary somewhat from the characteristics of the population from which they came – and from each other (Chapter 10). Consequently, estimates of the characteristics of a population based on a sample are best estimates and not precise. In previous chapters, we have used point estimates of population parameters based on sample statistics. To underline what we have already said, a point estimate is merely a single figure estimate as opposed to a range. Thus if the mean of a sample is 5.3 then the point estimate of the mean of the population from which the sample came is 5.3. Point estimates being best guesses, it rarely is exact despite looking like it must be.

The alternative to point estimates, the confidence interval approach, acknowledges the approximate nature of the estimates more clearly. Confidence intervals give the range of values likely to include the population value. This range of likely values is called the confidence interval since it reflects the range of values likely to include the true population mean (if we only knew this) 95% of times if you 100 separate samples. Instead of saying that our estimate of the population mean is 5.3, we say that the population mean is likely to be in the range 4.0–6.6. By expressing our inference or estimate in this way, we reinforce the notion of uncertainty as to the precise value. The size of the confidence interval depends on the variability of scores. The more variable the scores in a sample, the larger the confidence interval has to be for any level of confidence.

The precise definition of confidence intervals actually makes explaining it a little clumsy. Most psychologists tend to regard it as the range of scores which you can be 95% certain to contain the population mean. This is not quite correct but relatively easy to understand. The actual definition makes the explanation a little more difficult. The 95% confidence interval is based on repeatedly taking samples of a particular size from the population. Perhaps we take 100 samples and work out the mean of each one. If we exclude the extreme 5% of these means, the highest and lowest means of the remaining 95% of samples is the 95% confidence interval. Being a teeny bit imprecise or absolute (middle) pedantically accurate does not actually make much, if any, difference.

Actually we do not need to draw a lot of samples to calculate the confidence interval. We can make use of things we learned about earlier. Chapter 10 explained how we take the characteristics of a sample to infer the most likely characteristics of the population from which that sample was taken. Furthermore, we can even calculate the distributions of samples taken from that inferred population – using just one sample. Remember that the standard error is the usual index of the amount of variability in sample means drawn at random from a population. Standard error is simply the standard deviation of sample means. The calculation of standard error is a crucial phase in estimating confidence intervals for all parametric tests.

Normal distribution theory (Chapter 6) tells us that for *large* samples, 95% of sample means lie within plus or minus 1.96 standard errors from the population mean. Thus if the standard error for samples has been calculated as 2.6, then 95% of sample means lie between −5.096 and +5.096 (1.96 × 2.6 = 5.096) of the mean of our sample (i.e. the estimate of the population mean). If the sample mean is 10.00 then the confidence interval is 10.00 ± 5.096. That is, the confidence interval is between 4.904 and 15.096. Since this covers 95% of the most likely sample means, it is known as the 95% confidence interval. In other words, the 95% confidence interval is 4.90 to 15.10. However, this is approximate where the sample size is small.

Confidence intervals can be set at other levels such as 99%. The more stringent 99% confidence interval involves multiplying the standard error by 2.576 = 2.576 × 2.6 = 6.698. The resulting 99% confidence interval would be 10.00 (the sample mean) ± 6.698, or 3.30 to 16.70. So the more confident we want to be, the larger the confidence interval is. We can use tables of the z-distribution to work out other confidence intervals, but the 95% and 99% are conventional.

However, with small samples the z-distribution does not work perfectly. It is more usual to use the distribution of t (which is identical to that of z for large samples). With small samples, the value of t corresponding to our chosen confidence interval would be obtained from Table 16.1. This is distributed by the degrees of freedom. Thus if the degrees of

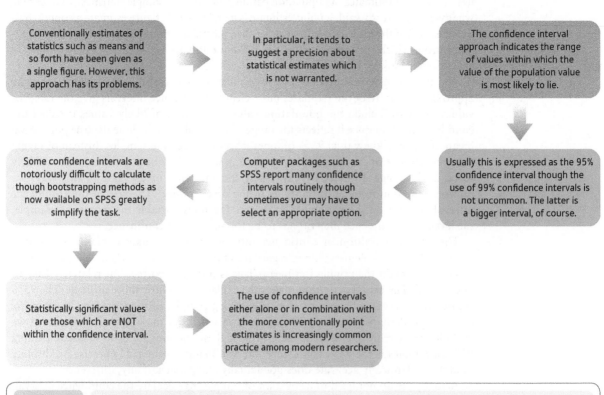

Conventionally estimates of statistics such as means and so forth have been given as a single figure. However, this approach has its problems.

In particular, it tends to suggest a precision about statistical estimates which is not warranted.

The confidence interval approach indicates the range of values within which the value of the population value is most likely to lie.

Usually this is expressed as the 95% confidence interval though the use of 99% confidence intervals is not uncommon. The latter is a bigger interval, of course.

Computer packages such as SPSS report many confidence intervals routinely though sometimes you may have to select an appropriate option.

Some confidence intervals are notoriously difficult to calculate though bootstrapping methods as now available on SPSS greatly simplify the task.

Statistically significant values are those which are NOT within the confidence interval.

The use of confidence intervals either alone or in combination with the more conventionally point estimates is increasingly common practice among modern researchers.

FIGURE 16.1   Conceptual steps for understanding confidence intervals

Table 16.1	Table of *t*-values for 95% and 99% confidence intervals	
Degrees of freedom	*t* for 95% confidence	*t* for 99% confidence
1	12.71	63.66
2	4.30	9.93
3	3.18	5.84
4	2.78	4.60
5	2.57	4.03
6	2.45	3.71
7	2.37	3.50
8	2.31	3.36
9	2.26	3.25
10	2.23	3.17
11	2.20	3.11
12	2.18	3.06
13	2.16	3.01
14	2.15	2.98
15	2.13	2.95
16	2.12	2.92
17	2.11	2.90
18	2.10	2.88
19	2.09	2.86
20	2.09	2.85
25	2.06	2.79
30	2.04	2.75
35	2.03	2.72
40	2.02	2.70
45	2.01	2.69
50	2.01	2.68
60	2.00	2.66
70	1.99	2.65
80	1.99	2.64
90	1.99	2.63
100	1.98	2.63
∞	1.96	2.58

Note: If the required number of degrees of freedom is missing, take the nearest lower number.

freedom for the sample were 25, then the value of *t* for 95% confidence is 2.06 (from Table 16.1). So the confidence interval would be 2.06 × 2.6 on either side of the estimated population mean of 10.00. That is, the 95% confidence interval would be 4.64 to 15.36. The degrees of freedom will vary according to the statistical estimate in question.

Sometimes the concept of confidence limits is used. Confidence limits are merely the extreme values of the confidence interval. In the above example, the 95% confidence limits are 4.64 and 15.36.

While this introduction explains confidence intervals in principle, their calculation varies from this pattern for some statistics. Figure 16.1 gives the key steps to consider in understanding confidence intervals.

16.2 Relationship between significance and confidence intervals

At first sight, statistical significance and confidence intervals appear dissimilar concepts. This is incorrect since they are both based on much the same inferential process. Remember that in significance testing we usually test the null hypothesis of no relationship between two variables. This usually boils down to a zero (or near-zero) correlation or to a difference of zero (or near-zero) between sample means. If the confidence interval does not contain this zero value then the obtained sample mean is statistically significant at 100% minus the confidence level. So if the 95% confidence interval is 2.30 to 8.16 but the null hypothesis would predict the population value of the statistic to be 0.00, then the null hypothesis is rejected at the 5% level of significance since it does not contain zero. In other words, confidence intervals contain enough information to judge statistical significance. However, statistical significance alone does not contain enough information to calculate confidence intervals.

Explaining statistics 16.1 to 16.5 illustrate the calculation of various confidence intervals.

Explaining statistics 16.1

How confidence intervals for a population mean based on a single sample work

Step 1 Calculate the standard error of the scores in the sample. The stages in doing this are given in Explaining statistics 12.1. You will also need to calculate the mean of the sample and the degrees of freedom (i.e. sample size −1).

Step 2 For the data in Table 12.3, the standard error is 0.58, the estimated population mean (the sample mean) is 5.00, and the degrees of freedom are 6 − 1 = 5 degrees of freedom.

Step 3 Decide what confidence level you require. We will use the 95% level. This is the minimum value of confidence in general use. If it was especially important that your confidence interval included the true population mean than you could use the 99% level or even the 99.9% level.

Step 4 Use Table 16.1 to find the value of t corresponding to the 95% confidence level. You need the row for the appropriate number of degrees of freedom (i.e. $N − 1 = 5$). This value of t is 2.57. Table 16.1 is merely a version of the table of the t-distribution that appears elsewhere in the book. It is included as it is initially less confusing to be able to look up the values directly.

Step 5 Calculate the confidence interval. It is the sample mean $\pm$ ($t \times$ the standard error). Therefore, the 95% confidence interval for the population mean is 5.00 $\pm$ (2.57 × 0.58). This gives us a 95% confidence interval of 3.51 to 6.49.

Reporting the results

The results of this analysis may be written up as follows: 'The 95% confidence interval for the population mean was 3.51 to 6.49. As this interval does not include 0.00 then the null hypothesis that the sample comes from a population with a

---

How confidence intervals for the unrelated *t*-test work

Step 1   As most of the major steps in calculating the confidence interval involve steps in the calculation of the unrelated *t*-test, use Explaining statistics 14.1 to calculate the necessary values.

Step 2   Make a note of the difference between the two sample means, the degrees of freedom ($N_1 + N_2 - 2$), and the standard error of the difference between two sample means. For the example in Explaining statistics 14.1 (Table 14.9), the difference between the sample means = 3.917, the degrees of freedom = 20 and the standard error = 1.392.

Step 3   Decide what level of confidence you require. This time we will use the 99% level of confidence.

Step 4   From Table 16.1, the *t*-value for 99% confidence with 20 degrees of freedom = 2.85.

Step 5   The confidence interval is obtained by taking the difference between the two sample means $\pm$ (*t* $\times$ the standard error). Thus the 99% confidence interval for the population of differences between sample means = 3.917 $\pm$ (2.85 $\times$ 1.392). Therefore the 99% confidence interval is 3.917 $\pm$ 3.97, which gives a 99% confidence interval of -0.05 to 7.89.

Reporting the results

The results of this analysis can be written up as follows: 'The 99% confidence interval for the difference in emotionality scores in two-parent and lone-parent families is -0.05 to 7.89. Since the null hypothesis holds that this difference is 0.00 then we can accept the null hypothesis at the 1% level of significance since the confidence interval includes the value 0.00. The hypothesis that emotionality is different in two-parent and lone-parent families is not supported at the 1% level of significance.'

How confidence intervals for the related *t*-test work

Step 1   Follow the calculation of the related *t*-test as described in Explaining statistics 13.1. We will use these data to obtain the 95% confidence interval for the difference between the means.

Step 2   Make a note of the difference between the sample means, the degrees of freedom and the standard error for your data. Explaining statistics 13.1 yields a value of the difference between the sample means of -1.50, a standard error of the difference of 0.756 with 7 degrees of freedom.

Step 3   Decide what level of confidence you require. This time we are using the 95% level of confidence.

Step 4   From Table 16.1, the *t*-value for 95% confidence with 7 degrees of freedom = 2.37.

Step 5 The confidence interval is obtained by taking the difference between the two sample means $\pm$ the (t-value $\times$ the standard error); i.e:

$$-1.50 \pm (2.37 \times 0.756) = -1.50 \pm 1.79$$

$$= -3.29 \text{ to } 0.29$$

Step 6 Thus the 95% confidence interval for the population of differences between sample means is -1.94 to 1.64.

Reporting the results

The results of this analysis can be written up as follows: 'The 95% confidence interval for the difference in eye contact at six months and nine months was -3.29 to 0.29. According to the null hypothesis, this difference should be 0.00. Consequently, as this value is included in the 95% confidence interval then the null hypothesis is supported and the alternative hypothesis that eye contact is related to age is rejected.'

Explaining statistics 16.4

How confidence intervals for the Pearson correlation coefficient work

Step 1 The calculation of the Pearson correlation coefficient is described in Explaining statistics 8.1. Work through these steps for your data or compute the value of r using a computer.

Step 2 Make a note of the value of the correlation coefficient and the sample size. For the data in Table 8.1, the value of the correlation coefficient is $-.90$ and the sample size is 10. We do not require the degrees of freedom for calculating the confidence interval for a Pearson correlation coefficient.

Step 3 To calculate the confidence interval, it is necessary to convert the correlation coefficient to its z_r using Table 36.5. Note that z_r is the Fisher normalised correlation coefficient (see Chapter 36). This table gives a value of z_r for a correlation of $-.90$ as -1.472. The negative sign is added because the correlation is negative.

Step 4 The standard deviation of z_r is obtained using the formula:

$$\text{standard deviation of } z_r = \frac{1}{\sqrt{N-3}}$$

Given that in our example the sample size N is 10, the standard deviation according to this formula is:

$$\text{standard deviation of } z_r = \frac{1}{\sqrt{10-3}} = \frac{1}{\sqrt{7}} = \frac{1}{2.646} = 0.378$$

This standard deviation is distributed as for z so that the 95% confidence interval is $1.96 \times$ the standard deviation. Thus the 95% confidence interval of z_r is the value of z_r for the correlation coefficient $\pm 1.96 \times 0.378$. That is, in our example, -1.472 ± 0.741. Therefore the 95% confidence interval for z_r is -0.731 to -2.213.

Step 5   The above is the confidence interval for z_r rather than for the original correlation coefficient. We can use Table 36.5 to convert this z_r back to the range of correlation coefficients. Thus the 95% confidence interval for the correlation coefficient is $-.62$ to $-.97$.

Interpreting the results

You will notice that this confidence interval is not symmetrical around the sample correlation of $-.90$. The correlation coefficient is not a linear variable so it cannot be added and divided as if it were. Hence the transformation to z_r which has linear characteristics.

Reporting the results

The results of this analysis can be written up as follows: 'The 95% confidence interval for the Pearson correlation between musical and mathematical ability was $-.62$ to $-.97$. The null hypothesis suggests that this relationship will be .00. Since the value under the null hypothesis was not included in the confidence interval, the null hypothesis of no relationship between musical and mathematical ability was rejected in favour of the alternative hypothesis that there is a negative correlation between mathematical and musical ability.'

16.3 | Regression

There are several confidence intervals for even a simple regression analysis since regression involves several estimates of population parameters – the slope of the regression line, the cut-point for the vertical axis and the predicted score from scores on the X variable.

Explaining statistics 16.5

How confidence intervals for a predicted score work

Step 1   Carry out the simple regression analysis according to Explaining statistics 9.1. This will give the slope and the intercept (cut-point) of the regression line. These can be used to calculate the most likely value of variable Y from a particular value of variable X. For a value of $X = 8$, the best prediction of Y is 3.37 for the data in Table 9.2.

Step 2   Calculate the Pearson correlation between variable X and variable Y in Table 9.2 using Explaining statistics 8.1. This gives r as $-.90$.

Step 3   Calculate the standard deviation of the Y variable scores using Explaining statistics 6.1. The standard deviation of the Y scores is 1.75.

Step 4   Using the information calculated in the previous three steps, the standard error of the estimate of Y from a particular value of X is given by the following formula:

$$\text{standard error of estimate of } Y = SD \text{ of } Y \times \sqrt{\frac{N(1 - r^2)}{N - 2}}$$

➜

$$= 1.75 \times \sqrt{\frac{10(1 - 0.90^2)}{10 - 2}}$$

$$= 1.75 \times \sqrt{\frac{10(1 - 0.81)}{8}}$$

$$= 1.75 \times \sqrt{0.2375}$$

$$= 1.75 \times 0.4873$$

$$= 0.853$$

Step 5 This standard error can be converted to the confidence interval by multiplying the value of the standard error by the appropriate value of t. The degrees of freedom for this are $N - 2$. Table 16.1 indicates that the t-value for $N - 2$. or 3 degrees of freedom is 3.18 for the 95% confidence interval. This gives us a value of the confidence interval around the predicted Y score of 3.37 of $\pm 0.85 \times 3.18 = \pm 2.70$. Thus we can be 95% sure that the population value of Y predicted from X is within the range of 0.67 to 6.07.

Interpreting the results

Of course, the confidence interval will vary numerically according to which X score is being used to predict Y. The size of the interval between the upper and lower confidence limits though does not vary. This is because the standard error is an average for all estimated Y scores.

Reporting the results

The results of this analysis can be written up as follows: 'The 95% confidence interval for predicting musical ability from maths score was 0.67 to 6.07 for a point-prediction of 3.37.'

Research examples

Confidence intervals

Confidence intervals are available for a substantial number of statistical methods. The basic principle is the same in all cases but expect to come across them in relation to statistics about which you know little. You should, nevertheless, be able to interpret them as a confidence interval is an indication of the spread of samples on that statistic.

Ang and Huan (2006) tested whether depression mediated the relation between academic stress and thoughts of killing oneself (suicidal ideation) in adolescents. They carried out a simple regression of academic stress with depression and suicidal ideation and a multiple regression of academic stress and depression with suicidal ideation. They presented the 95% confidence intervals for the unstandardised regression coefficients.

Hannaford, Thompson and Simpson (1996) evaluated an educational package which was designed to help general practitioners identify patients with depression. There was a 7% decrease in the number of cases of depression that were missed after receiving the educational package. The 95% confidence interval for this decrease varied from 2 to 12%.

Huisman, van Houwelingen and Kerkhof (2010) were interested in whether psychiatric diagnosis, gender and status as in- or out-patient were associated with particular types of suicide methods. They used multinomial logistic regression to determine which of these variables were related to suicide method when examined together. The dependent variables were the four categories of 1) self-poisoning, 2) jumping before a train, 3) jumping from a high place and 4) all other methods apart from hanging, which as the most common method was chosen to be the reference category. They reported the odds ratio of being in these categories together with the 95% confidence interval for the odds ratio. So, for example, the odds ratio for jumping before a train compared to hanging for patients with bipolar disorders was 5.53 with a 95% confidence interval of 1.23 to 24.82.

16.4   Writing up a confidence interval using APA style

We saw in Chapter 15 how simple it is to incorporate confidence intervals into writing up your statistical analysis when using APA style. For example, you could put:

95% CI [2.32. 4.44]

Or if you have several then you could put:

95% CI [2.32, 4.44], [−2.12, 1.13], and [4.26, 6.33], respectively.

The confidence interval follows the statistic as in the following example: $M = 38.6, 95\%$ CI [33.4, 43.7].

Two examples of published write-ups giving confidence intervals in APA style follow:

'These analyses revealed that within relationship goals, participants in the nostalgic past condition evinced greater goal importance, $t(82) = 2.47, p = .02, d = .54$, 95% CI [0.09, 0.79] and greater achievement likelihood, $t(82) = 2.54, p = .01, d = .56$, 95% CI [0.10, 0.81] than those in the ordinary past condition. However, participants in the two conditions did not differ in the extent to which they believed that they had already accomplished the relationship goals, $t(82) = 1.50, p = .14, 95\%$ CI [−0.14, 1.01].' (Abeyta, Routledge & Juhl, 2015, p. 1033.)

Notice how in the final sentence the confidence interval for the t-test passes through zero which means that the comparison is not significant. This is, of course, confirmed by the probability value of $p = .14$.

'In contrast, participants added information about a specific person in only 16% of the place-cued events, $M = 16\%, 95\%$ CI [6, 26]).' (Rubin, Wynn & Moscovitch, 2016, p. 310.)

The above is simpler and merely gives the confidence interval for the mean.

16.5   Other confidence intervals

In theory, any statistic (i.e. characteristic of a sample) will have a sampling distribution and, hence, a confidence interval. In practice, however, these can be obscure or unavailable though bootstrap statistics may make their estimation possible.

COMPUTER ANALYSIS

Examples of SPSS output containing confidence intervals

SPSS includes confidence intervals in much of its output. This is routinely done and so no special computer steps are needed generally. Screenshots 16.1 to 16.6 give a few examples of confidence intervals in SPSS output.

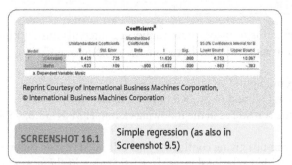

Reprint Courtesy of International Business Machines Corporation,
© International Business Machines Corporation

SCREENSHOT 16.1 Simple regression (as also in Screenshot 9.5)

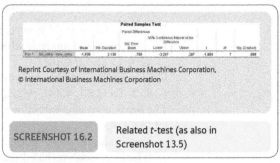

Reprint Courtesy of International Business Machines Corporation,
© International Business Machines Corporation

SCREENSHOT 16.2 Related t-test (as also in Screenshot 13.5)

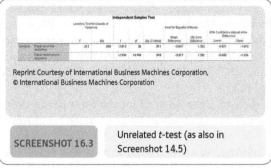

Reprint Courtesy of International Business Machines Corporation,
© International Business Machines Corporation

SCREENSHOT 16.3 Unrelated t-test (as also in Screenshot 14.5)

Descriptives

Depression

	N	Mean	Std. Deviation	Std. Error	95% Confidence Interval for Mean Lower Bound	95% Confidence Interval for Mean Upper Bound	Minimum	Maximum
Hormone 1	3	9.67	2.082	1.202	4.50	14.84	8	12
Hormone 2	3	3.67	1.528	.882	-.13	7.46	2	5
Placebo control	3	4.00	1.732	1.000	-.30	8.30	3	6
Total	9	5.78	3.308	1.103	3.23	8.32	2	12

Reprint Courtesy of International Business Machines Corporation,
© International Business Machines Corporation

SCREENSHOT 16.4 One-way ANOVA (as also in Screenshot 23.5)

Multiple Comparisons

Dependent Variable: Depression
Scheffe

(I) Condition	(J) Condition	Mean Difference (I-J)	Std. Error	Sig.	95% Confidence Interval Lower Bound	95% Confidence Interval Upper Bound
Hormone 1	Hormone 2	6.000*	1.466	.018	1.30	10.70
	Placebo control	5.667*	1.466	.023	.97	10.37
Hormone 2	Hormone 1	-6.000*	1.466	.018	-10.70	-1.30
	Placebo control	-.333	1.466	.975	-5.03	4.37
Placebo control	Hormone 1	-5.667*	1.466	.023	-10.37	-.97
	Hormone 2	.333	1.466	.975	-4.37	5.03

*. The mean difference is significant at the 0.05 level.

Reprint Courtesy of International Business Machines Corporation,
© International Business Machines Corporation

Estimated Marginal Means

Condition

Dependent Variable: Posttest

Condition	Mean	Std. Error	95% Confidence Interval Lower Bound	95% Confidence Interval Upper Bound
Psychotherapy	30.164a	2.119	24.716	35.611
Anti-depressant	35.423a	2.056	30.137	40.709
No treatment control	17.414a	3.561	8.261	26.566

a. Covariates appearing in the model are evaluated at the following values: Pretest = 42.22.

Reprint Courtesy of International Business Machines Corporation,
© International Business Machines Corporation

CHAPTER 17

Effect size in statistical analysis

Do my findings matter?

Overview

- Statistical significance is not the key attribute of a successful statistical analysis. Significance is merely a matter of whether the trend in the sample is likely if there is not a trend in the population. Too small a sample may be enough to produce non-significance.

- More important is the size of the relationship or difference obtained. This is not always easily appreciated on the basis of tests of significance.

- One standardised way of indicating the strength of a relationship is simply to turn the statistic into a correlation coefficient. This is easily done for chi-square, the t-test, nonparametric tests and the analysis of variance using the simple formulae presented in this chapter. There are other ways of doing this including Cohen's d, which is discussed in later chapters.

Preparation

Significance testing (Chapter 11) and the correlation coefficient (Chapter 8) are the basic ideas.

17.1 Introduction

One of the most neglected questions in statistical analysis is that of whether or not the researcher's findings are of any real substance. Obviously part of the answer depends very much on the particular research question being asked. One needs to address issues such as:

● Is this a theoretically important issue?

● Is this an issue of social relevance?

● Will this research actually help people?

These are not statistical matters. Statistics can help quantify the strength of the relationships established in research but it cannot evaluate its importance. Increasingly it is being required that measures of effect size are included in research reports.

Effect size can refer to a simple measure of the size of the effect in your study. For example, if the difference between women and men on a test of manual dexterity is 6.3 then 6.3 is the effect size. In many circumstances, such simple measures of effect size are perfectly adequate. Your findings are not meaningful unless you include them.

Standardised measures of effect size may also be included. This essentially involves putting your effect size onto a common scale. Standardised measure of effect size make it easy to compare the outcomes of studies with, say, different dependent variables. There is no single universal measure of effect size: it is said that there are up to about 80 different ones. Fortunately, not many are common. The correlation coefficient is a standardised effect size itself so you do not need a separate measure of effect size when dealing with correlations. The most common alternative to this is Cohen's d, which can be used when comparing two groups. There is a simple relationship between the Pearson correlation coefficient and Cohen's d (see Chapter 36). The third common measure of effect size is eta squared or partial eta squared. This is used for the ANOVA designs discussed later in this book.

SPSS does not always calculate measures of effect size so you may have to do a few, simple calculations in some cases.

17.2 Statistical significance and effect size

Students sometimes get confused as to the meaning of statistical significance. Perhaps it is a pity that the word significance was ever used in this context since all that it means is that it is reasonable to generalise from your sample data to the population. That is to say, significance merely gives you an estimate of the extent to which you can be confident that your findings are not simply artefacts of your particular sample or samples. It has absolutely nothing to do with whether or not there are really substantial trends in your data. Researchers tend to keep a little quiet about the substance of their findings, preferring to dwell on statistical significance. This is bad practice but encouraged by publication of research reports being substantially more likely if one's findings are statistically significant. Increasingly, however, journals are requiring the inclusion of effect size statistics in the articles they select for publication. But the bottom line is that the size of any effect (trend) that you find in your research is important in its own right.

The size of the samples being used profoundly influences the statistical significance of the findings. A correlation of .81 is needed to be statistically significant at the 5% level with a sample size of 6. However, with a much larger sample size (say, 100), a small correlation of .20 is statistically significant at the 5% level. In other words, with a large enough sample size quite small relationships can be statistically significant. This is discussed extensively in Chapter 39 on statistical power analysis.

We have already seen in Chapter 8 the *squared* correlation coefficient (the coefficient of determination) gives the proportion of the total variance shared by two variables. With a correlation of $r = 1.00$ the value of r^2 is still 1.00 (i.e. the total amount of variance). That means that all of the variation in one of the variables is predictable from the other variable. Expressed graphically, all of the points on a scattergram would fit perfectly on a straight line. If, however, the correlation between two variables is .2 then this means that r^2 equals .04. That is to say, the two variables have only 4% of their variance in common. This is not very much at all despite the fact that such a small correlation may well be statistically significant given a large enough sample size. The scatterplot of such a small correlation has points which deviate quite a lot from the best-fitting straight line between the points – in other words, there is a lot of error variance compared to the strength of the relationship between the two variables.

17.3 Size of the effect in studies

Although it is relatively easy to see the size of the relationships in correlation research, it is not quite so obvious in relation to experiments which have been analysed using *t*-tests, chi-square or a nonparametric test such as the Wilcoxon matched pairs. One of the approaches to this is to find ways of turning each of these statistics into a correlation coefficient. Generally this is computationally easy. The resulting correlation coefficient makes it very easy to assess the size of your relationships as it can be interpreted like any other correlation coefficient.

Some notes follow about the calculation of effect size statistics for different tests of significance. These can be referred to as appropriate when you wish to calculate effect sizes.

■ Chi-square

Read Chapter 18 on chi-square before attempting to understand this section. Turn a 2×2 chi-square into a sort of correlation coefficient by substituting the appropriate values in the following formula:

$$r_{\text{phi}} = \sqrt{\frac{\text{chi-square}}{N}}$$

The phi coefficient (r_{phi}) is simply a Pearson correlation coefficient for frequency scores. That is, phi is a special case of the Pearson correlation. Interpret it more or less like any other correlation coefficient. It is always positive because chi-square itself can only have positive values. Remember that N in the above formula refers to the number of observations and *not* to the degrees of freedom.

If the chi-square is bigger than 2×2, it is possible to use Cramér's V in place of the phi coefficient. This and phi are included in the output when you use SPSS to calculate chi-square so there is no need for any additional computational labour.

t-test

Essentially what is done here is to turn the independent variable into numerical values. That is to say, if the research design has, say, an experimental and a control group we code one group with the value 1 and the other group with the value 2. Take the data in Table 17.1, for example, which compares men and women in terms of level of job ambition (the dependent variable).

Of course, normally we would analyse the difference between the means in terms of the *t*-test or something similar. However, we can correlate the scores on the dependent variable (job ambition) if we code the independent variable as 1 for a man and 2 for a woman (Table 17.2). The two sets of scores can then be correlated using a Pearson correlation. This should be a simple calculation for you using SPSS. However, if you have already worked out your *t*-values for the *t*-test you can use the following formula to enable you to calculate the correlation quicker:

$$ r_{\text{bis}} = \sqrt{\frac{t^2}{t^2 + df}} $$

where *t* is the value of the *t*-statistic and *df* equals the degrees of freedom for the *t*-test.

Do not worry too much about r_{bis} since it is merely the Pearson correlation coefficient when one variable (e.g. gender) has just one of two values. It stands for the point biserial correlation coefficient.

Perhaps more frequently, Cohen's *d* is also used as the measure of effect size for the *t*-test. This is calculated by dividing the difference between the two conditions by a measure of the variance of the scores. It is discussed further in Chapter 36 where it is also explained how *d* can be calculated if you know the value of *r* and vice versa. Unfortunately, SPSS does not give the value of *d*. However, it is easy to calculate the correlation on SPSS between the scores on the dependent variable and the variable which indicates which group each of the scores belongs to. This correlation is a perfectly good measure of effect size though, if you wish, you can turn it correlation into the corresponding value of *d* (as described in Chapter 36).

Table 17.1	Scores of men and women on a dependent variable	
Men		**Women**
5		2
4		1
9		3
6		2
4		1
7		6
5		2
1		2
4		

Table 17.2	Rearranging the data in Table 17.1 so that gender can be correlated with the dependent variable

Score on dependent variable (job ambition)	Score on independent variable gender (men coded as 1, women coded as 2)
5	1
4	1
9	1
6	1
4	1
7	1
5	1
1	1
4	1
2	2
1	2
3	2
2	2
1	2
6	2
2	2
2	2

17.4 Approximation for nonparametric tests

We have to approximate to obtain a correlation coefficient for nonparametric tests such as the Mann–Whitney U-test. Before this section becomes clear, you need to read Chapter 21 on nonparametric tests of significance. One possible procedure is to work out the statistic (e.g. Mann–Whitney U-test), check its probability value (significance level) and then look up what the value of the t-test would be for that same significance level and sample size. For example, if we get a value of the Mann–Whitney U of 211 which is significant at the 5% level (two-tailed test) on a sample of 16 subjects, we could look up in the t-table the value of t which would be significant at the 5% level (two-tailed test) on a sample of 16 subjects (i.e. the degrees of freedom = 14). This value of t is 2.15 which could be substituted in the formula:

$$r_{\text{bis}} = \sqrt{\frac{t^2}{t^2 + df}}$$

17.5 Analysis of variance (ANOVA)

You need to read about ANOVA in Chapters 23 to 27 before this section will be clear. It is possible to compute from analysis of variance data a correlation measure called eta.

Table 17.3	Analysis of variance summary table				
Source of variance	Sum of squares	Degrees of freedom [df]	Mean square	F-ratio	Significance
Intelligence	1600	2	800	8.9	1%
Social class	2400	3	800	8.9	1%
Interaction	720	6	120	1.3	ns
Within (error)	9720	108	90		

This is analogous to a correlation coefficient but describes a curvilinear rather than the linear relationship which the Pearson correlation coefficient does. It is of particular use in the analysis of variance since it is sometimes difficult to know which of the independent variables explains the most variance. The probability value of an F-ratio in itself does not enable us to judge which of the independent variables accounts for the largest amount of the variance of the dependent variable. Table 17.3 is a summary table from an analysis of variance considering the influence of intelligence and social class on a dependent variable. It is difficult to know from the table whether intelligence or social class explains more of the variance as the degrees of freedom differ.

In order to calculate the value of eta for any of the variables all we need to do is substitute in the following formula:

$$\text{eta} = \sqrt{\frac{\text{treatment } df \times F\text{-ratio}}{(\text{treatment } df \times F\text{-ratio}) + \text{within } df}}$$

So, for example, if we take intelligence then we substitute the values from Table 17.3 in the formula:

$$\text{eta} = \sqrt{\frac{2 \times 8.9}{(2 \times 8.9) + 108}} = \sqrt{\frac{17.8}{17.8 + 108}}$$

$$= \sqrt{\frac{17.8}{125.8}} = \sqrt{0.1415} = 0.38$$

If we do a similar calculation for the two other sources of variation, we can extend our summary table to include eta (Table 17.4). What this extra information tells us is that

Table 17.4	Analysis of variance summary table with values of eta added					
Source of variance	Sum of squares	Degrees of freedom	Mean square	F-ratio	Significance	Eta
Intelligence	1600	2	800	8.9	1%	0.38
Social class	2400	3	800	8.9	1%	0.44
Interaction	720	6	120	1.3	ns	0.26
Within (error)	9720	108	90			

social class accounts for more variation in the dependent variable than does either intelligence or the interaction. In other words, social class has a bigger effect than intelligence or the interaction.

Some researchers prefer to use the value of eta squared (η^2) as this more directly reflects the amount of variance explained.

You will find references to something called partial eta squared (η_p^2) which is basically the value of eta squared adjusted in the following way: Instead of the variance due to each of the main effect being divided by total variance, it is divided by the total variance minus the error variance. SPSS will calculate partial eta squared for the analysis of variance if you request it but it does not do this using the one-way ANOVA. However, some statisticians caution against its use.

17.6 Writing up effect sizes using APA style

Effect sizes are easily incorporated into a research method using APA style. Here is a simple example though they do not get very difficult:

> 'Care was taken to match the pictures of snakes and the pictures of fish for peripheral details and for the size of the area covered by the animal, $t(62) = 0.15$, $p = .88$, $d = 0.04$. Each animal's color was manipulated to be either blue or red. All animals were presented on green backgrounds.' (Meyer, Bell, & Buchner, 2015, p. 727)

Based on what you read in Chapter 14, it should be clear that the researchers had used a *t*-test which was not significant ($p = .88$). The effect size, *d*, is 0.04 which is a very small effect size. You can find out about *d* in Chapter 36. This would have been what the researchers had hoped for since it refers to the matching of the two sets of pictures. Whatever the measure of effect size, it is merely inserted in the same way though perhaps *r* would be used or partial eta squared (η_p^2) for ANOVAs as in the following example:

> 'There was a significant main effect of activity type, $F(1, 46) = 16.07$, $p = .0002$, $\eta_p^2 = .26$, qualified by the predicted interaction between activity type and location, $F(1, 46) = 4.40$, $p = .041$, $\eta_p^2 = .09$.' (Zhang & Risen, 2014, p. 968)

Once you know the basic APA method for reporting statistical analyses succinctly, you will be able to understand the gist of what the researcher has written even for unfamiliar statistical tests.

17.7 Have I got a large, medium or small effect size?

The novice researcher may well not understand what the different values of effect size mean. Consequently, Table 17.5 offers verbal equivalents (small, medium and large).

Table 17.5	Verbal labels for different measures of effect size			
Standardised measure of effect size	**Test applied to**	**Verbal label for the size of effect**		
		Small	Medium	Large
r	Correlation coefficient, etc.	.1	.3	.5
Cohen's *d*	*t*-test	0.2	0.5	0.8
Phi	Chi-square	0.1	0.3	0.5
Eta squared	ANOVA	0.01	0.06	0.13
Cramér's V with 2 *df*	Chi-square	.07	.21	.35
Cramér's V with 3 *df*	Chi-square	.06	.17	.29

17.8   Method and statistical efficiency

Before going any further, we should emphasise that the quality of your research procedures is an important factor determining the strength of the relationships found in your research. Sloppy research methods or poor measurements are to be avoided at all costs. Anything which introduces measurement error into your research design will reduce the apparent trends in the research. So, for example, a laboratory experimenter must take scrupulous care in standardising her or his procedures as far as possible. Sloppy methods may lead to disappointment because they introduce error.

This is easily demonstrated if we consider a researcher trying to assess the relationship between children's ages and their heights in a sample of pre-school children. An excellent method for doing this would be to obtain each child's birth certificate so that their date of birth will give their precise age and to take the child down to the local clinic to have the child's height precisely measured by the clinic nurse who is experienced at doing this. In these circumstances, there is probably very little we can do further to maximise our chances of assessing the true relationship between age and height in children.

A much less satisfactory way of doing this research might be as follows: The researcher asks the child's nursery teacher to estimate the child's height and tells them to guess if they complain that they do not know. The children's ages are measured by asking the children themselves. It is pretty obvious that these measures of age and height are a little rough and ready. Using these approximate measures we would expect rather poor correlations between age and height – especially compared with the previous, very precise method. In other words, the precision of our measurement procedures has an important influence on the size of the relationships we obtain.

The difference between the two studies is that the second researcher is using very unreliable measures of height and age compared with the very reliable measures of the first researcher. There are a number of ways of measuring reliability in psychology including inter-rater reliability which is essentially the correlation between a set of measurements taken by person A with those taken by person B. So, for example, we would expect that the birth certificate method of measuring age would produce high correlations between two different researchers, and that asking the children themselves would not produce very reliable measures compared with the answer we would get from the same children even the next day.

If you can calculate the reliability of your measurements, it is possible to adjust the correlation between two measures for the unreliability of each of the measures. This essentially inflates the reliability coefficients upwards towards 1.00. In other words, you get the correlation between age and height assuming that the measures were totally reliable. The formula for doing this is:

$$r_{x_\infty y_\infty} = \frac{r_{xy}}{\sqrt{r_{xx}r_{yy}}}$$

The symbol $r_{x_\infty y_\infty}$ is the coefficient of attenuation. It is merely the correlation between variables x and y if these variables were perfectly reliable. The symbols r_{xx} and r_{yy} are the separate reliability coefficients of the variables x and y.

Often in research we do not have estimates of the reliability of our measures so the procedure is not universally applicable.

Research examples

Effect sizes

Effect sizes can be reported using a number of statistics. What is appropriate depends partly on the statistical design involved. So eta is used for ANOVA whereas Cohen's d or the correlation coefficient can be used for the t-test.

Gervais, Vescio and Allen (2012) in their study of people's interchangeability as sex objects (fungibility) report the effect size for one of their ANOVAs as follows: 'A main effect of body type, $F(1, 65) = 5.47$, $p = .02$, $\eta_p^2 = .08$, revealed that ideal targets ($M = 13.51$, $SD = 7.39$) were more fungible than average targets ($M = 12.79$, $SD = 7.06$). This effect, however, was modified by the presence of the hypothesised interaction between body type and target gender, $F(1, 65) = 6.11$, $p = .02$, $\eta_p^2 = .10$, indicating that the tendency for ideal targets to be perceived as more fungible than average targets was moderated by target gender.' (p. 507).

Lautamo and colleagues (2011), in an investigation of children with Specific Language Impairment (SLI), used Cohen's d as their measure of effect size: 'The results revealed significant differences between the two groups of 3.1 to 6.5-year-old children (with and without SLI). In the first analysis of differences in play performance (conducted with 38 items) independent samples t-tests confirmed that the means differed significantly ($t(108) = 5.80$, $p < .01$), and the effect size was large (Cohen's $d = 1.11$).' (p. 227).

Levine, Asada and Carpenter (2009) were interested in the effect sizes reported in the literature involving meta-analyses (see Chapter 36). They took a sample of 51 published meta-analyses which involved over 3600 separate studies. Levine et al. wanted to know what the correlation between effect sizes found in the analyses and the sample sizes involved. In approximately 80% of meta-analyses there was a negative correlation between effect size and sample size. In other words, the larger the effect size then the smaller the sample size was likely to be. For the researchers, the best interpretation of this involves a publication bias against non-significant results. That is, studies which do not reach statistical significance are systematically excluded from publication because the journals reject them or because the researchers do not attempt to publish them. The broader conclusion is that effect sizes reported in meta-analyses are likely to be overestimates of those found by the researchers doing research in an area.

Key points

- *Do not* expect the things in this chapter to feature regularly in other researchers' reports. They tend to get ignored despite their importance.

- Do be aware of the need to assess the degree of explanatory power obtained in your research as part of your interpretation of the value of your findings. All too frequently psychologists seek statistical significance and forget that their findings may be trivial in terms of the amount of variance explained.

- Do try to design your research in such a way that the error and unreliability are minimised as far as possible.

CHAPTER 18

Chi-square

Differences between samples of frequency data

Overview

- Chi-square is used with nominal (category) data. A minimum of two categories is involved.

- It tests whether the frequency counts in the various nominal categories could be expected by chance or whether there is a relationship.

- Chi-square is relatively uncommon in psychological research because psychologists tend to opt for score data. However, in some circumstances its use is necessary.

- One-sample chi-square compares the frequencies obtained in each category with a known expected frequency distribution. Two-sample chi-square uses a crosstabulation or frequency table for two variables. This contains the frequencies in the various possible combinations of categories for the two variables.

- The disparity between the actual frequencies in the data and what the frequencies would be if the null hypothesis were true is at the heart of the calculation. The bigger the disparity, the bigger the value of chi-square and the more one's findings are statistically significant.

- When the chi-square table has more than four cells (i.e. combinations of categories), interpretation becomes difficult. It is possible to subdivide a big table into a number of smaller chi-squares in order to facilitate interpretation. This is known as partitioning.

- Sometimes data may violate the mathematical foundations of chi-square too much. In these circumstances, the data may have to be modified to meet the mathematical requirements, or an alternative measure such as the Fisher exact test may be employed.

Preparation

You should be familiar with crosstabulation and contingency tables (Chapter 7) and samples and populations (Chapter 10).

18.1   Introduction

Often, chi-square is written as χ^2. However, we have avoided Greek letters as far as possible. If a researcher has several samples of data which involve frequencies rather than scores, a statistical test designed for frequency data must be used. The following are some examples of research of this sort:

- Male and female schoolchildren are compared in terms of wanting to be psychologists when they leave school (Table 18.1).

- The sexual orientations of a sample of religious men are compared with those of a non-religious sample (Table 18.2).

- Choosing to play with either a black or a white doll in black and white children (Table 18.3).

In each of these examples, both variables consist of a relatively small number of categories. Schematically each study approximates to the form shown in Table 18.4 in which the independent variable is the sample and the dependent variable consists of one of several categories.

The precise number of samples may vary from study to study and the number of categories of the dependent variable can be two or more. As a rule of thumb, *it is better to have just a few samples and a few categories,* since large tables can be difficult to interpret and generally require large numbers of participants or cases to be workable.

Table 18.1	Relationship between gender and wanting to be a psychologist		
Intention		**Male**	**Female**
Wants to be a psychologist		$f = 17$	$f = 98$
Does not want to be a psychologist		$f = 67$	$f = 35$

Table 18.2	Relationship between sexual orientation and religion	
Orientation	**Religious**	**Non-religious**
Heterosexual	57	105
Gay	13	27
Bisexual	8	17

Table 18.3	Relationship between doll choice and ethnicity		
Choice	**Black child**	**White child**	**Mixed-parentage**
Black doll	19	17	5
White doll	16	18	9

Table 18.4	Stylised table for chi-square		
Category	**Sample 1**	**Sample 2**	**Sample 3**
Category 1	27	21	5
Category 2	19	20	19
Category 3	9	17	65

The 'cells' of Table 18.4 (called a crosstabulation or contingency table) contain the frequencies of individuals in that particular sample and that particular category. So the 'cell' that corresponds to sample 2 and category 3 contains the frequency 17. This means that in your data there are 17 cases in sample 2 which also fit category 3. In other words, a cell is the intersection of a row and a column.

The statistical question is whether the distribution of frequencies in the different samples is so varied that it is unlikely that these all come from the same population. As ever, this population is defined by the null hypothesis (that there is no relationship between the independent and dependent variables).

18.2 Theoretical issues

Imagine a research study in which children are asked to choose between two television programmes, one violent and the other non-violent. Some of the children have been in trouble at school for fighting and the others have not been in trouble. The researcher wants to know if there is a relationship between the violence of the preferred television programme and having been in trouble for fighting at school. The data might look something like Table 18.5.

We can see from Table 18.5 that the fighters (sample 1) are more likely to prefer the violent programme and the non-fighters (sample 2) the non-violent programme. The frequencies obtained in the research are known as the observed frequencies because they are found from the data.

Assume that both of the samples come from the same population of data in which there is no relationship between the dependent and independent variables. This implies that any differences between the samples are merely due to the chance fluctuations of sampling. A useful index of how much the samples differ from each other is based on how different each sample is from the population distribution defined by the null hypothesis. As ever, since we do not know the population directly in most research, we have to estimate its characteristics from the characteristics of samples.

Table 18.5	Relationship between preferred TV programme and fighting	
Preference	**Sample 1 Fighters**	**Sample 2 Non-fighters**
Violent TV preferred	40	15
Non-violent TV preferred	30	70

With the chi-square test, we simply add together the frequencies for whatever number of samples we have. These sums are then used as an estimate of the distribution of the different categories in the population. Since differences between the samples under the null hypothesis are solely due to chance factors, by combining samples the best possible estimate of the characteristics of the population is obtained. In other words, we simply add together the characteristics of two or more samples as an estimate of the distribution of the categories in the population. The first stage of doing this is illustrated in Table 18.6.

Table 18.6	Relationship between preferred TV programme and fighting including the marginal frequencies (column and row frequencies)		
Preference	Sample 1 Fighters	Sample 2 Non-fighters	Row frequencies
Violent TV preferred	40	15	55
Non-violent TV preferred	30	70	100
Column frequencies	70	85	Overall frequency = 155

So in the null-hypothesis-defined population, we would expect 55 out of every 155 to prefer the violent programme and 100 out of 155 to prefer the non-violent programme. But we obtained 40 out of 70 preferring the violent programme in sample 1, and 15 out of 85 preferring the violent programme in sample 2. How do these figures match the expectations from the population defined by the null hypothesis? We need to calculate the expected frequencies of the cells in Table 18.6. This calculation is based on the assumption that the null hypothesis population frequencies are our best information as to the relative proportions preferring the violent and non-violent programmes if there truly was no difference between the samples.

Sample 1 contains 70 children. If the null hypothesis is true then we would expect 55 out of every 155 of these to prefer the violent programme. Thus our expected frequency of those preferring the violent programme in sample 1 is:

$$70 \times \frac{55}{155} = 70 \times 0.355 = 24.84$$

Remember that these figures have been rounded for presentation and give a slightly different answer from that generated by a calculator or computer.

Similarly, since we expect under the null hypothesis 100 out of every 155 to prefer the non-violent programme, then our expected frequency of those preferring the non-violent programme in sample 1, out of the 70 children in that sample, is:

$$70 \times \frac{100}{155} = 70 \times 0.645 = 45.16$$

Notice that the sum of the expected frequencies for sample 1 is the same as the number of children in that sample (24.84 + 45.16 = 70).

We can apply the same logic to sample 2 which contains 85 children. We expect that 55 out of every 155 will prefer the violent programme and 100 out of every 155 will prefer the non-violent programme. The expected frequency preferring the violent programme in sample 2 is:

$$85 \times \frac{55}{155} = 85 \times 0.355 = 30.18$$

The expected frequency preferring the non-violent programme in sample 2 is:

$$85 \times \frac{100}{155} = 85 \times 0.645 = 54.83$$

We can enter these expected frequencies (population frequencies under the null hypothesis) into our table of frequencies (Table 18.7).

Table 18.7	Contingency table including both observed and expected frequencies		
Preference	Sample 1 Fighters	Sample 2 Non-fighters	Row frequencies
Violent TV preferred	observed frequency = 40 expected frequency = 24.84	observed frequency = 15 expected frequency = 30.18	55
Non-violent TV preferred	observed frequency = 30 expected frequency = 45.16	observed frequency = 70 expected frequency = 54.83	100
Column frequencies (i.e. sum of observed frequencies in column)	70	85	Overall frequencies = 155

The chi-square statistic is based on the differences between the observed and the expected frequencies. It should be fairly obvious that the greater the disparity between the observed frequencies and the population frequencies under the null hypothesis, the less likely is the null hypothesis to be true. Thus if the samples are very different from each other, the differences between the observed and expected frequencies will be large. Chi-square is calculated from the overall disparity between the observed and expected frequencies. To be precise, the chi-square formula involves the squared deviations over the expected frequencies, but this is merely a slight diversion to make our formula fit a convenient statistical distribution which is called chi-square. The calculated value of chi-square is then compared with a table of critical values of chi-square (Significance Table 18.1) in order to estimate the probability of obtaining our pattern of frequencies by chance (if the null hypothesis of no differences between the samples was true). This table is organised according to the number of degrees of freedom, which is always (number of columns of data − 1) × (number of rows of data − 1). This would be (2 − 1) × (2 − 1) or 1 for Table 18.7. Figure 18.1 gives the key steps when carrying out a chi-square test.

Significance Table 18.1	5% and 1% significance values of chi-square (two-tailed test). Appendix F gives a fuller and conventional version of this table	
Degrees of freedom	Significant at 5% level Accept hypothesis	Significant at 1% level Accept hypothesis
1	3.8 or more	6.7 or more
2	6.0 or more	9.2 or more
3	7.8 or more	11.3 or more

→

Degrees of freedom	Significant at 5% level Accept hypothesis	Significant at 1% level Accept hypothesis
4	9.5 or more	13.3 or more
5	11.1 or more	15.1 or more
6	12.6 or more	16.8 or more
7	14.1 or more	18.5 or more
8	15.5 or more	20.1 or more
9	16.9 or more	21.7 or more
10	18.3 or more	23.2 or more
11	19.7 or more	24.7 or more
12	21.0 or more	26.2 or more

Your value must be in the listed ranges for your degrees of freedom to be significant at the 5% level (column 2) or the 1% level (column 3) (i.e. to accept the hypothesis).

Should you require more precise values than those listed above, these are to be found in the table in Appendix F.

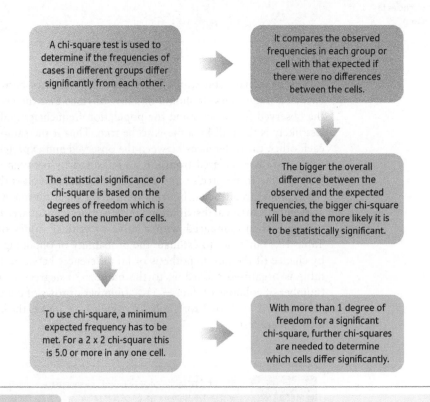

A chi-square test is used to determine if the frequencies of cases in different groups differ significantly from each other.

It compares the observed frequencies in each group or cell with that expected if there were no differences between the cells.

The bigger the overall difference between the observed and the expected frequencies, the bigger chi-square will be and the more likely it is to be statistically significant.

The statistical significance of chi-square is based on the degrees of freedom which is based on the number of cells.

To use chi-square, a minimum expected frequency has to be met. For a 2 x 2 chi-square this is 5.0 or more in any one cell.

With more than 1 degree of freedom for a significant chi-square, further chi-squares are needed to determine which cells differ significantly.

FIGURE 18.1   Conceptual steps for understanding the chi-square test

Explaining statistics 18.1

How chi-square works

The calculation of chi-square involves several relatively simple but repetitive calculations. For each cell in the chi-square table you calculate the following:

$$\frac{(\text{observed frequency}-\text{expected frequency})^2}{\text{expected frequency}}$$

The only complication is that this small calculation is repeated for each of the cells in your crosstabulation or contingency table. The formula in full becomes:

$$\text{chi-square} = \sum \frac{(O - E)^2}{E}$$

where O = observed frequency and E = expected frequency.

The following is an imaginary piece of research in which teenage boys and girls were asked to name their favourite type of television programme from a list of three: (1) soap operas, (2) crime dramas and (3) neither of these. The researcher suspects that gender may be related to programme preference (Table 18.8).

We next need to calculate the expected frequencies for each of the cells in Table 18.8. One easy way of doing this is to multiply the row total and the column total for each particular cell and divide by the total number of observations (i.e. total frequencies). This is shown in Table 18.9.

Table 18.8	Relationship between favourite type of TV programme and gender of respondent			
Respondents	**Soap opera**	**Crime drama**	**Neither**	**Totals**
Males	observed = 27	observed = 14	observed = 19	row 1 = 60
Females	observed = 17	observed = 33	observed = 9	row 2 = 59
Total	**Column 1 = 44**	**Column 2 = 47**	**Column 3 = 28**	**Total = 119**

Table 18.9	Calculation of expected frequencies by multiplying appropriate row and column totals and then dividing by overall total			
Respondents	**Soap opera**	**Crime drama**	**Neither**	**Total**
Males	observed = 27	observed = 14	observed = 19	row 1 = 60
	expected = 60 × 44 ÷ 119 = 22.185	expected = 60 × 47 ÷ 119 = 23.698	expected = 60 × 28 ÷ 119 = 14.118	
Females	observed = 17	observed = 33	observed = 9	row 2 = 59
	expected = 59 × 44 ÷ 119 = 21.815	expected = 59 × 47 ÷ 119 = 23.303	expected = 59 × 28 ÷ 119 = 13.882	
Total	**Column 1 = 44**	**Column 2 = 47**	**Column 3 = 28**	**Total = 119**

→

We then simply substitute the above values in the chi-square formula:

$$\text{chi-square} = \sum \frac{(O - E)^2}{E}$$

$$= \frac{(27 - 22.185)^2}{22.185} + \frac{(14 - 23.698)^2}{23.698} + \frac{(19 - 14.118)^2}{14.118}$$

$$+ \frac{(17 - 21.815)^2}{21.815} + \frac{(33 - 23.303)^2}{23.303} + \frac{(9 - 13.882)^2}{13.882}$$

$$= \frac{4.815^2}{22.185} + \frac{-9.698^2}{23.698} + \frac{4.882^2}{14.118} + \frac{-4.815^2}{21.815} + \frac{9.697^2}{23.303} + \frac{-4.882^2}{13.882}$$

$$= \frac{23.184}{22.185} + \frac{94.051}{23.698} + \frac{23.834}{14.118} + \frac{23.184}{21.815} + \frac{94.032}{23.303} + \frac{23.834}{13.882}$$

$$= 1.045 + 3.969 + 1.688 + 1.063 + 4.035 + 1.717$$

$$= 13.52$$

Note that this value is the same as that given by SPSS in Screenshot 18.5.

The degrees of freedom are (the number of columns − 1) × (the number of rows − 1) = (3 − 1) × (2 − 1) = 2 degrees of freedom.

We then check the table of the critical values of chi-square (Significance Table 18.1) in order to assess whether or not our samples differ among each other so much that they are unlikely to be produced by the population defined by the null hypothesis. The value must equal or exceed the tabulated value to be significant at the listed level of significance. Some tables will give you more degrees of freedom, but you will be hard pressed to do a sensible chi-square that exceeds 12 degrees of freedom.

Interpreting the results

Our value of chi-square is well in excess of the minimum value of 6.0 needed to be significant at the 5% level for 2 degrees of freedom, so we reject the idea that the samples came from the population defined by the null hypothesis. Thus we accept the hypothesis that there is a relationship between television programme preferences and gender.

Only if you have a 2 × 2 chi-square is it possible to interpret the significance level of the chi-square directly in terms of the trends revealed in the data table. As we will see in Section 18.3, if we have a bigger chi-square than this (say 3 × 2 or 3 × 3) then a significant value of chi-square merely indicates that the samples are dissimilar to each other overall without stipulating which samples are different from each other.

Because the sample sizes generally differ in contingency tables, it helps interpretation to convert the frequencies in each cell to percentages of the relevant sample size at this stage. It is important, though, never to actually calculate chi-square itself on these percentages as you will obtain the wrong significance level if you do. It seems from Table 18.10 that males prefer soap operas more often than females do, females have a preference for crime drama, and males are more likely than females to say that they prefer another type of programme. Unfortunately, as things stand we are not able to say which of these trends are statistically significant unless we partition the chi-square as described in Section 18.3.

Reporting the results

The results could be written up as follows: 'The value of chi-square was 13.52 which was significant at the 5% level with 2 degrees of freedom. Thus there is a gender difference in favourite type of TV programme. Compared with females, males were more likely to choose soap operas and less likely to choose crime dramas as their favourite programmes and more likely to prefer neither of these.'

Table 18.10	Observed percentages in each sample based on the observed frequencies in Table 18.8		
Respondents	**Soap opera**	**Crime drama**	**Neither**
Males	45.0%	23.3%	31.7%
Females	28.8%	55.9%	15.3%

However, as this table is bigger than a 2 × 2 table, it is advisable to partition the chi-square as discussed in Section 18.3 in order to say which of these trends are statistically significant.

Alternatively, following the recommendations of the APA (2010) Publication Manual we could write: 'There was a significant gender difference in favourite type of TV programme, $\chi^2(2, N = 119) = 13.52, p < .05$. Compared with females, males were more likely to choose soap operas and less likely to choose crime dramas as their favourite programmes and more likely to prefer neither of these.' Chapter 15 explains how to report statistical significance in the shorter, professional way used in this version.

18.3 Partitioning chi-square

There is no problem when the chi-square contingency table is just two columns and two rows. The chi-square in these circumstances tells you that your two samples are different from each other and how they differ. Examine your contingency table to see just what the difference is. But if you have, say, a 2 × 3 chi-square (e.g. you have two samples and three categories) then there is some uncertainty as to what a significant chi-square means – does it mean that all three samples are different from each other, that sample 1 and sample 2 are different, that sample 1 and sample 3 are different, or that sample 2 and sample 3 are different? In the television programmes example, although we obtained a significant overall chi-square, there is some doubt as to why we obtained this. The major differences between the genders are between the soap opera and crime drama conditions rather than between the soap opera and the 'other' conditions.

It is a perfectly respectable statistical procedure to break your large chi-square into a number of 2 × 2 chi-square tests to assess precisely where the significant differences lie. Thus in the TV programmes study you could generate three separate chi-squares from the 2 × 3 contingency table. These are illustrated in Table 18.11.

These three separate chi-squares each have just one degree of freedom (because they are 2 × 2 tables). If you calculate chi-square for each of these tables you hopefully should be able to decide precisely where the differences are between samples and conditions.

The only difficulty is the significance levels you use. Because you are doing three separate chi-squares, the normal significance level of 5% still operates, but it is divided between the three chi-squares you have carried out. In other words, we share the 5% between three to give us the 1.667% level for each – any of the three chi-squares would have to be significant at this level to be reported as being significant at the 5% level. Significance Table 18.2 gives the adjusted values of chi-square required to be significant at the 5% level (two-tailed test). Thus if you have three comparisons to make, the minimum value of chi-square that is significant is 5.73. The degrees of freedom for these comparisons will always be 1 as they are always based on 2 × 2 contingency tables.

Table 18.11	Three partitioned sub-tables from the 2 $\times$ 3 contingency table (Table 18.8)

Soap opera versus crime drama

Respondents	Soap opera	Crime drama	Totals
Males	27	14	row 1 = 41
Females	17	33	row 2 = 50
Totals	Column 1 = 44	Column 2 = 47	Total = 91

Soap opera versus neither

Respondents	Soap opera	Neither	Totals
Males	27	19	row 1 = 46
Females	17	9	row 2 = 26
Totals	Column 1 = 44	Column 3 = 28	Total = 72

Crime drama versus neither

Respondents	Crime drama	Neither	Totals
Males	14	19	row 1 = 33
Females	33	9	row 2 = 42
Totals	Column 2 = 47	Column 3 = 28	Total = 75

Significance Table 18.2	Chi-square 5% two-tailed significance values for 1–10 unplanned comparisons									
Degree of freedom	Number of comparisons being made									
	1	2	3	4	5	6	7	8	9	10
1	3.84	5.02	5.73	6.24	6.64	6.96	7.24	7.48	7.69	7.88

To use this table, simply look under the column for the number of separate comparisons you are making using chi-square. Your values of chi-square must equal or exceed the listed value to be significant at the 5% level with a two-tailed test.

18.4 Important warnings

Chi-square is rather less user friendly than it superficially suggests. The following are warning signs not to use chi-square or to take very great care:

- For a 2 $\times$ 2 crosstabulation table, all of the expected frequencies should be 5 or greater in order to use chi square. You may use the Fisher exact test if your data violate this requirement. For bigger crosstabulation tables, the rule is that no more than one-fifth of the expected frequencies should be lower than 5 and none should be less than 1. Some computers automatically print an alternative to chi-square if this assumption is breached – and if an alternative is available.

- Never do chi-square on percentages or anything other than frequencies. This invalidates the significance levels obtained.

- Always check that your total of frequencies is equal to the number of participants in your research. Chi-square should not be applied where participants in the research are contributing more than one frequency each to the total of frequencies.

You may come across something called Yates's correction which once was commonly applied when the expected frequencies in chi-square were small. It was supposed to make the data fit the theoretical distribution better. Unfortunately it overcompensated for the problem it was intended to deal with and made the value of chi square smaller and so less likely to be statistically significant. In short, it is outmoded and should not be used.

18.5   Alternatives to chi-square

Assume that your data violate the expected frequency rules given in the previous section. The following are the main alternatives for dealing with the situation but they will not work in every case:

- If you have a 2 × 2 or a 2 × 3 chi-square table then you can use the Fisher exact probability test which is not sensitive to small expected frequencies (see Explaining statistics 18.2).

- Apart from omitting very small samples or categories which may be all that is possible, sometimes you can save the day by combining samples and/or categories so that there are no small expected frequencies. So, for example, take the data set out in Table 18.12. It should be apparent that by combining two samples and/or two categories you are likely to increase the expected frequencies in the resulting chi-square table.

Table 18.12	3 × 3 contingency table		
Sample	Category 1	Category 2	Category 3
Sample 1	10	6	14
Sample 2	3	12	4
Sample 3	4	2	5

But you cannot simply combine categories or samples at a whim – the samples or categories have to be combined meaningfully. So, if the research was on the relationship between the type of degree that students take and their hobbies, you might have the following categories and samples:

category 1 – socialising
category 2 – dancing
category 3 – stamp collecting
sample 1 – English literature students
sample 2 – media studies students
sample 3 – physics students

Looking at these, it would seem reasonable to combine categories 1 and 2 and samples 1 and 2 since they seem to reflect rather similar things. No other combinations would seem appropriate. For example, it is hard to justify combining dancing and stamp collecting. As always in research, you need to be able to justify the decision that you make.

Explaining statistics 18.2

How the Fisher exact probability test works

Frequently students only have very small samples because they are working on learning exercises and there is not time to collect much data. As a consequence, the assumptions and requirements of the chi-square test are frequently broken. The Fisher exact probability test deals with small samples of frequency data much better than chi-square does because it is not subject to the expected frequencies requirement. We will only show the calculation of a 2 × 2 Fisher exact probability test although there is a version for 2 × 3 tables. SPSS prints these out together with your chi-square if appropriate. The interpretation of the Fisher exact test is much the same as for chi-square for the same data.

The calculation of the Fisher exact probability test is something of a nightmare by hand because it involves something called factorials. These are written as, for example, 5!. The exclamation mark is appropriate. What 5! means is 5 × 4 × 3 × 2 × 1, which is 120. Easy enough but as the basic formula involves four factorials multiplied by each other divided by five factorials multiplied by each other things get very cumbersome. Computers like cumbersome and repetitive tasks and this is one that we can best leave to SPSS.

Imagine a small study of the relationship between photographic memory and gender as illustrated in Table 18.13. The data are interesting because they suggest that photographic memory is more common among females than men. It is fairly obvious that the expected frequencies if this were a chi-square would be less than 5 – in fact 3 of them would be. So the chi-square rules are violated. Hence we turn to Fisher's exact test. You don't need to do anything special to calculate the Fisher exact test on SPSS as it is to be found in the Chi-Square Tests output tables such as Table 18.14 if appropriate for your data. Find the row for the Fisher's exact test and you can see that the two-sided exact significance is .091 or the 9.1% significance level. So the study is non-significant despite the data being interesting. You will also see that the Pearson chi-square value is 4.381 with a two-sided significance level of .036 or 3.6%. This is statistically significant but has to be disregarded because the data violate the assumptions of chi-square in terms of expected frequencies.

Table 18.13	Photographic memory and gender	
	Photographic memory	**No photographic memory**
Males	2	7
Females	4	1

Table 18.14 Fisher's exact test in SPSS output

Chi-Square Tests					
	Value	df	Asymp. Sig. (2-sided)	Exact Sig. (2-sided)	Exact Sig. (1-sided)
Pearson Chi-Square	4.381[a]	1	.036		
Continuity Correction[b]	2.340	1	.126		
Likelihood Ratio	4.583	1	.032		
Fisher's Exact Test				.091	.063
Linear-by-Linear Association	4.069	1	.044		
N of Valid Cases	14				

[a] 3 cells (75.0%) have expected count less than 5. The minimum expected count is 2.14.
[b]

Our two-tailed probability value of .091 is not statistically significant at the conventional 5% level (neither would the one-tailed test if that were appropriate).

Interpreting the results

We cannot reject the null hypothesis that the incidence of photographic memory is related to gender. It would be useful to convert the frequencies in Table 18.13 into percentages of the relevant sample size when interpreting these data as we have different numbers of males and females. Such a table would show that 80% of the females had photographic memories but only 22% of the males. Despite this, with such a small amount of data, the trend is not statistically significant.

Reporting the results

The following would be an appropriate description: 'Although photographic memory was nearly four times more common in females than in males, this proved not to be statistically significant using the Fisher exact probability test. The exact probability was .09 which is not significant at the .05 level. Thus we must reject the hypothesis that photographic memory is related to gender.'

Alternatively, following the recommendations of the APA (2010) Publication Manual we could write something like: 'Photographic memory was nearly four times more common in females than in males. However, the difference was not statistically significant, Fisher, $p = .091$. Thus we must reject the hypothesis that photographic memory is related to gender.' This style of presenting statistical significance is explained in detail in Chapter 15.

18.6   Chi-square and known populations

Sometimes, but rarely, in research we know the distribution in the population. If the population distribution of frequencies is known then it is possible to employ the single-sample chi-square. Usually the population frequencies are known as relative frequencies or percentages. So, for example, if you wished to know the likelihood of getting a sample of 40 university psychology students in which there are 30 female and 10 male students if you know that the population of psychology students is 90% female and 10% male, you simply use the latter proportions to calculate the expected frequencies of females and males in a sample of 40. If the sample were to reflect the population then 90% of the 40 should be female and 10% male. So the expected frequencies are $40 \times 90 \div 100$ for females and $40 \times 10 \div 100$ for males $= 36$ females and 4 males. These are then entered into the chi-square formula, but note that there are only two cells. The degrees of freedom for the one-sample chi-square is the number of cells minus 1 (i.e. $2 - 1 = 1$).

Explaining statistics 18.3

How the one-sample chi-square works

The research question is whether a sample of 80 babies of a certain age in foster care show the same level of smiling to their carer as a population of babies of the same age assessed on a developmental test. On this developmental test, 50% of babies at this age show clear evidence of the smiling response, 40% clearly show no evidence, and for 10% it is impossible to make a judgement. This is the population from which the foster babies are considered to be a sample. It is found that 35 clearly showed evidence of smiling, 40 showed no clear evidence of smiling and the remaining 5 were impossible to classify (Table 18.15).

Table 18.15	Data for a one-sample chi-square		
	Clear smilers	**Clear non-smilers**	**Impossible to classify**
Observed frequency	35	40	5
Expected frequency	40	32	8

We can use the population distribution to work out the expected frequency in the sample of 80 if this sample precisely matched the population. Thus 50% of the 80 (= 40) should be clear smilers, 40% of the 80 (= 32) should be clear non-smilers, and 10% of the 80 (= 8) should be impossible to classify. Table 18.15 gives the expected frequencies (i.e. population-based) and observed frequencies (i.e. sample-based).

These observed and expected frequencies are entered into the usual chi-square formula. The only difference is that the degrees of freedom are not quite the same – they are the number of conditions minus 1 (i.e. $3 - 1 = 2$ in the above example):

$$\text{chi-square} = \sum \frac{(O - E)^2}{E}$$

$$= \frac{(35 - 40)^2}{40} + \frac{(40 - 32)^2}{32} + \frac{(5 - 8)^2}{8}$$

$$= \frac{(-5)^2}{40} + \frac{8^2}{32} + \frac{(-3)^2}{8}$$

$$= \frac{25}{40} + \frac{64}{32} + \frac{9}{8}$$

$$= 0.625 + 2.000 + 1.125 = 3.75$$

But from Significance Table 18.1 we can see that this value of chi-square is far below the critical value of 6.0 required to be significant at the 5% level. Thus the sample of foster babies is not significantly different from the population of babies in terms of their smiling response.

Interpreting the results

A significant value of the one-sample chi-square means that the distribution over the various categories departs markedly from that of the known population. That is, the sample is significantly different from the population and is unlikely to come from that population. In our example, however, the sample does not differ significantly from the population. This shows that smiling behaviour in our sample of babies is no different from that of the population of babies. For the one-sample chi-square, it is sufficient to compare the observed frequencies with the expected frequencies (which are the population values). In our example, there seems to be little difference between the sample and the population values.

Reporting the results

The following would summarise the findings of this study effectively: 'It was possible to compare smiling behaviour in babies in foster care with population values of known smiling behaviour on a standard developmental test. A one-sample chi-square test yielded a chi-square value of 3.75 which was not statistically significant with two degrees of freedom. Thus it can be concluded that the fostered babies were no different in terms of smiling behaviour from the general population of babies of this age.'

Alternatively, following the recommendations of the APA (2010) Publication Manual we could write: 'It was found that smiling behaviour in babies in foster care was not different from population figures obtained from a standard developmental test, $\chi^2(2, N = 80) = 3.75$, p ns. Thus it can be concluded that the fostered babies were no different in terms of smiling behaviour from the general population of babies of this age.' This style of reporting statistical significance is

18.7 Chi-square for related samples – the McNemar test

It is possible to use chi-square to compare related samples of frequencies. Essentially, this involves arranging the data in such a way that the chi-square contingency table only includes two categories: those that change from the first to the second occasion. For example, data are collected on whether or not teenage students wish to go to university; following a careers talk favouring university education the same informants are asked again whether they wish to go to university. The data can be tabulated as in Table 18.16.

Table 18.16	Illustrative data for the McNemar test	
	Before talk 'yes'	Before talk 'no'
After talk 'yes'	30	50
After talk 'no'	10	32

We can see from this table that although some students did not change their minds as a consequence of the talk (30 wanted to go to university before the talk and did not change their minds, 32 did not want to go to university before the talk and did not change their minds), some students did change. Fifty changed their minds and wanted to go to university following the talk and 10 changed their minds and did not want to go to university after the talk.

The McNemar test simply uses the data on those who changed; non-changers are ignored. The logic of the test is that if the talk did not actually affect the teenagers, just as many would change their minds in one direction after the talk as change their minds in the other direction. That is, 50% should change towards wanting to go to university and 50% should change against wanting to go to university, if the talk had no effect. We simply create a new table (Table 18.17) which only includes changers and calculate chi-square on the basis that the null hypothesis of no effect would suggest that 50% of the changers should change in each direction.

The calculation is now exactly like that for the one-sample chi-square. This gives us a chi-square value of 25.35 with one degree of freedom (since there are two conditions). This is very significant when checked against the critical values in Significance Table 18.1. Thus there appears to be more change towards wanting to go to university following the careers talk than change towards not wanting to go to university.

Table 18.17	Table of those who changed in a positive or negative direction based on Table 18.16	
	Positive changers	Negative changers
Observed frequency	50	10
Expected frequency	30	30

18.8 Example from the literature

In a study of the selection of prison officers, Crighton and Towl (1994) found the relation-

were selected during the recruitment process.

Table 18.18	Relationship between ethnicity and selection	
	Selected	Not selected
Ethnic minority	1	3
Ethnic majority	17	45
	Chi-square $= 0.43$; $p = ns$	

The interpretation of this table is that there is no significant relationship ($p = ns$) between selection and ethnicity. In other words, the table does not provide evidence of a selection bias in favour of white applicants, for example. While this is not an unreasonable conclusion based on the data if we ignore the small numbers of ethnic minority applicants, the statistical analysis itself is not appropriate. In particular, if you calculate the expected frequencies for the four cells you will find that 50% of the expected frequencies are less than 5, and thus a rule has been violated. The Fisher exact probability test would be better for these data.

Research examples

Chi-square and Fisher's exact probability test

Remember that these tests require nominal category variables.

Huisman, van Houwelingen and Kerkhof (2010) investigated whether psychiatric diagnosis, gender and status as in- or out-patient were associated with particular types of suicide methods. Initially they examined the relation between suicide method and each of these three variables separately using chi-square. Six categories of suicide methods were used. Each of these chi-squares was significant. So, for the chi-square for gender and suicide method, significantly more male patients (41%) hanged themselves than female patients (26%). Significantly more female patients (27%) poisoned themselves than male patients (12%).

Kogan (2004) examined factors that predicted disclosure in women who had unwanted sexual experiences in their childhood or adolescence. The dependent variables were the timing of disclosure and the person disclosed to. Timing of disclosure consisted of the three categories of immediate, delayed and non-disclosure. The categories of the sorts of person disclosed to were adult, peers only and non-disclosure. Predictors of these two dependent variables included age at which the experience first occurred. The person disclosed to was then recategorised by the researcher into four groups – whether the person knew the other person, whether they were family and so on. Initially, chi-square tests were carried out between each of the dependent variables and each of the predictor variables. There were a number of significant findings. For example, whether the experience was with a family member was significantly related to both dependent variables. Women who had the experience with a family member were less likely to disclose or disclose immediately and less likely to disclose to peers only.

Kois and colleagues (2013) wished to explore whether the research on competency to stand trial among male inpatients extended to female inpatients. They used chi-square to look for significant relationships between findings of incompetence and other variables. They found significant associations, for example, between incompetence (versus competence) and the nominal category variables of active psychotic symptoms, diagnosis of a psychotic disorder, non-compliance with medication, and non-felony charges and competency.

Key points

- Avoid as far as possible designing research with a multiplicity of categories and samples for chi-square. Large chi-squares with many cells are often difficult to interpret without numerous sub-analyses.

- Always make sure that your chi-square is carried out on frequencies and that each participant contributes only one to the total frequencies.

- Check for expected frequencies under 5; if you have too many then take one of the escape routes described if possible.

- Effect size measures are phi for 2 $\times$ 2 chi square or Cramér's V for larger.

COMPUTER ANALYSIS

Chi-square using SPSS

Data
- Name the variables in 'Variable View' of the 'Data Editor'.
- Enter the data in table form under the appropriate variable names in 'Data View' of the 'Data Editor' (Screenshot 18.1).

Analysis
- For a one-sample chi-square, select 'Analyze', 'Nonparametric Tests', 'Legacy Dialogs' and 'Chi-Square Test...' (Screenshot 18.2).

2
- Move category variable to right hand box and enter 'Expected Values' of frequencies for the categories of that variable.
- Select 'OK'.

3
- For a more than one-sample chi-square, select 'Analyze', 'Descriptive Statistics' and 'Crosstabs...' (Screenshot 18.3).

4
- Move appropriate variables to 'Row(s):' and 'Column(s):' boxes.

5
- Select 'Statistics...', 'Chi-square' and 'Continue'.
- Select 'Cells...' 'Expected' and 'Unstandardized', 'Continue' and 'OK' (Screenshot 18.4).

6
- For a McNemar test, select 'Analyze', 'Nonparametric Tests', 'Legacy Dialogs' and '2-Related Samples...'.

7
- Move appropriate pair of variables to box to right and select 'McNemar' and 'OK'.

Output
- Check that the minimum expected frequencies have been met (Screenshot 18.5).
- Check that the test is statistically significant with $p = .05$ or less.

2
- Determine direction of significant difference.

Interpreting and reporting the output

There are two alternative ways of describing these results for the data in Table 18.8 and the output shown in Screenshot 18.5. To the inexperienced eye they may seem very different but they amount to the same thing:

- We could describe the results in the following way: 'There was a significant difference between the observed and expected frequency of teenage boys and girls in their preference for the three types of television programme, $\chi^2(2) = 13.51, p = .001.$'

- Alternatively, and just as accurate: 'There was a significant association between gender and preference for different types of television programme, $\chi^2(2) = 13.51, p = .001.$'

- In addition, we need to report the direction of the results. One way of doing this is to state that: 'Girls were more likely than boys to prefer crime programmes and less likely to prefer soap operas or both programmes.'

- With greater than 2 × 2 tables as in this case, it is most probably worthwhile presenting a table of the frequencies.

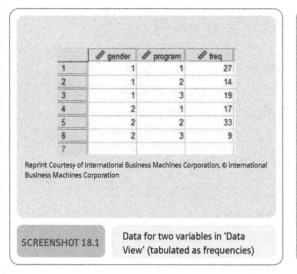

Reprint Courtesy of International Business Machines Corporation, © International Business Machines Corporation

SCREENSHOT 18.1 Data for two variables in 'Data View' (tabulated as frequencies)

Reprint Courtesy of International Business Machines Corporation, © International Business Machines Corporation

SCREENSHOT 18.2 On 'Analyze' select one-way 'Chi-square... '

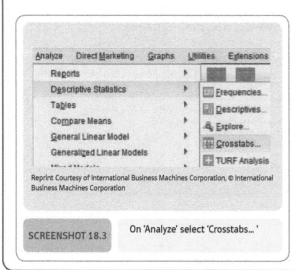

Reprint Courtesy of International Business Machines Corporation, © International Business Machines Corporation

SCREENSHOT 18.3 On 'Analyze' select 'Crosstabs... '

Reprint Courtesy of International Business Machines Corporation, © International Business Machines Corporation

Select 'Expected' frequencies

gender * program Crosstabulation

| | | | program | | | |
			Soap	Crime	Neither	Total
gender	Males	Count	27	14	19	60
		Expected Count	22.2	23.7	14.1	60.0
		Residual	4.8	-9.7	4.9	
	Females	Count	17	33	9	59
		Expected Count	21.8	23.3	13.9	59.0
		Residual	-4.8	9.7	-4.9	
Total		Count	44	47	28	119
		Expected Count	44.0	47.0	28.0	119.0

Chi-Square Tests

	Value	df	Asymptotic Significance (2-sided)
Pearson Chi-Square	13.518[a]	2	.001
Likelihood Ratio	13.841	2	.001
Linear-by-Linear Association	.000	1	.987
N of Valid Cases	119		

a. 0 cells (0.0%) have expected count less than 5. The minimum expected count is 13.88.

Reprint Courtesy of International Business Machines Corporation, © International Business Machines Corporation

SCREENSHOT 18.5	Two-way chi-square output

Recommended further reading

Maxwell, A. E. (1961). *Analysing qualitative data*. London: Methuen.

CHAPTER 19

Probability

Overview

- Although probability theory is at the heart of statistics, in practice researchers need to know relatively little of this.

- The addition rule basically suggests that the probability of, say, any of three categories occurring is the sum of the three individual probabilities for those categories.

- The multiplication rule suggests that the probability of different events occurring in a particular sequence is the product of the individual probabilities.

Preparation

General familiarity with previous chapters.

19.1 Introduction

From time to time, researchers need to be able to calculate the probabilities associated with certain patterns of events. One of us remembers being a student in a class that carried out an experiment based on newspaper reports of a Russian study in which people appeared to be able to recognise colours through their fingertips. So we designed an experiment in which a blindfolded person felt different colours in random order. Most of us did not do very well but some in the class seemed excellent. The media somehow heard about the study and a particularly good identifier in our experiment quickly took part in a live TV demonstration of her skills. She was appallingly bad at the task this time.

The reason why she was bad on television was that she had no special skills in the first place. It had been merely a matter of chance that she had done well in the laboratory. On the television programme, chance was not on her side and she turned out to be as hopeless as the rest of us. Actually, this reflects a phenomenon commonly referred to as *regression to the mean*. Choose a person (or group) because of their especially high (or, alternatively, especially low) scores and they will tend to score closer to the mean on the next administration of the test or measurement. This is because the test or measure is to a degree unreliable and by choosing exceptional scores you have to an extent capitalised on chance factors. With a completely unreliable test or measure, the reversion towards the mean will be dramatic. In our colour experiment the student did badly on TV because she had been selected totally on the basis of a criterion that was fundamentally unreliable – that is, completely at random.

Similar problems occur in any investigation of individual paranormal or psychic powers. For example, a spiritual medium who addresses a crowd of 500 people is doing nothing spectacular if in Britain she claims to be speaking to a dead relative of someone and that relative is Mary or Martha or Margaret. The chances of someone in the 500 having such a relative are very high.

19.2 Principles of probability

When any of us use a test of significance we are utilising probability theory. This is because statistical tests are based on it. Our working knowledge of probability does not have to be very great for us to function well. We have been using probability in previous chapters on significance testing when we talked about the 5% level of significance, the 1% level of significance and the 95% confidence intervals. Basically what we meant by a 5% level of significance is that a particular event (or outcome) would occur on five occasions out of 100. Although we have adopted the percentage system of reporting probabilities in this book, statisticians would normally not write of a 5% probability. Instead they would express it as being out of a *single* event rather than 100 events. Thus:

- .05 is an alternative way of writing 5%

- .10 is an alternative way of writing 10%

- 1.00 is an alternative way of writing 100%.

The difficulty for some of us with this alternative, more formal, way of writing probability is that it leaves everything in decimals, which does not appeal to the less mathematically skilled. However, you should be aware of the alternative notation since it appears in many research reports. Furthermore, much computer output can give probabilities to several decimal places which can be confusing. For example, what does a probability of .000 001 mean? The answer is one chance in 100 000 or a 0.0001% probability ($\frac{1}{1\,000\,000} \times 100 = 0.0001\%$).

There are two rules of probability with which psychologists ought to be familiar. They are the *addition rule* and the *multiplication rule*.

- The *addition rule* is quite straightforward. It merely states that for a number of mutually exclusive outcomes the sum of their probabilities adds up to 1.00. So if you have a set of 150 people of whom 100 are women and 50 are men, the probability of picking a woman at random is 100 ÷ 150 or .667. The probability of picking a man at random is 50 ÷ 150 or .333. However, the probability of picking either a man or a woman at random is .667 + .333 or 1.00. In other words, it is certain that you will pick either a man or a woman. The assumption is that the categories or outcomes are mutually exclusive, meaning that a person cannot be in both the man and woman categories. Being a man excludes that person from also being a woman. In statistical probability theory, one of the two possible outcomes is usually denoted p and the other is denoted q, so $p + q = 1.00$. Outcomes that are not mutually exclusive include, for example, the categories man and young since a person could be a man and young.

- The *multiplication rule* is about a set of events. It can be illustrated by our set of 150 men and women, in which 100 are women and 50 are men. Again the assumption is that the categories or outcomes are mutually exclusive. We could ask how likely it is that the first five people that we pick at random will all be women, given that the probability of choosing a woman on a single occasion is .667. The answer is that we multiply the probability associated with the first person being a woman by the probability that the second person will be a woman by the probability that the third person will be a woman by the probability that the fourth person will be a woman by the probability that the fifth person will be a woman:

Probability of all five being women $= p \times p \times p \times p \times p$

$$= .667 \times .667 \times .667 \times .667 \times .667$$

$$= .13$$

Therefore there is a 13% probability (.13) that we will choose a sample of five women at random. That is not a particularly rare outcome. However, picking a sample of all men from our set of men and women is much rarer:

Probability of all five being men $= p \times p \times p \times p \times p$

$$= .333 \times .333 \times .333 \times .333 \times .333$$

$$= .004$$

Therefore there is a 0.4% probability (.004) of choosing all men.

The multiplication rule as stated here assumes that once a person is selected for inclusion in the sample, he or she is replaced in the population and possibly selected again. This is called random sampling with replacement. However, normally we do not do this in psychological research, though if the population is big then not replacing the individual back into the population has negligible influence on the outcome. Virtually all statistical analyses assume replacement, but it does not matter that people are usually not selected more than once for a study in psychological research.

19.3 Implications

Such theoretical considerations concerning probability theory have a number of implications for research. They ought to be carefully noted.

- *Repeated significance testing within the same study* It is tempting to carry out several statistical tests on data. Usually we find that a portion of these tests are statistically significant at the 5% level whereas a number are not. Indeed, even if there were absolutely no trends in the population, we would expect, by chance, 5% of our comparisons to be significant at the 5% level. This is the meaning of statistical significance, after all. The more statistical comparisons we make on our data the more significant findings we would expect. If we did 20 comparisons we would expect one significant finding even if there are no trends in the population. In order to cope with this, the correct procedure is to make the statistical significance more stringent the more tests of significance we do. So, if we did two tests then our significance level per test should be 5%/2 or 2.5%; if we did four comparisons our significance level would be 5%/4 or 1.25% significance per test. In other words, we simply divide the 5% significance level by the number of tests we are doing. Although this is the proper thing to do, few psychological reports actually do it. However, the consequence of not doing this is to find more significant findings than you should.

- *Significance testing across different studies* An application of the multiplication rule in assessing the value of replicating research shows the dramatic increase in significance that this can achieve. Replication means the essential repeating of a study at a later date and possibly in radically different circumstances such as other locations. Imagine that the significance level achieved in the original study is 5% ($p = .05$). If one finds the same significance level in the replication, the probability of two studies producing this level of significance by chance is $p \times p$ or $.05 \times .05 = .0025$ or 0.25%. This considerably enhances our confidence that the findings of the research are not the result of chance factors but reflect significant trends.

Explaining statistics 19.1

Addition rule

A psychologist wishes to calculate the chance expectations of marks on a multiple choice test of general knowledge. Since a person could get some answers correct simply by sticking a pin into the answer paper, there has to be a minimum score below which the individual is doing no better than chance. If each question has four response options then one would expect that by chance a person could get one in four or one-quarter of the answers correct. That is intuitively obvious. But what if some questions have three possible answers and others have four? This is not quite so obvious, but we simply apply the law of addition and add together the probabilities of being correct for all of the questions on the paper. This entails adding together probabilities of .33 and .25 since there are three or four possible answers. So if there are 10 questions with three possible answers and five questions with four possible answers, the number of answers correct by chance is $(10 \times .33) + (5 \times .25) = 3.3 + 1.25 = 4.55$.

| Explaining statistics 19.2 |

Multiplication rule

A psychologist studies a pair of male twins who have been brought up separately and who have never met. The psychologist is surprised to find that the twins are alike on seven out of ten different characteristics, as presented below. The probability of their characteristics occurring in the general population is given in brackets:

1. They both marry women younger than themselves (.9).

2. They both marry brunettes (.7).

3. They both drive (.7).

4. They both swim (.6).

5. They have both spent time in hospital (.8).

6. They both take foreign holidays (.5).

7. They both part their hair on the left (.9).

However, they are different in the following ways:

8. One attends church (.4) and the other does not.

9. One has a doctorate (.03) and the other does not.

10. One smokes (.3) and the other does not.

The similarities between the two men are impressive if it is exceptional for two randomly selected men to be similar on each of the items. As stated above, the probabilities in brackets are the proportions of men in the general population demonstrating these characteristics. For many of the characteristics it seems quite likely that they will be similar. So two men taken at random from the general population are most likely to marry a younger woman. Since the probability of marrying a younger woman is .9, the probability of any two men marrying younger women is $.9 \times .9 = .81$. The probability of two men taken at random both being drivers is $.7 \times .7 = .49$. In fact the ten characteristics listed above are shared by randomly selected pairs of men with the following probabilities:

1. $.9 \times .9 = .81$

2. $.7 \times .7 = .49$

3. $.7 \times .7 = .49$

4. $.6 \times .6 = .36$

5. $.8 \times .8 = .64$

6. $.5 \times .5 = .25$

7. $.9 \times .9 = .81$

8. $.4 \times .4 = .16$

9. $.03 \times .03 = .0009$

10. $.3 \times .3 = .09$

The sum of these probabilities is 4.10. Clearly the twins are more alike than we might expect on the basis of chance. However, it might be that we would get a different answer if instead of taking the general population of men, we took men of the same age as the twins.

Key points

- Although probability theory is of crucial importance for mathematical statisticians, psychologists generally rely on an intuitive approach to the topic. This may be laziness on their part, but we have kept the coverage of probability to a minimum given the scope of this book. It can also be very deterring to anyone not too mathematically inclined. If you need to know more, especially if you need to estimate precisely the likelihood of a particular pattern or sequence of events occurring, we suggest that you consult books such as Kerlinger (1986) for more complete accounts of mathematical probability theory.

- However, it is important to avoid basic mistakes such as repeated significance testing on the same data without adjusting your significance levels to allow for the multitude of tests. This is not necessary for tests designed for multiple testing such as those for the analysis of variance, some of which we discuss later (Chapter 26), as the adjustment is built in.

CHAPTER 20

One-tailed versus two-tailed significance testing

Overview

- Hypotheses which do not or cannot stipulate the direction of the relationship between variables are called non-directional. So far we have only dealt with non-directional tests of hypotheses. These are also known as two-tailed tests.

- Some hypotheses stipulate the direction of the relationship between the variables – either a positive relation or a negative relation. These are known as directional hypotheses or one-tailed tests.

- Directional tests result in more significant findings than non-directional tests when applied to the same data. This is provided that the trend is in the direction stipulated.

- However, there are considerable restrictions on when directional tests are allowable. Without very carefully planning, it is wise to deal with one's data as if it were non-directional. Most student research is unlikely to meet the requirements of one-tailed testing.

Preparation

Revise the null hypothesis and alternative hypothesis (Chapter 11) and significance testing.

20.1   Introduction

Sometimes researchers are so confident about the likely outcome of their research that they make pretty strong predictions about the relationship between their independent and dependent variables. So, for example, rather than say that the *independent variable* age is correlated with verbal ability, the researcher predicts that the *independent variable* age is *positively* correlated with the *dependent variable* verbal ability. In other words, it is predicted that the older participants in the research will have better verbal skills. Equally the researcher might predict a *negative* relationship between the independent and dependent variables.

It is conventional in psychological statistics to treat such *directional* predictions differently from *non-directional* predictions. Normally psychologists speak of a directional prediction being one-tailed whereas a non-directional prediction is two-tailed. The crucial point is that if you have a directional prediction (one-tailed test) the critical values of the significance test become slightly different.

In order to carry out a one-tailed test you need to be satisfied that the criteria for one-tailed testing are fulfilled. These, as we will see, are rather stringent. In our experience, many one-tailed hypotheses put forward by students are little more than hunches and certainly not based on the required strong past research or strong theory. In these circumstances it is wrong to carry out one-tailed testing. It would be best to regard the alternative hypothesis as non-directional and choose two-tailed significance testing exactly as we have done so far in this book. One-tailed testing is a contentious issue and you may be confronted with different points of view; some authorities reject it although it is fairly commonplace if not frequent in psychological research.

20.2   Theoretical considerations

If we take a directional alternative hypothesis (such as that intelligence correlates positively with level of education) then it is necessary to revise our understanding of the null hypothesis somewhat. (The same is true if the directional alternative hypothesis suggests a negative relationship between the two variables.) In the case of the positively worded alternative hypothesis, the null hypothesis is:

Intelligence does not correlate *positively* with level of education.

Our previous style of null hypothesis would have left out the word *positively*. There are two different circumstances which support the null hypothesis that intelligence does not correlate *positively* with level of education:

If intelligence *does not correlate* at all with level of education, or

If intelligence correlates *negatively* with level of education.

That is, it is only research which shows a positive correlation between intelligence and education which supports the directional hypothesis – if we found an extreme negative correlation between intelligence and education this should lead to the rejection of the alternative hypothesis just as would zero or near-zero relationships. Because, in a sense, the dice is loaded against the directional alternative hypothesis, it is conventional to argue that we should not use the extremes of the sampling distribution in both directions for our test of significance for the directional hypothesis. Instead we should take the extreme

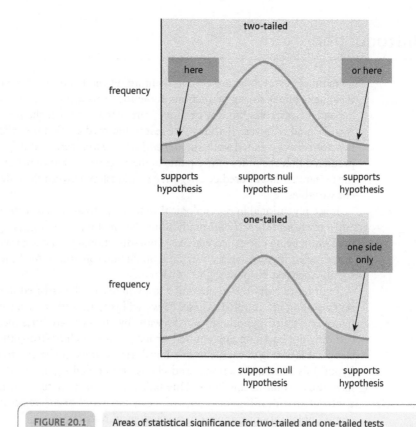

| FIGURE 20.1 | Areas of statistical significance for two-tailed and one-tailed tests |

samples in the positive direction (if it is positively worded) or the extreme samples in the negative direction (if it is negatively worded). In other words, our extreme 5% of samples which we define as significant should all be from one side of the sampling distribution, not 2.5% on each side as we would have done previously (see Figure 20.1).

Because the 5% of extreme samples, which are defined as significant, are all on the same side of the distribution, you need a smaller value of your significance test to be in that extreme 5%. Part of the attraction of directional or one-tailed significance tests of this sort is that basically you can get the same level of significance with a smaller sample or smaller trend than would be required for a two-tailed test. Essentially the probability level can be halved – what would be significant at the 5% level with a two-tailed test is significant at the 2.5% level with a one-tailed test, for example.

There is a big proviso to this. If you predicted a positive relationship but found what would normally be a significant negative relationship, with a one-tailed test you ought to ignore that negative relationship – it merely supports the null hypothesis. The temptation is, however, to ignore your original directional alternative hypothesis and pretend that you had not predicted the direction. Given that significant results are at a premium in psychology and are much more likely to get published, it is not surprising that psychologists seeking to publish their research might be tempted to 'adjust' their hypotheses slightly.

It is noteworthy that the research literature contains very few tests of significance of directional hypotheses which are rejected when the trend in the data is strongly (and significantly with a two-tailed test) in the opposite direction to that predicted. The only example we know of was written by one of us. Figure 20.2 gives the key steps to consider in understanding one- and two-tailed significance testing.

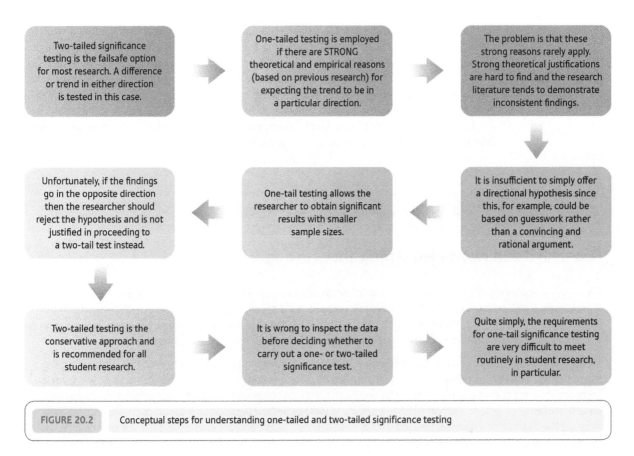

FIGURE 20.2   Conceptual steps for understanding one-tailed and two-tailed significance testing

20.3   Further requirements

A number of other rules are supposed to be followed if one is to use a directional hypothesis, including the following:

- The prediction should be based on strong and well-researched theory, and not on a whim or intuition.

- The prediction is based on previous similar research demonstrating consistent trends in the predicted direction.

- One should make the above predictions in advance of knowing the trends in the data. That is, for example, you do not look at your scattergrams and then 'predict' the direction of the correlation between your variables. That would be manifestly not a prediction. It is a cheat's way of getting significant results with a one-tailed test when a two-tailed test does not quite reach statistical significance.

There is another practical problem in the use of directional hypotheses. That is, if you have *more than two groups* of scores it is often very difficult to decide what the predicting trends between the groups should be. For essentially this reason, many statistical techniques are commonly regarded as directionless when more than two groups of scores or participants are involved. This often applies to techniques such as chi-square, the analysis of variance and other similar tests.

Although this is clearly a controversial area, you will probably find that as a student you rarely if ever have sufficient justification for employing a one-tailed test. As you might have gathered, most of these criteria for selecting a one-tailed test are to a degree subjective which is less than desirable. We would recommend that you choose a two-tailed or directionless test unless there is a pressing and convincing reason to do otherwise. Otherwise the danger of loading things in favour of significant results is too great.

In addition to two-tailed critical values, the significance tables in the appendices give the one-tailed values where these are appropriate.

Research examples

One-tailed and two-tailed significance testing

The use of one-tailed significance testing seems to be relatively uncommon in modern psychology research publications. Whether this is a good thing depends to some extent on one's point of view. It possibly indicates a diminished interest in testing highly specific hypotheses based on theory and past research in favour of a more exploratory approach to data analysis. With the latter, it is not really appropriate to make predictions about the direction of trends.

Meeten and Davey (2012) manipulated one of five moods by showing participants one of five films reflecting those moods. The five conditions were sad, happy, anxious, angry and neutral. Participants rated how they felt immediately after seeing the film and at the end of the study in terms of the four moods of sadness, happiness, anxiety and anger. Because each of the five conditions were expected to produce a particular mood immediately after seeing the film, one-tailed unrelated t-tests were carried out to compare each of the five conditions on each of the four moods. The five conditions were found to produce the expected mood. In order to see whether the induced mood was still present at the end of the study they carried out two-tailed related t-tests as they did not predict any particular results. There was only a significant change for anger, which was less at the end of the study.

Hoicka and Akhtar (2012) report in their study of early humour in children that 'Mann–Whitney U-tests revealed no effects of children's age or gender for whether children produced each humour type (all $p > .281$)' (p. 589). No indication is given of whether one- or two-tailed tests of significance were used but the default option is two-tailed tests. Only if the testing is indicated to be one-tailed do we assume that it is.

Key points

- Routinely make your alternative hypotheses two-tailed or directionless. This is especially the case when the implications of your research are of practical or policy significance. However, this may not be ideal if you are testing theoretical predictions when the direction of the hypothesis might be important. Nevertheless, it is a moot point whether you should take advantage of the 'less stringent' significance requirements of a one-tailed test.

- If you believe that the well-established theoretical or empirical basis for predicting the direction of the outcomes is strong enough, then still be a little cautious about employing one-tailed tests. In particular, do not formulate your hypothesis *after* collecting or viewing your data.

- You cannot be faulted for using two-tailed tests since they are less likely to show significant relationships. Thus they are described as being statistically more conservative. Student research often does not arise out of previous research or theory. Often the research is initiated before earlier research and theory have been reviewed. In these circumstances one-tailed tests are not warranted.

COMPUTER ANALYSIS

One- and two-tailed statistical significance using SPSS

- If there are good grounds for predicting the direction of the relationship between two variables, it is conventional to use a one-tailed rather than a two-tailed significance level. SPSS provides a one-tailed significance level for correlations and a 2 × 2 chi-square. It does not do this for t-tests and analysis of variance with two groups. To obtain the one-tailed level for these tests, the two-tailed significance level needs to be divided by 2.

CHAPTER 21

Ranking tests

Nonparametric statistics

Overview

- There are many statistical techniques which are not based on the normal curve.

- Some data violate the assumption of normality underlying many statistical tests. However, violations generally have modest impact on the outcomes of statistical analyses.

- Nonparametric and distribution-free statistics are often helpful where one's data violate the assumptions of other tests too much.

- For each of the tests discussed in the earlier chapters of this book, a nonparametric or distribution-free alternative is available.

- Unfortunately, in many cases there is no satisfactory alternative to the parametric tests.

Preparation

Be aware of the *t*-tests for related and unrelated samples. Revise ranking (Chapter 8).

21.1 Introduction

From time to time, any researcher will be faced with deciding between parametric and nonparametric significance tests. The difference is quite straightforward. Many statistical techniques require that the details are known or estimates can be made of the characteristics of the population. Almost invariably, as we have seen, the population is the population defined by the null hypothesis. These are known as parametric tests (a parameter is a characteristic of a population). Generally speaking, the numerical scores we used in previous chapters needed to roughly approximate to the normal (bell-shaped) distribution for parametric statistical tests to be satisfactory. The reason is that the statistician's theoretical assumptions, when developing the test, included the normal distribution of the data. Fortunately, the distribution of scores on a variable would have to be very lopsided (skewed) in order for the outcomes to be seriously misleading. Appendix A explains how to test for such skewness.

What can be done if the assumptions of parametric tests are substantially violated? One traditional alternative approach is called *nonparametric* testing because it makes few or no assumptions about the distribution in the population. Many nonparametric tests of significance are based on rankings given to the original numerical scores – it is unusual for researchers to collect their data in the form of ranks in the first place. Conventionally these tests for ranks were regarded as relatively easy computations for students – this was part of their appeal. However, in the age of computers this is hardly a compelling reason for their use. Nonparametric statistical tests also have their problems:

- Calculating them becomes disproportionately cumbersome with increasing amounts of data. This is not a problem for computers.

- They also suffer from the difficulty that many psychological data are gathered using rather restricted ranges of scores. This often results in the same values appearing several times in a set of data making ranking a little harder. Dealing with these tied scores produces many tied ranks which makes some nonparametric tests somewhat inaccurate to an unknown extent.

- Worst of all, the variety and flexibility of nonparametric statistical techniques are inferior to those of parametric statistics. For this reason it is generally best to err towards using parametric statistics in our opinion. Certainly current research practice seems to increasingly disfavour nonparametric statistics. The modern research literature overwhelmingly favours parametric statistics.

Figure 21.1 gives some of the key steps when deciding whether to use nonparametric statistics. Box 21.1 discusses bootstrapping which is an increasingly popular way of dealing with data which do not meet the requirements of parametric tests of significance.

21.2 Theoretical considerations

Ranking merely involves the ordering of a set of scores from the smallest to the largest. The smallest score is given the rank 1, the second smallest score is given the rank 2, the 50th smallest score is given the rank 50 and so on.

Since many nonparametric statistical techniques use ranks, the question is raised why this is so. The answer is very much the same as the reason for using the normal distribution as the basis for parametric statistics – it provides a standard distribution of scores

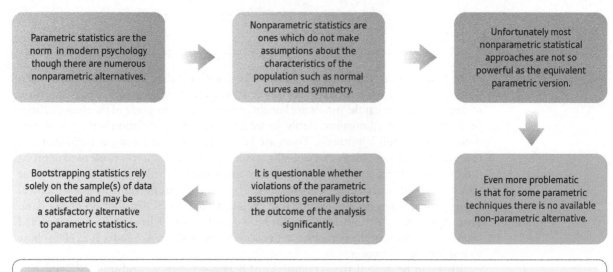

Parametric statistics are the norm in modern psychology though there are numerous nonparametric alternatives.

Nonparametric statistics are ones which do not make assumptions about the characteristics of the population such as normal curves and symmetry.

Unfortunately most nonparametric statistical approaches are not so powerful as the equivalent parametric version.

Bootstrapping statistics rely solely on the sample(s) of data collected and may be a satisfactory alternative to parametric statistics.

It is questionable whether violations of the parametric assumptions generally distort the outcome of the analysis significantly.

Even more problematic is that for some parametric techniques there is no available non-parametric alternative.

FIGURE 21.1   Conceptual steps for understanding nonparametric statistics

any given number of scores the ranks are always the same. So the ranks of 10 scores which represent the IQs of the 10 greatest geniuses of all time are exactly the same as the ranks for the scores on introversion of the 10 members of the local stamp collectors' club: 1, 2, 3, 4, 5, 6, 7, 8, 9 and 10.

Since all sets of 10 scores use exactly the same set of ranks, this considerably eases the statistician's calculations of the distribution of the ranks under the null hypothesis that there is no relationship between pairs of variables. Instead of an infinite variety of 10 scores, there is just this one set of 10 ranks on which to do one's calculations. Only sample size makes a difference to the ranks, not the precise numerical values of the scores themselves.

Box 21.1   Key concepts

Bootstrapping

Probably the history of statistics in psychology would have been somewhat different if computers had been available earlier. Many of the statistical techniques which modern psychologists routinely compute using powerful computer programs are actually quite elderly and, in some ways, creak a little when used in this digital age. In particular, the various standard statistical distributions, such as the *t*-distribution and the *F*-distribution, which are used in statistics were particularly important because they enabled calculations to be carried out relatively easily, long before electronic calculators, let alone computers, had been invented. But could things have been different if computers had been available to the early statisticians?

Bootstrapping refers to a number of techniques which do not assume a particular shape or distribution to the population. We have seen that, for example, the *t*-test assumes that the data are normally distributed. Instead bootstrapping simply assumes that a sample or sample of scores represents what is going on in the population. In other words, the population simply has the characteristics of the sample(s). So if the distribution of scores in a sample is 6, 8, 9, 9, 11, 12 and 13, then it is assumed that the population is exactly the same. Wait a minute, we cannot work out a sampling distribution of samples of seven scores if we only have seven scores, can we? There is only one sample of seven possible from seven scores. This is quite right. The 'trick' in bootstrapping is to take these seven scores and reproduce them, say, a thousand times, so that instead of seven scores we have 7000 scores. There is nothing in this bootstrapped 'population' that was not in the sample – everything is merely reproduced many times.

Doing this makes it possible to work out a sampling distribution of samples of seven taken from this bootstrapped population. Actually, literally hundreds if not thousands of samples are drawn and the distribution, say, of their means plotted. So it is possible to work out the likelihood of getting a particular sample mean given this bootstrapped sampling distribution. This is number crunching with a vengeance but the sort of work that computers excel at. The good news is that SPSS does bootstrapping as part of some of the statistical routines that it carries out – for example, the *t*-test. Where it is available, bootstrapping only requires the minimum effort of selecting the bootstrapping option.

Bootstrapping is capable of calculating things which are not easily calculated by traditional means – for example, it can work out the standard deviation of the median and any number of other statistics. From the point of view of the present chapter on nonparametric statistics, bootstrapping does not make assumptions about the data of the sort that parametric statistical tests do. Consequently, it can be seen as a powerful alternative to parametric testing but based on the same routines as the parametric test.

A problem with boot strapping is that the outcome is not absolutely reliable since different researchers analysing the same data will obtain statistical outcomes which differ a little. This is simply the consequence of the random selection process involved. This does not happen with more traditional statistics.

Many statistical procedures in SPSS have bootstrap options that you can choose. They give significance levels based on the bootstrapped population. These significance levels, obviously, are not identical to those calculated from, say, the *t*-distribution, etc., but constitute a perfectly valid approach to significance testing which does not make assumptions about the distribution of the population.

21.3   Nonparametric statistical tests

There is an extensive battery of nonparametric tests, although many are interchangeable with each other or rather obscure with very limited applications. In this chapter we will consider only a small number of tests which you may come across during your university courses or general reading. We have discussed chi-square (for frequencies) and Spearman's rho (for correlations) elsewhere in this book. The nonparametric tests discussed in this chapter are usually applicable in very much the same experimental designs as the parametric tests we have discussed elsewhere (see Table 21.1).

■ Tests for related samples

Two nonparametric tests are common in the literature – the sign test (which is not based on ranks) and the Wilcoxon matched pairs test (which is based on ranks). Because they would apply to data for the related *t*-test, we will use the data for Explaining statistics 13.1 to illustrate the application of both of these tests.

Table 21.1	Similar parametric and nonparametric tests	
Parametric test	**Nonparametric equivalent**
Related *t*-test	Wilcoxon matched pairs test
	Sign test
Unrelated *t*-test	Mann–Whitney *U*-test
One-way ANOVA	Kruskal–Wallis test (Appendix B2)
	Friedman test (Appendix B2)

Explaining statistics 21.1

How the sign test works

The sign test is like the related *t*-test in that it takes the differences between the two related samples of scores. However, instead of considering the size of the difference, the sign test merely uses the sign of the difference. In other words, it loses a lot of the information inherent in the size of the difference.

Step 1 Delete from the analysis any case which has identical scores for both variables. They are ignored in the sign test. Take the second group of scores away from the first group (Table 21.2). Remember to include the sign of the difference (+ or −)

Table 21.2	Steps in the calculation of the sign test		
Subject	Six months X_1	Nine months X_2	Difference $D = X_1 - X_2$
Baby Clara	3	7	−4
Baby Martin	5	6	−1
Baby Sally	5	3	+2
Baby Angie	4	8	−4
Baby Trevor	3	5	−2
Baby Sam	7	9	−2
Baby Bobby	8	7	+1
Baby Sid	7	9	−2

Step 2 Count the number of scores which are positively signed and then count the number of scores which are negatively signed. (Don't forget that zero differences are ignored in the sign test.)

Step 3 Take whichever is the smaller number – the number of positive signs or the number of negative signs.

Step 4 Look up the significance of this smaller number in Significance Table 21.1. You need to find the row which contains the sum of the positive and negative signs (i.e. ignoring zero differences). Your value has to be in the tabulated range to be statistically significant.

In our example, there are 6 negative and 2 positive signs; 2 is the smaller number. The sum of positive and negative signs is 8. Significance Table 21.1 gives the significant values of the smaller number of signs as 0 only. Therefore our value is not statistically unusual and we accept the null hypothesis.

It would be a good approximation to use the one-sample chi-square formula (Explaining statistics 13.1), given that you would expect equal numbers of positive and negative differences under the null hypothesis that 'the two samples do not differ'. That is, the distributions of the sign test and the McNemar test (Section 18.7) for the significance of changes are the same.

Significance Table 21.1	5% significance values for the sign test giving values of T (the smaller of the sums of signs) (two-tailed test). An extended table is given in Appendix G

Number of pairs of scores (ignoring any tied pairs)	Significant at 5% level Accept hypothesis
6–8	0 only
9–11	0 to 1
12–14	0 to 2
15–16	0 to 3
17–19	0 to 4
20–22	0 to 5
23–24	0 to 6
25	0 to 7
26–28	0 to 8
29–30	0 to 9
31–33	0 to 10
34–35	0 to 11
36–38	0 to 12
39–40	0 to 13
41–42	0 to 14
43–45	0 to 15
46–47	0 to 16
48–49	0 to 17
50	0 to 18

Your value must be in the listed ranges for your sample size to be significant at the 5% level (i.e. to accept the hypothesis).

Interpreting the results

The mean scores for eye contact at six months and nine months need to be checked in order to know what the trend is in the data. Although eye contact was greater at nine months, the sign test is not significant which means that we should accept the null hypothesis of no differences in eye contact at the two ages.

Reporting the results

Following the APA (2010) Publication Manual recommendations, we could write these results as follows: 'Eye contact was higher at nine months ($M = 6.75$) than at six months ($M = 5.25$). However, this difference was insufficient to cause us to reject the null hypothesis that the amount of eye contact is the same at six months and nine months of age, sign test (8), $p = 289$.'

The calculation steps for the Wilcoxon matched pairs (or signed ranks) test are similar. However, this test retains a little more information from the original scores by ranking the differences.

Explaining statistics 21.2

How the Wilcoxon matched pairs test works

The test is also known as the Wilcoxon signed ranks test. It is similar to the sign test except that when we have obtained the difference score we rank-order the differences ignoring the sign of the difference.

Step 1 The difference scores are calculated and then ranked ignoring the sign of the difference (Table 21.3). Notice that where there are tied values of the differences, we have allocated the average of the ranks which would be given if it were possible to separate the scores. Thus the two difference scores which equal 1 are both given the rank 1.5 since if the scores did differ minutely one would be given the rank 1 and the other the rank 2. Take care: zero differences are ignored and are not ranked.

Table 21.3	Steps in the calculation of the Wilcoxon matched pairs test			
Subject	Six months X_1	Nine months X_2	Difference $D = X_1 - X_2$	Rank of difference ignoring sign during ranking
Baby Clara	3	7	−4	7.5−
Baby Martin	5	6	−1	1.5−
Baby Sally	5	3	2	4.5+
Baby Angie	4	8	−4	7.5−
Baby Trevor	3	5	−2	4.5−
Baby Sam	7	9	−2	4.5−
Baby Bobby	8	7	1	1.5+
Baby Sid	7	9	−2	4.5−

Step 2 The ranks of the differences can now have the sign of the difference reattached.

Step 3 The sum of the positive ranks is calculated = 4.5 + 1.5 = 6. The sum of the negative ranks is calculated = 7.5 + 1.5 + 7.5 + 4.5 + 4.5 + 4.5 = 30.

Step 4 We then decide which is the smaller of the two sums of ranks – in this case it is 6. This is normally designated T.

Step 5 We then find the significance values of T (the smaller of the two sums of ranks) from Significance Table 21.2. This is structured in terms of the number of pairs of scores used in the calculation, which is 8 in the present case. The critical value for a two-tailed test at the 5% level is 4 or less. Our value is 6 which is not statistically significant.

If your sample size is larger than Significance Table 21.2 deals with, Appendix B1 explains how to test for significance.

Significance Table 21.2	5% significance values for the Wilcoxon matched pairs test (two-tailed test). An extended and conventional significance table is given in Appendix H
Number of pairs of scores (ignoring any tied pairs)	**Significant at 5% level Accept hypothesis**
6	0 only
7	0 to 2
8	0 to 4
9	0 to 6
10	0 to 8
11	0 to 11
12	0 to 14
13	0 to 17
14	0 to 21
15	0 to 25
16	0 to 30
17	0 to 35
18	0 to 40
19	0 to 46
20	0 to 52
21	0 to 59
22	0 to 66
23	0 to 74
24	0 to 81
25	0 to 90

Your value must be in the listed ranges for your sample size to be significant at the 5% level (i.e. to accept the hypothesis).

Interpreting the results

As always, it is important to examine the means of the two sets of scores in order to know what the trend in the data is. Although the amount of eye contact at nine months was greater than at six months, the Wilcoxon matched pairs test failed to reach statistical significance so it is not possible to reject the null hypothesis of no differences in eye contact at the two ages.

Reporting the results

Following the APA (2010) Publication Manual recommendations we could write the results as follows: 'Eye contact was slightly higher at nine months ($M = 6.75$) than at six months ($M = 5.25$). However, this difference did not reach statistical significance so it was not possible to reject the null hypothesis that eye contact does not change between these ages, $T(8) = 6, p = .088$.'

Generally speaking, it is difficult to suggest circumstances in which the sign test is to be preferred over the Wilcoxon matched pairs test. The latter uses more of the information contained within the data and so is more likely to detect significant differences where they exist.

The sign test can be applied in virtually any circumstance in which the expected population distribution under the null hypothesis is 50% of one outcome and 50% of another. In other words, the table of significance of the sign test can be used to check for departures from this 50/50 expectation.

■ Tests for unrelated samples

The major nonparametric test for differences between two groups of unrelated or uncor-related scores is the Mann–Whitney U-test.

Explaining statistics 21.3

How the Mann–Whitney U-test works

The Mann–Whitney U-test is used for much the same research designs as the unrelated or uncorrelated scores t-test (Chapter 14). In other words, it can be used whenever you have two groups of scores which are independent of each other (i.e. they are usually based on different samples of people). We will use the identical data upon which we demon-strated the calculation of the unrelated/uncorrelated scores t-test (Chapter 14).

Step 1 Rank all of the scores from the smallest to the largest (Table 21.4). Scores which are equal are allocated the average of ranks that they would be given if there were tiny differences between the scores. *Be careful! All of your scores are ranked irrespective of the group they are in. To avoid confusion, use the first column for the larger group of scores.* If both groups are equal in size then either can be entered in the first column. Group size $N_1 = 12$ for the two-parent families and $N_2 = 10$ for the lone-parent families.

Step 2 Sum the ranks for the larger group of scores. This is R_1. (If the groups are equal in size then either can be selected.)

Step 3 The sum of ranks (R_1) of Group 1 (174.5) (the larger group) and its sample size N_1 ($N_1 = 12$) together with the sample size N_2 of Group 2 ($N_2 = 10$) are entered into the following formula which gives you the value of the statistic U:

$$U = (N_1 \times N_2) + \frac{N_1 \times (N_1 + 1)}{2} - R_1$$

$$= (12 \times 10) + \frac{12 \times (12 + 1)}{2} - 174.5$$

$$= 120 + \frac{12 \times 13}{2} - 174.5$$

$$= 120 + \frac{156}{2} - 174.5$$

$$= 120 + 78 - 174.5$$

$$= 198 - 174.5$$

Table 21.4	Steps in the calculation of the Mann–Whitney U-test		
Two-parent families (X_1)	**Rankings**	**Lone-parent families (X_2)**	**Rankings**
(This column is for the larger group)		(This column is for the smaller group)	
12	12.5	6	2
18	21	9	6
14	16.5	4	1
10	8.5	13	14.5
19	22	14	16.5
8	3.5	9	6
15	18.5	8	3.5
11	10.5	12	12.5
10	8.5	11	10.5
13	14.5	9	6
15	18.5		
16	20		
	$\sum R_1 = 174.5$ (Note that this is the sum of ranks for the larger group)		

Step 4 Check the significance of your value of U by consulting Significance Table 21.3 (or Appendix I for the 1% significance level). In order to use this table, you need to find your value of N_1 in the column headings and your value of N_2 in the row headings. (However, since the table is symmetrical it does not matter if you use the rows instead of the columns and vice versa.) The table gives the two ranges of values of U which are significant. Your value must be in either of these two ranges to be statistically significant. (Appendix B1 explains what to do if your sample size exceeds the largest value in the table.)

The table tells us that for sample sizes of 12 and 10, the ranges are 0 to 29 or 91 to 120. Our value of 23.5 therefore is significant at the 5% level. In other words, we reject the null hypothesis that the independent variable is unrelated to the dependent variable in favour of the view that family structure has an influence on scores of the dependent variable.

Interpreting the results

The means of the two groups of scores must be examined to know which of the two groups has the higher scores on the dependent variable. In our example, greater emotionality was found in the children from the two-parent families. The significant value of the Mann–Whitney U-test suggests that we are reasonably safe to conclude that the two groups do differ in terms of their emotionality.

Reporting the results

The statistical analysis could be reported in the following APA (2010) Publication Manual style: 'It was found that emotionality was significantly higher, $U(22) = 23.5$, $p < .05$, in the two-parent families ($M = 13.42$) than in the lone-parent families ($M = 9.50$).'

→

Significance Table 21.3

5% significance values for the Mann–Whitney U-test (two-tailed test)

Sample size for smaller group	Sample size for larger group											
	5	6	7	8	9	10	11	12	13	14	15	20
5	0–2 23–25	0–3 27–30	0–5 30–35	0–6 34–40	0–7 38–45	0–8 42–50	0–9 46–55	0–11 49–60	0–12 53–65	0–13 57–70	0–14 61–75	0–20 80–100
6	0–3 27–30	0–5 31–36	0–6 36–42	0–8 40–48	0–10 44–54	0–11 49–60	0–13 53–66	0–14 58–72	0–16 62–78	0–17 67–84	0–19 71–90	0–27 93–120
7	0–5 30–35	0–6 36–42	0–8 41–49	0–10 46–56	0–12 51–63	0–14 56–70	0–16 61–77	0–18 66–84	0–20 71–91	0–22 76–98	0–24 81–105	0–34 106–140
8	0–6 34–40	0–8 40–48	0–10 46–56	0–13 51–64	0–15 57–72	0–17 63–80	0–19 69–88	0–22 74–96	0–24 80–104	0–26 86–112	0–29 91–120	0–41 119–160
9	0–7 38–45	0–10 44–54	0–12 51–63	0–15 57–72	0–17 64–81	0–20 70–90	0–23 76–99	0–26 82–108	0–28 89–117	0–31 95–126	0–34 101–135	0–48 130–180
10	0–8 42–50	0–11 49–60	0–14 56–70	0–17 63–80	0–20 70–90	0–23 77–100	0–26 84–110	0–29 91–120	0–33 97–130	0–36 104–140	0–39 111–150	0–55 145–200
11	0–9 46–55	0–13 53–66	0–16 61–77	0–19 69–88	0–23 76–99	0–26 84–110	0–30 91–121	0–33 99–132	0–37 106–143	0–40 114–154	0–44 121–165	0–62 158–220
12	0–11 49–60	0–14 58–72	0–18 66–84	0–22 74–96	0–26 82–108	0–29 91–120	0–33 99–132	0–37 107–144	0–41 115–156	0–45 123–168	0–49 131–180	0–69 171–240
13	0–12 53–65	0–16 62–78	0–20 71–91	0–24 80–104	0–28 89–117	0–33 97–130	0–37 106–143	0–41 115–156	0–45 124–169	0–50 132–182	0–54 141–195	0–76 184–260
14	0–13 57–70	0–17 67–84	0–22 76–98	0–26 86–112	0–31 95–126	0–36 104–140	0–40 114–154	0–45 123–168	0–50 132–182	0–55 141–196	0–59 151–210	0–83 197–280
15	0–14 61–75	0–19 71–90	0–24 81–105	0–29 91–120	0–34 101–135	0–39 111–150	0–44 121–165	0–49 131–180	0–54 141–195	0–59 151–210	0–64 161–225	0–90 210–300
20	0–20 80–100	0–27 93–120	0–34 106–140	0–41 119–160	0–48 130–180	0–55 145–200	0–62 158–220	0–69 171–240	0–76 184–260	0–83 197–280	0–90 210–300	0–127 273–400

Your value must be in the listed ranges for your sample sizes to be significant at the 5% level (i.e. to accept the hypothesis).

Source: Adapted and extended from Table I of R.P. Runyon and A. Haber (1989). *Fundamentals of behavioral statistics*. New York: McGraw-Hill.

21.4 Three or more groups of scores

The Kruskal–Wallis test and the Friedman test are essentially extensions of the Mann–Whitney U-test and the Wilcoxon matched pairs test, respectively. Appendix B2 gives information on how to calculate these nonparametric statistics.

Research examples

Ranking tests

Blackmore and her colleagues (2006) were interested in whether a number of factors such as how long the pregnancy had lasted were associated with developing post-pregnancy bipolar depression in women who had such depression. They compared the length of pregnancy in pregnancies which had resulted in depression with those which had not resulted in depression using a Wilcoxon matched pairs signed-rank test and found no significant difference.

Kenyon and her colleagues (2012) tested whether people with bulimia nervosa or other unspecified eating disorders were less able to infer the feelings, beliefs and knowledge of other people than people who did not have psychological disorders. As part of the study they assessed how depressed, anxious and stressed the three groups were (the two eating disorder groups and the control group). Because these three variables were not normally distributed thus violating an assumption of parametric statistics and could not be transformed to be so, the researchers carried out a Kruskal–Wallis test to determine if there was a statistical difference between the three groups. If there was a significant difference, they used a Mann–Whitney test to determine which groups differed from each other. They found that the two eating disorder groups did not differ from each other on these measures but were significantly more depressed, anxious and stressed than the healthy group.

Shafran and her colleagues (2006) were interested in determining whether being asked to have higher general personal standards such as working very hard would result in more dysfunctional eating than those who were asked to have lower general personal standards such as taking it easy at work. Some of the measures used to assess dysfunctional eating such as trying to restrict the intake of food and feeling regret after eating were significantly positively skewed. Because of this, Mann–Whitney tests were used to test for differences between these two groups before and after manipulating personal standards. After manipulation, those in the higher personal condition reported significantly more attempts to restrict their overall food intake and reported significantly more regret after eating.

Key points

- Often you will not require nonparametric tests of significance of the sort described in this chapter. The *t*-test will usually fit the task better.

- Only when you have marked symmetry problems in your data will you require the nonparametric tests. But even then remember that a version of the unrelated *t*-test is available to cope with some aspects of the problem (Chapter 14).

- The computations for the nonparametric tests may appear simpler. A big disadvantage is that when the sample sizes get large the problems in ranking escalate disproportionately.

- Some professional psychologists tend to advocate nonparametric techniques for entirely outmoded reasons.

- There is no guarantee that the nonparametric test will always do the job better when the assumptions of parametric tests are violated.

- There are large sample formulae for the nonparametric tests reported here for when your sample sizes are too big for the printed tables of significance. However, by the time this point is reached the computation is getting clumsy and can be better handled by a computer; also the advantages of the nonparametric tests are very reduced.

COMPUTER ANALYSIS

Two-group ranking tests using SPSS

Data
- Name the variables in 'Variable View' of the 'Data Editor'.
- Enter the data under the appropriate variable names in 'Data View' of the 'Data Editor'.

Analysis
- For the 2 related data tests, select 'Analyze', 'Nonparametric Tests', 'Legacy Dialogs' and '2-Related Samples…' (Screenshot 21.1).

2
- Move the appropriate pair of variables to the box to the right and select 'Sign'. Wilcoxon is already selected (Screenshot 21.2).
- Select 'OK'.

3
- For the Mann–Whitney test, select 'Analyze', 'Nonparametric Tests', 'Legacy Dialogs' and '2 Independent Samples…' (Screenshot 21.3).

4
- Move the appropriate test (dependent) and grouping (independent) variable to the two boxes to the right (Screenshot 21.4).
- Select 'Define Groups…' and select the two groups.
- Select 'Continue' and 'OK'.

Output
- Screenshot 21.5 shows the Wilcoxon output for data in Table 21.2.
- Screenshot 21.6 shows the output for the data in Table 21.4. Check to see if the *p* value is significant at .05 or less.
- If it is determine the direction of the difference.

FIGURE 21.2   SPSS steps for the sign, Wilcoxon and Mann–Whitney nonparametric tests

Interpreting and reporting the output

- We could report the Wilcoxon results for the data in Table 21.2 as follows: 'There was no significant difference in the amount of eye-contact by babies between 6 and 9 months, Wilcoxon, $z(8) = -1.71$, two-tailed $p = .088$.'

- We could report the Mann–Whitney results of the data in Table 21.4 as follows: 'The Mann–Whitney U-test found that the emotionality scores of children from two-parent families were significantly higher than those of children in lone-parent families, $U(10, 12) = 23.5$, two-tailed $p = .016$.'

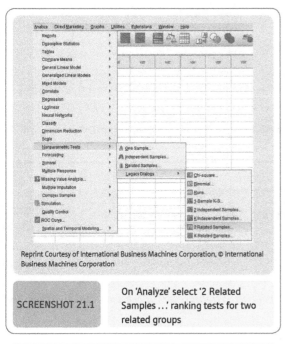

Reprint Courtesy of International Business Machines Corporation, © International Business Machines Corporation

| SCREENSHOT 21.1 | On 'Analyze' select '2 Related Samples ...' ranking tests for two related groups |

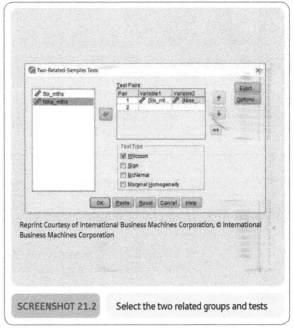

Reprint Courtesy of International Business Machines Corporation, © International Business Machines Corporation

| SCREENSHOT 21.2 | Select the two related groups and tests |

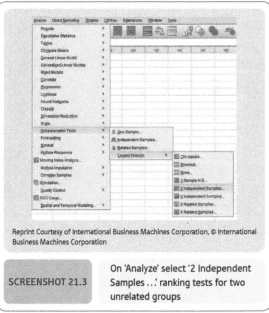

Reprint Courtesy of International Business Machines Corporation, © International Business Machines Corporation

| SCREENSHOT 21.3 | On 'Analyze' select '2 Independent Samples ...' ranking tests for two unrelated groups |

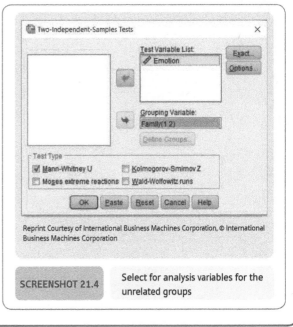

Reprint Courtesy of International Business Machines Corporation, © International Business Machines Corporation

| SCREENSHOT 21.4 | Select for analysis variables for the unrelated groups |

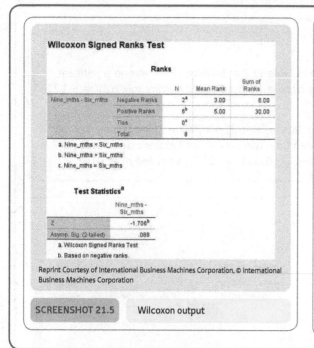

Wilcoxon Signed Ranks Test

Ranks

		N	Mean Rank	Sum of Ranks
Nine_mths - Six_mths	Negative Ranks	2[a]	3.00	6.00
	Positive Ranks	6[b]	5.00	30.00
	Ties	0[c]		
	Total	8		

a. Nine_mths < Six_mths
b. Nine_mths > Six_mths
c. Nine_mths = Six_mths

Test Statistics[a]

	Nine_mths - Six_mths
Z	-1.706[b]
Asymp. Sig. (2-tailed)	.088

a. Wilcoxon Signed Ranks Test
b. Based on negative ranks.

Reprint Courtesy of International Business Machines Corporation, © International Business Machines Corporation

SCREENSHOT 21.5   Wilcoxon output

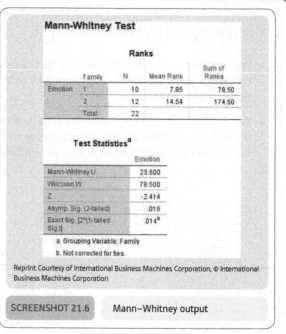

Mann-Whitney Test

Ranks

	Family	N	Mean Rank	Sum of Ranks
Emotion	1	10	7.85	78.50
	2	12	14.54	174.50
	Total	22		

Test Statistics[a]

	Emotion
Mann-Whitney U	23.500
Wilcoxon W	78.500
Z	-2.414
Asymp. Sig. (2-tailed)	.016
Exact Sig. [2*(1-tailed Sig.)]	.014[b]

a. Grouping Variable: Family
b. Not corrected for ties.

Reprint Courtesy of International Business Machines Corporation, © International Business Machines Corporation

SCREENSHOT 21.6   Mann–Whitney output

Recommended further reading

Mariscuilo, L. A., & McSweeney, M. (1977). *Nonparametric and distribution-free methods for the social sciences.* Monterey, CA: Brooks/Cole.

Siegel, S., & Castellan, N. J. (1988). *Nonparametric statistics for the behavioral sciences.* New York, NY: McGraw-Hill.

PART 3

Introduction to analysis of variance

CHAPTER 22

Variance ratio test

F-ratio to compare two variances

Overview

- The variance ratio test (the *F*-ratio test) assesses whether the variances of two different samples are significantly different from each other.

- That is, it tests whether the spread of scores for the two samples is significantly different. This is not dependent on the value of the means of each sample.

- However, it is more commonly used as part of other statistical techniques especially the analysis of variance. So understanding the *F*-ratio is an important step towards understanding the analysis of variance.

- It is also used to test one of the underlying assumptions of the unrelated *t*-test since this assumes that the variances of the two sets of scores are more or less equal (i.e. not significantly different).

Preparation

Make sure that you understand variance and the variance estimate (Chapters 4 and 12). Familiarity with the *t*-test will help with some applications (Chapters 13 and 14).

22.1   Introduction

Sometimes in research a researcher needs to compare the variances of two samples of scores. It is all too easy to become over-focused on comparing two sample means. This is to risk overlooking other important effects which may occur. For instance, it is perfectly possible to find that despite the means of two groups of scores being identical, their variances are radically different. Take the following simple experiment in which men and women are shown advertisements for women's underwear (tights), set out in Table 22.1. The dependent variable is the readers' degree of liking for the product rated on a scale from 1 to 7 (on which 1 means that they strongly disliked the advertisement and 7 means that they strongly liked the advertisement).

The big difference between the two groups is not in terms of their means – the men's mean is 4.4 whereas the women's mean is 4.3. This is a small and unimportant difference. What is more noticeable is that the women seem to be split into two camps. The women's scores tend to be large or small with little in the centre. There is more variance in the women's scores. The *F*-ratio test allows us to assess whether the difference in variance between women and men is significant.

There are other circumstances in which we compare variances:

- For the unrelated *t*-test, one should make sure that the two samples do not differ significantly in terms of their variances – if they do then it is better to opt for an 'unpooled' *t*-test which is easily computed using SPSS. It is to be found in Screenshot 14.5 in the bottom row beginning 'Equal variances not assumed'. In other words, SPSS presents you with a choice.

- Another major application is the analysis of variance in which variance estimates are compared (see Chapter 23). SPSS uses a slight variation on this which makes little difference for the analysis of variance.

In all of these circumstances the *F*-ratio test or the variance ratio test is appropriate. There is not a great deal that is new as it involves the variance estimate, which we have already discussed several times.

Table 22.1	Data comparing men and women on ratings of tights	
Men		**Women**
5		1
4		6
4		7
3		2
5		6
4		7
3		5
6		7
5		2
5		6
		1
		2

22.2 Theoretical issues and application

The variance ratio simply compares two variances in order to test whether they come from the same population. That is, are the differences between the variances simply the result of chance sampling fluctuations? Of course, since we are comparing samples from a population we need the variance estimate formula. In the simpler applications of the variance ratio test (F-ratio), the variance estimate involves using the sample size minus one ($N - 1$) as the denominator (lower part) of the variance estimate formula. (This does not apply in quite the same way in the more advanced case of the analysis of variance, as we will see in Chapter 23 onwards.)

The variance ratio formula is as follows:

$$F = \frac{\text{larger variance estimate}}{\text{smaller variance estimate}}$$

There is a table of the F-distribution (Significance Table 22.1) which is organised according to the degrees of freedom of the two variance estimates. Unlike the t-test, the F-ratio is a one-tailed test. It determines whether the numerator, the top part of the formula, is larger than the denominator, the lower part. The F-ratio cannot be smaller than one. The 5% or .05 applies to the upper or right-hand tail of the distribution. The larger the F-ratio is, the more likely it is that the larger variance estimate is significantly larger than the lower variance estimate.

Figure 22.1 shows the key steps in the variance test.

Significance Table 22.1	5% significance values of the F-distribution for testing differences in variance estimates between two samples (one-tailed test). Additional values are given in Significance Table 23.1					
Degrees of freedom for smaller variance estimate (denominator)	**Degrees of freedom for larger variance estimate (numerator)**					
	5	**7**	**10**	**20**	**50**	**∞**
5	5.1 or more	4.9	4.7	4.6	4.4	4.4
6	4.4	4.1	4.1	3.9	3.8	3.7
7	4.0	3.8	3.6	3.4	3.3	3.2
8	3.7	3.5	3.3	3.2	3.0	2.9
10	3.3	3.1	3.0	2.8	2.6	2.5
12	3.1	2.9	2.8	2.5	2.4	2.3
15	2.9	2.7	2.6	2.3	2.2	2.1
20	2.7	2.5	2.4	2.1	2.0	1.8
30	2.5	2.3	2.2	1.9	1.8	1.6
50	2.4	2.2	2.0	1.8	1.6	1.4
100	2.3	2.1	1.9	1.7	1.5	1.3
∞	2.2	2.0	1.8	1.6	1.4	1.0

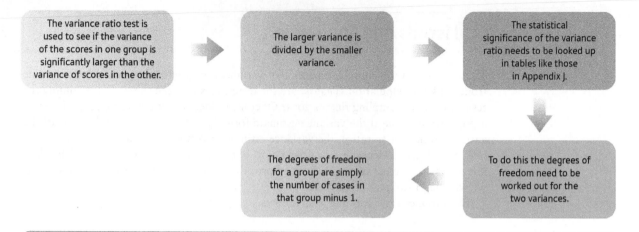

FIGURE 22.1	Conceptual steps for understanding the variance ratio test

Explaining statistics 22.1

How the variance ratio (*F*-ratio) works

It is not possible to calculate the variance ratio directly on SPSS so here are the steps in the calculation. You can use SPSS to calculate the variance estimates involved, as we show in the Computer Analysis.

Imagine a very simple piece of clinical research which involves the administration of electroconvulsive therapy (ECT). There are two experimental conditions: in one case the electric current is passed through the left hemisphere of the brain and in the other case it is passed through the right hemisphere of the brain. The dependent variable is scores on a test of emotional stability following treatment. Patients were assigned to one or other group at random. The scores following treatment were as listed in Table 22.2.

Quite clearly there is no difference in terms of the mean scores on emotional stability. Looking at the data, though, it looks as if ECT to the right hemisphere tends to push people to the extremes whereas ECT to the left hemisphere leaves a more compact distribution.

Table 22.2	Emotional stability scores from a study of ECT to different hemispheres of the brain

Left hemisphere	Right hemisphere
20	36
14	28
18	4
22	18
13	2
15	22
9	1
Mean = 15.9	Mean = 15.9

To calculate the variance ratio, the variance *estimates* of the two separate samples (left and right hemispheres) have to be calculated using the usual variance estimate formula. The following is the computational formula version of this:

$$\text{estimated variance} = \frac{\sum X^2 - \frac{(\sum X)^2}{N}}{N - 1}$$

Step 1 Calculate the variance of the first group of scores (i.e. the left hemisphere group), as in Table 22.3. The sample size (number of scores) is $N_1 = 7$. Substituting in the formula:

$$\text{variance estimate}_{[\text{group 1}]} = \frac{\sum X_1^2 - \frac{(\sum X_1)^2}{N_1}}{N_1 - 1} = \frac{1879 - \frac{111^2}{7}}{7 - 1} = \frac{1879 - \frac{12\,321}{7}}{6}$$

$$= \frac{1879 - 1760.143}{6} = \frac{118.857}{6}$$

$$= 19.81 \text{ (degrees of freedom} = N_1 - 1 = 6)$$

Table 22.3	Step 1 in the calculation of the variance estimate
X_1 = left hemisphere	$X_1{}^2$
20	400
14	196
18	324
22	484
13	169
15	225
9	81
$\sum X_1 = 111$	$\sum X_1{}^2 = 1879$

Step 2 The variance estimate of the right hemisphere group is calculated using the standard computational formula as in Table 22.4. The sample size $N_2 = 7$.

Table 22.4	Step 2 in the calculation of the variance estimate
X_2 = right hemisphere	$X_2{}^2$
36	1296
28	784
4	16
18	324
2	4
22	484
1	1
$\sum X_2 = 111$	$\sum X_2{}^2 = 2909$

Substituting in the formula:

$$\text{variance estimate}_{[\text{group 2}]} = \frac{\sum X_2^2 - \dfrac{(\sum X_2)^2}{N_2}}{N_2 - 1} = \frac{2909 - \dfrac{111^2}{7}}{7 - 1} = \frac{2909 - \dfrac{12\,321}{7}}{6}$$

$$= \frac{2909 - 1760.143}{6} = \frac{1148.857}{6}$$

$$= 191.48 \ (\text{degrees of freedom} = N_2 - 1 = 6)$$

Step 3 The larger variance estimate is divided by the smaller:

$$F = \frac{\text{larger variance estimate}}{\text{smaller variance estimate}}$$

$$= \frac{191.48}{19.81}$$

$$= 9.67 \ (df \text{ larger variance estimate} = 6, \ df \text{ smaller variance estimate} = 6$$

Step 4 We need to check whether or not a difference between the two variance estimates as large as this ratio implies would be likely if the samples came from the same population of scores. Significance Table 22.1 contains the critical values for the *F*-ratio. To use the table you find the intersection of the column for the degrees of freedom of the larger variance estimate and the degrees of freedom of the smaller variance estimate. Notice that the degrees of freedom we want are not listed for the numerator, so we take the next smaller listed value. Thus the table tells us we need a value of 4.4 at a minimum to be significant at the 5% level with a one-tailed test. Our calculated value of *F* is substantially in excess of the critical value. Thus we conclude that it is very unlikely that the two samples come from the same population of scores. We accept the hypothesis that the two sample variances are significantly different.

Interpreting the results

The interpretation of the *F*-ratio test is simply a matter of examining the two variance estimates to see which is larger. If the *F*-ratio is statistically significant then the larger of the variance estimates is significantly larger than the smaller one.

Reporting the results

The results could be written up according to the APA (2010) Publication Manual recommendations as follows: 'Despite there being no difference between the mean scores on emotionality following ECT to left and right brain hemispheres, the variance of emotionality was significantly higher for ECT to the right hemisphere, $F(6, 6) = 9.67$, $p < .05$. This suggests that ECT to the right hemisphere increases emotionality in some people but decreases it in others.'

Research examples

Comparing variances

Arden and Plomin (2006) were interested in determining whether greater variance in intelligence in males and females was found in early childhood. They compared the variance of intelligence in boys and girls at the ages of 2, 3, 4, 7, 9 and 10 and found greater variance in boys compared to girls at every age apart from at 2. In this analysis, they used Levene's test of homogeneity of variance rather than the F-ratio which would have been an alternative test.

Ruscio and Roche (2012) addressed the question of the extent to which the parametric assumptions of statistical tests in terms of equality of variances (and normality) are met by researchers. The past evidence is that normality assumptions are frequently violated but sample variance inequality has received little attention. Ruscio and Roche took 455 studies published in top psychology journals and noted the variances of the different groups in each study on the dependent variable. It is an assumption that the variances of groups used in statistics such as ANOVA and the regular version of the t-test should be equal – that is, not differ significantly. It was found that the variances of groups in a study often varied significantly using the F-ratio test and similar procedures.

Vista and Care (2011) point to the scarcity of research on gender differences in intelligence in non-Western countries and evidence from Southeast Asia is uncommon. They administered a non-verbal intelligence test (the Naglieri Non-verbal Ability Test) to a national sample of 2700 public schoolchildren in the Philippines in three different age groups. Studying mean scores from the research showed very little by way of gender differences. The trend is non-existent or, at most, very trivial. However, this was not at all the case when variance ratio tests (F-ratios) were calculated. There was evidence of greater variability of scores for males compared with females in the upper half of the distribution of scores and the reverse trend of greater variability of scores for females compared to males in the lower part of the distribution of scores. Although the research provides little evidence of gender differences in intelligence, it raises important questions about the distribution of intelligence between the genders in this context.

Key points

- Psychologists often fail to explore for differences in variances in their data. It is good practice to routinely examine your data for them where they might be meaningful.

- The F-ratio is a necessary adjunct to applying the unrelated t-test correctly. Make sure that you check that the variances are indeed similar before using the t-test.

- Be very careful when you use the F-ratio in the analysis of variance (Chapter 23 onwards). The F-ratio in the analysis of variance is not quite the same. In this you do not always divide the larger variance estimate by the smaller variance estimate.

COMPUTER ANALYSIS

F-ratio test using SPSS

Data
- Name the variables in 'Variable View' of the 'Data Editor'.
- Enter the data under the appropriate variable names in 'Data View' of the 'Data Editor' (Screenshot 22.1).

Analysis
- Select 'Analyze', 'Compare Means' and 'Means...' (Screenshot 22.2).
- Move the appropriate variable names to the 'Dependent' and 'Independent' boxes to the right (Screenshot 22.3).

2
- Select 'Options...' and move 'Variance' from the 'Statistics' to the 'Cell Statistics' box (Screenshot 22.4).
- Select 'Continue' and 'OK'.

Output
- The output is illustrated in Screenshot 22.5. As you cannot calculate the *F*-ratio directly on SPSS, divide the larger variance by the smaller variance and look up in the tables in Appendix J under the appropriate degrees of freedom whether the ratio is statistically significant.

FIGURE 22.2   SPSS steps for computing variance

Interpreting and reporting the output

- Decide which of the variance estimates is the larger. If the *F*-ratio is statistically significant then this variance is significantly larger than the smaller one.

- In APA recommended style you could write: 'Despite there being no difference between the mean scores on emotionality following ECT to left and right brain hemispheres, the variance of emotionality was significantly higher for ECT to the right hemisphere, $F(6, 6) = 9.67, p < .05$. This suggests that ECT to the right hemisphere increases emotionality in some people but decreases it in others.'

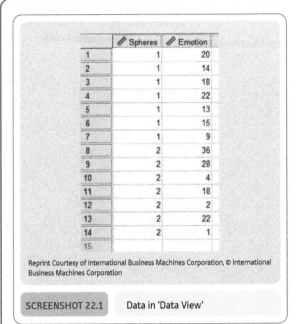

Reprint Courtesy of International Business Machines Corporation, © International Business Machines Corporation

SCREENSHOT 22.1   Data in 'Data View'

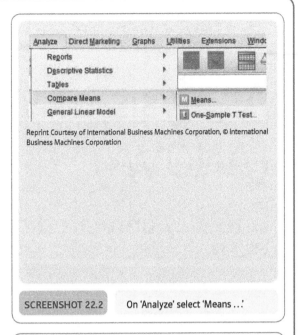

Reprint Courtesy of International Business Machines Corporation, © International Business Machines Corporation

SCREENSHOT 22.2   On 'Analyze' select 'Means ...'

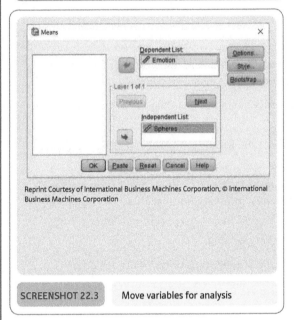

Reprint Courtesy of International Business Machines Corporation, © International Business Machines Corporation

SCREENSHOT 22.3   Move variables for analysis

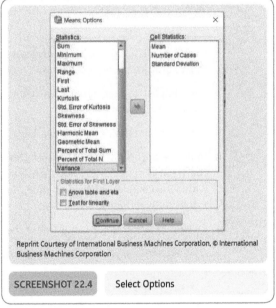

Reprint Courtesy of International Business Machines Corporation, © International Business Machines Corporation

SCREENSHOT 22.4   Select Options

Report

Emotion

Spheres	Mean	N	Std. Deviation	Variance
Left	15.86	7	4.451	19.810
Right	15.86	7	13.837	191.476
Total	15.86	14	9.875	97.516

Reprint Courtesy of International Business Machines Corporation, © International Business Machines Corporation

SCREENSHOT 22.5   Descriptive statistics output

CHAPTER 23

Analysis of variance (ANOVA)

One-way unrelated or uncorrelated ANOVA

Overview

- One-way analysis of variance (ANOVA) compares the variation in the means for a minimum of two groups. Usually used when there are three or more means to compare.

- This chapter concentrates on ANOVA for unrelated samples – usually when the samples consist of different people.

- The scores are the dependent variable; the groups are the independent variable.

- In essence, the ANOVA estimates the variance in the population due to the cell means (between variance) and the variance in the population due to random (or error) processes within the samples (within variance). The F-ratio test indicates whether these variances are significantly different.

- Error is variation which is not under the researcher's control.

- A significant analysis of variance means that some of the means differ from each other.

Preparation

It is pointless to start this chapter without a clear understanding of how to calculate the basic variance estimate formula and the computational formula for variance estimate (Chapter 4). A working knowledge of the variance ratio test (F-ratio test) is also essential (Chapter 22).

23.1 Introduction

Up to this chapter, research designs comparing the means of just two groups of scores have been covered. The analysis of variance (ANOVA) can do this but can compare three or more groups of scores. Analysis of variance takes varied forms but is primarily used to analyse the results of experiments. Nevertheless, the simpler versions of ANOVA are also routinely used in surveys and similar types of research. This chapter describes the one-way analysis of variance. This can be used whenever we wish to compare two or more groups in terms of their mean scores on a dependent variable. The scores must be independent (uncorrelated or unrelated). In other words, each respondent contributes just one score to the statistical analysis. Stylistically, Table 23.1 is the sort of research design for which the (uncorrelated or unrelated) one-way analysis of variance is appropriate.

Table 23.1	Stylised table of data for unrelated analysis of variance		
Group 1	**Group 2**	**Group 3**	**Group 4**
9	3	1	27
14	1	4	24
11	5	2	25
12	5	31	

The scores are those on the dependent variable. The groups are the independent variable. There are very few limitations on the research designs to which this is applicable:

- It is possible to have any number of groups, with the minimum being two.

- The groups consist of independent samples of scores. For example the groups could be:

  - men versus women

  - an experimental versus one control group

  - four experimental groups and one control group

  - three different occupational types – managers, office personnel and production workers.

- The scores (the dependent variable) can be for virtually any variable. The main thing is that they are numerical scores suitable for calculating the mean and variance.

- It is *not* necessary to have equal numbers of scores in each group. With other forms of analysis of variance, not having equal numbers can cause complications.

23.2 Some revision and some new material

You should be familiar with most of the following. Remember the formula for *variance*:

$$\frac{\sum (X - \overline{X})^2}{}$$

If you wish to estimate the variance of a population from the variation in a sample from that population, you use the *variance estimate* formula which is:

$$\text{variance estimate}_{[\text{definitional formula}]} = \frac{\sum (X - \overline{X})^2}{N - 1}$$

(By dividing by $N - 1$ we get an unbiased estimate of the population variance from the sample data.)

It is useful if you memorise the fact that the top part of the formula, i.e. $\sum (X - \overline{X})^2$ is called the *sum of squares*. It is the sum of the squared deviations from the mean. The phrase 'sum of squares' occurs repeatedly in all forms of the analysis of variance so cannot be avoided.

The bottom part of the variance formula (N) or variance estimate formula ($N - 1$) is called the *degrees of freedom*. In the analysis of variance things are a little complicated in that the value of the degrees of freedom can vary. Nevertheless, memorising that the phrase 'degrees of freedom' refers to the bottom part of the variance formulae is a useful start.

We can rewrite this formula as a *computational formula*:

$$\text{variance estimate}_{[\text{computational formula}]} = \frac{\sum X^2 - \dfrac{(\sum X)^2}{N}}{N - 1}$$

23.3 Theoretical considerations

Remember that the analysis of variance involves very few new ideas. However, some basic concepts are used in a relatively novel way. Unfortunately, most textbooks confuse readers by presenting the analysis of variance rather obscurely. In particular, they use a variant of the computational formula for the calculation of the variance estimate, which makes following the logic of what is happening very difficult. This is a pity since the analysis of variance is relatively simple in many respects. The main problem is the number of steps to be coped with.

All measurement assumes that a score is made up of two components:

● the 'true' value of the measurement

● an 'error' component.

In other words, the score that is obtained through measurement consists of a True Score plus an Error component. This is illustrated in Figure 23.1. The obtained score component

FIGURE 23.1   Components of a measured score in ANOVA

can take any value and so can the error component but they add up to the measured score. Error can take a positive or negative value.

Most psychological measurements tend to have a large error component compared with the true component. Error results from all sorts of factors – tiredness, distraction, unclear instructions and so forth. Normally we cannot say precisely to what extent these factors influence our scores. Nevertheless the assumption that the 'true' and 'error' components add together to give the obtained scores (i.e. the data) makes estimates possible. So, for example, an obtained score of 15 might be made up of:

$$15_{[\text{obtained score}]} = 12_{[\text{true}]} + 3_{[\text{error}]}$$

or an obtained score of 20 might be made up as follows:

$$20 = 24 + (-4)$$

We have no certain knowledge about anything other than the obtained scores. The true and error scores cannot be known directly. It is not difficult to understand how intelligent guesswork allows the true and error scores to be estimated in ANOVA. Look at the data of some fictitious research in Table 23.2. It is a study of the effects of two different hormones and an inert (placebo) control on depression scores in men. Tables 23.3 and 23.4 give the best estimates possible of the 'true' scores and 'error' scores in Table 23.2. Try to work out the simple 'tricks' we have employed. All we did to produce these two new tables was the following:

● In order to obtain a table of 'true' scores we have simply substituted the column mean for each group for the individual scores, the assumption being that the obtained scores deviate from the 'true' score because of the influence of varying amounts of error in the measurement. In statistical theory, error is assumed to be randomly distributed. Thus we have replaced all of the scores for Group 1 by the mean of 9.667. The column mean is simply the best estimate of what the 'true' score would be for the group if *we could get rid of the 'error' component*. As all of the scores are the same, there is absolutely no error component in any of the conditions of Table 23.3. The assumption in this is that the variability within a column is due to error so the average score in a column is our best estimate of the 'true' score for that column. Notice that the column means are unchanged by this.

● We have obtained the table of 'error' scores (Table 23.4) simply by subtracting the scores in the 'true' scores table away from the corresponding score in the original scores table (Table 23.2). What is not a 'true' score is an 'error' score by definition.

Table 23.2	Stylised table of data for unrelated analysis of variance with means	
Group 1 **Hormone 1**	**Group 2** **Hormone 2**	**Group 3** **Placebo control**
9	4	3
12	2	6
8	5	3
mean = 9.667	mean = 3.667	mean = 4.000
		Overall mean = 5.778

Table 23.3	'True' scores based on the data in Table 23.2	
Group 1 **Hormone 1**	**Group 2** **Hormone 2**	**Group 3** **Placebo control**
9.667	3.667	4.000
9.667	3.667	4.000
9.667	3.667	4.000
mean = 9.667	mean = 3.667	mean = 4.000
		Overall mean = 5.778

Table 23.4	'Error' scores based on the data in Table 23.2	
Group 1 **Hormone 1**	**Group 2** **Hormone 2**	**Group 3** **Placebo control**
− 0.667	0.333	− 1.000
2.333	− 1.667	2.000
− 1.667	1.333	− 1.000
mean = 0.000	mean = 0.000	mean = 0.000
		Overall mean = 0.000

Notice that the error scores show a mixture of positive and negative values, and that the sum of the error scores in each column (and the entire table for that matter) is zero. This is always the case with error scores and so constitutes an important check on your calculations should you wish to try out ANOVA for yourself. An alternative way of obtaining the error scores is to take the column (or group) mean away from each score in the original data table. This, of course, will give you exactly the same values for the error component.

So what do we do now that we have the 'true' scores and 'error' scores? The two derived sets of scores – the 'true' and the 'error' scores – are used separately to estimate the variance of the population of scores from which they are samples. (That is, the calculated variance estimate for the 'true' scores is an estimate of the 'true' variation in the population, and the calculated variance estimate of the 'error' scores is an estimate of the 'error' variation in the population.) Remember, the null hypothesis for this research would suggest that differences between the three groups are due to error rather than real differences related to the influence of the independent variable. The null hypothesis suggests that both the 'true' and 'error' variance estimates are similar since they are both the result of error. *If the null hypothesis is correct*, the variance estimate derived from the 'true' scores should be no different from the variance estimate derived from the 'error' scores. After all, under the null hypothesis the variation in the 'true' scores is due to error anyway. *If the alternative hypothesis is correct*, then there should be rather more variation in the 'true' scores than is typical in the 'error' scores.

We calculate the variance estimate of the 'true' scores and then calculate the variance estimate for the 'error' scores. See Chapter 22 for a discussion of variance estimates.

Next the two variance estimates are examined to see whether they are significantly different using the F-ratio test (the variance ratio test). This involves the following calculation:

$$F = \frac{\text{variance estimate}_{[\text{of true scores}]}}{\text{variance estimate}_{[\text{of error scores}]}}$$

(The error variance is always at the bottom in the analysis of variance. This is different from the F-ratio test described in the previous chapter. This is because we want to know if the variance estimate of the true scores is *bigger* than the variance estimate of the 'error' scores. We are not simply comparing the variances of two conditions.)

It is then a fairly straightforward matter to use Significance Table 23.1 for the F-distribution to decide whether or not these two variance estimates are significantly different from each other. We just need to be careful to use the appropriate numbers of degrees of freedom. The F-ratio calculation was demonstrated in Chapter 22. If the variance estimates are similar then the variance in 'true' scores is little different from the variance in the 'error' scores; since the estimated 'true' variance is much the same as the 'error' variance in this case, both can be regarded as 'error'. On the other hand, if the F-ratio is significant it means that the variation due to the 'true' scores is much greater than that due to 'error'; the 'true' scores represent reliable differences between groups rather than chance factors.

As mentioned in Chapter 22, the F-ratio, unlike the t-test, is a one-tailed test. It simply determines whether the true variance estimate is bigger than the error variance estimate. The F-ratio cannot be smaller than zero. In other words, it is always positive. The 5% or .05 probability only applies to the upper or right-hand tail of the distribution. The larger the F-ratio is, the more likely it is to be statistically significant.

Significance Table 23.1	5% significance values of the F-ratio for unrelated ANOVA. Additional values are given in Significance Table 22.1					
Degrees of freedom for error or within cells mean square (or variance estimate)	Degrees of freedom for true or between-treatment mean square (or variance estimate)					
	1	2	3	4	5	∞
1	161 or more	200	216	225	230	254
2	18.5	19.0	19.2	19.3	19.3	19.5
3	10.1	9.6	9.3	9.1	9.0	8.5
4	7.7	6.9	6.6	6.4	6.3	5.6
5	6.6	5.8	5.4	5.2	5.1	4.4
6	6.0	5.1	4.8	4.5	4.4	3.7
7	5.6	4.7	4.4	4.1	4.0	3.2
8	5.3	4.5	4.1	3.8	3.7	2.9
9	5.1	4.3	3.9	3.6	3.5	2.7
10	5.0	4.1	3.7	3.5	3.3	2.5
13	4.7	3.8	3.4	3.2	3.0	2.2
15	4.5	3.7	3.3	3.1	2.9	2.1
20	4.4	3.5	3.1	2.9	2.7	1.8
30	4.2	3.3	2.9	2.7	2.5	1.6
60	4.0	3.2	2.8	2.5	2.4	1.4
∞	3.8	3.0	2.6	2.4	2.2	1.0

Your value has to be equal or be larger than the tabulated value for an effect to be significant at the 5% level.

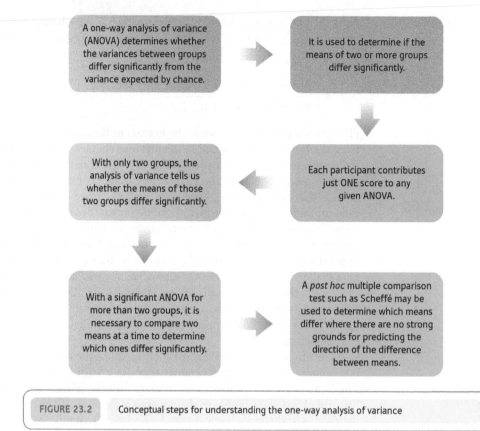

FIGURE 23.2   Conceptual steps for understanding the one-way analysis of variance

And that is just about it for the one-way analysis of variance. There is just one remaining issue: the *degrees of freedom*. If one were to work out the variance estimate of the original data in our study we would use the formula as given above:

$$\text{variance estimate}_{[\text{original data}]} = \frac{\sum X^2 - \dfrac{(\sum X)^2}{N}}{N - 1}$$

where $N - 1$ is the number of degrees of freedom.

However, the calculation of the number of degrees of freedom varies in the analysis of variance (it is not always $N - 1$). With the 'true' and 'error' scores the degrees of freedom are a little more complex although easily calculated using formulae. But the idea of degrees of freedom can be understood at a more fundamental level with a little work as shown in the next section. Figure 23.2 gives the key steps for an unrelated analysis of variance.

23.4   Degrees of freedom

This section gives a detailed explanation of degrees of freedom. You may find it easier to return to this section when you are a little more familiar with ANOVA.

Degrees of freedom refers to the distinct items of information contained in your data. By information we mean something which is new and not already known. For example, if we asked you what is the combined age of your two best friends and then asked you the age of the younger of the two, you would be crazy to accept a bet that we could tell you the age of your older best friend: the reason being that if you told us that the combined ages of your best friends was 37 years and that the younger was 16 years, any fool could work out that the older best friend must be 21 years. The age of your older best friend is contained within the first two pieces of information. The age of your older friend is redundant because you already know it from your previous information.

It is much the same sort of idea with degrees of freedom – which might be better termed the quantity of distinct information.

Table 23.5 repeats the table of the 'true' scores that we calculated earlier as Table 23.3. The question is how many items of truly new information the table contains. You have to bear in mind that what we are looking at is the variance estimate of the scores which is basically their variation around the overall mean of 5.778. Don't forget that the overall mean of 5.778 is our best estimate of the population mean under the null hypothesis that the groups do not differ.

Just how many of the scores in this table are we able to alter and still obtain this same overall mean of 5.778? For this table, we simply start rubbing out the scores one by one and putting in any value we like. So *if we start with the first person in group 1* we can arbitrarily set their score to 10.000 (or any other score you can think of). But, once we have done so, each score in group 1 has to be changed to 10.000 because the columns of the 'true' score table have to have identical entries. Thus the first column has to look like the column in Table 23.6 (the dashes represent parts of the table we have not dealt with yet).

Table 23.5	'True' scores based on the data in Table 23.2	
Group 1 **Hormone 1**	**Group 2** **Hormone 2**	**Group 3** **Placebo control**
9.667	3.667	4.000
9.667	3.667	4.000
9.667	3.667	4.000
mean = 9.667	mean = 3.667	mean = 4.000
		Overall mean = 5.778

Table 23.6	Insertion of arbitrary values in the first column	
Group 1	**Group 2**	**Group 3**
10.000	–	–
10.000	–	–
10.000	–	–
Mean = 10.000		
		Overall mean = 5.778

We have been free to vary just one score so far. We can now move on to the group 2 column. Here we can arbitrarily put in a score of 3.000 to replace the first entry. Once we do this then the remaining two scores in the column have to be the same because this is the nature of 'true' tables – all the scores in a column have to be identical (Table 23.7).

Thus so far we have managed to vary just two scores independently. We can now move on to group 3. We could start by entering, say, 5.000 to replace the first score, but there is a problem. The overall mean has to end up as 5.778 and the number 5.000 will not allow this to happen given that all of the scores in group 3 would have to be 5.000. There is only one number which can be put in the group 3 column which will give an overall mean of 5.778, that is 4.333 (Table 23.8).

We have not increased the number of scores we were free to vary by changing group 3 – we have changed the scores but we had no freedom other than to put one particular score in their place. Thus we have varied only *two* scores in the 'true' scores table – notice that this is one less than the number of groups we have which is a simple way of working out the degrees of freedom. We speak of *the 'true' scores having two degrees of freedom*.

It is a similar process with the error table. The requirements this time are (a) that the column averages equal zero and (b) that the overall average equals zero. This is because they are error scores which must produce these characteristics – if they do not they cannot be error scores. Just how many of the scores can we vary this time and keep within these limitations? (We have 'adjusted' the column means to ignore a tiny amount of rounding error.)

The answer is six scores (Table 23.9). The first two scores in each group can be varied to any values you like. However, having done this the value of the third score has to be fixed in order that the column mean equals zero. Since there are three equal-size groups then there are *six degrees of freedom for the error table* in this case.

Table 23.7	Insertion of arbitrary values in the second column	

Group 1	Group 2	Group 3
10.000	3.000	–
10.000	3.000	–
10.000	3.000	–
Mean = 10.000	Mean = 3.000	
		Overall mean = 5.778

Table 23.8	Forced insertion of a particular value in the third column because of the requirement that the overall mean is 5.778	

Group 1	Group 2	Group 3
10.000	3.000	4.333
10.000	3.000	4.333
10.000	3.000	4.333
Mean = 10.000	Mean = 3.000	Mean = 4.333
		Overall mean = 5.778

Table 23.9	'Error' scores based on the data in Table 23.2	

Group 1	Group 2	Group 3
−0.667	0.333	−1.000
2.333	−1.667	2.000
−1.667	1.333	−1.000
Mean = 0.000	Mean = 0.000	Mean = 0.000
		Overall mean = 0.000

Just in case you are wondering, for the *original data* table the degrees of freedom correspond to the number of scores minus one. This is because there are no individual column constraints – the only constraint is that the overall mean has to be 5.778. The lack of column constraints means that the first eight scores could be given any value you like and only the final score is fixed by the requirement that the overall mean is 5.778. In other words, the variance estimate for the original data table uses $N - 1$ as the denominator – thus the formula is the usual variance estimate formula for a sample of scores. Also note that the degrees of freedom for the 'error' and 'true' scores tables add up to $N - 1$.

Quick formulae for degrees of freedom

Anyone who has difficulty with the above explanation of degrees of freedom should take heart. Few of us would bother to work out the degrees of freedom from first principles. It is much easier to use simple formulae. For the one-way analysis of variance using unrelated samples, the degrees of freedom are as follows:

N = number of scores in the table

degrees of freedom$_{[\text{original data}]}$ = $N - 1$

degrees of freedom$_{[\text{'true' scores}]}$ = number of columns − 1

degrees of freedom$_{[\text{'error' scores}]}$ = $N -$ number of columns

This is not cheating – most textbooks largely ignore the meaning of degrees of freedom and merely give the formulae anyway.

Explaining statistics 23.1

How the unrelated/uncorrelated one-way analysis of variance works

Step-by-step, the following is the calculation of the analysis of variance.

Step 1   Draw up your data table using the format shown in Table 23.10. The degrees of freedom for this table are the number of scores minus one = $9 - 1 = 8$.

→

Table 23.10	Data table for an unrelated analysis of variance		
Group 1 **Hormone 1**	**Group 2** **Hormone 2**	**Group 3** **Placebo control**
9	4	3
12	2	6
8	5	3
mean = 9.667	mean = 3.667	mean = 4.000
		Overall mean = 5.778

Although this is not absolutely necessary you can calculate the variance estimate of your data table as a computational check – the sum of squares for the data table should equal the total of the sums of squares for the separate components. Thus, adding together the true and error sums of squares should give the total sum of squares for the data table. Similarly, the data degrees of freedom should equal the total of the true and error degrees of freedom. We will use the computational formula:

$$\text{variance estimate}_{[\text{original data}]} = \frac{\sum X^2 - \frac{(\sum X)^2}{N}}{df}$$

$\sum X^2$ means square each of the scores and then sum these individual calculations:

$$\sum X^2 = 9^2 + 4^2 + 3^2 + 12^2 + 2^2 + 6^2 + 8^2 + 5^2 + 3^2$$

$$= 81 + 16 + 9 + 144 + 4 + 36 + 64 + 25 + 9$$

$$= 388$$

$(\sum X)^2$ means add up all of the scores and then square the total:

$$(\sum X)^2 = (9 + 4 + 3 + 12 + 2 + 6 + 8 + 5 + 3)^2 = (52)^2 = 2704$$

The number of scores N equals 9. The degrees of freedom (df) equal $N - 1 = 9 - 1 = 8$. Substituting in the formula:

$$\text{variance estimate}_{[\text{original data}]} = \frac{\sum X^2 - \frac{(\sum X)^2}{N}}{df} = \frac{388 - \frac{2704}{9}}{8}$$

$$= \frac{388 - 300.444}{8} = \frac{87.556}{8} = 10.944$$

Step 2   Draw up Table 23.11 of 'true' scores by replacing the scores in each column by the column mean.

$$\sum X^2 = 9.667^2 + 3.667^2 + 4.000^2 + 9.667^2 + 3.667^2 + 4.000^2 + 9.667^2 + 3.667^2 + 4.000^2$$

$$= 93.451 + 13.447 + 16.000 + 93.451 + 13.447 + 16.000 + 93.451 + 13.447 + 16.000$$

$$= 368.694$$

$$(\sum Xa)^2 = (9.667 + 3.667 + 4.000 + 9.667 + 3.667 + 4.000 + 9.667 + 3.667 + 4.000)^2$$

$$= (52.000)^2 = 2704$$

Table 23.11	'True' scores based on the data in Table 23.10	
Group 1	Group 2	Group 3
9.667	3.667	4.000
9.667	3.667	4.000
9.667	3.667	4.000
mean = 9.667	mean = 3.667	mean = 4.000
		Overall mean = 5.778

The number of scores N equals 9. The degrees of freedom (df) are given by:

degrees of freedom$_{[\text{true scores}]}$ = number of columns − 1 = 3 − 1 = 2

We can now substitute in the formula:

$$\text{variance estimate}_{[\text{true scores}]} = \frac{\sum X^2 - \dfrac{(\sum X)^2}{N}}{df}$$

$$= \frac{368.694 - \dfrac{2704}{9}}{2}$$

$$= \frac{368.964 - 300.444}{2}$$

$$= \frac{68.250}{2} = 34.125$$

Step 3 Draw up the table of the 'error' scores (Table 23.12) by subtracting the 'true' scores table from the original data table (Table 23.10). Remember all you have to do is to take the corresponding scores in the two tables when doing this subtraction. The alternative is to take the appropriate column mean away from each score in your data table.

$$\text{variance estimate}_{[\text{error}]} = \frac{\sum X^2 - \dfrac{(\sum X)^2}{N}}{df}$$

$$\sum X^2 = (-0.667)^2 + 0.333^2 + (-1.000)^2 + 2.333^2$$

$$+ (-1.667)^2 + 2.000^2 + (-1.667)^2 + 1.333^2 + (-1.000)^2$$

$$= 0.445 + 0.111 + 1.000 + 5.443 + 2.779 + 4.000 + 2.779 + 1.777 + 1.000$$

$$= 19.334$$

$$(\sum X)^2 = [(-0.667) + 0.333 + (-1.000) + 2.333 + (-1.667) + 2.000$$

$$+ (-1.667) + 1.333 + (-1.000)]$$

$$= 0$$

Table 23.12	'Error' scores based on the data in Table 23.10	
Group 1	**Group 2**	**Group 3**
− 0.667	0.333	− 1.000
2.333	− 1.667	2.000
− 1.667	1.333	− 1.000
Mean = 0.000	Mean = 0.000	Mean = 0.000
		Overall mean = 0.000

The number of scores N equals 9. The degrees of freedom (df) equal N minus the number of columns, i.e. $9 - 3 = 6$. We can now substitute in the above formula:

$$\text{variance estimate}_{[error]} = \frac{\sum X^2 - \frac{(\sum X)^2}{N}}{df} = \frac{19.334 - \frac{0}{9}}{6} = 3.222$$

Step 4   We can now work out the F-ratio by dividing the variance estimate$_{[true\ scores]}$ by the variance estimate$_{[error\ scores]}$:

$$F\text{-ratio} = \frac{\text{variance estimate}_{[true\ scores]}}{\text{variance estimate}_{[error\ scores]}}$$

$$= \frac{34.125}{3.222}$$

$$= 10.59 \ (\text{degrees of freedom} = 2 \text{ for true and } 6 \text{ for error})$$

Note that this value is very similar to that provided by SPSS in Screenshot 23.5.

From Significance Table 23.1, we need a value of F of 5.1 or more to be significant at the 5% level of significance. Since our value of 10.59 is substantially larger than this, we can reject the null hypothesis and accept the hypothesis that the groups are significantly different from each other at the 5% level of significance.

23.5   Analysis of variance summary table

The analysis of variance calculation can get very complicated with complex experimental designs. In preparation for this, it is useful to get into the habit of recording your analysis in an analysis of variance summary table. This systematically records major aspects of the calculation. Table 23.13 is appropriate for this. Notice that the sums of squares for 'true' and 'error' added together are the same as the sum of squares of the original data (allowing for rounding errors). Don't forget that the sum of squares is simply the upper part of the variance estimate formula. Similarly the degrees of freedom of 'true' and 'error' scores added together give the degrees of freedom for the original data. The degrees of freedom are the lower part of the variance estimate formula.

In Table 23.13, we have used the terminology from our explanation. This is not quite standard in discussions regarding the analysis of variance. It is more usual to see the analysis of variance summary table in the form of Table 23.14 which uses slightly different terms.

Tables 23.13 and 23.14 are equivalent except for the terminology and the style of

Table 23.13	Analysis of variance summary table for unrelated ANOVAs				
Source of variation	Sum of squares	Degrees of freedom	Variance estimate	F-ratio	Significance
'True' scores	68.222	2	34.111	10.6	5%
'Error' scores	19.334	6	3.222		
Original data	87.556	8	10.944		

Table 23.14	Analysis of variance summary table for unrelated ANOVAs using alternative terminology			
Source of variation	Sum of squares	Degrees of freedom	Mean square	F-ratio
Between groups	68.222	2	34.111	10.6*
Within groups	19.334	6	3.222	
Total	87.556	8	10.944	

*Significant at 5% level.

- 'Mean square' is analysis of variance terminology for variance estimate. Unfortunately the name 'mean square' loses track of the fact that it is an estimate and suggests that it is something new.

- 'Between' is another way of describing the variation due to the 'true' scores. The idea is that the variation of the 'true' scores is essentially the differences between the groups or experimental conditions. Sometimes these are called the 'treatments'.

- 'Within' is just another way of describing the 'error' variation. It is called 'within' since the calculation of 'error' is based on the variation within a group or experimental condition.

- Total is virtually self-explanatory – it is the variation of the original scores which combine 'true' and 'error' components.

Interpreting the results

The most important step in interpreting your data is simple. You need a table of the means for each of the conditions such as Table 23.10. It is obvious from this table that two of the cell means are fairly similar whereas the mean of Group 1 is relatively high. This would suggest to an experienced researcher that if the one-way analysis of variance is statistically significant, then a multiple comparisons test (Chapter 26) is needed in order to test for significant differences between pairs of group means.

Reporting the results

The results of this analysis could be written up following the APA (2010) Publication Manual recommendations as: 'The data were analysed using an unrelated one-way analysis of variance. It was found that there was a significant effect of the independent variable drug treatment on the dependent variable depression, $F(2, 6) = 10.59$, $p < .05$. The mean for the hormone 1 group ($M = 9.67$, 95% CI [4.50, 14.84]), appears to indicate greater depression scores than for the hormone 2 group ($M = 3.67$, 95% CI [−0.13, 7.46]) and the placebo control ($M = 4.00$, 95% CI [−0.30, 8.30]).' (see Screenshot 23.5).

Of course, you can use Appendix J to test for significance at other levels.

In order to test whether the mean for group 1 is significantly greater than for the other two groups, it is necessary to apply a multiple comparisons test such as the Scheffé test or Tukey test (Chapter 26) if the differences had not been predicted. The outcome of this should also be reported.

Research examples

Unrelated one-way ANOVA

Frank and his colleagues (2012) tested whether intolerance for uncertainty is significantly higher in women with the eating disorders of 1) bulimia or 2) anorexia nervosa than 'healthy' women. They found a significant effect with a one-way analysis of variance. To determine which of the three groups differed significantly from one another the Tukey *post hoc* test was employed (see Chapter 26). Intolerance of uncertainty was significantly higher in women with bulimia or anorexia nervosa than in the healthy women.

Meeten and Davey (2012) researched the question of whether manipulating mood by showing participants one of five films influenced their emotions. The five mood conditions were sad, happy, anxious, angry and neutral. These five conditions were rated on the four mood scales of sadness, happiness, anxiety and anger. There was a significant one-way ANOVA effect for each mood rating. Planned *t*-tests showed that sadness was highest in the sad condition, happiness in the happy condition, anxiety in the anxious condition and anger in the angry condition (see Chapter 26).

Tyson and colleagues (2010) looked at the association between physical activity and anxiety and depression in a student sample. They broke down physical activity into three groups of low, medium and high physical activity and used a one-way analysis to determine whether anxiety and depression differed significantly between the three groups. They found a significant difference for both dependent variables – anxiety and depression. They used *post hoc* tests (see Chapter 26) to determine which groups differed significantly. They found that the lowest level of anxiety and depression was shown by the high physical activity group and the highest level of anxiety and depression was shown by the low physical activity group.

Key points

- The *t*-test is simply a special case of one-way ANOVA, so these tests can be used interchangeably when you have two groups of scores. They give identical significance levels. The square of the two-tailed *t*-value equals the one-tailed *F*-value (e.g. $1.96^2 = 3.8416$) and the square root of the one-tailed *F*-value equals the two-tailed *t*-value (e.g. $\sqrt{3.8416} = 1.96$).

- Do not be too deterred by some of the strange terminology used in the analysis of variance. Words like treatments and levels of treatment merely reveal the agricultural origins of these statistical procedures; be warned that it gets worse. Levels of treatment simply refer to the number of different conditions for each independent variable. Thus if the independent variable has three different values it is said to have three different levels of the treatment.

- The analysis of variance with just two conditions or sets of scores is relatively easy to interpret. You merely have to examine the difference between the means of the two conditions. It is not so easy where you have three or more groups. Your analysis may not be complete until you have employed a multiple comparisons procedure as in Chapter 26. Which multiple comparisons test you use may be limited by whether your ANOVA is significant or not.

- When the F-ratio is statistically significant for a one-way analysis of variance with more than two groups, you need to determine which groups differ significantly from each other. If you had good grounds for predicting which groups differed, you could use an unrelated t-test to see if the difference was significant (see Chapter 14). If you did not have a sound basis for predicting which groups differed, you would use a multiple comparison test such as the Scheffé test (Chapter 26).

COMPUTER ANALYSIS

Unrelated one-way analysis of variance using SPSS

Data
- Name the variables in 'Variable View' of the 'Data Editor'.
- Enter the data under the appropriate variable name in 'Data View' of the 'Data Editor' (Screenshot 23.1).

Analysis
- Select 'Analyze', 'Compare Means' and 'One-Way ANOVA...' (Screenshot 23.2).
- Move the dependent and independent variable names to the appropriate boxes to the right.

2
- Move the appropriate variable names to the 'Dependent' and 'Independent' boxes to the right (Screenshot 23.3).

3
- Select 'Options', 'Descriptive', 'Homogeneity of variance test', 'Continue' and 'OK' (Screenshot 23.4).
- Select 'Post hoc' test, the test you want and continue.

Output
- Check if the F-ratio is significant at .05 or less (Screenshot 23.5).

- If so, check that the Sig(nificance) of the homogeneity of variances is not significant at more than .05. The variances of the conditions should be similar for ANOVA.

2
- Check which means differ significantly with the *post hoc* test or further unrelated t-tests (See Chapter 26).

FIGURE 23.3   SPSS steps for one-way analysis of variance

Interpreting and reporting the output

- Start with the table of means for each of the conditions of study. Ask yourself what the pattern of different means implies. In this case, one of the means seems to be very different from the other two. The implication of this is that a multiple comparison test such as is explained in Chapter 26 would be helpful.

- An APA (2010) style write-up for this analysis might be: 'Using a one-way analysis of variance, it was found that there was a significant effect of the independent variable drug treatment on the dependent variable depression, $F(2, 6) = 10.59, p < .05$. The mean for the hormone 1 group ($M = 9.67$, 95% CI [4.50, 14.84]) appears to indicate greater depression scores than for the hormone 2 group ($M = 3.67$, 95% CI [−0.13, 7.46]) and the placebo control ($M = 4.00$, 95% CI [−0.30, 8.30]).'

- The partial eta squared η_p^2) effect size can be obtained by conducting this analysis with the General Linear Model (see Box 9.1).

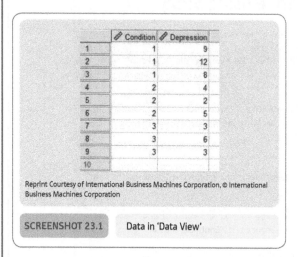

Reprint Courtesy of International Business Machines Corporation, © International Business Machines Corporation

SCREENSHOT 23.1   Data in 'Data View'

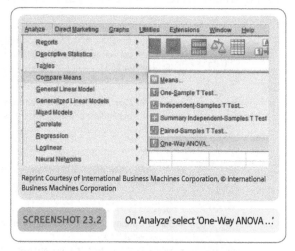

Reprint Courtesy of International Business Machines Corporation, © International Business Machines Corporation

SCREENSHOT 23.2   On 'Analyze' select 'One-Way ANOVA ...'

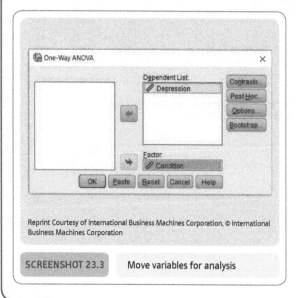

Reprint Courtesy of International Business Machines Corporation, © International Business Machines Corporation

SCREENSHOT 23.3   Move variables for analysis

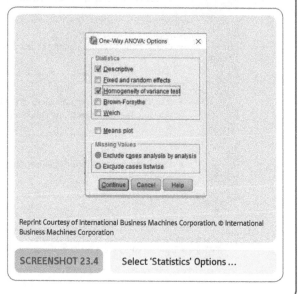

Reprint Courtesy of International Business Machines Corporation, © International Business Machines Corporation

SCREENSHOT 23.4   Select 'Statistics' Options ...

Descriptives

Depression

	N	Mean	Std. Deviation	Std. Error	95% Confidence Interval for Mean Lower Bound	Upper Bound	Minimum	Maximum
Hormone 1	3	9.67	2.082	1.202	4.50	14.84	8	12
Hormone 2	3	3.67	1.528	.882	-.13	7.46	2	5
Placebo control	3	4.00	1.732	1.000	-.30	8.30	3	6
Total	9	5.78	3.308	1.103	3.23	8.32	2	12

Test of Homogeneity of Variances

Depression

Levene Statistic	df1	df2	Sig.
.293	2	6	.756

ANOVA

Depression

	Sum of Squares	df	Mean Square	F	Sig.
Between Groups	68.222	2	34.111	10.586	.011
Within Groups	19.333	6	3.222		
Total	87.556	8			

Reprint Courtesy of International Business Machines Corporation, © International Business Machines Corporation

SCREENSHOT 23.5   One-way ANOVA output

CHAPTER 24

ANOVA for correlated scores or repeated measures

Overview

- The related analysis of variance is used to compare two or more related samples of means: for example, when the same group of participants is assessed three times on a measure. That is, measurement takes place under a number of conditions.

- The scores are the dependent variable, the different occasions on which the measure is taken constitute the independent variable.

- Because individuals are measured more than once, it is possible to estimate the impact of the characteristics of the individual on the scores. This allows a separate assessment of the variation in the data due to these individual differences. Effectively this variation can be removed from the data.

- The amount of error variance is lower in related designs since the variation due to individual differences is removed. What remains of the error is known as the 'residual' or residual error. The value of the residual is compared to the variation due to the condition using the F-ratio.

- A significant value of the F-ratio shows that the means in the conditions differ from each other overall. It does not tell you that all the means differ overall or that different pairs of means differ from each other. These differences are tested for separately using a multiple comparisons procedure.

Preparation

You need a good understanding of the unrelated/uncorrelated analysis of variance (Chapter 23). In addition, the difference between correlated/related samples and unrelated/uncorrelated samples (or repeated measures) should be revised.

24.1 Introduction

The analysis of variance covered in this chapter is also called the related, related scores, related samples, repeated measures and matched analysis of variance.

Correlated or related research designs are held to be efficient forms of planning research. Usually these designs involve the same group of participants being assessed in two or more research conditions. The assumption is that by doing so, many of the differences between people are 'allowed for' by having each person 'serve as their own control' – that is, appear in all of the research conditions.

The different sets of scores in the related or correlated analysis of variance are essentially different treatment conditions. We can describe them as either different levels of the treatment or different experimental conditions (Table 24.1).

Table 24.1	Stylised research design for the analysis of variance			
Case	**Treatment 1**	**Treatment 2**	**Treatment 3**	**Treatment 4**
Case 1 (John)	9	14	6	18
Case 2 (Heather)	7	12	9	15
Case 3 (Jane)	5	11	6	17
Case 4 (Tracy)	10	17	12	24
Case 5 (Paul)	8	15	7	19

The numerical scores are scores on the *dependent variable*. They can be any measures for which it is possible to calculate their means and variances meaningfully, in other words basically numerical scores. The treatments are the *levels* of the independent variable. There are very few limitations to the use of this research design:

- It is possible to have any number of treatments with two being the minimum.

- The groups should consist of related or correlated sets of scores. For example:

  - Children's IQs assessed at the age of 5 years, then again at 8 years and finally at 10 years (Table 24.2).

  - Studies with several experimental and control conditions such as that illustrated in Table 24.3 in which each participant takes part in every condition. The study is one of reaction time to emotive words. It is usual to counterbalance the order in which the participants are run through the different conditions.

  - A group of weight-watchers' weights before and after dieting. The dependent variable is their weight in pounds (Table 24.4).

Table 24.2	Research design of IQ assessed sequentially over time		
Child	**Age 5 years**	**Age 8 years**	**Age 10 years**
John	120	125	130
Paula	93	90	100
Sharon, etc.	130	140	110

Table 24.3	Reaction time in seconds comparing two experimental conditions with two control conditions			
Subject	Four-letter words	Mild swear words	Neutral words	Nonsense syllables
Darren	0.3	0.5	0.2	0.2
Lisa, etc.	0.4	0.3	0.3	0.4

Table 24.4	Weight in pounds before and after dieting	
Dieter	Before diet	After diet
Ben	130	120
Claudine, etc.	153	141

- It is necessary to have equal numbers of scores in each group since this is a related subjects or repeated measures design. Obviously in the above examples we have used small numbers of cases.

The related/correlated analysis of variance can also be applied when you have *matched sets* of people (Table 24.5). By this we mean that although there are different people in each of the treatment conditions, they are actually very similar. Each set is as alike as possible on specified variables such as age or intelligence. One member of each matched set is assigned at random to each of the treatment conditions. The variables forming the basis of the matching are believed or known to be correlated with the dependent variable. There is no point in matching if they are not. The purpose of matching is to reduce the amount of 'error' variation.

Table 24.5	Stylised ANOVA design using matched samples			
Matched set	Treatment 1	Treatment 2	Treatment 3	Treatment 4
Matched set 1	9	14	6	18
Matched set 2	7	12	9	15
Matched set 3	5	11	6	17
Matched set 4	10	17	12	24
Matched set 5	8	15	7	19

One advantage of using matched sets of people in experiments rather than the same person in several different treatment conditions is their lack of awareness of the other treatment conditions. That is, they only respond in one version of the experimental design and so cannot be affected by their experience of the other conditions. Matching can be done on any variables you wish but it can get cumbersome if there are too many variables on which to match. So, for example, if you believed that age and sex were related to the dependent variable, you could control for these variables by using matched sets which contained people of the same sex and a very similar age. In this way variation due to sex and age is equally spread between the different treatments or conditions. Thus, matched set 1 might consist of four people matched in that they are all females in the age range 21–25 years. Each one of these is randomly assigned to one of the four treatment conditions. Matched set 2 might consist of four males in the age range 16–20 years. Once again, one of each of these four people is randomly assigned to one of the four treatment conditions.

Modern usage is to describe participants in research as participants, not subjects. Unfortunately, the use of the word subject is hard to avoid in statistics as the terms used are almost 100 years old.

24.2   Theoretical considerations underlying the computer analysis

It is a very small step from the uncorrelated to the correlated analysis of variance. All that is different in the correlated ANOVA is that the error scores are reduced (or adjusted) by removing from them the contribution made by individual differences. The basic idea is shown in Figure 24.1. By an individual difference we mean the tendency of a particular person to score generally high or generally low irrespective of the research treatment or condition they are being tested in. So, for example, bright people will tend to score higher on tests involving intellectual skills no matter what the test is. Less bright people may tend to score relatively poorly no matter what the intellectual test is. In uncorrelated research designs there is no way of knowing the contribution of individual differences. In effect, the individual differences have to be lumped together with the rest of the variance which we have called error. But repeated/related/correlated designs allow us to subdivide the error variance into two sorts: a) that which is explained (as individual differences) and b) that which remains unexplained (or residual error variance).

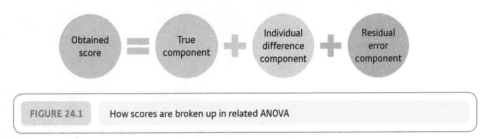

| FIGURE 24.1 | How scores are broken up in related ANOVA |

So far we have discussed error variance as if it were purely the result of chance factors, but error variance is to some extent explicable in theory – the problem is that we do not know what causes it. If we can get an estimate of the contribution of an individual's particular characteristics to their scores in our research we should be able to revise the error scores so that they no longer contain any contribution from the individual differences of that participant. (Remember that individual differences are those characteristics of individuals which tend to encourage them to score generally high or generally low on the dependent variable.)

Once we have measured the same participant twice (or more) then it is possible to estimate the individual difference. Take the data from two individuals given in Table 24.6. Looking at these data, we can see the participants' memory ability for both words and numbers. It is clear that Ann Jones tends to do better on these memory tasks irrespective of the precise

Table 24.6	Individual differences for two people		
Subject	**Memory for words**	**Memory for numbers**	**Row mean**
Ann Jones	17	20	18.5
John Smith	11	14	12.5
			Overall mean = 15.5

nature of the task; John Smith generally does worse no matter what the task. Although both of them seem to do better on memory for numbers, this does not alter the tendency for Ann Jones to generally do best overall. This is not measurement error but a general characteristic of Ann Jones. On average, Ann Jones tends to score six points above John Smith or three points above the overall mean of 15.5 and John Smith tends to score three points below the overall mean of 15.5. In other words, we can give a numerical value to their individual difference relative to the overall mean. So if we subtract 3 from each of Ann Jones's scores and add 3 to each of John Smith's scores we have essentially removed their individual differences components. Figure 24.2 shows the key steps in related ANOVA.

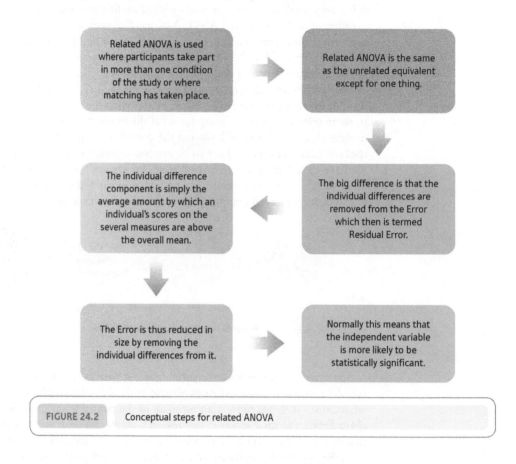

Related ANOVA is used where participants take part in more than one condition of the study or where matching has taken place.

Related ANOVA is the same as the unrelated equivalent except for one thing.

The individual difference component is simply the average amount by which an individual's scores on the several measures are above the overall mean.

The big difference is that the individual differences are removed from the Error which then is termed Residual Error.

The Error is thus reduced in size by removing the individual differences from it.

Normally this means that the independent variable is more likely to be statistically significant.

FIGURE 24.2 Conceptual steps for related ANOVA

24.3 Examples

A physiological psychologist is researching the effects of different pain-relieving drugs on the amount of relief from pain that people experience in a controlled trial. In one condition people are given aspirin, in another condition they are given the trial drug product X, and in the third condition (the control condition) they are given a dummy tablet which contains no active ingredient (this is known as a placebo). The amount of relief from pain experienced in these conditions is rated by each of the participants. The higher the score, the more pain relief. Just to be absolutely clear, participant 1 (Bob Robertson) gets a relief from pain score of 7 when given one aspirin, 8 when given product X and 6 when given the inactive placebo tablet (Table 24.7). It is obvious that Bob Robertson tends to get the most relief from pain (the row mean for Bob is the highest there is) because of the tablets whereas Bert Entwistle tends to get the least relief from pain (his row mean is the lowest there is).

Table 24.7	Pain relief scores from a drugs experiment			
Participant	Aspirin	Product X	Placebo	Row mean
Bob Robertson	7	8	6	7.000
Mavis Fletcher	5	10	3	6.000
Bob Polansky	6	6	4	5.333
Ann Harrison	9	9	2	6.667
Bert Entwistle	3	7	5	5.000
Column mean	6.000	8.000	4.000	Overall mean = 6.000

Table 24.8	Amount of adjustment of Table 24.7 for individual differences		
Participant	Overall mean	Row mean	Adjustment needed to error scores to allow for individual differences (overall mean − row mean)
Bob Robertson	6.000	7.000	−1.000
Mavis Fletcher	6.000	6.000	0.000
Bob Polansky	6.000	5.333	0.667
Ann Harrison	6.000	6.667	−0.667
Bert Entwistle	6.000	5.000	1.000

The related/correlated scores analysis of variance is different in that we make adjustments for these tendencies for individuals to typically score generally high or generally low or generally in the middle. We simply subtract each person's row mean from the table's overall mean of 6.000 to find the amount of adjustment needed to each person's score in order to 'eliminate' individual differences from the scores. Thus for Bob Robertson we need to add −1 (i.e. 6.000 − 7.000) to each of his scores in order to overcome the tendency of his scores to be 1.000 higher than the overall mean (i.e. average score in the table). Do not forget that adding −1 is the same as subtracting 1. Table 24.8 shows the amount of adjustment needed to everyone's scores in order to eliminate individual differences.

Apart from the adjustment for individual differences, the rest of the analysis of variance is much as in Chapter 23.

Explaining statistics 24.1

How correlated samples analysis of variance works

The end point of our calculations is the analysis of variance summary table (Table 24.9). Hopefully by the time we reach the end of our explanation you will understand all of the entries in this table.

Step 1   To begin, you need to tabulate your data. We will use the fictitious relief from pain experiment described above. This is given in Table 24.10.

Table 24.9	Analysis of variance summary table				
Source of variation	Sum of squares	Degrees of freedom	Mean square (or variance estimate)	F-ratio	Probability (sig.)
Between treatments	40.00	2	20.00	5.10	5% (i.e. drugs)
Between people (i.e. individual differences)	8.67	4	2.17		
Error (i.e. residual)	31.33	8	3.92		
Total	80.00	14			

Table 24.10	Pain relief scores from a drugs experiment			
	Aspirin	Product X	Placebo	Row mean
Bob Robertson	7	8	6	7.000
Mavis Fletcher	5	10	3	6.000
Bob Polansky	6	6	4	5.333
Ann Harrison	9	9	2	6.667
Bert Entwistle	3	7	5	5.000
Column mean	6.000	8.000	4.000	Overall mean = 6.000

If you wish, you may calculate the variance estimate of this table using the standard variance estimate formula. As this is generally only a check on your calculations, it is unnecessary for our present purposes since it contains nothing new. If you do the calculation then you should find that the sum of squares is 80 and the degrees of freedom 14 which would give a variance estimate value of 5.71 (i.e. 80 divided by 14). The first two pieces of information are entered into the analysis of variance summary table.

Step 2 We then produce a table of the 'true' scores. Remember that 'true' scores are usually called the 'between' or 'between groups' scores in analysis of variance. To do this, we simply substitute the column mean for each of the individual scores in that column so leaving no variation within the column – the only variation is between the columns. The results are given in Table 24.11.

Table 24.11	'True' scores (obtained by replacing each score in a column by its column mean)			
Participant	Aspirin	Product X	Placebo	Row mean
Bob Robertson	6.000	8.000	4.000	6.000
Mavis Fletcher	6.000	8.000	4.000	6.000
Bob Polansky	6.000	8.000	4.000	6.000
Ann Harrison	6.000	8.000	4.000	6.000
Bert Entwistle	6.000	8.000	4.000	6.000
Column mean	6.000	8.000	4.000	Overall mean = 6.000

The estimated variance of these data can be calculated using the standard computational formula:

$$\text{estimated variance}_{[\text{true/between scores}]} = \frac{\sum X^2 - \dfrac{(\sum X)^2}{N}}{df}$$

$$\sum X^2 = 6.000^2 + 8.000^2 + 4.000^2 + 6.000^2 + 8.000^2 + 4.000^2 + 6.000^2 + 8.000^2 + 4.000^2$$
$$+ 6.000^2 + 8.000^2 + 4.000^2 + 6.000^2 + 8.000^2 + 4.000^2$$

$$= 36.000 + 64.000 + 16.000 + 36.000 + 64.000 + 16.000 + 36.000 + 64.000$$
$$+ 16.000 + 36.000 + 64.000 + 16.000 + 36.000 + 64.000 + 16.000$$

$$= 580$$

$$\sum X^2 = (6.000 + 8.000 + 4.000 + 6.000 + 8.000 + 4.000 + 6.000 + 8.000 + 4.000$$
$$+ 6.000 + 8.000 + 4.000 + 6.000 + 8.000 + 4.000)^2$$
$$= (90)^2$$
$$= 8100$$

The number of scores N equals 15. The degrees of freedom (df) equals the number of columns of data minus 1 ($3 - 1 = 2$). Substituting in the formula:

$$\text{estimated variance}_{[\text{true/between scores}]} = \frac{\sum X^2 - \dfrac{(\sum X)^2}{N}}{df}$$

$$= \frac{580 - \dfrac{8100}{15}}{2}$$

$$= \frac{580 - 540}{2} = \frac{40}{2}$$

$$= 20.0$$

Note that this is the same value as given by SPSS in the first line of **factor1** in the output table in Screenshot 24.5.

Step 3   The error table is now calculated as an intermediate stage. As ever, this is done by subtracting the true/between scores from the scores in the original data table (see Table 24.12). Alternatively, we subtract the column mean from each of the scores in the data table.

Table 24.12	'Error' scores (original data table minus true/between scores)			
Participant	**Aspirin**	**Product X**	**Placebo**	**Row mean**
Bob Robertson	1.000	0.000	2.000	1.000
Mavis Fletcher	−1.000	2.000	−1.000	0.000
Bob Polansky	0.000	−2.000	0.000	−0.667
Ann Harrison	3.000	1.000	−2.000	0.667
Bert Entwistle	−3.000	−1.000	1.000	−1.000
Column mean	**0.000**	**0.000**	**0.000**	Overall mean = 0.000

This is essentially our table of 'error' scores, but since the row means vary (Bert Entwistle's is -1.000 but Mavis Fletcher's is 0.000) then we still have to remove the effects of the individual differences. This we do simply by taking away the row mean from each of the error scores in the row. That is, we take 1.000 away from Bob Robertson's error scores, 0.000 from Mavis Fletcher's, -0.667 from Bob Polansky's, 0.667 from Ann Harrison's and -1.000 from Bert Entwistle's. (Don't forget that subtracting a negative number is like adding a positive number.) This gives us a revised table of error scores without any individual differences. It is usually called the residual scores table in analysis of variance, but it is just a more refined set of error scores (Table 24.13).

Table 24.13	'Residual (error)' scores (obtained by subtracting individual differences or row means from Table 24.12)			
Participant	Aspirin	Product X	Placebo	Row mean
Bob Robertson	0.000	−1.000	1.000	0.000
Mavis Fletcher	−1.000	2.000	−1.000	0.000
Bob Polansky	0.667	−1.333	0.667	0.000
Ann Harrison	2.333	0.333	−2.667	0.000
Bert Entwistle	−2.000	0.000	2.000	0.000
Column mean	0.000	0.000	0.000	Overall mean = 0.000

Notice that both the column and row means now equal zero. This is because not only have the 'true' or between scores been removed from the table but the individual differences are now gone. We need to check out the degrees of freedom associated with this table. There are more constraints now because the row totals also have to equal zero. Thus in the aspirin column we can adjust four scores, but the fifth score is fixed by the requirement that the mean equals zero. In the product X condition we can again vary four scores. However, once we have made these changes, we cannot vary any of the scores in the placebo condition because the row means have to equal zero. In other words, there is a total of eight degrees of freedom in the residual error scores.

The formula for the degrees of freedom is quite straightforward:

$$\text{degrees of freedom}_{[\text{residual error scores}]} = (\text{number of columns of error scores} - 1)$$
$$\times (\text{number of rows of error scores} - 1)$$

The variance estimate of this residual error can be calculated using the standard formula:

$$\text{variance estimate}_{[\text{residual error scores}]} = \frac{\sum X^2 - \dfrac{(\sum X)^2}{N}}{df}$$

$$\sum X^2 = 0.000^2 + (-1.000)^2 + 1.000^2 + (-1.000)^2 + 2.000^2 + (-1.000)^2$$
$$+ 0.667^2 + (-1.333)^2 + 0.667^2 + 2.333^2 + 0.333^2 + (-2.667)^2 + (-2.000)^2$$
$$+ 0.000^2 + 2.000^2$$
$$= 0.000 + 1.000 + 1.000 + 1.000 + 4.000 + 1.000 + 0.445 + 1.777 + 0.445 + 5.443$$
$$+ 0.111 + 7.113 + 4.000 + 0.000 + 4.000$$
$$= 31.334$$

$$(\sum X)^2 = [0.000 + (-1.000) + 1.000 + (-1.000) + 2.000$$

$$+ (-1.000) + 0.667 + (-1.333) + 0.667 + 2.333 + 0.333 + (-2.667)$$

$$+ (-2.000) + 0.000 + 2.000]^2$$

$$= 0$$

The number of scores N equals 15 as before. The degrees of freedom are given by:

$$\text{degree of freedom} = (\text{number of columns} - 1) \times (\text{number of rows} - 1)$$

$$= (3 - 1) \times (5 - 1)$$

$$= 2 \times 4 = 8$$

Substituting in the formula:

$$\text{variance estimate}_{[\text{residual error scores}]} = \frac{\sum X^2 - \dfrac{(\sum X)^2}{N}}{df}$$

$$= \frac{31.334 - \dfrac{0}{15}}{8}$$

$$= \frac{31.334}{8} = 3.92$$

Once again, note that this is the same value as that provided by SPSS in the first line of Error(factor1) in the output table in Screenshot 24.5.

Step 4

This is not absolutely necessary, but the conventional approach to correlated/repeated measures analysis of variance calculates the variance estimate of the individual differences. This is usually described as the between-people variance estimate or 'blocks' variance estimate. (The word 'blocks' originates from the days when the analysis of variance was confined to agricultural research. Different amounts of fertiliser would be put on a single area of land and the fertility of these different 'blocks' assessed. The analysis of variance contains many terms referring to its agricultural origins such as split plots, randomised plots, levels of treatment and so forth.)

If you wish to calculate the between-people (or individual differences) variance estimate, you need to draw up Table 24.14, which consists of the individual differences component in each score (this is obtained by the difference between the row means and the overall mean in the original data). In other words, it is a table of the amount of adjustment required to everyone's scores in order to remove the effect of their individual characteristics.

Table 24.14	Between-people (individual difference) scores (obtained by taking the difference between the row means and overall mean in the original data)			
Participant	Aspirin	Product X	Placebo	Row mean
Bob Robertson	1.000	1.000	1.000	1.000
Mavis Fletcher	0.000	0.000	0.000	0.000
Bob Polansky	−0.667	−0.667	−0.667	−0.667
Ann Harrison	0.667	0.667	0.667	0.667
Bert Entwistle	−1.000	−1.000	−1.000	−1.000
Column mean	0.000	0.000	0.000	Overall mean = 0.000

We calculate the variance estimate of this using the usual variance estimate formula for the analysis of variance. The degrees of freedom are constrained by the fact that the column means have to equal zero and that all the scores in the row are the same. In the end, this means that the degrees of freedom for this table are the number of rows minus one. We have five rows so therefore the number of degrees of freedom is four.

The sum of squares for Table 24.14 is 8.67 and the degrees of freedom are 4; therefore the variance estimate is $8.67 \div 4 = 2.17$. These values can be entered in the analysis of variance summary table. (Strictly speaking, this is another unnecessary stage in the calculation, but it does provide a check on the accuracy of your calculations.)

Step 5   We can enter the calculations into an analysis of variance summary table. It might be more conventional to see an analysis of variance summary table written in the form shown in Table 24.15. Some calculations are unnecessary and we have omitted them.

Table 24.15	Analysis of variance summary table			
Source of variation	Sum of squares	Degrees of freedom	Mean square (or variance estimate)	F-ratio
Between treatments (i.e. drugs)	40.00	2	20.00	5.10*
Between people (i.e. individual differences)	8.67	4	2.17	–
Error (i.e. residual)	31.33	8	3.92	–
Total	80.00	14	–	–

* Significant at 5% level.

Notice that the total sum of squares (80.00) is the same as the sum of the individual components of this total $(40.00 + 8.67 + 31.33)$ and this applies also to the degrees of freedom. This can provide a useful check on the accuracy of your calculations.

Interpreting the results

The most important part of the analysis is the F-ratio. This is the between-groups variance estimate divided by the error (residual) variance estimate. In other words, it is $20.00 \div 3.92 = 5.10$. The statistical significance of this value can be assessed by the use of Significance Table 24.1. With two degrees of freedom for between treatments and eight for the error, a minimum F-ratio of 4.5 is needed to be statistically significant. Thus the obtained F-ratio of 5.10 is significant at the 5% level.

The significant probability value of 5% tells us that the variance in the between-groups scores is substantially greater than the error (residual) variance. Thus the null hypothesis that the drugs have no effect on the amount of relief from pain is rejected and the hypothesis that the drugs treatments have an effect at the 5% level of significance is accepted. What you do not know as a result of this analysis is which of the particular groups or conditions differ from each other. The F-ratio is just an overall test. Further analyses using multiple comparisons tests are necessary to say just where the significant differences lie (see Chapter 26).

The use of SPSS and other computer programs make very sophisticated statistical analyses to be computed which are very difficult without them. One of these which is applicable here is the test of sphericity. This simply tests whether certain assumptions about your data are met. If they are, then the test of significance is slightly different and, for the same data, more likely to be statistically significant. This is discussed further in the Computer Analysis section at the end of this chapter.

Significance Table 24.1	5% significance values of the *F*-ratio for related ANOVA (one-tailed test). Additional values are to be found in Significance Table 22.1					
Degrees of freedom for residual or residual error mean square (or variance estimate)	Degrees of freedom for between-treatments mean square (or variance estimate)					
	1	2	3	4	5	∞
1	161 or more	200	216	225	230	254
2	18.5	19.0	19.2	19.3	19.3	19.5
3	10.1	9.6	9.3	9.1	9.0	8.5
4	7.7	6.9	6.6	6.4	6.3	5.6
5	6.6	5.8	5.4	5.2	5.1	4.4
6	6.0	5.1	4.8	4.5	4.4	3.7
7	5.6	4.7	4.4	4.1	4.0	3.2
8	5.3	4.5	4.1	3.8	3.7	2.9
9	5.1	4.3	3.9	3.6	3.5	2.7
10	5.0	4.1	3.7	3.5	3.3	2.5
13	4.7	3.8	3.4	3.2	3.0	2.2
15	4.5	3.7	3.3	3.1	2.9	2.1
20	4.4	3.5	3.1	2.9	2.7	1.8
30	4.2	3.3	2.9	2.7	2.5	1.6
60	4.0	3.2	2.8	2.5	2.4	1.4
∞	3.8	3.0	2.6	2.4	2.2	1.0

Your value has to equal or be larger than the tabulated value for an effect to be significant at the 5% level.

Reporting the results

There are a number of ways of reporting this output. 'One-way repeated measures analysis of variance was used to compare the treatment means. A significant treatment effect was found for the three conditions, $F(2, 8) = 5.10, p < .05$. The Aspirin mean was 6.00, the Product X mean 8.00, and the Placebo mean was 4.00.' The results of Bonferroni related *t*-tests could be added. These are discussed in Chapter 26.

Research examples

Correlated/related ANOVA

Dumont and Louw (2009) analysed the impact of the work of Henri Tajfel (1919–1982) on social psychology. They suggest that his work formed the infrastructure to European social psychology over a long period of time. They collected data on the citations to his work in five prominent psychology journals. Six time periods starting with 1972–1976 and ending with 1997–2002 formed the conditions for a related samples one-way analysis of variance. This showed that the percentages of articles published in these journals varied significantly over the six time periods. Furthermore, multi-comparisons employing Bonferroni correction showed that the percentage for each time period was significantly greater than that of the preceding one.

→

Hunter, Schellenberg and Griffith (2011) manipulated mood by showing the same participants pictures that were designed to elicit happy, neutral or sad feelings. To check whether these pictures evoked these feelings, participants rated each picture on a 7-point bipolar sad–happy scale. A one-way repeated measures ANOVA was carried out which found a significant effect. Related t-tests were used to show that the happy pictures made participants feel significantly happier than the neutral pictures, which made them feel significantly happier than the sad pictures.

Perlman (2011) points out that research suggests that teachers often use teaching styles which undermine the motivation of students. Using what is known as self-determination theory teachers' behaviours have been changed to be more motivationally supportive. The purpose of Perlman's research was to assess the influence of using a Sport Education approach as opposed to a skill-drill game approach on the teaching behaviour of pre-service physical education teachers. An observation protocol was used to code teacher–student interaction episodes employing 15 different categories. Furthermore, the teachers were given a breakdown of their use of autonomy supportive, controlling and neutral comments. The Learning Climate Questionnaire and the Sport Motivation Scale were completed by the students which provided scores on their perceptions of autonomy–support and individual motivation. The data were collected on a repeated basis over time from this group of participants including the questionnaire data. Related analysis of variance was used to assess the data. The use of the Sport Education approach resulted in higher levels of autonomy supportive interactions on the part of the teachers.

Key points

- Working out this analysis of variance by hand is quite time-consuming and extremely repetitive. Computers will save most people time.

- Do not be deterred by some of the strange terminology used in the analysis of variance. Words like blocks, split-plots and levels of treatment have their origins in agricultural research, as does ANOVA.

- The analysis of variance in cases in which you have just two conditions or sets of scores is relatively easy to interpret. It is not so easy where you have three or more groups; then your analysis is not complete until you have employed a multiple comparisons procedure as in Chapter 26.

COMPUTER ANALYSIS

Related analysis of variance using SPSS

Data
- Name the variables appropriately in 'Variable View' of the 'Data Editor'.

- Enter the data under the appropriate variable name in 'Data View' of the 'Data Editor' (Screenshot 24.1).

Analysis
- Select 'Analyze', 'General Linear Model' and 'Repeated Measures...' (Screenshot 24.2).

2
- Enter the number of groups in the 'Number of Levels:' and select 'Add' and 'Define' (Screenshot 24.3).

3
- Move the appropriate variables to the top box on the right and select 'Options' (Screenshot 24.4).

4
- Then on the same screen, select 'Descriptive statistics', 'Estimates of effect size', 'Continue' and 'OK'.

Output
- Check if Mauchly's test of sphericity is not significant with Sig. greater than .05. (This is to be found in computer output.) If it were significant, then there is spherecity.

2
- If it is not significant, check that the Sig(nificance) of the Factor for 'Sphericity Assumed' in the 'Tests of Within-Subjects Effects' table is .05 or less (Screenshot 24.5).

3
- If there are more than 2 means, check with related t-tests which means differ significantly. See Chapter 26.

FIGURE 24.3   SPSS steps for a repeated measures analysis of variance

Interpreting and reporting the output

- In this example, assuming sphericity, the exact significance level for F is .037, which means that the analysis is significant at the 5% output (.05 probability). If sphericity cannot be assumed then use one of the other three tests in Screenshot 24.5 (e.g. Greenhouse–Geisser). Since we have three groups, it is appropriate to compare each group using the related t-test adjusted for the number of comparisons (three in this case). In this situation, this would mean that the significance obtained has to be smaller than $.05 \div 3 = .0167$ in order to be reported statistically significant at the .05 level. None of them is statistically significant.

- We could describe the results of this analysis in the following way: 'A one-way repeated measures analysis of variance showed a significant treatment effect for the three conditions, $F(2, 8) = 5.10, p = .037, \eta_p^2 = .56$. The Aspirin mean was 6.00, the Product X mean 8.00, and the Placebo mean was 4.00. None of the three treatments differed significantly from one another with related t-tests when a Bonferroni adjustment was made for the number of comparisons.'

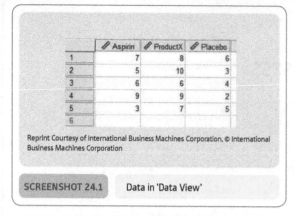

Reprint Courtesy of International Business Machines Corporation, © International
Business Machines Corporation

SCREENSHOT 24.1   Data in 'Data View'

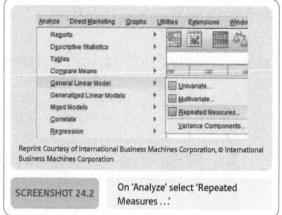

Reprint Courtesy of International Business Machines Corporation, © International
Business Machines Corporation

SCREENSHOT 24.2   On 'Analyze' select 'Repeated
Measures …'

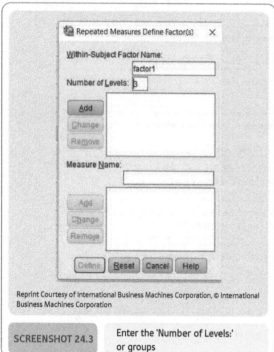

Reprint Courtesy of International Business Machines Corporation, © International
Business Machines Corporation

SCREENSHOT 24.3   Enter the 'Number of Levels:'
or groups

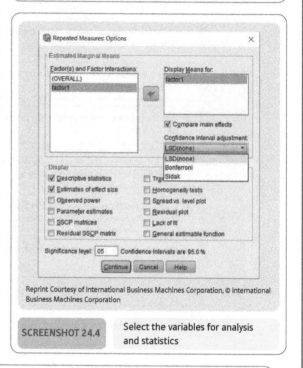

Reprint Courtesy of International Business Machines Corporation, © International
Business Machines Corporation

SCREENSHOT 24.4   Select the variables for analysis
and statistics

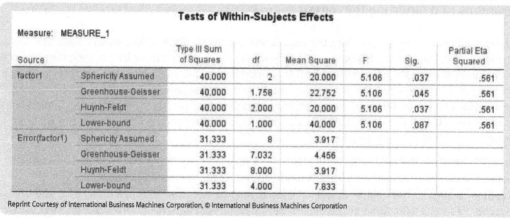

Tests of Within-Subjects Effects

Measure: MEASURE_1

Source		Type III Sum of Squares	df	Mean Square	F	Sig.	Partial Eta Squared
factor1	Sphericity Assumed	40.000	2	20.000	5.106	.037	.561
	Greenhouse-Geisser	40.000	1.758	22.752	5.106	.045	.561
	Huynh-Feldt	40.000	2.000	20.000	5.106	.037	.561
	Lower-bound	40.000	1.000	40.000	5.106	.087	.561
Error(factor1)	Sphericity Assumed	31.333	8	3.917			
	Greenhouse-Geisser	31.333	7.032	4.456			
	Huynh-Feldt	31.333	8.000	3.917			
	Lower-bound	31.333	4.000	7.833			

Reprint Courtesy of International Business Machines Corporation, © International Business Machines Corporation

SCREENSHOT 24.5   Most important part of the output

CHAPTER 25

Two-way or factorial ANOVA for unrelated/ uncorrelated scores

Two studies for the price of one?

Overview

- The two-way analysis of variance involves two independent variables and a single dependent variable which is the score. ANOVAs with two or more independent variables are called factorial ANOVAs.

- Factorial designs potentially indicate the extent to which the two independent variables when combined influence scores on the dependent variable.

- The main effects are the influence of the independent variables acting separately, the interaction is the influence of the independent variables acting in combination.

- Much of the two-way analysis of variance proceeds like two separate one-way analyses. However, there is the interaction which assesses the multiplicative (rather than additive) influence of the two independent variables acting in combination.

- Two-way analysis of variance requires some care in its interpretation. It is not possible to adopt a purely mechanical approach. Judgement is required. The problem is that the main effects are estimated before the interaction effects. Sometimes interaction effects become subsumed as main effects. Care is needed to examine the graph of the interaction to identify this possibility.

- The two-way analysis of variance can be extended to any number of independent variables though the process rapidly becomes very cumbersome with each additional independent variable.

Preparation

Chapter 23 on the one-way analysis of variance contains material essential to the full understanding of this chapter.

25.1 Introduction

Often researchers wish to assess the influence of more than a single independent variable at a time in experiments and other studies. The one-way analysis of variance deals with a single independent variable which can have two or more levels. However, analysis of variance copes with several *independent* variables in a research design. These are known as multi-factorial ANOVAs. The number of 'ways' is the number of independent variables. Thus a two-way analysis of variance allows two independent variables to be included, three-way analysis of variance allows three independent variables and five-way analysis of variance means that there are five independent variables. *There is only one dependent variable no matter how many 'ways' in each analysis of variance.* If you have two or more *dependent* variables, each of these will normally entail a separate analysis of variance (though see Chapter 29 on MANOVA). Although things can get very complicated conceptually, two-way analysis of variance is relatively straightforward and introduces just one major new concept – interaction.

In this chapter we will be concentrating on examples in which all of the scores are independent (uncorrelated). Each participant therefore contributes just one score to the analysis. In other words, it is an *uncorrelated* design.

Generally speaking, the two-way analysis of variance is best suited to experimental research in which it is possible to allocate participants at random into the various conditions. Although this does not apply to the one-way analysis of variance, there are problems in using two-way and multi-way analyses of variance in survey and other non-experimental research. The difficulty is that ideally you need equal numbers of scores in each cell otherwise the calculation involves estimates. It is hard to do these calculations by hand, though easy on the computer as no extra effort is involved. However, the ideal still would be equal numbers in each cell.

A typical research design for a two-way analysis of variance is the effect of the *independent variables* alcohol *and* sleep deprivation on the *dependent variable* of people's comprehension of complex video material expressed in terms of the number of mistakes made on a test of understanding of the video material. The research design and data might look like that shown in Table 25.1.

Table 25.1	Data for typical two-way analysis of variance: number of mistakes on video test		
	Sleep deprivation		
	4 hours	**12 hours**	**24 hours**
Alcohol	16	18	22
	12	16	24
	17	25	32
No alcohol	11	13	12
	9	8	14
	12	11	12

In a sense, one could regard this experiment conceptually as two separate experiments, one studying the effects of sleep deprivation and the other studying the effects of alcohol. The effects of each of the two independent variables are called the *main* effects. Additionally, the analysis normally looks for *interactions* which are basically findings that cannot be explained on the basis of the distinctive effects of alcohol level and sleep deprivation acting separately. For example, it could be that people do especially badly if they have been deprived of a lot of sleep *and* have been given alcohol. They do more badly than the additive effects of alcohol and sleep deprivation would predict. Interactions are about the effects of specific combinations of variables. If we look carefully at Table 25.1, it is possible to see that the scores in the Alcohol–24 hours cell seem to be rather higher on average than the scores in any of the other cells. Similarly, the scores in the No alcohol–4 hours cell seem to be rather smaller, typically, than the other cells. This is an example of what we mean by an interaction – an outcome which does not seem to be the consequence of the two main variables acting separately. We will return to the concept of interaction later.

In the analysis of variance, we sometimes talk of the *levels of a treatment* – this is simply the number of values that any independent variable can take. In the above example, the alcohol variable has two different values – that is, there are two levels of the treatment or variable alcohol. There are three levels of the treatment or variable sleep deprivation. Sometimes, a two-way ANOVA is identified in terms of the numbers of levels of treatment for each of the independent variables. So a 2 × 3 ANOVA has two different levels of the first variable and three for the second variable. This corresponds to the above example.

25.2 Theoretical considerations

Much of the two-way analysis of variance is easy if it is remembered that it largely involves two separate 'one-way' analyses of variance as if there were two separate experiments. Imagine an experiment in which one group of subjects is given iron supplements in their diet to see if iron has any effect on their depression levels. In the belief that women have a greater need for iron than men, the researchers included gender as their other independent variable. The data are given in Table 25.2. Figure 25.1 gives the key steps in a two-way ANOVA.

Table 25.2	Data table for study of dietary supplements		
	Iron supplement	**No iron supplement**	
Males	3	9	
	7	5	
	4	6	
	6	8	
	Cell mean = 5.00	Cell mean = 7.00	Row mean = 6.00
Females	11	19	
	7	16	
	10	18	
	8	15	
	Cell mean = 9.00	Cell mean = 17.00	Row mean = 13.00
	Column mean = 7.00	Column mean = 12.00	Overall mean = 9.50

Table 25.2 represents a 2 × 2 ANOVA. Comparing the four condition means (cell means), the depression scores for females not receiving the supplement seem rather higher than those of any other groups. In other words, it would appear that the lack of the iron supplement has more effect on women. Certain gender and iron supplement conditions

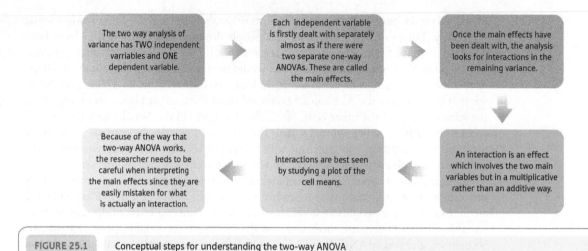

FIGURE 25.1   Conceptual steps for understanding the two-way ANOVA

in combination have a great effect on depression scores. This suggests an interaction. That is, particular cells in the analysis have much higher or lower scores than can be explained simply in terms of the gender trends or dietary supplement trends acting separately.

The assumption in the two-way analysis of variance is that the variation in Table 25.2 comes from four sources:

● 'error' (often referred to as residual error)

● the main effect of gender

● the main effect of iron supplement

● the interaction of gender and iron supplement.

The first three components above are dealt with exactly as they were in the one-way unrelated analysis of variance. The slight difference is that instead of calculating the variance estimate for one independent variable we now calculate two variance estimates – one for each independent variable. However, the term main effect should not cause any confusion. It is merely the effect of an independent variable acting alone as it would if the two-way design were turned into two separate one-way designs. The only difference is that the error term may be smaller than in a one-way ANOVA as part of the error may now be accounted for by the other independent variable and the interaction of the two independent variables. A smaller error term makes it more likely that significant effects will be obtained.

The interaction consists of any variation in the scores which is left after we have taken away the 'error' and main effects for the gender and iron supplements sub-experiments. That is, priority is given to finding main effects at the expense of interactions. This is important and can lead to incorrectly interpreted analyses if it is not appreciated.

25.3   Steps in the analysis

■ Step 1

To produce an 'error' table we simply take our original data and subtract the cell mean from every score in the cell. Thus, for instance, we need to subtract 5.00 from each score in the cell for males receiving the iron supplement and 17.00 from each cell for the females not receiving the iron supplement, etc. In the present example the 'error' table is as in Table 25.3.

Table 25.3	'Error' scores for study of dietary supplements		
	Iron supplement	**No iron supplement**	
Males	3 − 5 = −2	9 − 7 = 2	
	7 − 5 = 2	5 − 7 = −2	
	4 − 5 = −1	6 − 7 = −1	
	6 − 5 = 1	8 − 7 = 1	
	Cell mean = 0.00	Cell mean = 0.00	Row mean = 0.00
Females	11 − 9 = 2	19 − 17 = 2	
	7 − 9 = −2	16 − 17 = −1	
	10 − 9 = 1	18 − 17 = 1	
	8 − 9 = −1	15 − 17 = −2	
	Cell mean = 0.00	Cell mean = 0.00	Row mean = 0.00
	(i) Column mean = 0.00	Column mean = 0.00	Overall mean = 0.00

We calculate the 'error' variance estimate for this in the usual way. The formula, as ever, is:

$$\text{variance estimate}_{[\text{error}]} = \frac{\sum X^2 - \dfrac{(\sum X)^2}{N}}{df}$$

The degrees of freedom (*df*), analogously to the one-way analysis of variance, are the number of scores minus the number of conditions or cells. This leaves 12 degrees of freedom (16 scores minus 4 conditions or cells).

■ Step 2

To produce a table of the main effects for the iron supplement treatment, simply substitute the column means from the original data for each of the scores in the columns. The iron supplement mean was 7.00 so each iron supplement score is changed to 7.00, thus eliminating any other source of variation. Similarly, the no-iron supplement mean was 12.00 so each score is changed to 12.00 (see Table 25.4).

Table 25.4	Diet main effect scores for study of dietary supplements		
Iron supplement	**No iron supplement**		
7.00	12.00	
7.00	12.00	
7.00	12.00	
7.00	12.00	Row mean = 9.50
7.00	12.00	
7.00	12.00	
7.00	12.00	
7.00	12.00	Row mean = 9.50
Column mean = 7.00	Column mean = 12.00	Overall mean = 9.50

The variance estimate of the above scores can be calculated using the usual variance estimate formula. The degrees of freedom are calculated in the familiar way – the number of columns minus one (i.e. $df = 1$).

■ Step 3

To produce a table of the main effect of gender, remember that the independent variable gender is tabulated as the rows (not the columns). In other words, we substitute the row mean for the males and the row mean for the females for the respective scores (Table 25.5).

Table 25.5	Gender main effect scores for study of dietary supplements								
Males	6.00	6.00	6.00	6.00	6.00	6.00	6.00	6.00	Row mean = 6.00
Females	13.00	13.00	13.00	13.00	13.00	13.00	13.00	13.00	Row mean = 13.00

The variance estimate of the above scores can be calculated with the usual variance estimate formula. Even the degrees of freedom are calculated in the usual way. However, *as the table is on its side* compared to our usual method, the degrees of freedom are the number of *rows* minus one in this case (2 − 1 or 1 degree of freedom).

The calculation of the main effects (variance estimates) for gender and the iron supplement follows exactly the same procedures as in the one-way analysis of variance.

■ Step 4

The remaining stage is to calculate the interaction. This is simply anything which is left over after we have eliminated 'error' and the main effects. So for any score, the interaction score is found by taking the score in your data and subtracting the 'error' score and the gender score and the iron supplement score.

Table 25.6 is our data table less the 'error' variance, in other words a table which replaces each score by its cell mean. It is obvious that the row means for the males and females are not the same. The row mean for males is 6.00 and the row mean for females is 13.00. To get rid of the gender effect, we can subtract 6.00 from each male score and 13.00 from each female score in the previous table. The results of this simple subtraction are found in Table 25.7.

Table 25.6	Data table with 'error' removed		
	Iron supplement	**No iron supplement**	
Males	5.00	7.00	
	5.00	7.00	
	5.00	7.00	
	5.00	7.00	Row mean = 6.00
Females	9.00	17.00	
	9.00	17.00	
	9.00	17.00	
	9.00	17.00	Row mean = 13.00
	Column mean = 7.00	Column mean = 12.00	Overall mean = 9.50

Table 25.7	Data table with 'error' and gender removed			
	Iron supplement	**No iron supplement**		
Males	−1.00	1.00		
	−1.00	1.00		
	−1.00	1.00		
	−1.00	1.00	Row mean = 0.00	
Females	−4.00	4.00		
	−4.00	4.00		
	−4.00	4.00		
	−4.00	4.00	Row mean = 0.00	
	Column mean = −2.50	Column mean = 2.50	Overall mean = 0.00	

You can see that the male and female main effect has been taken into account since now both row means are zero. That is, there remains no variation due to gender. But you can see that there remains variation due to iron treatment. Those getting the supplement now score −2.50 on average and those not getting the iron treatment score +2.50. To remove the variation due to the iron treatment, subtract −2.50 from the iron supplement column and 2.50 from the non-iron supplement column (Table 25.8). Do not forget that *subtracting a negative number is like adding a positive number.*

Looking at Table 25.8, although the column and row means are zero throughout, the scores in the cells are not. This shows that there still remains a certain amount of variation in the scores even after 'error' and the two main effects have been taken away. That is, there is an interaction, which may or may not be significant. We have to check this using the *F*-ratio test.

Table 25.8	Interaction table, i.e. data table with 'error', gender and iron supplement all removed			
	Iron supplement	**No iron supplement**		
Males	1.5	−1.5		
	1.5	−1.5		
	1.5	−1.5		
	1.5	−1.5	Row mean = 0.00	
Females	−1.5	1.5		
	−1.5	1.5		
	−1.5	1.5		
	−1.5	1.5	Row mean = 0.00	
	Column mean = 0.00	Column mean = 0.00	Overall mean = 0.00	

What the interaction table implies is that women *without* the iron supplement and men *with* the iron supplement are getting the higher scores on the dependent variable.

We can calculate the variance estimate for the interaction by using the usual formula. Degrees of freedom need to be considered. The degrees of freedom for the above table of the interaction are limited by:

● all scores in the cells having to be equal (i.e. no 'error' variance)

all marginal means (i.e. row and column means) having to equal zero.

In other words, there can be only one degree of freedom in this case.

There is a general formula for the degrees of freedom of the interaction: degrees of freedom$_{[interaction]}$ = (number of rows − 1) × (number of columns − 1). Since there are two rows and two columns in this case, the degrees of freedom are:

$$(2 − 1) \times (2 − 1) = 1 \times 1 = 1$$

■ Step 5

All of the stages in the calculation are entered into an analysis of variance summary table (Table 25.9).

Table 25.9	Analysis of variance summary table			
Source of variation	**Sums of squares**	**Degrees of freedom**	**Mean square**	**F-ratio**
Main effects				
Gender	196.00	1	196.00	58.96*
Iron supplement	100.00	1	100.00	30.00*
Interaction				
Gender with iron supplement	36.00	1	36.00	10.81*
'Error'	40.00	12	3.33	–
Total (data)	372.00	15	–	–

*Significant at the 5% level.

Notice that there are several F-ratios because you need to know whether there is a significant effect of gender, a significant effect of the iron supplement and a significant interaction of the gender and iron supplement variables. In each case, you divide the appropriate mean square by the 'error' mean square. If you wish to check your understanding of the processes involved, see if you can obtain the above table by going through the individual calculations.

The significant interaction indicates that some of the cells or conditions are getting exceptionally high or low scores which cannot be accounted for on the basis of the two main effects acting independently of each other. In this case, it would appear that females getting the iron supplement and males not getting the iron supplement are actually getting higher scores than the gender or supplement acting separately and independently of each other would produce. In order to interpret an interaction, you have to remember that the effects of the independent variables are separately removed from the table (i.e. the main effects are removed first). It is only after this has been done that the interaction is calculated. In other words, ANOVA gives priority to main effects, and sometimes it can confuse interactions for main effects. Table 25.10 presents data from the present experiment in which the cell means have been altered to emphasise the lack of main effects.

In this example, it is absolutely clear that all the variation in the cell means is to do with the female/no-supplement condition. All the other three cell means are identical at 5.00. Quite clearly the males and females in the iron supplement condition have exactly the same average score. Similarly, males in the iron supplement and no-supplement conditions are obtaining identical means. In other words, there seem to be no main effects at all. The females in the no-supplement condition are the only group getting exceptionally high scores.

Table 25.10	Alternative data table showing different trends		
	Iron supplement	**No iron supplement**	
Males	Cell mean = 5.00	Cell mean = 5.00	Row mean = 5.00
Females	Cell mean = 5.00	Cell mean = 17.00	Row mean = 11.00
	Column mean = 5.00	Column mean = 11.00	

This would suggest that there is an interaction but no main effects. However, if you do the analysis of variance on these data you will find that there are two main effects and an interaction! The reason for this is that the main effects are estimated before the interaction, so the exceptionally high row mean for females and the exceptionally high column mean for the no-supplement condition will lead to the interaction being mistaken for main effects as your ANOVA summary table might show significant main effects. So you need to examine your data with great care as you carry out your analysis of variance; otherwise you will observe main effects which are an artefact of the method, and ignore interactions which are actually there! The analysis of variance may be tricky to execute, but it can be even trickier for the novice to interpret properly – to be frank, many professional psychologists are unaware of the problems.

It is yet another example of the importance of close examination of the data alongside the statistical analysis itself.

Explaining statistics 25.1

How two-way unrelated analysis of variance works

Without a safety net we will attempt to analyse the sleep and alcohol experiment mentioned earlier. It is described as a 2×3 analysis of variance because one independent variable has two values and the other has three values (Table 25.11).

Table 25.11	Data for sleep deprivation experiment: number of mistakes on video test		
	Sleep deprivation		
	4 hours	**12 hours**	**24 hours**
Alcohol	16	18	22
	12	16	24
	17	25	32
No alcohol	11	13	12
	9	8	14
	12	11	12

→

Step 1   *Total variance estimate.* We enter the row and column means as well as the means of each of the six cells (Table 25.12).

Table 25.12	Data for sleep deprivation experiment with the addition of cell, column and row means			
	Sleep deprivation			
	4 hours	**12 hours**	**24 hours**	
Alcohol	16	18	22	
	12	16	24	
	17	25	32	
	Cell mean = 15.000	Cell mean = 19.667	Cell mean = 26.000	Row mean = 20.222
No alcohol	11	13	12	
	9	8	14	
	12	11	12	
	Cell mean = 10.667	Cell mean = 10.667	Cell mean = 12.667	Row mean = 11.333
	Column mean = 12.833	Column mean = 15.167	Column mean = 19.333	Overall mean = 15.777

$$\text{variance estimate}_{[\text{data}]} = \frac{\sum X^2 - \dfrac{(\sum X)^2}{N}}{df}$$

$$\sum X^2 = 16^2 + 18^2 + 22^2 + 12^2 + 16^2 + 24^2 + 17^2 + 25^2 + 32^2 + 11^2 + 13^2 + 12^2 + 9^2 + 8^2$$
$$+ 14^2 + 12^2 + 11^2 + 12^2$$
$$= 256 + 324 + 484 + 144 + 256 + 576 + 289 + 625 + 1024 + 121 + 169 + 144 + 81$$
$$+ 64 + 196 + 144 + 121 + 144$$
$$= 5162$$

$$(\sum X)^2 = (16 + 18 + 22 + 12 + 16 + 24 + 17 + 25 + 32 + 11 + 13 + 12 + 9 + 8 + 14 + 12$$
$$+ 11 + 12)^2$$
$$= (284)^2 = 80\ 656$$

The number of scores N equals 18. The degrees of freedom (df) equal the number of scores minus one, i.e. 17. Substituting in the formula:

$$\text{variance estimate}_{[\text{data}]} = \frac{\sum X^2 - \dfrac{(\sum X)^2}{N}}{df} = \frac{5162 - \dfrac{80\ 656}{18}}{17}$$

$$= \frac{5162 - 4480.889}{17}$$

$$= \frac{681.111}{17} = 40.065$$

The sum of squares here (i.e. 681.111) is called the total sum of squares in the ANOVA summary table. (Strictly speaking, this calculation is unnecessary in that its only function is a computational check on your other calculations.)

Step 2   *'Error' variance estimate.* Subtract the cell mean from each of the scores in a cell to obtain the 'error' scores (Table 25.13).

Table 25.13	'Error' scores			
	Sleep deprivation			
	4 hours	**12 hours**	**24 hours**	
Alcohol	1.000	−1.667	−4.000	
	−3.000	−3.667	−2.000	
	2.000	5.333	6.000	Alcohol mean = 0.000
No alcohol	0.333	2.333	−0.667	
	−1.667	−2.667	1.333	
	1.333	0.333	−0.667	No alcohol mean = 0.000
	Column mean = 0.000	Column mean = 0.000	Column mean = 0.000	Column mean = 0.000

Apart from rounding errors, the cell means, the row means, the column means and the overall mean are all zero – just as required of an 'error' table.

We calculate the 'error' variance estimate using the usual variance estimate formula:

$$\text{variance estimate}_{[\text{data}]} = \frac{\sum X^2 - \frac{(\sum X)^2}{N}}{df}$$

$$\sum X^2 = 1.000^2 + (-1.667)^2 + (-4.000)^2 + (-3.000)^2 + (-3.667)^2 + (-2.000)^2 + 2.000^2$$
$$+ 5.333^2 + 6.000^2 + 0.333^2 + 2.333^2 + (-0.667)^2 + (-1.667)^2 + (-2.667)^2 + 1.333^2$$
$$+1.333^2 + 0.333^2 + (-0.667)^2$$

$$= 1.000 + 2.779 + 16.000 + 9.000 + 13.447 + 4.000 + 4.000 + 28.444 + 36.000 + 0.111$$
$$+5.443 + 0.445 + 2.779 + 7.113 + 1.777 + 1.777 + 0.111 + 0.445$$

$$= 134.671$$

$$(\sum X)^2 = [1.000 + (-1.667) + (-4.000) + (-3.000) + (-3.667) + (-2.000) + 2.000 + 5.333$$
$$+6.000 + 0.333 + 2.333 + (-0.667) + (-1.667) + (-2.667) + 1.333 + 1.333$$
$$+0.333 + (-0.667)]^2$$

$$= 0$$

(Notice that this latter calculation is unnecessary as it will always equal 0 for 'error' scores.) The number of scores N equals 18. The degrees of freedom (df) equal the number of scores minus the number of cells, i.e. $18 - 6 = 12$. We can now substitute these values in the formula:

$$\text{variance estimate}_{[\text{'error scores'}]} = \frac{\sum X^2 - \frac{(\sum X)^2}{N}}{df}$$

$$= \frac{134.671 - \frac{0}{18}}{12}$$

$$= \frac{134.671}{12}$$

$$= 11.223$$

Step 3   *Sleep deprivation variance estimate.* We now derive our table containing the scores in the three sleep deprivation conditions (combining over alcohol and non-alcohol conditions) simply by replacing each score in the column by the column mean (Table 25.14).

$$\text{variance estimate}_{[\text{'sleep deprivation' scores}]} = \frac{\sum X^2 - \frac{(\sum X)^2}{N}}{df}$$

$$\begin{aligned}
\sum X^2 &= 12.833^2 + 15.167^2 + 19.333^2 + 12.833^2 + 15.167^2 + 19.333^2 + 12.833^2 + 15.167^2 \\
&\quad + 19.333^2 + 12.833^2 + 15.167^2 + 19.333^2 + 12.833^2 + 15.167^2 + 19.333^2 + 12.833^2 \\
&\quad + 15.167^2 + 19.333^2 \\
&= 164.686 + 230.038 + 373.765 + 164.686 + 230.038 + 373.765 + 164.686 + 230.038 \\
&\quad + 373.765 + 164.686 + 230.038 + 373.765 + 164.686 + 230.038 + 373.765 \\
&\quad + 164.686 + 230.038 + 373.765 \\
&= 4610.934
\end{aligned}$$

Table 25.14	Scores due to sleep deprivation		
Sleep deprivation			
4 hours	**12 hours**	**24 hours**	
12.833	15.167	19.333	
12.833	15.167	19.333	
12.833	15.167	19.333	
12.833	15.167	19.333	
12.833	15.167	19.333	
12.833	15.167	19.333	
Column mean = 12.833	Column mean = 15.167	Column mean = 19.333	

$$\begin{aligned}
(\sum X)^2 &= (12.833 + 15.167 + 19.333 + 12.833 + 15.167 + 19.333 + 12.833 + 15.167 \\
&\quad + 19.333 + 12.833 + 15.167 + 19.333 + 12.833 + 15.167 + 19.333 + 12.833 + 15.167 \\
&\quad + 19.333)^2 \\
&= (284)^2 \\
&= 80\,656
\end{aligned}$$

The number of scores N equals 18. The degrees of freedom (df) equal the number of columns minus one, i.e. $3 - 1 = 2$. We can now substitute these values in the formula:

$$\begin{aligned}
\text{variance estimate}_{[\text{'sleep deprivation' scores}]} &= \frac{[C]\sum X^2 - \frac{(\sum X)^2}{N}}{df} = \frac{4610.934 - \frac{80\,656}{18}}{2} \\
&= \frac{4610.934 - 4480.889}{2} \\
&= \frac{130.045}{2} = 65.023 \\
&= \frac{134.671}{12} \\
&\quad\; 11.223
\end{aligned}$$

Step 4 | *Alcohol variance estimate.* The main effect for alcohol (or the table containing scores for the alcohol and no-alcohol comparison) is obtained by replacing each of the scores in the original data table by the row mean for alcohol or the row mean for no-alcohol as appropriate. In this way the sleep deprivation variable is ignored (Table 25.15).

Table 25.15	Scores due to alcohol effect alone		
Alcohol	20.222	20.222	20.222
	20.222	20.222	20.222
	20.222	20.222	20.222
No alcohol	11.333	11.333	11.333
	11.333	11.333	11.333
	11.333	11.333	11.333

The variance estimate of these 18 scores gives us the variance estimate for the independent variable alcohol. We calculate:

$$\text{variance estimate}_{[\text{`alcohol' scores}]} = \frac{\sum X^2 - \frac{(\sum X)^2}{N}}{df}$$

$$\sum X^2 = 20.222^2 + 20.222^2 + 20.222^2 + 20.222^2 + 20.222^2 + 20.222^2 + 20.222^2 + 20.222^2$$
$$+ 20.222^2 + 11.333^2 + 11.333^2 + 11.333^2 + 11.333^2 + 11.333^2 + 11.333^2 + 11.333^2$$
$$+ 11.333^2 + 11.333^2$$

$$= 408.929 + 408.929 + 408.929 + 408.929 + 408.929 + 408.929 + 408.929 + 408.929$$
$$+ 408.929 + 128.437 + 128.437 + 128.437 + 128.437 + 128.437 + 128.437 + 128.437$$
$$+ 128.437 + 128.437$$

$$= 4836.294$$

$$(\sum X)^2 = (20.222 + 20.222 + 20.222 + 20.222 + 20.222 + 20.222 + 20.222 + 20.222$$
$$+ 20.222 + 11.333 + 11.333 + 11.333 + 11.333 + 11.333 + 11.333 + 11.333 + 11.333$$
$$+ 11.333)^2$$

$$= (284)^2$$

$$= 80\ 656$$

The number of scores N equals 18. The degrees of freedom (df) equal the number of conditions for the alcohol variable (i.e. alcohol and no alcohol) minus one, i.e. $2 - 1 = 1$. We can now substitute these values in the formula:

$$\text{variance estimate}_{[\text{`alcohol' scores}]} = \frac{\sum X^2 - \frac{(\sum X)^2}{N}}{df} = \frac{4836.294 - \frac{80\ 656}{18}}{1}$$

$$= \frac{4836.294 - 4480.889}{1}$$

$$= \frac{355.405}{1} = 355.405$$

Step 5

Interaction variance estimate. The final stage is to calculate the interaction. This is obtained by getting rid of 'error', getting rid of the effect of sleep deprivation and then getting rid of the effect of alcohol:

- Remove 'error' by simply replacing our data scores by the cell mean (Table 25.16).

- Remove the effect of the alcohol versus no-alcohol treatment. This is done simply by subtracting the row mean (20.222) from each of the alcohol scores and the row mean (11.333) from each of the no-alcohol scores (Table 25.17).

- Remove the effect of sleep deprivation by subtracting the column mean for each sleep deprivation condition from the scores in the previous table. In other words, subtract -2.944, -0.611 or 3.556 as appropriate. (Do not forget that subtracting a negative number is like adding the absolute value of that number.) This leaves us with the interaction (Table 25.18).

The variance estimate from the interaction is computed using the usual formula:

$$\text{variance estimate}_{[\text{'interaction' scores}]} = \frac{\sum X^2 - \frac{(\sum X)^2}{N}}{df}$$

Table 25.16 Data minus 'error' (each data score replaced by its cell mean)

	Sleep deprivation			
	4 hours	12 hours	24 hours	
Alcohol	15.000	19.667	26.000	
	15.000	19.667	26.000	
	15.000	19.667	26.000	Row mean = 20.222
No alcohol	10.667	10.667	12.667	
	10.667	10.667	12.667	
	10.667	10.667	12.667	Row mean = 11.333
	Column mean = 12.833	Column mean = 15.167	Column mean = 19.333	Overall mean = 15.777

Table 25.17 Data minus 'error' and alcohol effect (row mean subtracted from each score in Table 25.16)

	Sleep deprivation			
	4 hours	12 hours	24 hours	
Alcohol	−5.222	−0.555	5.778	
	−5.222	−0.555	5.778	
	−5.222	−0.555	5.778	Row mean = 0.000
No alcohol	−0.666	−0.666	1.334	
	−0.666	−0.666	1.334	
	−0.666	−0.666	1.334	*Row mean* = 0.000
	Column mean = −2.944	Column mean = −0.611	Column mean = 3.556	Overall mean = 0.000

Table 25.18	Interaction table: data minus 'error', alcohol and sleep deprivation (column mean subtracted from each score in Table 25.17)			
	Sleep deprivation			
	4 hours	**12 hours**	**24 hours**	
Alcohol	−2.278	0.056	2.222	
	−2.278	0.056	2.222	
	−2.278	0.056	2.222	Row mean = 0.000
No alcohol	2.278	−0.056	−2.222	
	2.278	−0.056	−2.222	
	2.278	−0.056	−2.222	Row mean = 0.000
	Column mean = 0.000	Column mean = 0.000	Column mean = 0.000	Overall mean = 0.000

$$\Sigma X^2 = (-2.278)^2 + 0.056^2 + 2.222^2 + (-2.278)^2 + 0.056^2 + 2.222^2 + (-2.278)^2 + 0.056^2$$
$$+ 2.222^2 + 2.278^2 + (-0.056)^2 + (-2.222)^2 + 2.278^2 + (-0.056)^2 + (-2.222)^2 + 2.278^2$$
$$+ (-0.056)^2 + (-2.222)^2$$
$$= 5.189 + 0.003 + 4.937 + 5.189 + 0.003 + 4.937 + 5.189 + 0.003 + 4.937 + 5.189$$
$$+ 0.003 + 4.937 + 5.189 + 0.003 + 4.937 + 5.189 + 0.003 + 4.937$$
$$= 60.774$$

$$(\Sigma X)^2 = [(-2.278) + 0.056 + 2.222 + (-2.278) + 0.056 + 2.222 + (-2.278) + 0.056$$
$$+ 2.222 + 2.278 + (-0.056) + (-2.222) + 2.278 + (-0.056) + (-2.222)$$
$$+ 2.278 + (-0.056) + (-2.222)]^2$$
$$= 0$$

(This latter calculation is an unnecessary calculation as it will always equal 0.) The number of scores N equals 18. The degrees of freedom (df) are given by the following formula:

$$df = (\text{number of rows} - 1) \times (\text{number of columns} - 1)$$
$$= (2 - 1) \times (3 - 1)$$
$$= 1 \times 2$$
$$= 2$$

We can now substitute the above values in the formula:

$$\text{variance estimate}_{[\text{'interaction' scores}]} = \frac{\sum X^2 - \dfrac{(\sum X)^2}{N}}{df} = \frac{60.774 - \dfrac{0}{18}}{2}$$

$$= \frac{60.774 - 0}{2} = 30.387$$

Step 6   Table 25.19 is the analysis of variance summary table. The F-ratios are always the mean square of either one of the main effects or the interaction divided by the variance estimate (mean square) due to 'error'.

→

Table 25.19	Analysis of variance summary table			
Source of variation	**Sums of square**	**Degrees of freedom**	**Mean square**	**F-ratio**
Main effects				
Sleep deprivation	130.045	2	65.023	5.79[a]
Alcohol	355.405	1	355.405	31.67[a]
Sleep deprivation with alcohol	60.774	2	30.387	2.71
'Error'	134.668	12	11.222	–
Total (data)	681.111[b]	17	–	–

[a] Significant at 5% level.
[b] This form of calculation has introduced some rounding errors.

Significance Table 25.1	5% significance values of the F-ratio for unrelated ANOVA. Additional values are to be found in Significance Table 22.1					
Degrees of freedom for error or mean square (or variance estimate)	**Degrees of freedom for between-treatments mean square (or variance estimate)**					
	1	**2**	**3**	**4**	**5**	**∞**
1	161 or more	200	216	225	230	254
2	18.5	19.0	19.2	19.3	19.3	19.5
3	10.1	9.6	9.3	9.1	9.0	8.5
4	7.7	6.9	6.6	6.4	6.3	5.6
5	6.6	5.8	5.4	5.2	5.1	4.4
6	6.0	5.1	4.8	4.5	4.4	3.7
7	5.6	4.7	4.4	4.1	4.0	3.2
8	5.3	4.5	4.1	3.8	3.7	2.9
9	5.1	4.3	3.9	3.6	3.5	2.7
10	5.0	4.1	3.7	3.5	3.3	2.5
13	4.7	3.8	3.4	3.2	3.0	2.2
15	4.5	3.7	3.3	3.1	2.9	2.1
20	4.4	3.5	3.1	2.9	2.7	1.8
30	4.2	3.3	2.9	2.7	2.5	1.6
60	4.0	3.2	2.8	2.5	2.4	1.4
∞	3.8	3.0	2.6	2.4	2.2	

Your value has to equal or be larger than the tabulated value for an effect to be significant at the 5% level for a two-tailed test (i.e. to accept the hypothesis).

The significance of each F-ratio is checked against Significance Table 25.1. Care must be taken to use the appropriate degrees of freedom. The degrees of freedom error in this case is 12, which means that alcohol (with one degree of freedom) must have an F-ratio of 4.8 or more to be significant at the 5% level. (As the significance table does not contain a row for 12 degrees of freedom, the value 4.8 has been estimated by interpolation.) Sleep deprivation and the sleep deprivation with alcohol interaction (both of which have two degrees of freedom) need to have a value of 3.9 or more to be significant at the 5% level. Thus the interaction is not significant, but sleep deprivation is.

Interpreting the results

At first glance, the interpretation of the analysis of variance summary table and thus the results of the analysis appear to be quite straightforward in this case:

* Alcohol has a significant influence on the number of mistakes in the understanding of the video.

* The amount of sleep deprivation has a significant influence on the number of mistakes in the understanding of the video.

* There is apparently no significant interaction – that is, the differences between the conditions are fully accounted for by alcohol and sleep deprivation acting independently.

But this only tells us that there are significant differences; we have to check the column and row means in order to say precisely which condition produces the greatest number of mistakes. In other words, the analysis of variance summary table has to be interpreted in the light of the original data table with the column, row and cell means all entered.

Carefully checking the data suggests that the above interpretation is rather too simplistic. It seems that sleep deprivation actually has little effect unless the person has been taking alcohol. The high cell means are associated with alcohol and sleep deprivation. In these circumstances, there is some doubt that the main effects explanation is good enough.

Reporting the results

We would conclude, in these circumstances, 'Although, in the ANOVA, only the main effects were significant, there is reason to think that the main effects are actually the results of the interaction between the main effects. Careful examination of the cell means suggests that especially high scores are associated with taking alcohol and undergoing higher amounts of sleep deprivation. In contrast, those in the no-alcohol condition were affected only to a much smaller extent by having high amounts of sleep deprivation.'

This is tricky for a student to write up since it requires a rather subtle interpretation of the data which might exceed the statistical skills of the readers of their work.

25.4 More on interactions

A conventional way of illustrating interactions is through the use of graphs such as those in Figures 25.2 to 25.5. These graphs deal with the sleep and alcohol study just analysed. Notice that the means are given for each of the cells of the two-way ANOVA. Thus the

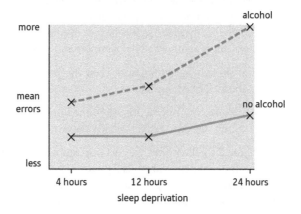

FIGURE 25.2   ANOVA graph illustrating possible interactions

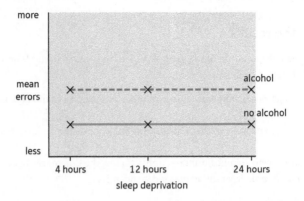

FIGURE 25.3   ANOVA graph illustrating lack of interactions

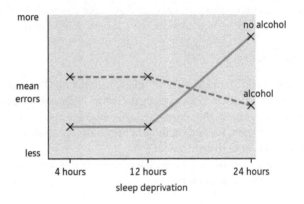

FIGURE 25.4   ANOVA graph illustrating an alternative form of interaction

vertical axis is a numerical scale commensurate with the scale of the dependent variable; the horizontal axis simply records the different levels of *one* of the independent variables. In order to indicate the different levels of the second independent variable, the different cell means for each level are joined together by a distinctively different line.

The main point to remember is that main effects are assumed to be effects which can be added directly to the scores in the columns or rows for that level of the main effect and that the effect is assumed to be common and equal in all of the cells involved. This implies that:

● if there is *no* interaction, then the lines through the points should move more or less parallel to each other

● if there *is* an interaction, then the lines through the points will not be parallel; they may touch, move together or move apart.

Figure 25.3 illustrates the sort of pattern we might expect if there is no interaction between the independent variables. Figure 25.4 shows that it is possible for an interaction to involve the crossing of the lines through the points.

Crucially, the pattern illustrated in Figure 25.5 demonstrates the circumstances in which the risk of confusing main effects for the interaction is minimal. This is because, although the two lines are definitely not parallel, the evidence for main effects is not strong but there is evidence of an interaction. Thus there seems to be no sleep deprivation

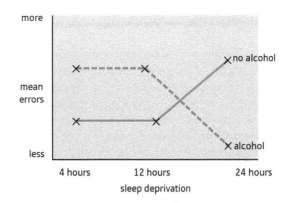

| FIGURE 25.5 | ANOVA graph illustrating interaction when it cannot be mistaken for main effects |

main effect since the means of the no alcohol and alcohol groups combined vertically are more or less the same. Thus there is no main effect of sleep deprivation in Figure 25.5 because of this similarity. In much the same way, if the three means for the no-alcohol condition are averaged and the three means for the alcohol condition are averaged, these two overall means are very similar. In other words, if the means of the combined conditions are the same, this implies, by definition, there is no interaction. In any of the other circumstances such as in Figures 25.2–25.4, combining the means vertically and combining the means horizontally produces combined means which differ. So be comforted if you obtain the pattern shown in Figure 25.5 in your research; there is no element of judgement involved in its interpretation. In the end, simple statistics usually tell you more about your data than many of the more complex statistics. If, when doing ANOVA, you look at graphs like these then you should be able to work out what is happening in your study. The *F*-ratios and the like simply confirm whether or not what you see is significant.

■ Interpreting the results

Remember that the interpretation of any data should be based first of all on an examination of cell means and variances (or standard deviations) as in Table 25.20. The tests of significance merely confirm whether or not your interpretations can be generalised. It would appear from Table 25.20 that the cell means for the no-alcohol condition are relatively unaffected by the amount of sleep deprivation. However, in the alcohol conditions increasing levels of sleep deprivation produce a greater number of mistakes. There also appears to be a tendency for there to be more mistakes when the participants have taken alcohol than when they have not.

Table 25.20	Table of means for the two-way ANOVA			
	Sleep deprivation			
	4 hours	**12 hours**	**24 hours**	
Alcohol	15.000	19.667	26.000	Row mean = 20.222
No alcohol	10.667	10.667	12.667	Row mean = 11.333
	Column mean = 12.833	Column mean = 15.167	Column mean = 19.333	Overall mean = 15.777

■ Reporting the results

The results of this analysis may be written up according to the APA (2010) Publication Manual's recommendation as follows: 'A two-way ANOVA was carried out on the data. The two main effects of sleep deprivation, $F(2, 12) = 31.67$, $p < .05$, and alcohol, $F(1, 12) = 5.79$, $p < .05$, were statistically significant. The number of errors related to the number of hours of sleep deprivation. Four hours of sleep deprivation resulted in an average of 12.83 errors, 12 hours of sleep deprivation resulted in an average of 15.17 errors, and 24 hours of sleep deprivation resulted in 19.33 errors on average. Consuming alcohol before the test resulted on average in 20.22 errors and the no-alcohol condition resulted in substantially fewer errors ($M = 11.33$). The interaction between sleep deprivation was not significant despite the tendency of the scores in the alcohol condition with 24 hours of sleep deprivation to be much higher than those in the other conditions, $F(2, 12) = 2.71$, p ns. Inspection of the graph (Figure 25.2) suggests that there is an interaction since the alcohol and no-alcohol lines are not parallel. It would appear that the interaction is being hidden by the main effects in the ANOVA.'

The significant F-ratio for the main effect of sleep deprivation needs to be explored further by the use of multiple comparisons tests (Chapter 26). This is only necessary when there are more than two levels of an independent variable. Given the possibility of an interaction in this study, it would be sensible to carry out multiple comparisons comparing all of the six cell means of the 2 × 3 ANOVA with each other (Chapter 26 and Computer Analysis in Chapter 31).

25.5 Three or more independent variables

The two-way ANOVA can be extended to include three or more independent variables although you are always restricted to analysing a single dependent variable. Despite this, it should be noted that the complexity of experimental research is constrained by a number of factors including the following:

● Having a lot of different conditions in an experiment may involve a lot of research and planning time. Preparing complex sets of instructions for participants in the different experimental conditions, randomly assigning individuals to these groups and many other methodological considerations usually limit our level of ambition in research designs. In non-psychological disciplines, the logistics of experiments are different since the units may not be people but, for example, seedlings in pots containing one of several different composts, with different amounts of fertiliser, and one of several different growing temperatures. These are far less time-consuming.

● Interpreting ANOVA is more skilful than many researchers realise. Care is needed to interpret even a two-way analysis properly because main effects are prioritised in the calculation, which results in main effects being credited with variation which is really due to interaction.

Since theoretically but not practically there is no limit to the number of independent variables possible in the analysis of variance, the potential for complexity is enormous.

However, caution is recommended when planning research. The problems of interpretation get somewhat more difficult the more independent variables there are. The complexity is largely the result of the number of possible *interactions*. Although there is just one interaction with a two-way analysis of variance, there are four with a three-way analysis of variance. The numbers accelerate rapidly with greater numbers of independent variables. As far as possible, we would recommend any psychologist to be wary of going far beyond a two-way analysis of variance without very careful planning and without some experience with these less complex designs.

It is possible to disregard the interactions and simply to analyse the different variables in the experiment as if they were several one-way experiments carried out at the same time. The interpretations would be simpler by doing this. However, this is rarely if ever done in psychological research and it is conventional always to consider interactions.

Imagine the following three-way or three-factor analysis of variance. The three independent variables are:

● age – coded as either young or old

● gender – coded as either male or female

● noise – the research takes place in either a noisy or a quiet environment.

So this is a three-way ANOVA with a total of eight different conditions (2 ages × 2 genders × 2 different noise levels). The dependent variable is the number of errors on a numerical memory test in the different conditions. The main features of this research are presented in Table 25.21.

The sheer number of comparisons possible between sections of the data causes problems. These comparisons are:

● *The main effect of gender* that is, comparing males and females irrespective of age or noise.

● *The main effect of age* that is, comparing young and old irrespective of gender or noise.

● *The main effect of noise* that is, comparing noisy and quiet conditions irrespective of age or gender.

● *The interaction of age and gender* that is, comparing age and gender groups ignoring the noise conditions. This would look like Table 25.22.

● *The interaction of age and noise* that is, comparing age and noise groups ignoring gender. This is shown in Table 25.23.

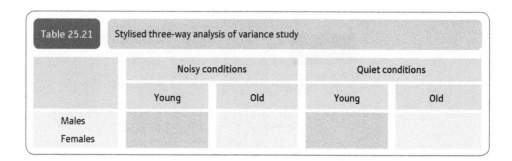

Table 25.21   Stylised three-way analysis of variance study

	Noisy conditions		Quiet conditions	
	Young	Old	Young	Old
Males				
Females				

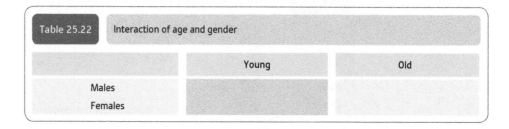

Table 25.22   Interaction of age and gender

	Young	Old
Males		
Females		

- *The interaction of noise and gender* that is, comparing the noise and gender groups ignoring age. This is shown in Table 25.24.

- *There is a fourth interaction* the interaction of noise and gender and age which is represented by Table 25.25. Notice that the cell means of each of the conditions are involved in this.

Although Table 25.25 looks like the format of the original data table (Table 25.21), the scores in the cells will be very different because all of the other sources of variation will have been removed.

The steps in calculating this three-way analysis of variance follow the pattern demonstrated earlier in this chapter but with extra layers of complexity:

1. The error term is calculated in the usual way by subtracting the cell mean from each score in a particular cell. The variance estimate of this table can then be calculated.

2. The main effect of gender is calculated by substituting the male mean for each of the male scores and the female mean for each of the female scores. The variance estimate of this table can then be calculated.

3. The age main effect is calculated by substituting the mean score of the young people for each of their scores and substituting the mean score of the old people for each of their scores. The variance estimate of this table can then be calculated.

4. The noise main effect is obtained by substituting the mean score in the noisy conditions for each score in the noisy conditions and substituting the mean score in the quiet

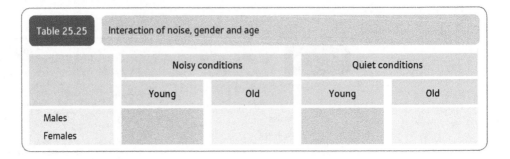

Table 25.23   Interaction of age and noise

	Noisy conditions		Quiet conditions	
	Young	Old	Young	Old

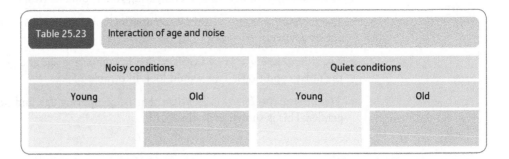

Table 25.24   Interaction of noise and gender

	Noisy conditions	Quiet conditions
Males		
Females		

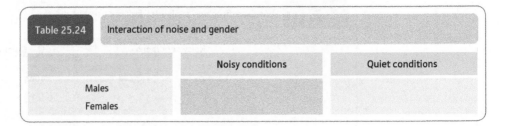

Table 25.25   Interaction of noise, gender and age

	Noisy conditions		Quiet conditions	
	Young	Old	Young	Old
Males				
Females				

conditions for each score in the quiet conditions. The variance estimate of this table can then be calculated.

5. The interaction of age and gender is arrived at by taking the table of scores with the error removed and then removing the age and gender difference simply by taking away the column mean and then the row mean. This is the same procedure as we applied to get the interaction in the two-way analysis of variance. The variance estimate of this table can then be calculated.

6. We arrive at the interaction of age and noise by drawing up a similar table and then taking away the appropriate age and noise means in turn. The variance estimate of this table can then be calculated.

7. We arrive at the interaction of noise and gender by drawing up a similar table and then taking away the appropriate noise and gender means in turn. The variance estimate of this table can then be calculated.

8. The three-way interaction (age × noise × gender) is obtained by first of all drawing up our table of the age × noise × gender conditions. We then take away the main effects by subtracting the appropriate age, noise and gender means from this table. But we also have to take away the two-way interactions of age × noise, age × gender and noise × gender by subtracting the appropriate means. Whatever is left is the three-way interaction. The variance estimate of this final table can then be calculated.

Research examples

Two-way unrelated analysis of variance

Curseu, Schruijer and Boros (2012) explain that groups in which a minority dissent from the dominant view are complex situations in which the dissent might lead to greater complexity of thinking by the majority but also the rejection and relationship conflict which may ensue also has its influence. Groups need to deal with this. The research involved a design in which some groups experienced minority dissent whereas others did not and some groups retained all members and others lost the dissenting member or a random other member where there was no dissent. These conditions were manipulated by the researchers. Using two-way analysis of variance, it was found that groups with dissent where the deviant left the group tended to have the highest complexity of cognitions about the topic under discussion. It may be that the absence of the dissenting member reduced the need to deal with the ill feelings and upset that their presence would have caused. The group then might be better placed to think about the nature of the disagreement in a positive and stimulating way.

Harinck and Van Kleef (2012) argue that emotion is an important component of conflict resolution. Anger can lead to the other party conceding. The researchers make a case that anger is effective when the matter is one concerning conflicts of interest but not so when conflicts of values are involved. The research design was a 2 × 2 factorial design with one unrelated independent variable being the conflict issue (interest versus values) and the other unrelated independent variable was emotion (anger versus neutral). Psychology students participated for course credit. The experimental manipulation was achieved through the use of scenarios containing different information pertinent to the various experimental conditions. The goal of the negotiation was a pay rise. This could be for self-interest reasons or for reasons of fairness (i.e. the value reason). People perceive anger as unfair in value conflicts to a greater extent than if the conflict is one of interest. That is, there was a significant interaction.

Wyrick and Bond (2011) were interested in the influence of the mode of administration of a questionnaire on the amount of disclosure. They used the POSIT (Problem Oriented Screening Instrument for Teenagers) Instrument in either pencil and paper form or in a web-based administration method. They used as one independent variable age (middle versus high school students) and the two modes of administration as the other to give a 2 × 2 ANOVA design. One dependent variable was the number of items omitted by the respondents and another was the perceived risk involved in answering the questions. There was no evidence that risk was related to the experimental manipulation. Contrary to expectations, the students were more likely to skip items on the web than in the pencil and paper version.

Key points

- Only when you have a 2 × 2 unrelated analysis of variance is the interpretation of the data relatively straight-forward. For 2 × 3 or larger analyses of variance, you need to read Chapter 26 as well.

- Although at heart simple enough, the two-way analysis of variance is cumbersome to calculate by hand and is best done on a computer.

- Analysis of variance always requires a degree of careful interpretation of the findings and cannot always be interpreted in a hard-and-fast way. This is a little disconcerting given its apparent mathematical sophistication.

- Before calculating the analysis of variance proper, spend a good deal of effort trying to make sense of the pattern of column, row and cell means in your data table. This should alert you to the major trends in your data. You can use your interpretation in combination with the analysis of variance summary table to obtain as refined an interpretation of your data as possible.

COMPUTER ANALYSIS

Unrelated two-way analysis of variance using SPSS

Data
- Name the variables in 'Variable View' of the 'Data Editor'.
- Enter the data as appropriate in 'Data View' (Screenshot 25.1).

Analysis
- Select 'Analyze', 'General Linear Model' and 'Univariate…' (Screenshot 25.2).

2
- Move the dependent variable to the 'Dependent Variable:' box.
- Move the independent variables to the 'Fixed Factor(s):' box.

3
- Select 'Plots…'. Move one independent variable (Factor) to the 'Horizontal Axis:' box and the other to the 'Separate Lines:' box. Select 'Add' and 'Continue' (Screenshot 25.3).

4
- Select 'Options…', factors and interactions to put in 'Display Means for:' box, 'Descriptive statistics', 'Estimates of effect size', 'Homogeneity tests', 'Continue' and 'OK' (Screenshot 25.4).

Output
- Check which *F*-ratios are significant by having a Sig(nificance) of .05 or less (Screenshot 25.5).

2
- Check that Levene's test shows the variances are homogeneous by having a Sig(nificance) level of more than .05.

3
- If a significant main effect has more than 2 groups, use further tests to determine which means differ.

4
- With a significant interaction use further tests to determine which means differ.

FIGURE 25.6   SPSS steps for two-way analysis of variance

Interpreting and reporting the output

- Make sure that you examine the cell means in particular together with the row and column means in order to understand what is going on in the data. Such an inspection would appear to suggest that the cell means for the no-alcohol condition are not related to the amount of sleep deprivation. Where alcohol is consumed, sleep deprivation leads to greater numbers of errors. More mistakes occur, apparently, when alcohol has been taken.

- Following APA Publication Manual (2010) style, one might write: 'A two-way ANOVA revealed that the main effects for sleep deprivation, $F(2, 12) = 5.80, p < .05, \eta_p^2 = .49$, and alcohol, $F(1, 12) = 31.68, p < .05, \eta_p^2 = .73$, were statistically significant. The more sleep deprivation the greater the number of errors. Four hours of sleep deprivation gave an average of 12.83 errors, 95% CI [9.85, 15.81], 12 hours of sleep deprivation 15.17 errors, 95% CI [12.19, 18.15], and 24 hours of sleep deprivation 19.33 errors, 95% CI [16.35, 22.31]. Consuming alcohol led to an average of 20.22 errors, 95% CI [17.79, 22.66], compared to a mean of 11.33, 95% CI [8.90, 13.77], for the no alcohol condition. There was not a significant interaction, though scores in the alcohol condition with 24 hours of sleep deprivation were much higher than those in the other conditions, $F(2, 12) = 2.71, p \, ns, \eta_p^2 = .31$. Inspection of the graph (Figure 25.2) suggests that there is an interaction since the alcohol and no-alcohol lines are not parallel. It would appear that the interaction is being disguised by the main effects in the ANOVA.'

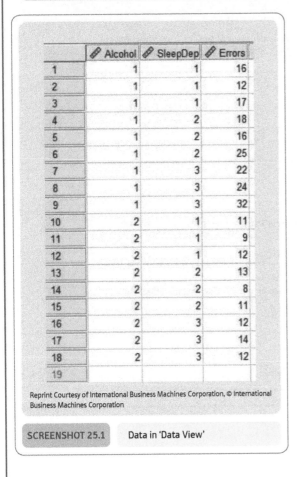

Reprint Courtesy of International Business Machines Corporation, © International Business Machines Corporation

SCREENSHOT 25.1   Data in 'Data View'

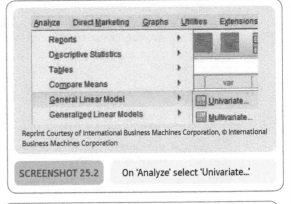

Reprint Courtesy of International Business Machines Corporation, © International Business Machines Corporation

SCREENSHOT 25.2   On 'Analyze' select 'Univariate...'

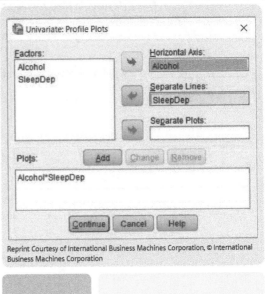

Reprint Courtesy of International Business Machines Corporation, © International Business Machines Corporation

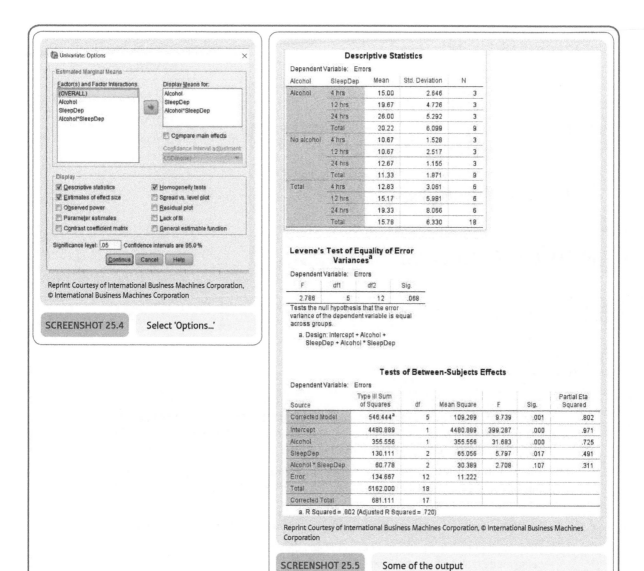

SCREENSHOT 25.4   Select 'Options...'

Reprint Courtesy of International Business Machines Corporation, © International Business Machines Corporation

Descriptive Statistics

Dependent Variable: Errors

Alcohol	SleepDep	Mean	Std. Deviation	N
Alcohol	4 hrs	15.00	2.646	3
	12 hrs	19.67	4.726	3
	24 hrs	26.00	5.292	3
	Total	20.22	6.099	9
No alcohol	4 hrs	10.67	1.528	3
	12 hrs	10.67	2.517	3
	24 hrs	12.67	1.155	3
	Total	11.33	1.871	9
Total	4 hrs	12.83	3.061	6
	12 hrs	15.17	5.981	6
	24 hrs	19.33	8.066	6
	Total	15.78	6.330	18

Levene's Test of Equality of Error Variances[a]

Dependent Variable: Errors

F	df1	df2	Sig.
2.786	5	12	.068

Tests the null hypothesis that the error variance of the dependent variable is equal across groups.

a. Design: Intercept + Alcohol + SleepDep + Alcohol * SleepDep

Tests of Between-Subjects Effects

Dependent Variable: Errors

Source	Type III Sum of Squares	df	Mean Square	F	Sig.	Partial Eta Squared
Corrected Model	546.444[a]	5	109.289	9.739	.001	.802
Intercept	4480.889	1	4480.889	399.287	.000	.971
Alcohol	355.556	1	355.556	31.683	.000	.725
SleepDep	130.111	2	65.056	5.797	.017	.491
Alcohol * SleepDep	60.778	2	30.389	2.708	.107	.311
Error	134.667	12	11.222			
Total	5162.000	18				
Corrected Total	681.111	17				

a. R Squared = .802 (Adjusted R Squared = .720)

Reprint Courtesy of International Business Machines Corporation, © International Business Machines Corporation

SCREENSHOT 25.5   Some of the output

CHAPTER 26

Multiple comparisons within ANOVA

A *priori* and *post hoc* tests

Overview

- Analyses of variance are straightforward to interpret if the independent variables each have just two different values. If there are only two values of each independent variable, then statistical significance means that those two values are significantly different.

- Interpretation of ANOVA becomes more demanding when any independent variable has three or more different categories. ANOVA itself does not stipulate which means are significantly different in these circumstances.

- Multiple comparison tests are available which indicate just where the differences lie.

- These multiple comparison tests have built-in adjustment for the numbers of comparisons being made making them preferable to using multiple *t*-tests.

- Choosing the best multiple comparison test for any particular data or purpose is not straight-forward. Consequently, different tests might be used. Only when the different tests yield different conclusions is there a problem.

- When the analysis has been preplanned prior to data collection, *a priori* tests may be appropriate. They are known as planned contrasts. However, only a minority of research meets the strictures of pre-planning required.

- If the categories of the independent variable can be ordered from smallest to largest meaningfully, then it is possible to test for trends in the ordering of the means. Possible trends include linear and U-shaped.

Preparation

You will need a working knowledge of Chapters 23, 24 and 25 on the analysis of variance. Chapter 18 introduces the problem of multiple comparisons in the context of partitioning chi-square tables.

26.1 Introduction

When in research there are *more than two levels* of an *independent* variable, which conditions are significantly different from the others may not be obvious. There is no problem when you have only two groups of scores to compare in a one-way or a 2×2 ANOVA, for example. However, if there are three or more different levels of any independent variable the interpretation problems begin. Take, for example, Table 26.1 of means for a one-way analysis of variance. Although the analysis of variance for the data which are summarised in this table may well be statistically significant, there remains a very obvious problem. Groups 1 and 2 have virtually identical means and it is group 3 which has the exceptionally large scores. Quite simply we would be tempted to assume that groups 1 and 2 do not differ significantly and that any differences are due to group 3. Our eyes are telling us that only parts of the data are contributing to the significant ANOVA.

Although the above example is very clear, it becomes a little more fraught if the data are less clear-cut than this (Table 26.2). In this case, it may well be that all three groups differ from each other. Just by looking at the means we cannot know for certain since they may just reflect sampling differences.

Table 26.1	Sample means in a one-way ANOVA		
	Group 1	Group 2	Group 3
Mean	5.6	5.7	12.9

Table 26.2	Sample means in another one-way ANOVA		
	Group 1	Group 2	Group 3
Mean	5.6	7.3	12.9

Obviously it is essential to test the significance of the differences between the means for all *three* possible *pairs* of sample means from the three groups.

These are:

group 1 with group 2

group 1 with group 3

group 2 with group 3

If there had been *four* groups then the pairs of comparisons would be:

group 1 with group 2

group 1 with group 3

group 1 with group 4

group 2 with group 3

group 2 with group 4

group 3 with group 4

This is getting to be a lot of comparisons! It is worthwhile asking yourself whether you

26.2   Planned (*a priori*) versus unplanned (*post hoc*) comparisons

In the fantasy world of statisticians, there is a belief that researchers meticulously plan down to the last detail of their statistical analysis in advance of collecting their data. As such an ideal researcher, one would have planned in advance precisely what pairs of cells or conditions in the research are to be compared and any unnecessary ones excluded. These choices are based on the hypotheses and other considerations which do not depend on the data. In other words, they are planned comparisons. The term for this is *a priori* comparisons. More usual, in our experience, is the researcher who decides in retrospect and in the light of the data collected what the analysis should be. Psychological theory is rarely so powerful that we can predict from it the precise pattern of outcomes to expect. Comparisons decided upon after the data have been collected and tabulated are called *a posteriori* or *post hoc* comparisons.

Different statistical tests are used for planned and unplanned comparisons. For planned comparisons *contrasts* are used; for unplanned comparisons *multiple comparisons tests* are used. You do not use both in the same analysis. In the unlikely circumstances that you have planned the comparisons in advance then a simple approach would be as follows: Compare the pairs of means using several *t*-tests. No adjustments need to be made to the significance levels if you make sure that the number of comparisons is less than the number of conditions. Of course, in no circumstances should you retrospectively add in unplanned comparisons. However, circumstances like these rarely occur in most student research. The more formal way of doing *a priori* comparisons (planned comparisons) is discussed in Section 26.5. Since most researchers in psychology do not pre-plan in this way, we will give priority to the more usual situation in which comparisons are made after the data are inspected. The big problem here is the number of comparisons that are usually made in *post hoc* analyses. The more significance tests we do the more likely we are to obtain statistical significance. The consequence is that the normal significance levels are inappropriate, so whatever test is used needs to take this into account. As their name suggests, multiple comparison tests do just that.

SPSS has a substantial number of multiple comparisons tests and you can do several at the same time for comparison, if you wish. They include LSD, Bonferroni, Ryan–Einot–Gabriel–Welsch Q (REGWQ), Tukey, Scheffé and the Duncan test. Each of these assumes that the variance within each of the groups is the same. Where the variances are not equal then the Games–Howell and Dunnett's T3 can be selected. They do not give exactly the same answer in every circumstance. The main difference is in terms of how conservative they are – that is, tending to favour the null hypothesis.

Box 26.1   Focus on

Does it matter that the *F*-ratio is not significant?

Traditionally, the advice was that unless the ANOVA itself was statistically significant, no further analyses should be carried out. That is, a significant ANOVA is a prerequisite before comparing pairs of means. This advice no longer applies since the introduction of multiple comparisons tests like the Newman–Keuls test and Duncan's new multiple range test. If one is operating within the strictures of preplanned (*a priori*) testing then issues of multiple comparisons do not apply.

26.3   Methods of multiple comparisons testing

Before leaping into what SPSS can do, it is worthwhile looking at the basic procedures involved in multiple comparisons testing. One intuitively obvious and traditional multiple comparisons method is to compare each of the pairs of groups using a *t*-test. So for the four-group experiment there would be up to six separate *t*-tests to calculate (group 1 with group 2, group 1 with group 3, etc.). The problem with this procedure (which is not so bad really) is the number of separate comparisons being made. The more comparisons you make between pairs of means the more likely is a significant difference merely due to chance (always the risk in inferential statistics). This has to be dealt with.

To cope with this problem a relatively simple procedure, the *Bonferroni* method, can be employed. It has the advantage that it is fairly intuitive unlike many of the procedures used by SPSS. The obvious procedure is to share the 5% (.05) significance between all of the comparisons. The more comparisons, the smaller the share. So, if you are making four comparisons (i.e. conducting four separate *t*-tests) then the appropriate significance level for the individual tests is as follows:

$$\text{significance level for each test} = \frac{\text{overall significance level}}{\text{number of comparisons}}$$

$$= \frac{5\%}{4}$$

$$= 1.25\%$$

In other words, a comparison actually needs to be significant at the 1.25% level according to the significance tables (or more likely the computer output) before we accept that it is significant at the *equivalent* of the 5% level. This essentially compensates for our generosity in doing many comparisons and reduces the risk of inadvertently capitalising on chance differences. (We adopted this procedure for chi-square in Chapter 18.)

So long as you adjust your critical values to allow for the number of comparisons made, in this way there is nothing much wrong with using multiple *t*-tests. Indeed, this procedure, properly applied, is a 'conservative' one in that it errs in favour of the null hypothesis. Appendix K contains a table of *t*-values for use when there are a number of comparisons being made (i.e. multiple comparisons). Say you wished to test the statistical significance of the differences between pairs of groups in a three-group one-way analysis of variance. This gives three different comparisons between the pairs. The significant *t*-test values for this are found under the column for three comparisons. Or if you have the exact significance level, then adjust this by dividing by the number of comparisons. As SPSS includes Bonferroni in its multiple comparisons procedures use that.

SPSS has a smorgasbord of methods of doing multiple comparisons. Choosing between them is no easy task. The Bonferroni option may be best when the sample sizes are small as is the case with much student work. REGWQ generally would be a good option for the style of analysis that students tend to do. The Games–Howell would be an appropriate choice where the variances of the groups differ significantly.

Instructions for multiple comparisons testing on SPSS are given in the Computer Analysis at the end of the chapter.

26.4   Multiple comparisons for multifactorial ANOVA

The procedure is much the same when we have two or more independent variables in our ANOVA design except that we have more than one independent variable. Each of these independent variables (factors) is treated separately. Essentially this is like treating each factor as a separate study. You can compare pairs of groups within any of the main effects by using a *t*-test. This is only appropriate for independent variables with more than two levels. The reason is, of course, that if we only have two levels of the independent variable then a significant main effect for this variable can only mean that the two levels or groups differ significantly. Figure 26.1 shows the key steps for multiple comparison tests. Box 26.1 discusses the outmoded idea that the overall ANOVA needs to be statistically significant if multiple comparisons are going to be made.

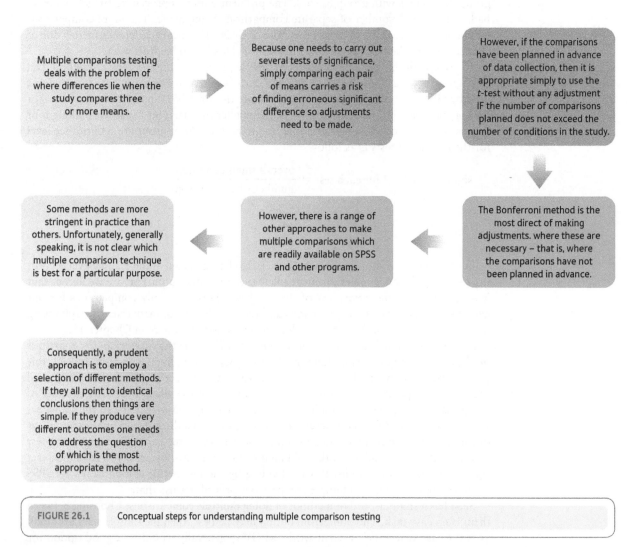

Multiple comparisons testing deals with the problem of where differences lie when the study compares three or more means.

Because one needs to carry out several tests of significance, simply comparing each pair of means carries a risk of finding erroneous significant difference so adjustments need to be made.

However, if the comparisons have been planned in advance of data collection, then it is appropriate simply to use the *t*-test without any adjustment IF the number of comparisons planned does not exceed the number of conditions in the study.

Some methods are more stringent in practice than others. Unfortunately, generally speaking, it is not clear which multiple comparison technique is best for a particular purpose.

However, there is a range of other approaches to make multiple comparisons which are readily available on SPSS and other programs.

The Bonferroni method is the most direct of making adjustments. where these are necessary – that is, where the comparisons have not been planned in advance.

Consequently, a prudent approach is to employ a selection of different methods. If they all point to identical conclusions then things are simple. If they produce very different outcomes one needs to address the question of which is the most appropriate method.

FIGURE 26.1   Conceptual steps for understanding multiple comparison testing

26.5 Contrasts

Super psychology student of the year has probably decided in detail the statistical comparisons that she wants in advance of collecting her data. For example, in the study involving Group 1 given hormone 1, Group 2 given hormone 2 and Group 3 a Placebo control (see Table 26.1) she may have prepared the following plan: She will compare the control group (placebo group) with Group 1 and Group 2 combined because they think that depression scores will be higher in the hormone conditions. She also plans to compare

Group 1 and Group 2 to see if two hormones differ in their effects. When comparisons are preplanned (*a priori*) like this then the statistics change and we do not make adjustments to the significance levels. To be truthful, we have never met a student who carries out such thoughtful and meticulous statistical planning. But the clever folk at SPSS clearly have as they provide the procedures for carrying out *planned contrasts*. For most of us, we suspect, planning research, collecting data and analysing data are done in a somewhat more erratic fashion, so *planned contrasts* are not appropriate. It is completely wrong to check the data, see what looks interesting and then decide on the contrasts to make. Planned contrasts require discipline on the part of the researcher.

There is one basic thing that you need to know. Planned comparisons involve the use of weights. You need to understand this system in order to tell SPSS what comparisons you want but the weights are intrinsically part of planned comparisons. The bad news is that you cannot have all possible comparisons (which is very different from the *post hoc* multiple comparison tests). So if you wished to Compare Group 1 with the placebo control group (Group 3) we give weights as follows:

Group 1 weight = 1; Group 2 weight = 0; Group 3 weight = −1

So the groups to be compared have been given a value of 1 and −1 but Group 2 is given a weight of zero, which means it is excluded from the analysis as it is given no (zero) weighting. This contrast compares the mean of Group 1 with the mean of Group 3. Also notice that the sum of the three weights totals 0. This is always the case if your comparisons are going to be orthogonal (uncorrelated with each other). If, instead, you wished to compare Group 3 (the placebo control group) with Group 1 and Group 2 combined together then the weights would be as follows:

Group 1 weight = 1; Group 2 weight = 1; Group 3 weight = −2

These weights indicate that the mean of Group 3 is compared with the combined average of Group 1 and Group 2. Notice how the weights have been set so that they add up to zero in this case too.

This sort of *a priori* significance testing involves quite hard rules. Rule 1 is that the maximum number of contrasts is one less than the number of groups. So in our example, since there are three groups we can plan for no more than two contrasts. Rule 2 is that a group on its own cannot appear in more than one contrast (though it can be used in combination with another group). So you may have realised that the above two contrasts for our study are not legitimate since Group 3 appears as a separate group twice, which violates Rule 2. There is a simple test to see if the contrasts you choose are within the rules. That is, you simply multiply the weights for each mean by each other and check whether the total comes to zero. If we do this with the two contrasts in the previous paragraph we get $(1 \times 1) + (0 \times 1) + (-1 \times -2) = 1 + 0 + 2 = 3$. It does not add up to zero so there is something wrong because you have broken a rule. Quickly we should be able to see that Group 3 has been used on its own twice in the contrasts. Of course, if you only planned one of the above two contrasts then the rule would not be broken. One possible legitimate pair of contrasts are possible as follows:

CONTRAST 1: Group 1 weight = 1; Group 2 weight = 1; Group 3 weight = −2

CONTRAST 2: Group 1 weight = 1; Group 2 weight = −1; Group 3 weight = 0

Now if we multiply the weights together we get $(1 \times 1) + (1 \times -1) + (-2 \times 0) = 1 + -1 + 0 = 0$. So this pair of contrasts would be legitimate. The reason for the rules is that the tests between the means need to be independent of each other in order for the significance level to be correct. That is, there is no correlation between the two sets of weights. You can do the Pearson correlation to show this. When the rules are broken then the result is that the error rates (significance levels) are above the usual 5% level. Not sticking to the rules would mean that your reported significance levels for the contrasts are wrong – too generous in favour of finding support for the hypothesis/ses. Another important thing is that you do not have all the comparisons that in the end you would like. But this should not come as a surprise as this is the analysis you planned.

Should you wish to use contrasts on SPSS, select 'Contrasts. . .' (Screenshot 26.3) and enter or add the weights into the 'Coefficients' box one at a time. The important table in the output is Contrast Tests. The final column gives the significance level of the contrast. The coefficients you used can be found in the Contrast Coefficients table.

26.6 Trends

In some areas of psychological research, it is possible that the different levels of the independent variable can be put in order from the smallest to the largest. Often, though, such ordering is impossible. But if it is, then it is possible to seek trends in the means of the dependent variable over the different levels of the independent variable. If you wanted to compare the effect of different levels of music played in the back-ground while studying for a stats test then such an ordering is possible. The music might in one condition be at 40 decibels, in another 60 decibels, in another 80 decibels, in another 100 decibels, and in the last condition 120 decibels. Here there is a clear, natural progression of loudness so a trend analysis is possible on these five conditions. The trend may be a linear one but it could be a curve of some sort. If you plotted the means of the conditions on a graph you would be able to get some idea of the shape of the trend. You need several levels of the independent variable to fit a trend if the result is to be meaningful. With three conditions the only trend that could be fitted is a linear one. This would indicate that there is a steady, equal increase in the means as the music loudness increases from its lowest level to its highest. SPSS will calculate linear, quadratic, cubic and quartic trends for you if you have reason to want them. Of these, the linear trend is probably the most useful. The quadratic trend might some-times be of interest. It is basically a U-shaped relationship. Very little medicine will leave the patient feeling very unwell and a bigger dose will leave the patient unwell, and the ideal dose will do the most good and stop the patient feeling unwell. However, a bigger dose than that might make the patient feel somewhat unwell and a bigger dose than that may leave the patient feeling very unwell. In other words, this would be an inverted U relationship.

It is not difficult to assess any or all of these trends tested using SPSS as part of your ANOVA. However, you must have the groups ordered from the smallest to the largest in your variable list for it to work properly. To conduct a trend analysis on SPSS select 'Contrasts. . .' (Screenshot 26.3) and the appropriate contrast (Linear, Quadratic, Cubic, 4th or 5th) in 'Polynomial'. In the output, look for the table labelled ANOVA and you can check for the trend that you requested – if it is significant then you have that sort of trend in your data. If not, you haven't. But before you incorporate trends into your ana-lysis, make sure that your categories can be put in order from low to high and, if they can, then enter your categories in this order.

Research examples

Multiple comparison tests

Ivancevich (1976) conducted a field experiment in which sales personnel were assigned to various goal setting groups. One was a participative goal-setting situation, another was an assigned goal group, and a third group served as a comparison group. Various measures of performance and satisfaction were collected at various data collection points which included a before training baseline, then 6 months, 9 months and 12 months after training. ANOVA was used together with the Duncan's multiple range test to examine where the significant differences were to be found between the experimental and control conditions. The results suggested that for up to nine months both the participative and assigned goal setting groups had higher performance and satisfaction levels. At 12 months, this advantage no longer applied.

Touliatos and Lindholm (1981) compared the ratings on the Behavior Problem Checklist for parents and teachers. Some of the children rated were in counselling and others were not in counselling. Using ANOVA, it was found that the youngsters in counselling were more likely to exhibit deviant behaviour. The independent variables for the ANOVA were counselling versus not in counselling and ratings by mothers versus fathers versus teachers. The researchers wanted to know just where in their data the differences lay. So they used Duncan's Multiple Range Test which showed that more behavioural problems were seen by parents than by the children's teachers.

Yildirim (2008) investigated the relationship between occupational burnout and the availability of various sources of social support among school counsellors in Turkey. The analysis included other sociodemographic variables. There was a significant negative relationship between burnout and sources of social support. However, burnout was not related to age, gender or marital status in this study. Some of the subdimensions of burnout were related to some of these variables. The Scheffé test was employed to make finer comparisons between the conditions of the ANOVA. For example, it was found that counsellors with only up to three years of experience had higher levels of depersonalisation of burnout than those with more experience in this sort of counselling.

Key points

- If you have more than two sets of scores in the analysis of variance (or any other test for that matter), it is important to employ one of the procedures for multiple comparisons.

- Even simple procedures such as multiple t-tests are better than nothing, especially if the proper adjustment is made for the number of t-tests being carried out and you adjust the critical values accordingly.

- Modern computer packages, especially SPSS, have a range of multiple comparison tests. It is a fine art to know which is the most appropriate for your particular circumstances. Usually it is expedient to compare the results from several tests; often they will give much the same results, especially where the trends in the data are clear.

COMPUTER ANALYSIS

Multiple comparison tests using SPSS

Data
- Name the variables in 'Variable View' of the 'Data Editor'.
- Enter data under the appropriate variable names in 'Data View' of the 'Data Editor' (Screenshot 26.1).

Analysis
- Select 'Analyze', 'General Linear Model' and 'Univariate...' (Screenshot 26.2).

2
- Enter dependent and independent variables in boxes to the right (Screenshot 26.3).

3
- Select 'Options', factor to put in 'Display Means for:' box, 'Descriptive statistics', 'Estimates of effect size', 'Homogeneity tests', 'Continue' and 'OK' (Screenshot 26.4).
- Select 'Post Hoc...', the test/s wanted, 'Continue' and 'OK' (Screenshot 26.5).

Output
- Check which means differ significantly by seeing if the Sig(nificance) is .05 or less (Screenshot 26.6).
- Note the direction of the difference.

FIGURE 26.2   SPSS steps for multiple comparison tests

Interpreting and reporting the output

- Screenshot 26.6 is one way in which SPSS gives multiple comparisons. The table gives all of the possible comparisons between the conditions of the study. It is a little repetitive so you will find similar comparisons included twice. The significance column tells you which means are significantly different from the others.

- Following APA Publication Manual (2010) guidelines, we might write: 'The main effect was significant, $F(2, 6) = 10.59, p < .05, \eta_p^2 = .78$. Consequently, the Scheffé test was used to compare pairs of group means. The mean for Hormone 1 ($M = 9.67$) was significantly higher than Hormone 2 ($M = 3.67$) and the placebo group ($M = 4.00$) at the 5% level of significance but no other groups differed significantly.'

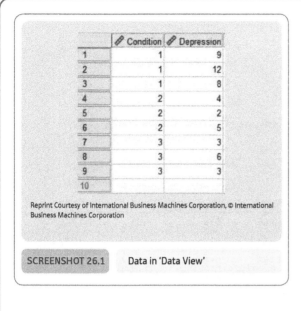

SCREENSHOT 26.1   Data in 'Data View'

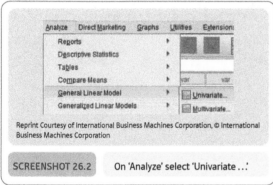

SCREENSHOT 26.2   On 'Analyze' select 'Univariate …'

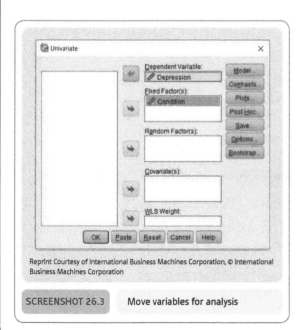

SCREENSHOT 26.3   Move variables for analysis

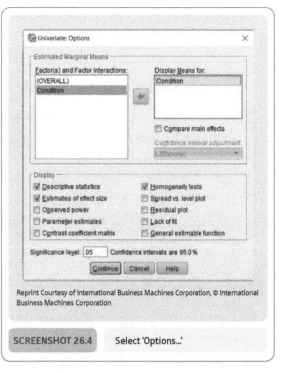

SCREENSHOT 26.4   Select 'Options…'

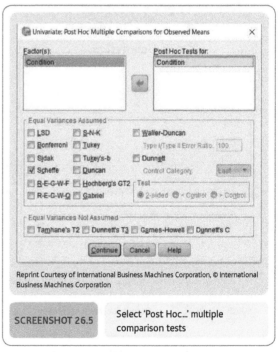

SCREENSHOT 26.5   Select 'Post Hoc…' multiple comparison tests

Post Hoc Tests

Condition

Multiple Comparisons

Dependent Variable: Depression

Scheffe

(I) Condition	(J) Condition	Mean Difference (I-J)	Std. Error	Sig.	95% Confidence Interval Lower Bound	95% Confidence Interval Upper Bound
Hormone 1	Hormone 2	6.00*	1.466	.018	1.30	10.70
	Placebo control	5.67*	1.466	.023	.97	10.37
Hormone 2	Hormone 1	-6.00*	1.466	.018	-10.70	-1.30
	Placebo control	-.33	1.466	.975	-5.03	4.37
Placebo control	Hormone 1	-5.67*	1.466	.023	-10.37	-.97
	Hormone 2	.33	1.466	.975	-4.37	5.03

Based on observed means.
 The error term is Mean Square(Error) = 3.222.

 *. The mean difference is significant at the .05 level.

Homogeneous Subsets

Depression

Scheffe[a,b]

Condition	N	Subset 1	Subset 2
Hormone 2	3	3.67	
Placebo control	3	4.00	
Hormone 1	3		9.67
Sig.		.975	1.000

Means for groups in homogeneous subsets are displayed.
 Based on observed means.
 The error term is Mean Square(Error) = 3.222.

 a. Uses Harmonic Mean Sample Size = 3.000.

 b. Alpha = .05.

SCREENSHOT 26.6   Output for the Scheffé test

Recommended further reading

Mixed-design ANOVA

Related and unrelated variables together

Overview

- The analysis of variance has variants dealing with a variety of research designs.

- Mixed designs are those which involve a mixture of related and unrelated independent variables.

- There is just a single dependent variable.

- Mixed designs involve the complication that there is more than one error term. That is, different error terms apply for the unrelated variables and the related variables.

Preparation

Chapters 23 to 25 are essential as this chapter utilises many of the ideas from different types of ANOVA.

27.1   Introduction

This chapter deals with a useful variant of the analysis of variance: the mixed design. Although we are moving into quite advanced areas of statistics, the key to most statistical analysis lies more in the interpretation of simple statistics such as cell means. Avoid letting the complex calculations employed blind you to the major purpose of your analysis – understanding what your data say. The mixed-design analysis of variance is similar to the two-way ANOVA described in Chapter 25. The big difference is that *one* of the independent variables is related and *one* is unrelated – hence the term mixed design. Thus it is used when participants take part in *all* of the conditions of one independent variable but in just *one* condition of the other variable. A good example of this type of design is when a pre-test has been given on the dependent variable before the different experimental treatments and a post-test given afterwards. So all participants are measured on both the pre-test and post-test, making pre-test/post-test a related measure. Of course, the unrelated independent variable involves the important experimental manipulation. This design may be extended to involve more than one independent variable and more than one related variable. Box 27.1 explains an important issue about cell sizes in ANOVA.

Although we greatly prefer not to refer to participants in research as subjects, it is unavoidable with ANOVA at times as ANOVA's terminology was developed nearly 100 years ago when attitudes were different.

Box 27.1   Focus on

Equal cell sizes?

Before the introduction of computers, it was conventional in many of the variants of the analysis of variance to ensure that all conditions or cells had the same number of scores. The reason for this was that the hand calculations are simpler if this is the case. When carrying out laboratory studies, equal cell sizes are relatively easy to achieve even if it involves randomly discarding scores from some cells. However, it is possible to do any analysis of variance with unequal numbers of scores in each condition or cell. The calculations tend to be cumbersome and so it is best to use a computer package such as SPSS to reduce the computational load.

The exception to this is the one-way analysis of variance described in Chapter 23, which can be calculated with no adjustments for unequal sample size. Of course, with the related one-way analysis of variance it is not possible to have different numbers of participants in different conditions of the experiment since participants have to take part in all conditions.

One issue remains, though, and that is whether it is better to have equal cell sizes no matter whether a computer package is being used or not. The answer to the question is that it is always better to have equal cell sizes for the simple reason that if data are not there then the computer package has to employ estimates. While the bias caused by this is probably minimal in most cases, anyone employing really complex ANOVA designs would be well advised to try to ensure that equal sample sizes are used.

27.2   Mixed designs and repeated measures

Repeated measures designs have the same participants (or matched groups of participants) measured in *all* conditions just as in the repeated measures one-way analysis of variance except that there are two or more independent variables. The repeated measures design is intended to increase the precision of research by measuring the error variance (residual variance) in a way which excludes the individual differences component. The individual difference component is obtained from the general tendency of individual participants to score relatively high or relatively low irrespective of the experimental condition. The trend for each individual can simply be deducted from the error scores to leave (residual) error.

Fully repeated measures designs can be analysed, but they are beyond the scope of this book (see Howell, 2013, for calculation methods). Some independent variables do not allow for repeated measures – gender, for example, is not a repeated measure since a person cannot change their gender during the course of an experiment. Only where matching of groups on the basis of gender has been carried out is it possible to have gender as a repeated measure.

Much more common in psychology are *mixed designs* in which the repeated measure is on just some of the independent variables. Mixed designs are two- or more-way analyses of variance in which participants are measured in more than one experimental condition but not *every* experimental condition. (This means that for at least one of the independent variables in a mixed design, scores on different participants will be found in the different levels of this independent variable.) Usually you will have to check through the experimental design carefully in order to decide whether a researcher has used a mixed design, although many will stipulate the type of design. Box 27.2 explains a potentially confusing aspect of ANOVA that you may come across – the difference between fixed and random effects models.

One common mixed design is the pre-test/post-test design. Participants are measured on the dependent variable before and after the experimental treatment. This is clearly a

---

| Box 27.2 | Key concepts |

Fixed and random effects

The issue of fixed versus random effects is a typical analysis of variance misnomer. It really means fixed or random choice of the different levels of an independent variable. The implication is that you can select the levels of a treatment (independent variable) either by a systematic decision or by choosing the levels by some random procedure.

Most psychological research assumes a fixed effects model, and it is hard to find instances of the use of random effects. A fixed effect is where you as the researcher choose or decide or fix what the different values of the independent variable are going to be. In some cases you have no choice at all – a variable such as gender gives you no discretion since it has just two different values (male and female). Usually we just operate as if we have the choice of the different treatments for each independent variable. We simply decide that the experimental group is going to be deprived of sleep for five hours and the control group not deprived of sleep at all.

But there are many different possible amounts of sleep deprivation – no hours, one hour, two hours, three hours, four hours and so forth. Instead of just selecting the number of hours of sleep deprivation on the basis of a particular whim, practicality or any other similar basis, it is possible to choose the amounts of sleep deprivation at random. We could draw the amount out of a hat containing the possible levels. In circumstances like these we would be using a random effects model. Because we have selected the hours of sleep deprivation at random, it could be said that our ability to generalise from our experiment to the effects of sleep deprivation in general is enhanced. We have simply chosen an unbiased way of selecting the amount of sleep deprivation after all.

Since the random effects model rarely corresponds to practice in psychological research it is not dealt with further in this book. Psychologists' research is more likely to be the result of agonising about time, money and other practical constraints on the choices available.

related design since the same people are measured twice on the same dependent variable. However, since the experimental and control groups consist of different people, this comparison is unrelated. Hence this form of the pre-test/post-test design is a mixed design. This sort of design is illustrated in Table 27.1. Imagine that the dependent variable is self-esteem measured in children before and after the experimental manipulation. The experimental manipulation involves praising half the children (the experimental group) for good behaviour but telling the other half (the control group) nothing. Obviously this type of design allows the researcher to test whether the two groups are similar prior to the experimental manipulation by comparing the experimental and control groups on the pre-test measure. The hypothesis that praise affects self-esteem suggests that the post-test measure should be different for the two groups. (Notice that the hypothesis predicts an interaction effect in which the related and unrelated independent variables interact to yield rather different scores for the experimental group and the control group on the post-test.)

In virtually all respects, the computation of the mixed design is like that for the two-way (unrelated) ANOVA described in Chapter 25. Both main effects and the interaction are calculated as previously. The error is treated differently though as shown in Tables 27.13 and 27.14 (Explaining statistics 27.1). Although the *total* error is calculated by subtracting the cell mean from each of the data scores to leave the error score (as in Chapter 25), in the mixed design this error is then subdivided into two component parts: (a) the individual differences component and (b) the (residual) error component:

- the error due to individual differences is calculated and then used as the error term for the *unrelated* independent variable (this error term is often called 'subjects within groups')

- the (residual) error term is used as the error term when examining the effects of the related independent variable (this error term is often called 'B × subjects within groups').

Note the slight amendments made to the tables such as Table 27.3 (Explaining statistics 27.1) compared with those given in Chapter 25; columns headed 'subject' and 'subject mean' have been added. If there is variation in the subject mean column it shows that there is still an individual differences component in the scores in the main body of the table. Careful examination of a) the column means and row means, b) cell means, c) subject means and d) the individual scores in the cells will hint strongly whether there remains any variation due to a) the main effects, b) interaction, c) individual differences and d) (residual) error. Table 27.2 shows a typical ANOVA summary table for the mixed design. The main effects are A and B and there is an interaction AB. However, there are additional rows such as Subjects within groups and B × subjects within groups. These

Table 27.1	Stylised version of the mixed ANOVA design		
Unrelated variable	**Related variable**		
		Pre-test	Post-test
Experimental condition Control condition			

are used as error terms in the mixed design ANOVA – that is, more than one error term is used (Figure 27.1). Figure 27.2 shows the key steps in a mixed ANOVA.

If you feel confident with the two-way unrelated ANOVA described in Chapter 25, we suggest that you need to concentrate on steps 2 and 7 overleaf as these tell you how to calculate the error terms. The other steps should be familiar.

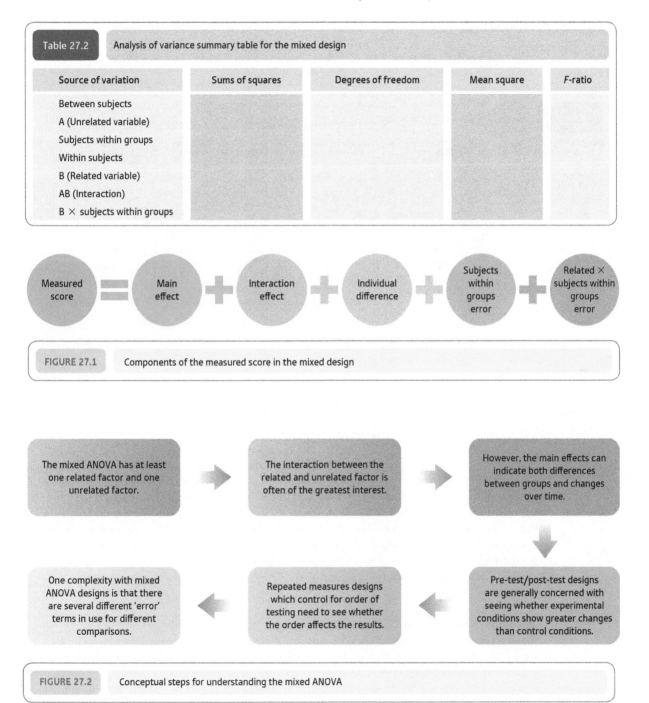

| Table 27.2 | Analysis of variance summary table for the mixed design |

Source of variation	Sums of squares	Degrees of freedom	Mean square	F-ratio
Between subjects				
A (Unrelated variable)				
Subjects within groups				
Within subjects				
B (Related variable)				
AB (Interaction)				
B × subjects within groups				

FIGURE 27.1   Components of the measured score in the mixed design

FIGURE 27.2   Conceptual steps for understanding the mixed ANOVA

Explaining statistics 27.1

How the mixed-design two-way analysis of variance works

The variance estimate for the data in Table 27.3 for $N - 1$ degrees of freedom is $76.89 \div 11 = 6.99$. N is the number of scores.

Table 27.3	Example of a mixed ANOVA design			
	Subject	**Pre-test measure**	**Post-test measure**	**Subject mean**
Control	S1	6	5	5.500
	S2	4	6	5.000
	S3	5	7	6.000
		Mean = 5.000	Mean = 6.000	Mean = 5.500
Experimental	S4	7	10	8.500
	S5	5	11	8.000
	S6	5	12	8.500
		Mean = 5.667	Mean = 11.000	Mean = 8.333
		Mean = 5.333	Mean = 8.500	Overall mean = 6.917

Just to remind you, 6.99 is the variance estimate (or mean square) based on the 12 scores in Table 27.3. To avoid repetitious calculations with which you should now be familiar, we have given only the final stages of the calculation of the various variance estimates. This is to allow you to work through our example and check your calculations.

In the mixed-design ANOVA the following steps are then calculated.

Step 1 *Between-subjects scores.* Between-subjects scores are the data but with the pre-test/post-test difference eliminated. In other words, each participant's scores in the pre-test and post-test conditions are replaced by the corresponding subject mean. Thus the column means for the pre-test and post-test have the (residual) error removed since the remaining variation within the cells is due to individual differences. However, there still remains variation within the table due to individual differences as well as the main effects and interaction. (To be absolutely clear, the first entry of 5.500 for both the pre-test and post-test measure is obtained by averaging that first person's scores of 5 and 6 in Table 27.3.)

The variance estimate for the between-subjects scores is $25.40 \div 5 = 5.08$ (df = number of subjects − 1, i.e. 6 − 1 = 5).

Step 2 *Subjects within groups scores, i.e. individual difference component.* If we take away the cell mean from the scores in Table 27.4, we are left with the individual difference component for each participant for each score. Thus, S2's scores are on average −0.500 below the row mean. Table 27.5 gives the individual difference component of every score in the original data.

The variance estimate for the subject within groups scores is $1.32 \div 4 = 0.33$ (the df is the number of subjects − number of rows of data, i.e. 6 − 2 = 4).

Table 27.4	Table of between-subjects scores, i.e. with (residual) error removed			
	Subject	Pre-test	Post-test	Subject mean
Control	S1	5.500	5.500	5.500
	S2	5.000	5.000	5.000
	S3	6.000	6.000	6.000
		Mean = 5.500	Mean = 5.500	Mean = 5.500
Experimental	S4	8.500	8.500	8.500
	S5	8.000	8.000	8.000
	S6	8.500	8.500	8.500
		Mean = 8.333	Mean = 8.333	Mean = 8.333
		Mean = 6.917	Mean = 6.917	Overall mean = 6.917

Table 27.5	Subjects within-groups scores, i.e. error due to individual differences removed			
	Subject	Pre-test	Post-test	Subject mean
Control	S1	5.500 − 5.500 = 0.000	0.000	0.000
	S2	5.000 − 5.500 = −0.500	−0.500	−0.500
	S3	6.000 − 5.500 = 0.500	0.500	0.500
				Mean = 0.000
Experimental	S4	8.500 − 8.333 = 0.167	0.167	0.167
	S5	−0.333	−0.333	−0.333
	S6	0.167	0.167	0.167
				Mean = 0.000
		Mean = 0.000	Mean = 0.000	Overall mean = 0.000

You will see that these individual difference scores seem rather like error scores – they add to zero for each cell. Indeed they are error scores – the individual differences component of error. The variance estimate of the individual differences is used as the error variance estimate for calculating the significance of the control/experimental comparison (i.e. the unrelated independent variable).

Step 3   *Experimental/control scores: main effect.* The best estimate of the effects of the experimental versus the control condition involves simply replacing each score for the control group with the control group mean (5.500) and each score for the experimental group by the experimental group mean (8.333). This is shown in Table 27.6.

The variance estimate for the experimental/control main effect is $24.08 \div 1 = 24.08$ (the *df* is the number of rows of data −1, i.e. $2 − 1 = 1$).

The statistical significance of the main effect of the experimental versus control manipulation independent variable involves the variance estimate for the main effects scores in Table 27.6 and the variance estimate for the individual differences error scores in Table 27.5. By dividing the former by the latter variance estimate, we obtain the *F*-ratio for testing the effects of the experimental versus control conditions. If this is significant then there is an overall difference between the control and experimental group scores.

Table 27.6	Main effect (experimental/control comparison)			
	Subject	Pre-test	Post-test	Subject mean
Control	S1	5.500	5.500	5.500
	S2	5.500	5.500	5.500
	S3	5.500	5.500	5.500
				Mean = 5.500
Experimental	S4	8.333	8.333	8.333
	S5	8.333	8.333	8.333
	S6	8.333	8.333	8.333
				Mean = 8.333
		Mean = 6.917	Mean = 6.917	Overall mean = 6.917

Step 4

Within-subjects scores. Subtract the between-subjects scores (Table 27.4) from the data table (Table 27.3) and you are left with the within-subjects scores. In other words, the scores in Table 27.7 are what is left when the effects of the experimental/control comparison and the individual difference component of the scores are removed. Notice that the subject means in Table 27.7 are all zero as are the row means. This indicates that there are no individual differences or differences due to the experimental/control comparison remaining in Table 27.7.

The variance estimate for this table is $51.54 \div 6 = 8.59$ (*df* is the number of scores minus the number of subjects $= 12 - 6 = 6$).

Step 5

Within-subjects independent variable main effect: pre-test/post-test scores. This is the main effect of the repeated measure. It is obtained simply by substituting the appropriate column average from the data table (Table 27.3) for each of the scores (Table 27.8).

The variance estimate for the pre-test/post-test main effect is $30.09 \div 1 = 30.09$ (the *df* is the number of columns of data $- 1$, i.e. $2 - 1 = 1$).

Table 27.7	Within-subjects scores (i.e. the scores with individual differences and control/experimental differences eliminated)			
	Subject	Pre-test	Post-test	Subject mean
Control	S1	0.5	−0.5	0.000
	S2	−1.0	1.0	0.000
	S3	−1.0	1.0	0.000
				Mean = 0.000
Experimental	S4	−1.5	1.5	0.000
	S5	−3.0	3.0	0.000
	S6	−3.5	3.5	0.000
				Mean = 0.000
		Mean = −1.583	Mean = 1.583	Overall mean = 0.000

Table 27.8 — Main effects of the pre-test/post-test comparison

	Subject	Pre-test	Post-test	Subject mean
Control	S1	5.333	8.500	6.917
	S2	5.333	8.500	6.917
	S3	5.333	8.500	6.917
				Mean = 6.917
Experimental	S4	5.333	8.500	6.917
	S5	5.333	8.500	6.917
	S6	5.333	8.500	6.917
				Mean = 6.917
		Mean = 5.333	Mean = 8.500	Overall mean = 6.917

Step 6

Interaction of experimental/control with pre-test/post-test. The calculation of the interaction is much as for the two-way unrelated ANOVA (Chapter 25):

- We can eliminate error by making every score in the data table the same as the cell mean (Table 27.9).

- We can eliminate the effect of the control versus experimental treatment by simply taking the corresponding row means away from all of the scores in Table 27.9 (Table 27.10).

- Note that Table 27.10 still contains variation between its pre-test and post-test columns. We eliminate this by subtracting the corresponding column mean from each of the scores in the pre-test and post-test columns (Table 27.11).

Table 27.11 contains the scores for the interaction. The variance estimate for the interaction is $14.08 \div 1 = 14.08$ (the *df* is the number of rows of data $- 1 \times$ the of columns of data $- 1$ (i.e. $(2 - 1) \times (2 - 1) = 1 \times 1 = 1$)).

Table 27.9 — Removing (total) error from the data table

	Subject	Pre-test	Post-test	Subject mean
Control	S1	5.000	6.000	5.500
	S2	5.000	6.000	5.500
	S3	5.000	6.000	5.500
				Mean = 5.500
Experimental	S4	5.667	11.000	8.333
	S5	5.667	11.000	8.333
	S6	5.667	11.000	8.333
				Mean = 8.333
		Mean = 5.333	Mean = 8.500	Overall mean = 6.917

Table 27.10		Removing experimental/control main effect (total error removed in previous step)		
	Subject	Pre-test	Post-test	Subject mean
Control	S1	$5.000 - 5.500 = -0.500$	0.500	0.000
	S2	-0.500	0.500	0.000
	S3	-0.500	0.500	0.000
				Mean = 0.000
Experimental	S4	$5.667 - 8.333 = -2.666$	2.667	0.000
	S5	-2.666	2.667	0.000
	S6	-2.666	2.667	0.000
				Mean = 0.000
		Mean = -1.583	Mean = 1.583	Overall mean = 0.000

Table 27.11		Removing pre-test/post-test differences (error and experimental/control main effect already removed in previous two steps)		
	Subject	Pre-test	Post-test	Subject mean
Control	S1	$-0.500 - (-1.583) = 1.083$	-1.083	0.000
	S2	1.083	-1.083	0.000
	S3	1.083	-1.083	0.000
				Mean = 0.000
Experimental	S4	$-2.666 - (-1.583) = -1.083$	1.083	0.000
	S5	-1.083	1.083	0.000
	S6	-1.083	1.083	0.000
				Mean = 0.000
		Mean = 0.00	Mean = 0.00	Overall mean = 0.00

Step 7

Pre-test/post-test × subjects within groups. Earlier we explained that pre-test/post-test × subjects within groups is an error term which is in essence the (residual) error that we calculated in Chapter 24. It is actually quite easy to calculate the (residual) error simply by:

● drawing up a total error table by subtracting the cell means from each score in the data table (Table 27.9) as we did for the two-way unrelated ANOVA in Chapter 25 and then

● taking away from these (total) error scores the corresponding (residual) error in Table 27.4. In other words,

(Residual) error = (Total) error − Individual difference error

Most statistical textbooks present a rather more abstract computational approach to this which obscures what is really happening. However, to facilitate comparisons with other textbooks, if required, we will present the calculation using essentially the computational method.

The calculation of this error term involves taking the data (Table 27.3) and then a) subtracting the interaction score (Table 27.9), b) subtracting the individual differences score (Table 27.4) and c) adding the

Table 27.12	Pre-test/post-test $\times$ subjects within groups scores (i.e. (residual) error)			
	Subject	Pre-test	Post-test	Subject mean
Control	S1	$6 - 5.000 - 5.500 + 5.500 = 1.000$	$5 - 6.000 - 5.500 + 5.500 = -1.000$	0.000
	S2	$4 - 5.000 - 5.000 + 5.500 = -0.500$	$6 - 6.000 - 5.000 + 5.500 = 0.500$	0.000
	S3	$5 - 5.000 - 6.000 + 5.500 = -0.500$	$7 - 6.000 - 6.000 + 5.500 = 0.500$	0.000
				Mean = 0.000
Experi-mental	S4	$7 - 5.667 - 8.500 + 8.333 = 1.167$	$10 - 11.000 - 8.500 + 8.333 = -1.167$	0.000
	S5	$5 - 5.667 - 8.000 + 8.333 = -0.333$	$11 - 11.000 - 8.000 + 8.333 = 0.333$	0.000
	S6	$5 - 5.667 - 8.500 + 8.333 = -0.833$	$12 - 11.000 - 8.500 + 8.333 = 0.833$	0.000
				Mean = 0.000
		Mean = 0.000	Mean = 0.000	Overall mean = 0.000

between-subjects score (Table 27.6). Notice that the scores in Table 27.12 are just as we would expect of error scores – the cells all add up to zero. It is (residual) error since there is no variation left in the subject mean column.

The variance estimate for the pre-test/post-test $\times$ subjects within groups (or residual error) is $7.37 \div 4 = 1.84$ (the *df* is (number of subjects − number of rows) $\times$ (number of columns −1) = (6−2) $\times$ (2−1) = 4 $\times$ 1 = 4).

This (residual) error term is used in assessing the significance of the pre-test/post-test comparison as well as the interaction.

The various calculations in steps 1–7 can be made into an analysis of variance summary table. Table 27.13 is a summary table using the basic concepts we have included in this book; Table 27.14 is the same except that it uses the conventional way of presenting mixed designs in statistics textbooks.

You might be wondering about the reasons for the two error terms. The (residual) error is merely that with no individual differences remaining, and in Chapter 24 we examined how removing individual differences helps to control error

Table 27.13	Analysis of variance summary table (using basic concepts)			
Source of variation	Sums of squares	Degrees of freedom	Variance estimate	F-ratio
Unrelated				
Main effect (unrelated variable)	24.08	1	24.08	$\dfrac{24.08}{0.33} = 72.97$[a]
Individual differences error	1.32	4	0.33	
Related				
Main effect (related variable)	30.09	1	30.09	$\dfrac{30.09}{1.84} = 16.35$[a]
Interaction (related $\times$ unrelated variables)	14.08	1	14.08	$\dfrac{14.08}{1.84} = 7.65$[a]
(Residual) error	7.37	4	1.84	

[a] Significant at the 5% level.

Table 27.14	Analysis of variance summary table (with layout in the conventional form)			
Source of variation	Sums of squares	Degrees of freedom	Variance estimate	F-ratio
Between subjects				
A (Praise)	24.08	1	24.08	$\frac{24.08}{0.33} = 72.97^{a}$
Subjects within groups	1.32	4	0.33	
Within subjects				
B (Time)	30.09	1	30.09	$\frac{30.09}{1.84} = 16.35^{a}$
AB	14.08	1	14.08	$\frac{14.08}{1.84} = 7.65^{a}$
B × subjects within groups	7.37	4	1.84	

[a] Significant at the 5% level. The above which is conceptually correct is based on calculations subject to compounded rounding errors. But the figures correspond closely to those in Screenshot 27.6 for example.

variation in related designs. Not surprisingly, it is used for the main effect and interaction which include related components. However, since the individual differences error contains only that source of variation, it makes a good error term for the unrelated scores comparison. After all, by getting rid of 'true' error variation the design allows a 'refined' error term for the unrelated comparison. For a simpler way of analysing this data see Box 27.3.

Perhaps we ought to explain why rather unusual names are used conventionally for the error terms in mixed ANOVAs. The reason is that the individual differences component of the scores cannot be estimated totally independently of the interaction between the main variables since they are both dependent on pre-test/post-test differences. Consequently, the estimate of individual differences cannot be totally divorced from the interaction. It follows that both error terms ought to be labelled in ways which indicate this fact. On balance, then, you would be wise to keep to the conventional terminology.

Interpreting the results

The interpretation of the mixed-design two-way ANOVA is virtually identical to the interpretation of any two-way ANOVA design such as the unrelated two-way ANOVA in Chapter 25. It is the calculation of the error terms which is different and this does not alter the interpretation although obviously may affect the significance level.

Remember that the interpretation of any data should be based first of all on an examination of cell means and variances (or standard deviations) such as those to be found in Table 27.15. It is the pattern that you find in these which tells you just what the data say. The tests of significance merely confirm whether or not your interpretations may be generalised. An examination of Table 27.15 suggests that it is the experimental group at the post-test which has by far the highest mean score. There appears to be little difference between the other cells. This seems to suggest that there is an interaction between the two independent variables. The ANOVA summary table confirms this.

Table 27.15	Table of means for mixed ANOVA design		
	Pre-test measure	**Post-test measure**	
Control	Cell mean = 5.000	Cell mean = 6.000	Row mean = 5.500
Experimental	Cell mean = 5.667	Cell mean = 11.000	Row mean = 8.333
	Column mean = 5.333	Column mean = 8.500	Overall mean = 6.917

Reporting the results

These results may be written up according to the APA (2010) Publication Manual's recommendations as follows: 'A mixed-design analysis of variance with praise as the unrelated independent variable and pre-test versus post-test as the related independent variable was carried out on the dependent variable self-esteem. The independent variable praise had a significant effect on self-esteem, $F(1, 4) = 72.97, p < .05$. The scores in the control group ($M = 5.50$) were significantly lower than those in the experimental group which was given praise ($M = 8.33$). Similarly, scores at the post-test were significantly higher in the post-test ($M = 8.50$) than in the pre-test ($M = 5.33$), $F(1, 4) = 16.35, p < .05$.

However, the hypothesis suggests that there is an interaction between the two independent variables such that the post-test measures of the experimental group given praise score more highly on the dependent variable than the other cells. There was a significant interaction, $F(1, 4) = 7.65, p < .05$. Furthermore, it would seem that it is the experimental groups following the praise manipulation which had the highest self-esteem scores. Table 27.15 shows the cell means for the four conditions of the experiment. It would appear that the variation between the cells is the result of the interaction effect and that the main effects are slight in comparison.'

| Box 27.3 | Focus on |

Simpler alternative

The sort of mixed design dealt with in this chapter requires a significant interaction for the experimental hypothesis to be supported. However, it has the drawback that the main effect of the pre-test/post-test comparison may well be affected by this interaction. (Remember that ANOVA takes out main effects first and interactions can be confused for these unless you keep your eye firmly on the descriptive output for the means, etc.) Furthermore, the unrelated comparison can also be affected in the same way. A simpler analysis of these same data, although not so thorough as the mixed design ANOVA, would be a *t*-test comparing the differences between the pre-test and post-test scores for the experimental and control groups. In other words, you have two groups of scores based on the change from pre-test scores. So you can compare the amount of change in your experimental group compared to the amount of change in the control group using an unrelated *t*-test. Of course, if you had three groups then you could use one-way ANOVA to much the same effect.

■ 'Risks' in related subjects designs

The advantage of related designs is that the error component of the data can be reduced by the individual differences component. Similarly, in matched-subject designs the matching variables, if they are carefully selected because they correlate with the dependent variable, reduce the amount of error in the scores. However, there is a trade-off between reducing the error term and the reduction in degrees of freedom involved (Glantz & Slinker, 1990) since the degrees of freedom in an unrelated ANOVA error term are higher than for the related ANOVA error term. If one's matching variables are poorly related to the dependent variable or if the individual differences component of error is very small, there may be no advantage in using the related or matched ANOVA. Indeed, there can be a reduction in the power of the related ANOVA to reject your null hypothesis. This is a complex matter. The most practical advice is:

● Do not employ matching unless you know that there is a strong relationship between

matching participants by their gender if you know that there is a gender difference in scores on the dependent variable).

- Do whatever you can to reduce the error variance by standardising your methods and using highly reliable measures of the dependent variable.

Research examples

Mixed-design ANOVA

Blankenship, Wegener and Murray (2012) pointed out that much of the research on persuasion deals with the attitude of interest directly. There are circumstances where indirect methods could work better. They suggest that tackling persuasion through the indirect method of changing values might be more effective than directly dealing with attitudes. By dealing with values directly, confidence in the value might be undermined and this may lead to attitude change. Undermining the attitude might lead to resistance. In research related to these ideas, Blankenship et al. used psychology students as participants. Two independent variables were created: a) the target of the persuasive attack, which was either on pertinent values or a policy attack on the issue of affirmative action, and b) the time which was either a pre-attack measure or a post-attack measure. In other words, their attitudes to affirmative action were measured both before and after the persuasive communication. The type of persuasive communication was randomly assigned but the pre-test and post-test measure was a correlated variable since all participants provided both measures. So the appropriate ANOVA was a mixed design. The study showed that attitudes towards affirmative action changed more when equality was attacked as a value than when affirmative action as a policy was attacked directly using the same arguments. As this was a 2×2 design there was no need for multiple comparison testing.

Fitneva, Lam and Dunfield (2013) were interested in children's strategies for information gathering. The sources of information may be asking other people for the information but they can involve direct experience. What is not known from previous research is the extent to which children understand when it is better to ask and when it is better to find out. The researchers set up a situation in which the children were asked questions about 'moozle' figures. They could seek the answer by looking at the figure or by asking an adult who was 'the moozle expert'. The questions asked could be about physical properties (such as hair colour) or invisible properties (such as whether the moozle spoke French). The analysis was basically a repeated measures analysis of variance. The age of the children was one independent variable (4-year-olds versus 6-year-olds) and the related measures independent variable was visible versus invisible aspects of the moozle. The dependent variable was the number of times that the child chose to look at the moozle. It was found that children were significantly more likely to look at the moozle for information in the visible condition. There was an interaction showing the stronger tendency for the older children to look for visible properties and ask the expert for invisible properties.

Signal and colleagues (2012) discuss the transitory state following waking from sleep. This is a period of poor functioning, confusion and low levels of arousal. This occurs despite the opportunity for recovery that might be expected to follow sleep. It is of particular concern where a worker performs a critical task immediately after being woken up (e.g. when called out to an emergency at night). During such periods, performance at tasks can be inferior to before going to sleep. The study investigated the extent and course of sleep inertia. Participants were awakened after a short nap of 20 minutes, 40 minutes or 60 minutes. This was a simulation study taking place in a controlled setting of the laboratory. There was a no nap control condition. Dependent measures included a short test battery including a Sleepiness Scale and a Working Memory Task repeated several times after waking. The statistical analysis employed the mixed-model analyses of variance using time post-nap (a repeated measure), duration of nap and order of completing protocols as the independent variables. There was no effect of sleep inertia on the Sleepiness Scale. Nevertheless, the Working Memory task showed impairment in the form of slower reaction time, fewer correct responses and increased omissions due to sleep inertia.

Key points

- Research designs which require complex statistics such as the above ANOVAs are difficult and cumbersome to implement. Use them only after careful deliberation about what it is you really need from your research.

- Avoid the temptation to include basic demographic variables such as age and gender routinely as independent variables in the analysis of variance. If they are key factors then they should be included; otherwise they can merely lead to complex interactions which may be hard to interpret and not profitable when you have done so.

COMPUTER ANALYSIS

Mixed design analysis of variance using SPSS

Data	• Name the variables in 'Variable View' of the 'Data Editor'. • Enter the data under the appropriate variable names in 'Data View' of the 'Data Editor' (Screenshot 27.1).
Analysis	• Select 'Analyze', 'General Linear Model' and 'Repeated Measures. . .' (Screenshot 25.2). • Enter number of conditions for related independent variable in 'Number of Levels:' box (Screenshot 25.3). Select 'Add' and 'Define'.
2	• Move the related or repeated measures variables to the 'Within-Subjects Variables:' box (Screenshot 25.4). • Move the unrelated factor to the 'Between-Subjects Factor(s):' box.
3	• Select 'Plots. . .'. Move related variable to 'Horizontal Axis:' box and unrelated variable to 'Separate Lines:' box. Select 'Add' and 'Continue'.
4	• Select 'Options', move factors and interactions to 'Display means for:', 'Descriptive statistics', 'Estimates of effect size', 'Homogeneity tests', 'Continue' and 'OK'.
Output	• The most important effect in a pretest-posttest design is the interaction between the related and the unrelated variable. Check its significance in the 'Tests of Within-Subjects Contrasts' table. Carry out further tests to see which means differ significantly if it is.
2	• In a repeated measures design where the order of conditions is controlled, it is important to determine if there is a carryover effect.

FIGURE 27.3   SPSS steps for a mixed ANOVA

Interpreting and reporting the output

- The post-test mean for the experimental condition is higher than the other means in the Descriptive Statistics output suggesting an interaction. This is confirmed in the Tests of Within-Subjects Contrasts table. Both the main effect of order and the interaction between order and condition are statistically significant. It is important that Box's Test of Equality of Covariance Matrices and Levene's Test of Equality of Error Variances are non-significant.

- In line with APA (2010) conventions and after carrying out some t-tests to determine which means of the interaction differ, the results could be written as follows: 'The interaction between the two conditions and the change over time was statistically significant, $F(1, 4) = 7.68, p < .05, \eta_p^2 = .66$. While the pre-test means did not differ significantly, $t(4) = 0.76$, two-tailed $p < .492$, the post-test mean for the experimental condition ($M = 11.00, SD = 1.00$) was significantly higher, $t(4) = 6.12$, two-tailed $p < .004$, than that for the control condition ($M = 6.00, SD = 1.00$). The increase from pre-test ($M = 5.67, SD = 1.15$) to post-test ($M = 11.00, SD = 1.00$) was significant for the experimental condition, $t(2) = 4.44$, two-tailed $p < .047$, but not for the control condition, $t(2) = 1.00$, two-tailed $p < .423$.'

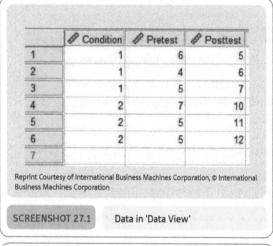

Reprint Courtesy of International Business Machines Corporation, © International Business Machines Corporation

SCREENSHOT 27.1   Data in 'Data View'

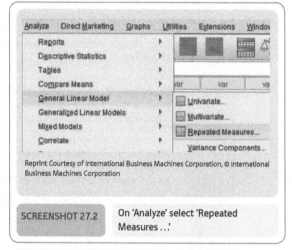

Reprint Courtesy of International Business Machines Corporation, © International Business Machines Corporation

SCREENSHOT 27.2   On 'Analyze' select 'Repeated Measures ...'

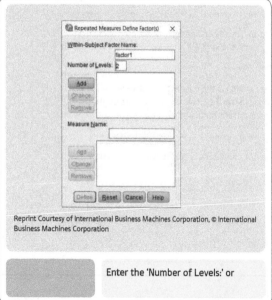

Reprint Courtesy of International Business Machines Corporation, © International Business Machines Corporation

Enter the 'Number of Levels:' or

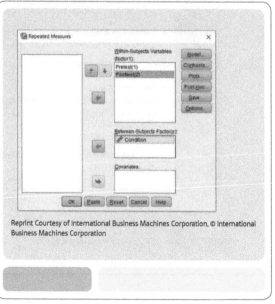

Reprint Courtesy of International Business Machines Corporation, © International Business Machines Corporation

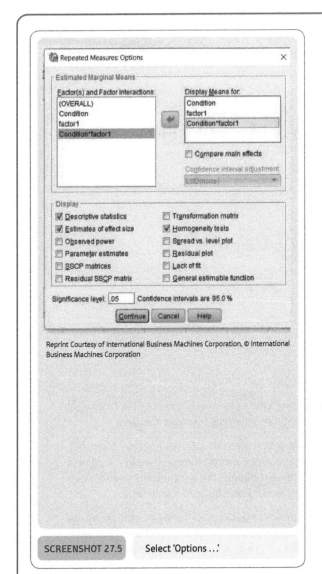

SCREENSHOT 27.5   Select 'Options ...'

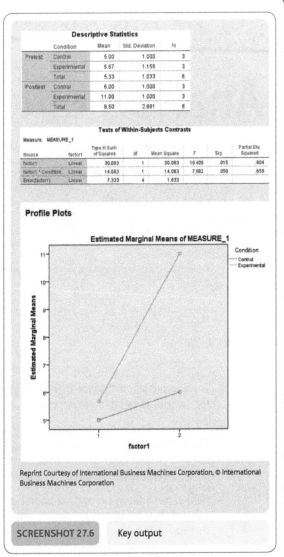

SCREENSHOT 27.6   Key output

Recommended further reading

Glantz, S. A., & Slinker, B. K. (1990). *Primer of applied regression and analysis of variance.* New York, NY: McGraw-Hill.

CHAPTER 28

Analysis of covariance (ANCOVA)

Controlling for additional variables

Overview

- The analysis of covariance (ANCOVA) involves procedures by which it is possible to control for additional variables which may be influencing the apparent trends in the data.

- Analysis of covariance designs often include a pre-test measure of the dependent variable. The analysis adjusts for these pre-test differences. Very approximately speaking, it adjusts or controls the data so that the pre-test scores are equal. This is especially useful when participants cannot be randomly allocated to different conditions of the design.

- Remember that in properly randomised experimental designs, extraneous influences are controlled partly by this process of randomly assigning participants to conditions. Of course, this may not always have the desired outcome which is why some researchers will use a pre-test to check that the participants are similar on the dependent variable prior to actually running the experiment. If the pre-test data suggest that the participants are not equated on the dependent variable then ANCOVA may be employed to help correct this.

Preparation

Chapters 23 to 25 are essential as this chapter utilises many of the ideas from different types of ANOVA.

28.1 Introduction

Another useful variant of the analysis of variance is the analysis of covariance (ANCOVA). This adds extra complexity but is especially valuable when there is reason to believe that the randomisation process cannot be relied on to have equated participants in the various conditions (cells) prior to the experimental manipulation. Of course, in non-randomised studies using analysis of variance (ANOVA) this is especially likely to be the case.

The analysis of covariance described in this chapter is basically an elaboration of the unrelated analysis of variance (Chapter 23). The crucial difference is that an additional variable known as the covariate is measured as well as the dependent variable and independent variable(s). This covariate is a variable which correlates potentially with the *dependent* variable. That is, the researcher suspects that the covariate is an uncontrolled source of variation which is affecting the outcome of the study. The participants in the various conditions of the experiment may be different in terms of a covariate, for example. Thus not all differences between the experimental conditions are due to the influence of the independent variable (experimental manipulation) on the dependent variable if the covariate is having an influence. In the analysis of covariance the scores on the dependent variable are 'adjusted' so that they are equated on the covariate. Although the procedures do not actually use the adjusted scores, the cell means for the adjusted scores are obtained as part of an additional stage in the statistical analysis.

In almost all psychology experiments random assignment of participants to different conditions of the experiment is used so that any pre-existing differences between participants are randomly distributed – hopefully. However, randomisation does not fully guarantee that participants are similar in all conditions for every study. Randomisation avoids systematic biases, but it cannot ensure that there are no differences between participants in the different conditions prior to the experimental manipulation which affect their scores on the dependent variable. Furthermore, non-experimental studies cannot employ randomisation properly. In one common application of analysis of covariance, pre-test measures can be thought of as covariates of the post-test measure and thus handled using the analysis of covariance as an alternative to the mixed design described in the previous chapter. Figure 28.1 shows the key steps in ANCOVA.

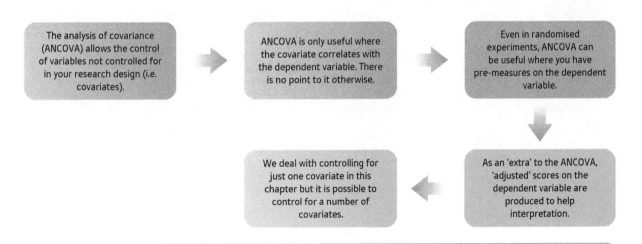

The analysis of covariance (ANCOVA) allows the control of variables not controlled for in your research design (i.e. covariates).

ANCOVA is only useful where the covariate correlates with the dependent variable. There is no point to it otherwise.

Even in randomised experiments, ANCOVA can be useful where you have pre-measures on the dependent variable.

We deal with controlling for just one covariate in this chapter but it is possible to control for a number of covariates.

As an 'extra' to the ANCOVA, 'adjusted' scores on the dependent variable are produced to help interpretation.

FIGURE 28.1   Conceptual steps for understanding ANCOVA

28.2   Analysis of covariance

Regard the analysis of covariance as being very much like the analysis of variance. The big difference is that it allows any variable(s) which might correlate with the dependent variable to be taken into account (apart, of course, from any independent variables in your analysis of variance design). In other words, it is possible to adjust the analysis of variance for differences between your groups that might affect the outcome. For example, you might find that social class correlates with your dependent variable, and that social class differs for the groups in your analysis of variance. Using analysis of covariance you can effectively 'adjust' the scores on your dependent variable for these social class differences. This is, in essence, to equate all of the groups so that their mean social class is the same. Although it is possible to calculate analysis of covariance by hand, we would recommend the use of a computer package since you are likely to want to equate for several variables, not just one. Furthermore, you should check to see that your covariate does, in fact, correlate with the dependent variable otherwise your analysis may become less sensitive, not more so. In any form of analysis of variance, there is a balance between the gains from additional controls on variance and the loss of degrees of freedom as a consequence of doing so. Controlling for covariates which do not correlate with the dependent variable effectively reduces the degrees of freedom but can do nothing to remove these sources of variance – because they simply do not correlate with the dependent variable. Reducing degrees of freedom reduces the likelihood of statistical significance all other things being equal.

Table 28.1 gives data that could be analysed using the analysis of covariance. The study is of the effects of different types of treatment on the dependent variable depression. For each participant, a pre-test measure of depression taken prior to therapy is also given. Notice that the pre-test scores of group 3, the no-treatment control group, tends to score higher on this pre-measure. Therefore, it could be that the apparent effects of therapy are to do with pre-existing differences between the three groups. Analysis of covariance could be used to allow for these pre-existing differences.

Table 28.1	Example of analysis of covariance data				
Group 1 Psychotherapy		Group 2 Anti-depressant		Group 3 No-treatment control	
Dependent variable Depression	Covariate Pre-test	Dependent variable Depression	Covariate Pre-test	Dependent variable Depression	Covariate Pre-test
27	38	30	40	40	60
15	32	27	34	29	52
22	35	24	32	35	57

Explaining statistics 28.1

How the one-way analysis of covariance works

The data are found in Table 28.1. The analysis of covariance involves a number of steps which essentially remove the influence of the covariate on the dependent variable prior to calculating the analysis of variance on these adjusted scores. It is unnecessary to calculate the adjusted scores directly and adjusted sums of squares are used instead. The one-way analysis of covariance involves three major steps:

- Calculating a one-way ANOVA on the dependent variable (depression) using exactly the same methods as found in Explaining statistics 23.1

- Calculating a one-way ANOVA on the covariate (in this case the pre-test scores) again using exactly the same methods as found in Explaining statistics 23.1.

- Calculating a variation on the one-way ANOVA which involves the regression of the covariate on the dependent variable. In essence this is the covariation which is subtracted from the variation in the scores on the dependent variable to adjust them for the effect of the covariate.

The outcomes of the above steps are then used to calculate the analysis of covariance (ANCOVA).

Finally, in order to judge what the data say after the influence has been removed, we also need a table of the adjusted cell means for the dependent variable, i.e. what is left when the covariate is removed from the dependent variable.

Step 1   *One-way unrelated ANOVA on the dependent variable.* For clarity we have given the data on the dependent variable in Table 28.2. Consult Explaining statistics 23.1 for fuller details of calculating the one-way ANOVAs.

1. Calculate the sum of the squared scores by squaring each score on the dependent variable and adding to give the total:

$$\Sigma X^2 = 27^2 + 15^2 + 22^2 + 30^2 + 27^2 + 24^2 + 40^2 + 29^2 + 35^2 = 7309$$

2. Sum the scores to give:

$$G = 27 + 15 + 22 + 30 + 27 + 24 + 40 + 29 + 35 = 249$$

3. Calculate the total number of scores on the dependent variable, $N = 9$.

4. Calculate the correction factor using the following formula:

$$\frac{G^2}{N} = \frac{249^2}{9} = 6889.000$$

Table 28.2	Scores on the dependent variable		
	Group 1	**Group 2**	**Group 3**
	27	30	40
	15	27	29
	22	24	35

Table 28.3	Analysis of variance summary table for scores on the dependent variable			
Source of variation	Sum of squares	Degrees of freedom	Mean square (variance estimate)	F-ratio
Between groups[dependent]	268.667	2	134.333	5.33[a]
Error[dependent]	151.333	6	25.222	
Total[dependent]	420.000	8		

[a] Significant at the 5% level.

5. Obtain the total sum of squares for the dependent variable by taking the sum of the squared scores minus the correction factor. This is $7309 - 6889.000 = 420.000$. This is entered into the ANOVA summary table for the dependent variable (Table 28.3).

6. Enter the degrees of freedom for the total sum of squares for the dependent variable. This is always $N - 1$ or the number of scores $- 1 = 9 - 1 = 8$.

7. The sum of squares between groups ($SS_{[between]}$) can be calculated as follows using the correction factor calculated above, the totals of each column and the number of scores in each column (e.g. N_1):

$$SS_{[between]} = \frac{T_1^2}{N_1} + \frac{T_2^2}{N_2} + \frac{T_3^2}{N_3} - \frac{G^2}{N}$$

$$= \frac{64^2}{3} + \frac{81^2}{3} + \frac{104^2}{3} - 6889.000$$

$$= 268.667$$

This value of the between-groups sum of squares for the dependent variable is entered into the ANOVA summary table (Table 28.3).

8. Enter the degrees of freedom for the between-groups sum of squares $=$ columns $- 1 = c - 1 = 3 - 1 = 2$.

9. Calculate the error (i.e. error or within) sum of squares ($SS_{[error]}$) by subtracting the between-groups sum of squares from the total sum of squares:

$$SS_{[error]} = SS_{[total]} - SS_{[between]}$$

$$= 420.000 - 268.667$$

$$= 151.333$$

10. The degrees of freedom for error are the number of scores minus the number of columns $= N - c = 9 - 3 = 6$.

Step 2 *Unrelated ANOVA on the covariate.* Again we can create a table of the covariate scores (Table 28.4) and carry out an unrelated ANOVA in exactly the same way as above for the dependent variable.

1. Calculate the sum of the squared scores by squaring each score on the covariate and adding to give the total:

$$\Sigma X^2 = 38^2 + 32^2 + 35^2 + 40^2 + 34^2 + 32^2 + 60^2 + 52^2 + 57^2 = 17\,026$$

2. Sum the scores to give:

$$G = 38 + 32 + 35 + 40 + 34 + 32 + 60 + 52 + 57 = 380$$

Table 28.4	Scores on the covariate		
	Group 1	**Group 2**	**Group 3**
	38	40	60
	32	34	52
	35	32	57

3. Calculate the total number of scores for the covariate, $N = 9$.

4. Calculate the correction factor using the following formula:

$$\frac{G^2}{N} = \frac{380^2}{9} = 16\ 044.444$$

5. Obtain the sum of squared scores for the covariate by taking the sum of the squared scores minus the correction factor. This is $17\ 026 - 16\ 044.444 = 981.556$. This is entered into the ANOVA summary table for the covariate (Table 28.5).

6. Enter the degrees of freedom for the total sum of squares for the dependent variable. This is always $N - 1$ or the number of scores $- 1 = 9 - 1 = 8$.

7. The sum of squares between groups ($SS_{[between]}$) can be calculated as follows using the correction factor which has already been calculated, the totals of each column and the number of scores in each column for the covariate (e.g. N_1):

$$SS_{[between]} = \frac{T_1^2}{N_1} + \frac{T_2^2}{N_2} + \frac{T_3^2}{N_3} - \frac{G^2}{N} = \frac{105^2}{3} + \frac{106^2}{3} + \frac{169^2}{3} - 16\ 044.444 = 896.223$$

This value of the between-groups sum of squares for the covariate is entered into the ANOVA summary table (Table 28.5).

8. Also, enter the degrees of freedom for the between-groups sum of squares for the covariate = columns $- 1 = c - 1 = 3 - 1 = 2$.

9. Calculate the error (i.e. error or within) sum of squares ($SS_{[error]}$) by subtracting the between-groups sum of squares from the total sum of squares:

$$SS_{[error]} = SS_{[total]} - SS_{[between]} = 981.556 - 896.223 = 85.333$$

The degrees of freedom for error are the number of scores minus the number of columns = $N - c = 9 - 3 = 6$.

Table 28.5	Analysis of variance summary table for scores on the covariate			
Source of variation	**Sum of squares**	**Degrees of freedom**	**Mean square (variance estimate)**	**F-ratio**
Between groups[covariate]	896.223	2	448.112	31.51[a]
Error[covariate]	85.333	6	14.222	
Total[covariate]	981.556	8		

[a] Significant at the 0.1% level.

Step 3 *Calculating the covariation summary table.* This is very similar to the calculation of the unrelated ANOVA but is based on the cross-products of the dependent variable and covariate scores (Table 28.6). Basically it involves multiplying each dependent variable score by the equivalent covariate score. In this way it is similar to the calculation of the Pearson correlation coefficient which involves the calculation of the covariance. Table 28.6 can be used to calculate a summary table for the cross-products (Table 28.7). The calculation is analogous to that for ANOVA in steps 1 and 2 above. The only substantial difference is that it involves calculation of the cross-products of $X \times Y$ instead of X^2.

1. Calculate the overall (or grand) total of the X scores:

$$G_X = 27 + 15 + 22 + 30 + 27 + 24 + 40 + 29 + 35 = 249$$

2. Calculate the overall (or grand) total of the Y scores:

$$G_Y = 38 + 32 + 35 + 40 + 34 + 32 + 60 + 52 + 57 = 380$$

3. Calculate the number of scores for the dependent variable, $N = 9$.

4. Calculate the correction factor by substituting the already calculated values:

$$\text{Correction factor} = \frac{G_X \times G_Y}{N} = \frac{249 \times 380}{9} = \frac{94\,620}{9} = 10\,513.333$$

Table 28.6	Data and cross-products table

	Group 1			Group 2			Group 3		
	X Dependent	Y Covariate	$X \times Y$	X Dependent	Y Covariate	$X \times Y$	X Dependent	Y Covariate	$X \times Y$
	27	38	1026	30	40	1200	40	60	2400
	15	32	480	27	34	918	29	52	1508
	22	35	770	24	32	768	35	57	1995
	$\Sigma X = 64$	$\Sigma Y = 105$	$\Sigma XY = 2276$	$\Sigma X = 81$	$\Sigma Y = 106$	$\Sigma XY = 2886$	$\Sigma X = 104$	$\Sigma Y = 169$	$\Sigma XY = 5903$
	$\Sigma X \Sigma Y = 64 \times 105 = 6720$			$\Sigma X \Sigma Y = 81 \times 106 = 8586$			$\Sigma X \Sigma Y = 104 \times 169 = 17\,576$		
	$N_1 = 3$			$N_2 = 3$			$N_3 = 3$		

Grand total of all X scores $= \Sigma X = G_X = 64 + 81 + 104 = 249$

Grand total of all Y scores $= \Sigma Y = G_Y = 105 + 106 + 169 = 380$

Table 28.7	Summary table for the covariation

Source of variation	Sum of squares	Degrees of freedom	Mean square (variance estimate)	F-ratio
Between groups[covariation]	447.334	2		
Error[covariation]	104.333	5	Not needed here	Not needed here
Total[covariation]	551.667	8		

5. Calculate the number of scores for each group (N_1, N_2, N_3). In our example these are all 3 as the group sizes are equal, but this does not have to be so.

6. Total degrees of freedom for the data table = the number of scores $- 1 = 9 - 1 = 8$.

7. Multiply each X score by the equivalent Y score to give the cross-products and sum these cross-products to give ΣXY which is the sum of cross-products:

$$\Sigma XY = (27 \times 38) + (15 \times 32) + (22 \times 35) + (30 \times 40) + (27 \times 34) + (24 \times 32)$$
$$+ (40 \times 60) + (29 \times 52) + (35 \times 57)$$
$$= 1026 + 480 + 770 + 1200 + 918 + 768 + 2400 + 1508 + 1995$$
$$= 11\,065$$

8. Obtain the total sum of covariation by subtracting the correction factor from the sum of cross-products:

$$\text{Total sum of covariation} = \sum XY - \frac{G_X \times G_Y}{N}$$
$$= 11065 - 10\,513.333$$
$$= 551.667$$

9. These values of the total sum of covariation (551.667) and the degrees of freedom (8) can be entered into Table 28.7 (the summary table for covariation).

10. Sum the scores on the dependent variable and covariate separately for each of the groups as in Table 28.6. This gives us ΣX_1, ΣX_2, ΣX_3, ΣY_1, ΣY_2, ΣY_3, since we have three groups in our instance.

11. The sum of the covariation between groups is calculated as follows:

$$\text{Sum of covariation between groups} = \frac{\sum X_1 \sum Y_1}{N_1} + \frac{\sum X_2 \sum Y_2}{N_2} + \frac{\sum X_3 \sum Y_3}{N_3} - \frac{G_X G_Y}{N}$$
$$= \frac{64 \times 105}{3} + \frac{81 \times 106}{3} + \frac{104 \times 169}{3} - 10\,513.333$$
$$= \frac{6720}{3} + \frac{8586}{3} + \frac{17\,576}{3} - 10\,513.333$$
$$= 2240.000 + 2862.000 + 5858.667 - 10\,513.333$$
$$= 447.334$$

12. The degrees of freedom for the covariation between groups is the number of groups $- 1 = 3 - 1 = 2$.

13. These values of the sum of covariation between groups and degrees of freedom between groups can be entered in Table 28.7.

14. The sum of the covariation of error can be obtained now by subtracting the sum of the between-groups covariation from the total covariation:

$$\text{Sum of the covariation of error} = \text{Total of covariation} - \text{Covariation between groups}$$
$$= 551.667 - 447.334$$
$$= 104.333$$

➔

15. This value of the covariation for error can now be entered into Table 28.7.

16. The degrees of freedom for error are calculated in a way which removes one degree of freedom for the covariation. This is simply the total number of scores − the number of groups − 1 = 9 − 3 − 1 = 5. This can be entered in Table 28.7.

The above calculation steps for covariation are only superficially different from those for the analysis of variance in steps 1 and 2. They are actually different only so far as variance and covariance differ (pp. 106–107).

Step 4   *Calculating the ANCOVA summary table, i.e. the dependent table with the covariate partialled out.* This is achieved by taking away the variation in the scores due to the covariate from the variation in the dependent variable. Once we have the three summary tables (dependent variable, covariate and cross-products) then it is a fairly simple matter to calculate the adjusted dependent variable sums of squares and enter them into Table 28.8, the summary table for a one-way ANCOVA.

The formulae are:

$$SSError_{[adjusted]} = SSError_{[dependent]} - \frac{(Error_{[covariation]})^2}{SSError_{[covariate]}}$$

$$SSTotal_{[adjusted]} = SSTotal_{[dependent]} - \frac{(Total_{[covariation]})^2}{SSError_{[covariate]}}$$

Be very careful to distinguish between the covariation and the covariate.

These calculations are as follows:

$$SSError_{[adjusted]} = SSError_{[dependent]} - \frac{(Error_{[covariation]})^2}{SSError_{[covariate]}}$$

$$= 151.333 - \frac{104.333^2}{85.333}$$

$$= 151.333 - \frac{10\,885.375}{85.333}$$

$$= 151.333 - 127.563$$

$$= 23.77$$

Table 28.8	ANCOVA summary table			
Source of variation	Sum of squares	Degrees of freedom	Mean square (variance estimate)	F-ratio
Between[adjusted]	86.175	2	43.088	$\frac{43.088}{4.754} = 9.06$[a]
Error[adjusted]	23.770	5	4.754	
Total[adjusted]	109.945	8		

[a] Significant at the 5% level.

$$SSTotal_{[adjusted]} = SSTotal_{[dependent]} - \frac{(Total_{[covariation]})^2}{SSError_{[covariate]}}$$

$$= 420.000 - \frac{551.667^2}{981.556}$$

$$= 420.000 - \frac{304\,336.479}{981.556}$$

$$= 420.000 - 310.055$$

$$= 109.945$$

Enter these values into the ANCOVA summary table (Table 28.8) and the between sum of squares obtained by subtracting the error sum of squares from the total sum of squares.

Note that the degrees of freedom for the error term in the ANCOVA summary table are listed as 5. This is because we have constrained the degrees of freedom by partialling out the covariate. The formula for the degrees of freedom for the adjusted error is number of scores - number of groups $- 1 = 9 - 3 - 1 = 5$.

Step 5

The F-ratio in the ANCOVA summary table is calculated in the usual way. It is the between mean square divided by the error mean square. This is 9.06. Note that this is the same value as that produced by SPSS in Screenshot 28.8 for 'Condition'. The significance of this is obtained from Significance Table 25.1 for 2 and 5 degrees of freedom (or Appendix J if other levels of significance are required). We look under the column for 2 degrees of freedom and the row for 5 degrees of freedom. This indicates that our F-ratio is above the minimum value for statistical significance and is therefore statistically significant.

Step 6

Adjusting group means. No analysis of variance can be properly interpreted without reference to the means of the data table. This is not simple with ANCOVA as the means in the data are the means unadjusted for the covariate. Consequently it is necessary to adjust the means to indicate what the mean would be when the effect of the covariate is removed. The formula for this is as follows:

Adjusted group mean = Unadjusted group mean

$$- \frac{(Error_{[covariance]})}{SSError_{[covariate]}} \times (Group\ mean_{[covariate]}) - Grand\ mean_{[covariate]}$$

The unadjusted group means are merely the means of the scores on the dependent variable for each of the three groups in our example. These can be calculated from Table 28.2. The three group means are: group 1 = 21.333, group 2 = 27.000 and group 3 = 34.667.

The group means for the covariate can be calculated from Table 28.4. They are group 1 = 35.000, group 2 = 35.333 and group 3 = 56.333.

The grand mean of the covariate is simply the mean of all of the scores on the covariate in Table 28.4 which equals 42.222 for our example.

The sums of squares for error have already been calculated. The sum of squares for error for the cross-products is 104.333 and is found in Table 28.7. The sum of squares for error for the covariate is 85.333 and is found in Table 28.5.

We can now substitute all of these values into the formula and enter these values into Table 28.9.

Group 1: Adjusted mean = 30.17 obtained as follows:

$$21.333 - \left[\frac{104.333}{85.333} \times (35.000 - 42.222) \right] = 21.333 - [1.223 \times (-7.222)]$$

$$= 21.333 - (-8.833)$$

$$= 30.166$$

Table 28.9	Unadjusted and adjusted means for depression		
Means	**Group 1 Psychotherapy**	**Group 2 Antidepressants**	**Group 3 Control**
Unadjusted	21.33	27.00	34.67
Adjusted	30.17	35.43	17.41

Group 2: Adjusted mean $= 35.43$ obtained as follows:

$$27.000 - \left[\frac{104.333}{85.333} \times (35.333 - 42.222) \right] = 27.000 - [1.223 \times (-6.889)]$$

$$= 27.000 - (-8.425)$$

$$= 35.425$$

Group 3: Adjusted mean $= 17.41$ obtained as follows

$$34.667 - \left[\frac{104.333}{85.333} \times (56.333 - 42.222) \right] = 34.667 - (1.223 \times 14.111)$$

$$= 34.667 - 17.258$$

$$= 17.41$$

Notice how the adjusted means in Table 28.9 show a completely different pattern from the unadjusted means in this case.

Step 7   The simplest way of testing which of the adjusted means are different from the others is to use the Fisher protected LSD (least significant difference) test (Huitema, 1980). It is convenient since the component parts have largely been calculated by now. This test gives us an F-ratio with always one degree of freedom for the comparison and N − the number of groups − $1 = 9 - 3 - 1 = 5$ in our example for the error. Because we have three groups, there are three possible comparisons between pairs of groups. We will show the calculation in full for the comparison between groups 1 and 2:

$$F = \frac{(\text{Adjusted group}_1 \text{ mean} - \text{Adjusted group}_2 \text{ mean})^2}{\text{Mean square error adjusted} \times \left[\left(\frac{1}{N_1} + \frac{1}{N_2} \right) + \left(\frac{(\text{Covariate group}_1 \text{ mean} - \text{Covariate group}_2 \text{ mean})^2}{\text{Sum of squares of error for the covariate}} \right) \right]}$$

where:

Adjusted group$_1$ mean is found in Table 28.9.

Adjusted group$_2$ mean is found in Table 28.9.

Mean square error adjusted is found in Table 28.8.

Covariate group$_1$ mean is found by consulting Table 28.4 and dividing the sum of covariate scores for group 1 by the number of scores for group $1 = \sum Y/N = 105 \div 3 = 35.000$.

Covariate group$_2$ mean is found in exactly the same way. Consult Table 28.4 and divide the sum of covariate scores for group 2 by the number of scores $= 106 \div 3 = 35.333$.

Sum of squares of error for the covariate is found in Table 28.5.

$$F = \frac{(30.17 - 35.43)^2}{4.754\left[\left(\dfrac{1}{3} + \dfrac{1}{3}\right) + \dfrac{(35.000 - 35.333)^2}{85.333}\right]}$$

$$= \frac{5.26^2}{4.754\left[(0.333 + 0.333) + \dfrac{(-0.333)^2}{85.333}\right]}$$

$$= \frac{27.668}{4.754\left(0.666 + \dfrac{0.111}{85.333}\right)}$$

$$= \frac{27.668}{4.754(0.666 + 0.001)}$$

$$= \frac{27.668}{4.754(0.667)} = \frac{27.668}{3.171} = 8.725$$

This value of the F-ratio with 1 and 5 degrees of freedom is statistically significant at the 5% level. So the adjusted means of group 1 and group 2 are significantly different from each other.

We also carried out the comparisons between group 1 and group 3 (the obtained F-ratio was not significant at the 5% level) and group 2 and group 3 (the obtained F-ratio was statistically significant at the 5% level).

Interpreting the results

The analysis of covariance makes it clear that the post-test measures of depression differ overall once the pre-test differences are controlled. However, by considering the means of the adjusted levels of depression it seems clear that the depression scores of the control group were actually lower than those of either of the treatment groups. In other words, once pre-test levels of depression are adjusted for, then the obvious interpretation is that depression is actually being increased by the treatment rather than being reduced relative to the control group. The multiple comparisons test indicates that the significant differences are between the anti-depressant group and the control group and the psychotherapy group and the control group. The two treatment groups did not differ significantly from each other.

Reporting the results

This analysis may be written up according to the APA (2010) Publication Manual's recommendations as follows: 'Analysis of covariance (ANCOVA) was applied to the three groups (psychotherapy, anti-depressant and no-treatment control) in order to see whether the different treatments had an effect on post-test levels of depression controlling for pre-test depression. There was found to be a significant effect of the type of treatment, $F(2, 5) = 9.06, p < .05$. The unadjusted means indicated that depression was higher in the control group ($M = 34.67$) than with psychotherapy ($M = 21.33$) or with anti-depressant treatment ($M = 27.00$). However, this seems to be the result of the influence of the covariate (pre-therapy levels of depression as measured at the pre-test) since the adjusted means for the groups indicate that the least depression is found in the untreated control group ($M = 17.41$), compared with the psychotherapy group ($M = 30.27$) and the anti-depressant group ($M = 35.11$). Thus, the two treatment conditions increased depression relative to the control group. This was confirmed in a comparison of the adjusted means using the Fisher protected LSD test. The analysis indicated that group 1 (psychotherapy) and group 2 (anti-depressant) differed significantly, $F(1, 5) = 8.73, p < .05$. Group 2 (anti-depressant) and group 3 (control condition) differed significantly, $F(1, 5) = 12.09, p < .05$. Group 1 (psychotherapy) and group 3 (control) did not differ significantly, $F(1, 5) = 5.98, p\ ns$.'

Research examples

ANCOVA

Cumming and co-workers (2012) studied the effect of physically maturing early in adolescence on the physical activity of girls. Research has suggested that girls reduce their amounts of physical activity during adolescence and the health-related issues that this entails are obvious. Is there a role for early maturation in this? The study compared early and late maturing adolescent girls with an average age of 12.7 years. The dependent variables were health-related matters such as physical activity behaviour, physical self-concept, and health-related quality of life. In each case it was expected that early maturing girls would score lower. The analysis employed several ANCOVA analyses comparing early and late maturing girls on these variables. Chronological age was included as the covariate since obviously maturation and age correlate together. Although the size of the differences tended to be small to moderate, the ANCOVAs repeatedly showed that early maturing girls scored lower on the health-related variables. It is noteworthy that early maturing girls rated themselves lower in terms of body attractiveness. This may have a bearing on their lower levels of involvement in physical activity.

Estevis, Basso and Combs (2012) investigated the effect of practice on the Wechsler Adult Intelligence Scale–IV. The participants were given the test at the start of the study and again a few months later. For some it was three months later and for the others it was six months later. They used various subscales from the test including Verbal Comprehension, Working Memory, Perceptual Reasoning and Processing Speed as well as the Full Scale IQ. They analysed the data using an ANCOVA design in which test versus retest and the various subscales were the related factors and three months versus six months was the independent factor. Gender was entered as the covariate. Bonferroni adjustment was employed to deal with the repeated significance testing problem. The interval between testing and retesting did not have a significant effect.

Wright and Hardie (2012) write that the previous research on the relationship between handedness and anxiety fails to indicate a clear conclusion. One reason for expecting a relationship between anxiety and handedness is that the right-hand side hemisphere of the brain is involved in negative emotional states and inhibition. Anxiety is often classified as being situational in nature or alternatively as a personality trait of the individual. The researchers found that left-handed people have statistically significantly higher scores on state anxiety, which supports the idea of the role of the right hemisphere. No trait anxiety differences were found but trait and state anxiety were significantly correlated. So ANCOVA was employed with trait anxiety as the control variable because of this correlation. The handedness relationship to state anxiety remained even in this analysis. The authors suggest that left-handers are more reactive personalities and so respond with state anxiety to the new situation that they were experiencing in the research laboratory as part of the research.

Key points

- Relying on ANCOVA to deal with the problems due to employing non-randomised allocation to the cells of the ANOVA ignores the basic reason for doing randomised experiments in the first place – that the researcher does not know what unknown factors influence the outcome of the research. Random allocation to conditions is the only practical and sound way of fully controlling for variables not included in the design.

- It is not wise to use ANCOVA to try to correct for the sloppiness of your original design or procedures. Although, especially when using computers, you can include many covariates, it is best to be careful when planning your research to reduce the need for this. In randomised experiments, probably the control of the pre-test measure is the only circumstance requiring ANCOVA. Of course, there are circumstances in which pre-tests are undesirable, especially as they risk sensitising participants as to the purpose of the study or

COMPUTER ANALYSIS

Analysis of covariance using SPSS

Data	• Name the variables in 'Variable View' of the 'Data Editor'. • Enter the data under the appropriate variable names in 'Data View' of the 'Data Editor' (Screenshot 28.1).
Analysis	• If the potential covariate is reasonably strongly related to the dependent variable, proceed with ANCOVA. Use Pearson correlation for this.
2	• Select 'Analyze', 'General Linear Model' and 'Univariate...' (Screenshot 28.2). • Move dependent variable to 'Dependent Variable:' box, independent variable to 'Fixed Factor:' box and covariate variable to 'Covariate:' box (Screenshot 28.3).
3	• To check that the slope of the regression line is similar in each condition, select 'Model' and 'Custom'. Move the independent variable, the covariate and the interaction between the independent variable and covariate box to the box on the right.
4	• If the interaction between the independent variable and the covariate is not significant by having a Sig(nificance) of greater than .05, proceed with the ANCOVA.
5	• Select 'Analyze', 'General Linear Model', 'Univariate...', 'Model', 'Full factorial' and 'Continue' (Screenshot 28.4). • Select 'Options...', 'Descriptive statistics', 'Estimates of effect size', 'Compare main effects' and 'LSD' (Screenshot 26.5). • Move the independent variable to the 'Display Means for:' box.
6	• Select 'Continue' and 'OK'.
Output	• Check if the independent variable is significant by seeing if its Sig(nificance) is .05 or less (Screenshot 28.8). • If it is and there are more than 2 conditions, conduct further tests to determine which adjusted means differ significantly (Screenshot 28.9). • Compare adjusted means (Screenshot 28.6) with unadjusted ones (Screenshot 28.5) to see effect of ANCOVA.

FIGURE 28.2	SPSS steps for ANCOVA

Interpreting and reporting the output

● Firstly check that the covariate is related to the dependent variable. If not, then do not use ANCOVA. Also the relation between the covariate and the dependent variable should be similar across the conditions of the independent variable. This assumption is known as homogeneity of regression lines. Otherwise the effect of controlling will be different for each condition.

● Using APA (2010) style, one might write: 'Analysis of covariance (ANCOVA) in which the effect of treatment on post-treatment depression was examined controlling for pre-treatment depression. The treatment effect was significant, $F(2, 5) = 9.06, p < .05, \eta_p^2 = .78$. The Fisher protected LSD test showed the adjusted post-treatment mean for the anti-depressant group ($M = 35.52$) was significantly higher than that for the psychotherapy group ($M = 30.27$) and the no-treatment control group ($M = 17.21$).'

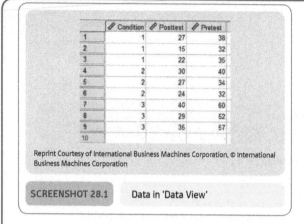

Reprint Courtesy of International Business Machines Corporation, © International Business Machines Corporation

SCREENSHOT 28.1 Data in 'Data View'

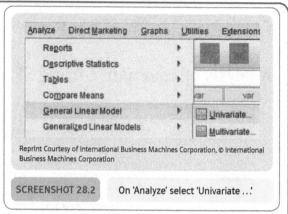

Reprint Courtesy of International Business Machines Corporation, © International Business Machines Corporation

SCREENSHOT 28.2 On 'Analyze' select 'Univariate ...'

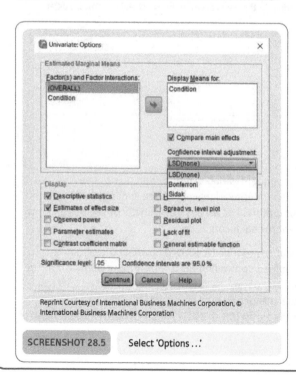

Reprint Courtesy of International Business Machines Corporation, © International Business Machines Corporation

SCREENSHOT 28.3 Select variables for analysis

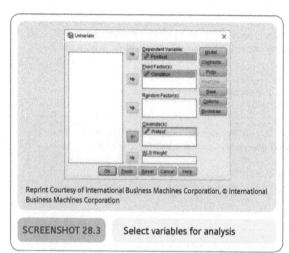

Reprint Courtesy of International Business Machines Corporation, © International Business Machines Corporation

SCREENSHOT 28.4 Select 'Model ...'

Descriptive Statistics

Dependent Variable: Posttest

Condition	Mean	Std. Deviation	N
Psychotherapy	21.33	6.028	3
Anti-depressant	27.00	3.000	3
No treatment control	34.67	5.508	3
Total	27.67	7.246	9

Reprint Courtesy of International Business Machines Corporation, © International Business Machines Corporation

SCREENSHOT 28.6 Important output – basic descriptives

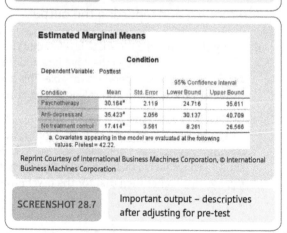

Reprint Courtesy of International Business Machines Corporation, © International Business Machines Corporation

SCREENSHOT 28.5 Select 'Options ...'

Estimated Marginal Means

Condition

Dependent Variable: Posttest

Condition	Mean	Std. Error	95% Confidence Interval Lower Bound	Upper Bound
Psychotherapy	30.164[a]	2.119	24.716	35.611
Anti-depressant	35.423[a]	2.056	30.137	40.709
No treatment control	17.414[a]	3.561	8.261	26.566

a. Covariates appearing in the model are evaluated at the following values: Pretest = 42.22.

Reprint Courtesy of International Business Machines Corporation, © International Business Machines Corporation

SCREENSHOT 28.7 Important output – descriptives after adjusting for pre-test

Tests of Between-Subjects Effects

Dependent Variable: Posttest

Source	Type III Sum of Squares	df	Mean Square	F	Sig.	Partial Eta Squared
Corrected Model	396.230[a]	3	132.077	27.783	.002	.943
Intercept	27.326	1	27.326	5.748	.062	.535
Pretest	127.564	1	127.564	26.833	.004	.843
Condition	86.176	2	43.088	9.064	.022	.784
Error	23.770	5	4.754			
Total	7309.000	9				
Corrected Total	420.000	8				

a. R Squared = .943 (Adjusted R Squared = .909)

Reprint Courtesy of International Business Machines Corporation, © International Business Machines Corporation

SCREENSHOT 28.8   ANCOVA summary table

Pairwise Comparisons

Dependent Variable: Posttest

(I) Condition	(J) Condition	Mean Difference (I-J)	Std. Error	Sig.[b]	95% Confidence Interval for Difference[b]	
					Lower Bound	Upper Bound
Psychotherapy	Anti-depressant	-5.259[*]	1.782	.032	-9.840	-.678
	No treatment control	12.750	5.341	.063	-.979	26.479
Anti-depressant	Psychotherapy	5.259[*]	1.782	.032	.678	9.840
	No treatment control	18.009[*]	5.267	.019	4.471	31.547
No treatment control	Psychotherapy	-12.750	5.341	.063	-26.479	.979
	Anti-depressant	-18.009[*]	5.267	.019	-31.547	-4.471

Based on estimated marginal means

*. The mean difference is significant at the .05 level.

b. Adjustment for multiple comparisons: Least Significant Difference (equivalent to no adjustments).

Reprint Courtesy of International Business Machines Corporation, © International Business Machines Corporation

SCREENSHOT 28.9   LSD pairwise comparisons

Recommended further reading

Cramer, D. (2003). *Advanced quantitative data analysis* (Chapter 11). Buckingham, UK: Open University Press.

Glantz, S. A., & Slinker, B. K. (1990). *Primer of applied regression and analysis of variance.* New York, NY: McGraw-Hill.

CHAPTER 29

Multivariate analysis of variance (MANOVA)

Overview

- The multivariate analysis of variance (MANOVA) is very much like the analysis of variance (ANOVA). The big difference is that it involves several different dependent variables simultaneously. These dependent variables are all score variables. The independent variable is a category variable (or variables).

- There are versions of MANOVA which are equivalent to the various ANOVA designs covered in Chapters 23 to 25. Thus it is possible to have one-way MANOVAs, two-way and more (factorial) MANOVAs, and MANCOVAs in which the effects of one or more covariates can be removed from the data. Related designs are possible but beyond the scope of this book, as is MANCOVA.

- Essentially MANOVA combines the dependent variables to see whether the different groups (conditions) differ in terms of their 'means' on this combined set of dependent variables.

- A MANOVA summary table is produced which includes a multivariate test of significance. Commonly these include Pillai's trace, Wilks' lambda, Hotelling's trace and Roy's largest root. Computer software such as SPSS gives all of these making the output look a little complex.

- MANOVA may not be the ideal choice in circumstances in which the dependent variables are highly correlated and could be combined by totalling into a single score, for example, and used in ANOVA. In these circumstances, ANOVA may yield a slightly more powerful test.

- If MANOVA is significant, then this indicates that the groups in the study differ in terms of a combination(s) of the dependent variables. This leaves the researcher to examine the data in more detail by doing ANOVAs on the individual dependent variables or, much better, discriminant function analysis which will allow you to better know just how the dependent variables have been combined for the MANOVA. This is dealt with in Chapter 30.

- If MANOVA fails to reach statistical significance, then no further analyses are needed or are appropriate.

- Potential problems with MANOVA may be avoided by ensuring that each group (cell) are of equal size. Violating the assumptions of MANOVA becomes less problematic if you do.

Preparation

Revise Chapters 23 to 25 on analysis of variance (ANOVA). MANOVA adds little to this in terms of conceptual difficulty and so cannot be adequately carried out without understanding ANOVA which is also part of the MANOVA procedures.

29.1 Introduction

ANOVA looks for differences in group means on a single dependent variable. The dependent variable is always a score variable. MANOVA is essentially similar but examines the influence of the independent variable on a set of several dependent variables (all scores) simultaneously. As a very simple example, the research question may be whether a new drug, Therapazine supplement, affects motor skills in patients with Alzheimer's disease (see Table 29.1). Thus, at random, some patients are given Therapazine, others are given a placebo (inactive) pill and others are given nothing at all. Now there are

Table 29.1	Data table for a study of effects of Therapazine on motor skills										
Group (independent variable)											
Therapazine condition				**Placebo condition**				**No treatment condition**			
RT[a]	Sp	Hd	W	RT	Sp	Hd	W	RT	Sp	Hd	W
8[b]	5	7	7	1	3	2	2	4	3	5	4
7	7	6	5	4	5	3	3	1	2	3	6
9	8	5	9	7	2	1	2	3	5	2	6
7	5	8	8	2	5	6	1	1	4	6	2

[a] RT = reaction time, Sp = clarity of speech, Hd = steadiness of hand and W = writing speed. Scores are from four cases in each column.
[b] The scores are for the four dependent variables.

many different motor skills that the researcher might wish to assess in this study – for example, reaction time, clarity of speech, steadiness of the hand and writing speed. All of these motor skills seem related conceptually, at least, to the research question and it would seem somewhat short-sighted simply to select one. MANOVA allows the researcher to include a number of variables which may be affected by the drug treatment.

Better and clearer outcomes will be achieved in your analysis if you avoid the trap of throwing variables into the MANOVA simply because you can. Carefully selecting the dependent variables because they have a strong conceptual or theoretical bearing on the research question will yield dividends. For example, as the Alzheimer's research is about motor skills then adding in variables about social class or social networking to the list of dependent variables would add nothing to the MANOVA analysis.

Thus, MANOVA is simply an extension of the analysis of variance to cover circumstances where there are multiple dependent variables measured in the form of scores. In the analysis of variance (Chapters 23 to 27) we have seen that it is possible to analyse research designs with the following:

- Just one independent variable. This is known as a one-way analysis of variance. The independent variable is that which forms the different groups. (See Table 23.1 for an example.)

- Two or more independent variables. It would be possible to extend our Alzheimer's study to include more than one independent variable. So the next step might be to have a second independent variable. We previously referred to this design as a two-way ANOVA design. If we added a third grouping variable (independent variable) then this would be termed a three-way ANOVA design and so forth. These two-way, three-way and so forth designs are sometimes referred to as factorial designs, of course.

- Any of the above designs with additional covariates controlled for. So, for example, age of participants might be added as a covariate in the above designs. This is known as the analysis of covariance (ANCOVA) (Chapter 28).

MANOVA can deal with all three of the above types of design and more. If you have only two groups then Hotelling's two-sample t^2 may be appropriate (Box 29.1).

Box 29.1	Focus on

Hotelling's two sample t^2

You may have a very simple study with just two groups (e.g. experimental and control conditions) yet have several dependent variables which relate to your hypothesis. Such designs are usually analysed using the t-test (Chapter 14). There is a multivariate version of the t-test for research designs having just two groups of participants but several dependent variables. This is known as Hotelling's two sample t^2 (If you want to do this analysis, just remember it is the same as MANOVA, which reduces effectively to Hotelling's two sample t^2 if you just have two groups in your study. So simply follow the MANOVA procedures.) This is, of course, much the same as for the t-test and ANOVA.

There are two obvious questions to ask about MANOVA at this stage:

1. Just why would one wish to analyse several different dependent variables at the same time rather than do a number of separate ANOVAs?

2. Just how does one combine several dependent variables?

The answers to these questions are not simple or straightforward but are important things to understand:

- *Why not do several ANOVAs?* The answer to this question partly lies in the common comment in statistics that the more tests of significance one carries out then the more likely that significant findings emerge *by chance*. These do not represent real differences and, consequently, are not meaningful. So the more ANOVAs one does on one's data the more likely that a statistically significant finding will emerge. The consequence of multiple testing of this sort has been dealt with elsewhere when dealing with multiple comparisons (Chapter 26). But multiple testing can create other difficulties which do not at first appear to be statistical in nature. The purpose of research is not primarily to obtain significant findings but to provide an account or narrative or theoretical explanation which links together the findings of the researcher. Thus if the findings are not reliable then one may be trying to explain chance findings thinking that they are meaningful findings representing something happening in the real world.

- One obvious solution may strike you. Why not apply the Bonferroni adjustment (Section 26.3) to the significance levels of the ANOVAs carried out on each dependent variable? That is, adjust the probability levels to take into account the number of comparisons made. This is sensible thinking but not entirely satisfactory in this case because multiple significance testing is most problematic when the dependent variables correlate with each other poorly (or not at all). Where the dependent variables correlate highly then the risk of a spurious significant ANOVA is not so great. More technically, there is a risk of Type I errors (accepting the hypothesis when it is in fact false) which increases when the dependent variables do not correlate with each other beyond a minimal level. So the use of MANOVA can be thought of as a way of replacing several ANOVAs with one blanket test on a set of dependent variables. It thus protects against Type I errors.

- *How to combine dependent variables?* At first sight, the answer to this question seems self-evident if the scores are positively correlated – just add up the scores for each participant to give a total score. In this way, a single dependent variable is produced which can be entered into a regular ANOVA and thus eliminating the need for MANOVA. In some circumstances this would be a good way to proceed. However, doing something like this risks losing some of the information in your data. If this is not clear then imagine you ask your participants six questions, the answers to which are scored on a five-point Likert scale from strongly disagree to strongly agree. Then you give a score from 1 to 5 for each of the different points on the rating scales. Finally you add up each individual's scores to give a total score. Usually, information is lost from the data by doing so. So if someone scores 17 on the scale you simply do not know from that total what answers they gave. There are many possible ways of scoring 17 on the six questions. The total score does represent something, but it has lost some of the fine detail of the original replies. In much the same way, ANOVA carried out on the total of scores on the dependent variables also loses information.

This is not always a problem. It is a difficulty when more than one dimension underlies

variables show some high correlations but also some low correlations then probably more than one underlying dimension is involved. However, if the variables are all highly inter-correlated reflecting a single underlying dimension, totalling the scores and then subject-ing the resultant total scores to ANOVA may be extremely effective. It also has the advantage that there is no loss of degrees of freedom in the analysis – loss of degrees of freedom can be a problem in MANOVA, but this is dependent on the total picture of the analysis. What it is best to do is a judgement call, as is common in statistics.

On a sort of loss–gains analysis, if your dependent variables are highly correlated then more is lost than gained through the use of MANOVA. MANOVA is somewhat more abstract than ANOVA so perhaps best avoided if there is not a clear gain. It would also be legitimate to use just one dependent variable if it is highly intercorrelated with the other dependent variables. However, since psychological measures tend to be unreliable, one cannot generally expect extremely high intercorrelations between variables. Furthermore, there is no advantage of this over the summation approach of adding up the dependent variables to get a total score if the variables correlate highly.

29.2   MANOVA's two stages

Actually MANOVA is a two-stage process. These stages are usually separate. SPSS does have a method for doing MANOVA in the GLM procedures, but that only does half the job. In addition, you probably will need to carry out a discriminant function analysis which is a different SPSS procedure. Let us look at these two stages in turn.

■ Stage 1: MANOVA

In ANOVA the researcher wants to know whether the different groups defined by the independent variable(s) are associated with different mean scores on the dependent variable. This is generally discussed in terms of the sums of squares associated with the different group means compared with the estimated sums of squares due to error variance. The ratio between the sums of squares due to the different groups of participants and the sum of squares due to error provides the basis of the statistical significance testing using the F-ratio or something similar. We have illustrated the calculation of this from basics in previous chapters on ANOVA. This is a somewhat tedious and unnecessary process given that the work is better done by computers.

Much the same process is involved in MANOVA except that we have several dependent variables to examine at the same time. So the question is whether the various groups are different in terms of the means that they have on several dependent variables. Once again, these differences in means are turned into sums of squares. But there is a big problem in doing this for a MANOVA design. It is not merely that there are several dependent vari-ables, but also the several dependent variables may well be correlated with each other – that is, they measure, in part, the same thing. The analysis needs to make allowance for the extent to which the dependent variables are correlated. If it did not do so then the analysis would be claiming the same variance several times over. The extent of this depends on the size of the correlations between variables and the number of variables which cor-relate. Once the sums of squares associated with the different groups in the research design have been calculated, then multivariate tests of significance are computed and a signifi-cance level(s) provided. If the analysis is significant, then this shows that the groups of participants differ in terms of their scores over the set of dependent variables combined. It does not tell us which dependent variables are responsible for the differences. That is the job of the second stage.

Things are more complicated than this, of course. Life is never simple halfway through a statistics textbook. Like all tests of significance, MANOVA was subject to a set of assumptions by the person who developed the procedures. Parts of the computer output for MANOVA simply tell the user whether these assumptions have been met.

Stage 2: The relative importance of each dependent variable

From the MANOVA procedure, we know whether the groups in our research are different overall on the several dependent variables combined. That is the basic test of the hypothesis. Of course, if the multivariate test of significance in MANOVA is not significant, this basically is the end of the story. The researcher has drawn a blank in terms of their hypothesis and the null hypothesis is preferred over the alternative hypothesis. Even if we get a significant result from the multivariate test of significance, it is not clear what our analysis means since this tells us nothing as such about which groups vary and on what variables. We really need to understand something more about the pattern of variables on which the groups differ – that is, what combinations of variables tend to produce differences in group means?

A less than perfect but intuitively reasonable approach to this is to do a number of ANOVAs – one for each dependent variable. Hold on a minute, you may be thinking, didn't we decide at the start of the chapter that it was not a good idea to do this? The problem was the multitude of tests of significance being employed which is partly why MANOVA was opted for in the first place. But MANOVA gives us protection from Type I errors (accepting the hypothesis when it is in fact false) so we do not need to worry. If the MANOVA is not significant then the analysis is protected from the risk of Type I error simply because no further analyses are carried out on the individual dependent variables.

If the MANOVA is statistically significant, then this supposedly 'protects' the analysis from Type I errors and indicates that it is legitimate to do ANOVAs on each of the various dependent variables. In other words, a significant MANOVA puts a cap on the risk of finding a significant result by chance – that is, the Type I error. Unfortunately, this is just not adequate for a number of reasons. The main one is that often there is one variable which is affected by the independent variable and the rest of the dependent variables are not affected. In these circumstances, the significant MANOVA protects the affected dependent variable from Type I errors, but the other variables are not protected. So one of the ANOVAs would be protected but the rest not. Quite what will happen depends on the details of the data and analysis. Some textbooks still recommend doing this second stage analysis but there is an alternative approach, so you may choose that instead (unless your local statistical expert advises otherwise, in which case it would be politic to follow their advice).

Another problem with it is that even if you test each dependent variable separately, in the end you do not quite know what was affected by the independent variable(s). Although you could name the various significant dependent variables, this does not tell you what it is about the dependent variable which is affected. That is, what do the dependent variables have in common which produces the differences between the groups of participants?

Ideally, the problem of finding which dependent variables are influential on the findings is addressed through the use of discriminant function analysis (see Box 29.2 and Chapter 30). In this chapter, we will simply describe the MANOVA procedure followed up by ANOVAs.

29.3 Doing MANOVA

If you have mastered the basics of ANOVA then you may regard MANOVA, in its essence, as involving just a small step further. Ignoring discriminant function analysis for now, the major problem in implementing MANOVA lies in seeing the wood for the trees in the computer output. But by this stage, you have probably developed skill in dealing with SPSS output. MANOVA is essentially easy because the important new thing to understand is multivariate tests. These are analogous to the *F*-ratios (or Levene's test which is used by SPSS) familiar from ANOVA. Actually there are several multivariate tests which do much the same – they indicate whether your group 'means' are different on the set of dependent variables as a whole. These multivariate tests include Pillai's trace, Wilks' lambda, Hotelling's trace and Roy's largest root. You don't have to choose between them – SPSS computes them all for you. Figure 29.1 gives the key steps in understanding a MANOVA analysis.

Let's look at the research summarised in Table 29.2. This is basically a one-way ANOVA design in which we have a single independent variable – the group – but several dependent variables. So apart from having several dependent variables, this is much the same as the design in Chapter 23 for one-way ANOVA. The study investigates the efficiency of team-building sessions with a sports psychologist, team-building sessions with a sports coach or no team building. Participants were randomly assigned to these three different conditions. Gender is regarded as a second independent variable. There are equal numbers of male and female participants. If you can, it is best to have equal group sizes for MANOVA as it helps you to avoid problems (see later). Three dependent measures were used: 1) the difference between the liking ratings for the participant's favourite and least favourite team member which is believed to be a measure of team cohesion, 2) the number of voluntary gym sessions the player attends and 3) the number of games each player plays in a season.

The three dependent variables correlate at the levels indicated in Table 29.3. As can be seen, all three measures intercorrelate positively, but there is some considerable variation in the size of the correlations. This suggests that more than one dimension underlies these

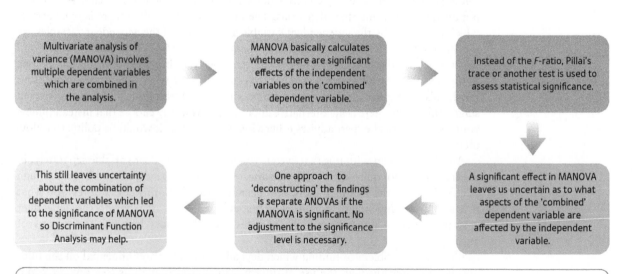

| Multivariate analysis of variance (MANOVA) involves multiple dependent variables which are combined in the analysis. | → | MANOVA basically calculates whether there are significant effects of the independent variables on the 'combined' dependent variable. | → | Instead of the *F*-ratio, Pillai's trace or another test is used to assess statistical significance. |

| This still leaves uncertainty about the combination of dependent variables which led to the significance of MANOVA so Discriminant Function Analysis may help. | ← | One approach to 'deconstructing' the findings is separate ANOVAs if the MANOVA is significant. No adjustment to the significance level is necessary. | ← | A significant effect in MANOVA leaves us uncertain as to what aspects of the 'combined' dependent variable are affected by the independent variable. |

FIGURE 29.1   Conceptual steps for understanding MANOVA

| Table 29.2 | Data for the MANOVA analysis |

Group (independent variable)								
Team building with sports psychologist Dependent variables			Team building with sports coach Dependent variables			No team building controls Dependent variables		
Like[a]	Gym	Game	Like	Gym	Game	Like	Gym	Game
9[b]	12	14	4	6	15	9	6	10
5	9	14	5	4	12	1	2	5
8	11	12	4	9	15	6	10	12
4	6	5	3	8	8	2	5	6
9	12	3	4	9	9	3	6	7
9	11	14	5	3	8	4	7	8
6	13	14	2	8	12	1	6	13
6	11	18	6	9	11	4	9	12
8	11	22	4	7	15	3	8	15
8	13	22	4	8	28	3	2	14
9	15	18	5	7	10	2	8	11
7	12	18	4	9	9	6	9	10
8	10	13	5	18	18	3	8	13
6	11	22	7	12	24	6	14	22

[a] Like = difference between ratings of most and least liked team members, Gym = number of gym sessions voluntarily attended and Game = number of games played.
[b] The scores are the scores on the three dependent variables.

variables – that is, the variables are measuring several things. The variables cannot convincingly be totalled in this case given the wide range in the size of the correlations. So a MANOVA analysis seems appropriate.

The MANOVA analysis of the data produces primarily a MANOVA summary table which is similar to the ANOVA summary table in Chapter 23. There are even values of the F-ratio much as in ANOVA. However, this is based on different calculations from ANOVA since it is applied to the multivariate test (e.g. Pillai's trace, Wilks' lambda,

| Table 29.3 | Correlations between the three dependent variables |

	Difference between ratings of most/least liked team members	Number of gym sessions voluntarily attended	Number of games played
Difference between ratings of most/least liked team members	–	.60	.30
Number of gym sessions voluntarily attended		–	.51
Number of games played			–

Table 29.4	Result of multivariate tests				
Effect	**Value**	**F**	**Hypothesis df**	**Error df**	**Sig.**
Intercept Pillai's trace	.94	184.71	3.00	37.00	.00
Group's Pillai's trace	.49	4.11	6.00	76.00	.00

Hotelling's trace and Roy's largest root). Pillai's trace is probably the one to rely on because it is more robust and less affected by the data not meeting its requirements. To keep the tables as simple as possible, we have confined our analysis to Pillai's trace only. In MANOVA you do not calculate the sums of squares but the value of Pillai's trace (and possibly the others). The MANOVA summary table (Table 29.4) gives the results of this analysis. Apart from that, you will find much the same statistics as for analysis of variance.

So it should be self-evident from Table 29.4 that we have a significant effect of group (type of team building). Generally speaking, Pillai's trace gives much the same outcome as Wilks' lambda, Hotelling's trace and Roy's largest root. It does not much matter which you choose – and, of course, you can use all four if you so wish though this will clutter your report to no advantage. If you do not get any significant findings then this is the end of MANOVA – your hypothesis has been rejected.

Of course, if you have significant findings, then you need to know what they indicate. There are several steps in order to do this.

Step 1

The simplest interpretation would be to conclude that there are differences on the composite of the three dependent variables related to the independent variables (groups). This may be sufficient to confirm the hypothesis. In our particular example, there are differences in the 'means' of the composite of the three dependent variables due to the independent variable group (condition).

Step 2

In order to have a better understanding of more precisely what is going on in the data, you need the corresponding univariate ANOVAs to the MANOVA. SPSS gives you these as part of the basic output from MANOVA. An example is given in Table 29.5. As you can see, there is an ANOVA for each dependent variable. It may look confusing at first, but by taking one dependent variable at a time a basic understanding of one-way ANOVA will suffice. What seems clear from Table 29.5 is that two of the three dependent variables show virtually identical significant patterns. That is, the summary table shows that the two main effects for 1) difference between ratings of most and least liked team members and 2) number of gym sessions voluntarily attended are significant. The third dependent variable, number of games played, does not reach significance. This would suggest that the significant MANOVA is largely the result of the first two variables rather than the third variable. But it should be noted that you may obtain a significant MANOVA yet none of the ANOVAs is statistically significant. This means exactly what it says, but you also need to realise that a linear combination of the dependent variables is related to group

Table 29.5	Part of a table of the individual ANOVAs for the three dependent variables				
Dependent variable	Sum of squares	Degrees of freedom	Mean square	F-ratio	Significance
Number of games played	98.14	2	49.07	1.67	0.20
Difference between ratings of most liked and least liked team members	97.19	2	48.60	15.71	0.00
Number of gym sessions voluntarily attended	122.33	2	61.16	6.86	0.03

membership despite the fact that individually the dependent variables may fail to be related to group membership. Using these methods, you do not know much about that linear combination of variables. Discriminant function analysis would help you with this (see Chapter 30 and Box 29.2).

(see Chapter 30 and Box 29.2).

Box 29.2 Focus on

Discriminant function analysis and MANOVA

In the present chapter, we have concentrated on the very basics of MANOVA. A significant MANOVA means that the groups defined by your independent variable are different in terms of the composite of the dependent variables you have used. The next question is just what aspects of the dependent variable(s) are responsible for the significant MANOVA. The approach used in the present chapter is to do a number of ANOVA analyses for the different dependent variables. This tells you if the means for your groups are different for any of the dependent variables. The trouble with this is that one is left somewhat unclear about the nature of the underlying combination variable derived from the several dependent variables.

An improvement in understanding can be achieved using discriminant function analysis (which is covered in detail in Chapter 30). This analysis helps you to understand how your dependent variables were combined to give the significant MANOVA. These combinations of variables are known as discriminant functions. In other words, the analysis creates artificial variables which it

derives from one or more of the original dependent variables. This is usually done on a computer program such as SPSS as the calculations are tedious to do by hand – and you would be ill-advised to spend time doing so with the attendant risk of computational errors. There is one centroid (which is a sort of mean score) for each group of participants on each of the discriminant functions. Discriminant functions are obviously abstractions from the original dependent variables and, as such, they cannot be expected to be as clear initially as the variables that you included in the set of dependent variables. Interpretation is involved and using your intelligence, insight, and other thinking skills may be unexpected to those who wish to believe that statistics is a purely mechanical process.

There can be several discriminant functions based on a set of dependent variables as already indicated. If there is just one dependent variable, as in ANOVA, then there is just one discriminant function which is the same as that single dependent variable. With two dependent variables there can be two discriminant functions and so forth. The

→

number of discriminant functions is the smaller number of the number of dependent variables or one less than the number of groups. Each discriminant function that emerges in an analysis is unrelated to the other discriminant functions that emerge. That is, discriminant functions do not correlate with each other.

The term discriminant function seems odd at first, but it means just what it says on the label. It is a mathematical equation (function) which discriminates things. What does it discriminate? Well, it is the mathematical function of the dependent variables which best discriminate between the different groups (i.e. levels of the independent variable). Basically the calculation (computer) works out the pattern of weights to give to each of the dependent variables in order to produce the maximum discrimination between the various groups on the discriminant function. Of course, there are many different possible discriminant functions since it is basically a pattern of weights to apply to the different dependent variables, but only one function will give the greatest degree of discrimination between the different groups. In other words, discriminant function analysis produces a new measure (function) which maximises the difference between the groupings of participants on that measure (function).

As indicated, there may be several discriminant functions. The first discriminant function essentially emerges from the original data whereas the second discriminant function is calculated on the data after the first discriminant function has been taken into account. The third discriminant function is calculated from the data after the first and second discriminant functions have been removed.

There is a conceptual problem when we move from MANOVA to discriminant function analysis. In MANOVA we tend to speak of the scores as being the dependent variable and the variable on which the groups differ is the independent variable. Well, discriminant function analysis, like the various forms of regression, works the other way round. In this case, the score variables become the independent variables and the dependent variable is the variable on which the different groups are categorised. Yes, this is confusing, but if you concentrate on the nature of the variable in question (category variable or score) then Chapter 30 should be straightforward.

■ Step 3

A table of estimated marginal means is helpful at this stage. SPSS generates separate tables for each of the main effects and each interaction. In the present case, we have reproduced only the estimated marginal means for the significant main effect (the team building variable). This can be seen in Table 29.6. It is clear from this that scores on each of the first two dependent variables are lowest for the control, second highest for team building by a coach, and highest for team building by the psychologist. It is not immediately obvious which of the three dependent variables best discriminates the three conditions.

Table 29.6	Estimated marginal means for groups on each dependent variable		
	Difference between ratings of most and least liked team members	Number of gym sessions voluntarily attended	Number of games played
Teamwork training by sports psychologist	7.29	11.21	14.93
Teamwork training by coach	4.43	8.36	13.86
Control – no teamwork training	3.79	7.14	11.29

Table 29.7	Box's M test for covariance homogeneity (equality)
Box's M	18.70
F	1.38
df_1	12
df_2	7371
Significance	0.17

Remember that this is a down-to-basics account of MANOVA. We do not pretend that it offers the most sophisticated approach. You might wish, especially, to check whether your data actually meet the requirements of MANOVA in terms of the characteristics of the data. One quite important thing is the Box's test of equality of the covariance matrix. We don't need to know too much about this test, but we do need to know what to do if the test is statistically significant. The Box's test is illustrated in Table 29.7. If it yields a significant value (as it does in our case), this means that the covariances are not similar, which violates one of the assumptions on which MANOVA was built. This can affect the probability levels obtained in the MANOVA. However, this is crucial only if the MANOVA significance levels just reach the .05 level of significance. If your MANOVA findings are very significant then there is not a great problem. You should not worry if the different cells (groupings) of your MANOVA have equal sample sizes as violating the requirements of the MANOVA makes no practical difference to the significance level in this case. If you have very different sample sizes and your findings are close to the boundary between statistical significance and statistical non-significance, then you should worry more – one solution is to equate the sample sizes by randomly dropping cases from cells as necessary. But this could have as much effect on your findings as violating the equal covariances principle anyway. So bear this in mind when designing your MANOVA.

29.4 Reporting your findings

If your MANOVA was not significant, you could write the following, after the APA (2010) Publication Manual's recommendations: 'MANOVA was used to test the hypothesis that team work training had an effect on sporting behaviours, but the null hypothesis was supported, Pillai's $F(6, 76) = 1.08$, p ns.'

However, since the findings were significant, you could write: 'MANOVA showed that teamwork training was effective in improving sporting behaviours, Pillai's $F(6, 76) = 4.11$, $p < .01$. The individual dependent variables were subject to ANOVAs in order to assess whether the three dependent variables showed the same trend. For the measure of the difference between favourite and least favourite team member measure it was found that the psychologist teamwork sessions ($M = 7.29$) were superior to the coach team work sessions ($M = 4.43$) and the control condition ($M = 3.79$), $F(2, 39) = 15.71$, $p < .01$. The mean number of gym sessions attended was higher for the psychologist ($M = 11.21$) than the coach ($M = 8.36$) and control ($M = 7.14$), $F(2, 39) = 6.86$, $p < .05$.' The value of Pillai's F was obtained from Screenshot 29.5.

Research examples

MANOVA

Guzman and Kingston (2012) studied sport dropout. At one point in time, variables believed to be predictors of sport dropout were measured and whether the individual had persisted with the sport or dropped out was assessed after 19 months. The participants were 857 young athletes with a mean age of around 15 years. Part of the study involved a MANOVA analysis. The design was dropout or persistence × male or female × age (three categories). The several dependent variables analysed at the same time were psychological need satisfaction from sport, intention to practise sport, perceived conflict between sport and study, and the self-determination index. Drop-out was related to these dependent variables in MANOVA as was age. There were no interaction effects.

Lowe and Ang (2012) were interested in the experience of test anxiety (fear of evaluation) in elementary students in the USA and Singapore. Culture and gender were the independent variables, making this a 2 × 2 design. MANOVA was used for the statistical analysis because several dependent variables were employed – physiological hyperarousal, social concerns, task-irrelevant behaviour and worry. The MANOVA (and additional regular ANOVAs) showed that Singapore males had more test anxiety than US males whereas the US females scored more highly than the Singapore females on the overall test anxiety scale and the physiological hyperarousal subscale. Singapore males had higher anxiety on the Worry subscale.

Casidy (2012) chose to examine differences in the personality of consumers which were related to the variables of a) fashion consciousness – which is the individual's involvement in fashionable dressing and so forth and b) prestige sensitivity – preference for the high-priced, higher-quality, designer clothes. The data were collected from undergraduate students using self-completion questionnaires. She included items from what she calls the big five scales used to measure consumer personality in the literature. Using cluster analysis, she found four clusters of highly related items in the responses of the students to these items. These clusters she identified as 'openness to experience, extraversion, agreeableness and consciousness'. The data were analysed using MANOVA. The independent variables in this study were each of the personality clusters. The multiple dependent variables were fashion consciousness and prestige sensitivity. There were personality differences in terms of the prestige sensitivity/fashion consciousness dependent variable.

Key points

- MANOVA basically deals with a very simple problem – the risk of falsely accepting a hypothesis because you have carried out multiple tests of significance.

- Try to avoid an unfocused approach to MANOVA. It is *not* a particularly useful technique for sorting out what to do with numerous dependent variables that you have measured merely because you could.

- MANOVA is not appropriate if all of your dependent variables are highly intercorrelated. It may be better in these circumstances to combine the dependent variables to give a total score which is then analysed using ANOVA, for example.

- A complete MANOVA would preferably involve a discriminant function analysis. This is described in Chapter 30.

COMPUTER ANALYSIS

Multivariate analysis of variance using SPSS

Data
- Name the variables in 'Variable View' of the 'Data Editor'.
- Enter the data under the appropriate variable names in 'Data View' of the 'Data Editor' (Screenshot 29.1).

Analysis
- Select 'Analyze', 'General Linear Model' and 'Multivariate...' (Screenshot 29.2).
- Move the dependent variables to the 'Dependent Variables:' box and the independent variable(s) to the 'Fixed Factor(s):' box (Screenshot 29.3).

2
- Select 'Options...' and move the independent variable to the 'Display Means for:' box (Screenshot 29.4).

3
- Select 'Descriptive statistics', 'Estimates of effect size', 'Continue' and 'OK'.

Output
- Check in the 'Multivariate Tests' table if Pillai's *F* for the independent variable is significant with a Sig(nificance) of .05 or less (Screenshot 29.5).

2
- If it is significant, check in the 'Tests of Between-Subjects Effects' table which of the dependent variables the independent variable has a significant effect on with a Sig(nificance) of .05 or less (Screenshot 29.5).

3
- If there are more than 2 groups use further tests to determine which means differ significantly from each other.

FIGURE 29.2   SPSS steps for MANOVA

Interpreting and reporting the output

- A number of different multivariate tests are given in the Multivariate Tests output. Pillai's trace is as good as any for most purposes. For the Tests for Between-Subjects Effects output you only need to concentrate on the row for Group in this example.

- You could write: 'MANOVA showed that teamwork training was effective in improving sporting behaviours, Pillai's $F(6, 76) = 4.11, p < .01, \eta_p^2 = .25$'

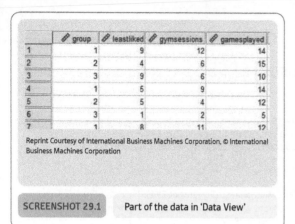

Reprint Courtesy of International Business Machines Corporation, © International Business Machines Corporation

SCREENSHOT 29.1 Part of the data in 'Data View'

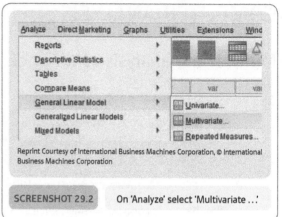

Reprint Courtesy of International Business Machines Corporation, © International Business Machines Corporation

SCREENSHOT 29.2 On 'Analyze' select 'Multivariate . . .'

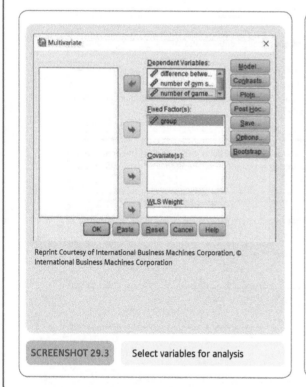

Reprint Courtesy of International Business Machines Corporation, © International Business Machines Corporation

SCREENSHOT 29.3 Select variables for analysis

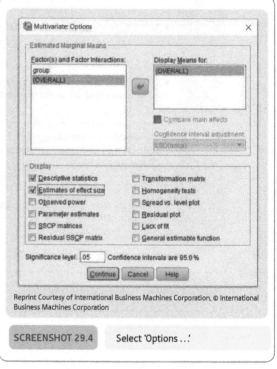

Reprint Courtesy of International Business Machines Corporation, © International Business Machines Corporation

SCREENSHOT 29.4 Select 'Options . . .'

Multivariate Tests[a]

Effect		Value	F	Hypothesis df	Error df	Sig.	Partial Eta Squared
Intercept	Pillai's Trace	.937	184.710[b]	3.000	37.000	.000	.937
	Wilks' Lambda	.063	184.710[b]	3.000	37.000	.000	.937
	Hotelling's Trace	14.976	184.710[b]	3.000	37.000	.000	.937
	Roy's Largest Root	14.976	184.710[b]	3.000	37.000	.000	.937
group	Pillai's Trace	.490	4.109	6.000	76.000	.001	.245
	Wilks' Lambda	.522	4.733[b]	6.000	74.000	.000	.277
	Hotelling's Trace	.892	5.349	6.000	72.000	.000	.308
	Roy's Largest Root	.865	10.953[c]	3.000	38.000	.000	.464

a. Design: Intercept + group

b. Exact statistic

c. The statistic is an upper bound on F that yields a lower bound on the significance level.

Tests of Between-Subjects Effects

Source	Dependent Variable	Type III Sum of Squares	df	Mean Square	F	Sig.	Partial Eta Squared
Corrected Model	difference between ratings of most and least liked team members	97.190[a]	2	48.595	15.709	.000	.446
	number of gym sessions voluntarily attended	122.333[b]	2	61.167	6.869	.003	.260
	number of games played	98.143[c]	2	49.071	1.668	.202	.079
Intercept	difference between ratings of most and least liked team members	1121.167	1	1121.167	362.438	.000	.903
	number of gym sessions voluntarily attended	3330.381	1	3330.381	374.000	.000	.906
	number of games played	7493.357	1	7493.357	254.676	.000	.867
group	difference between ratings of most and least liked team members	97.190	2	48.595	15.709	.000	.446
	number of gym sessions voluntarily attended	122.333	2	61.167	6.869	.003	.260
	number of games played	98.143	2	49.071	1.668	.202	.079
Error	difference between ratings of most and least liked team members	120.643	39	3.093			
	number of gym sessions voluntarily attended	347.286	39	8.905			
	number of games played	1147.500	39	29.423			
Total	difference between ratings of most and least liked team members	1339.000	42				
	number of gym sessions voluntarily attended	3800.000	42				
	number of games played	8739.000	42				
Corrected Total	difference between ratings of most and least liked team members	217.833	41				
	number of gym sessions voluntarily attended	469.619	41				
	number of games played	1245.643	41				

a. R Squared = .446 (Adjusted R Squared = .418)

b. R Squared = .260 (Adjusted R Squared = .223)

c. R Squared = .079 (Adjusted R Squared = .032)

SCREENSHOT 29.5   Important output

Recommended further reading

Diekhoff, G. (1992). *Statistics for the social and behavioral sciences* (Chapter 15). Dubuque, IL: Wm. C. Brown.

Hair, J. F., Jr, Anderson, R. E., Tatham, R. L., & Black, W. C. (2018). *Multivariate data analysis* (8th ed., Chapter 6). Upper Saddle River, NJ: Pearson Prentice Hall.

MA: Allyn & Bacon.

CHAPTER 30

Discriminant (function) analysis – especially in MANOVA

Overview

- Discriminant function analysis uses a set of score variables to assess the extent to which they are associated with the different groups in a study. Is it possible to discriminate between groupings of participants (conditions) on the basis of a set of independent variables?

- It is similar to logistic regression (Chapters 41 and 42) in terms of what it does, though it cannot use category variables as predictor variables and is based on more restrictive assumptions.

- The main use of discriminant function analysis is when a significant MANOVA is obtained (Chapter 29).

- A discriminant function is a variable derived from a set of variables which maximises the differences between the groups. It computes a set of weights which are applied to each variable in the set of score variables. More than one discriminant function may emerge.

- It is important to avoid extremely highly correlated variables since this creates high collinearity which distorts the analysis, putting the meaning of the findings in doubt. If two variables highly correlate then one could be omitted from the analysis (it contains no different information from the other variable with which it correlates highly). To check, repeat this analysis but using the previously omitted variable instead then compare the outcomes.

- Discriminant function analysis can classify participants into groups on the basis of their 'scores' on the discriminant functions. This classification can then be compared with the group that the participants actually belong to.

- Discriminant function analysis has concepts which are new – especially those of centroids and canonical correlation. But a centroid is nothing more than the mean of a group on a discriminant function (which is just a special sort of variable) and canonical correlation is just a single correlation coefficient but between one set of variables and another set.

Preparation

Read Chapter 29 on MANOVA, but understanding something about regression (Chapters 9 and 34) and especially logistic regression (Chapters 41 and 42) will be beneficial.

30.1 Introduction

Discriminant function analysis once did the job for which logistic regression is now the preferred technique. For most purposes, logistic regression is preferable since its underlying basic assumptions are less demanding (restricting). Both techniques tell the researcher whether different groups of participants (categories of the dependent variable) can be accurately classified on the basis of a number of other variables (the independent variables) in combination. For discriminant function analysis, these independent variables must be scores (logistic regression can handle nominal or category variables in addition). The main (perhaps only) reason why discriminant function analysis is included in this textbook is its role in MANOVA (see Chapter 29). In many ways, discriminant function analysis and MANOVA are built on the same basic mathematical calculations. Consequently, it is not surprising that when MANOVA cannot answer a particular question, discriminant function analysis is used to fill in the information gap. Apart from that, we would not recommend its use. In relation to MANOVA, discriminant function analysis indicates the combination of variables which best differentiates between the various groups of participants. In doing so, the researcher's task is to understand what each discriminant function represents. This is done by focusing on the variables which correlate best with the discriminant function. In this regard, it is a little like factor analysis (Chapter 33).

Table 30.1 illustrates a study for which discriminant function analysis is appropriate. It deals with three drug conditions (including one no-treatment control). Much the same

Table 30.1	Data table for a study of effects of Tritherop on motor skills											
Group (dependent variable)												
Tritherop condition Independent variables				**Placebo condition Independent variables**				**No-treatment condition Independent variables**			
RT[a]	Sp	Hd	W	RT	Sp	Hd	W	RT	Sp	Hd	W
8[b]	5	7	7	1	3	2	2	4	3	5	4
7	7	6	5	4	5	3	3	1	2	3	6
9	8	5	9	7	2	1	2	3	5	2	6
7	5	8	8	2	5	6	1	1	4	6	2

[a] RT = Reaction time, Sp = clarity of speech, Hd = steadiness of hand and W = writing speed. Scores are from four cases in each column.
[b] The scores are for the four independent variables.

data were previously discussed in Chapter 29 on MANOVA, though notice that we have reversed the labelling of the independent variable and the dependent variables. There are four independent variables (reaction time, clarity of speech, steadiness of hand and writing speed). The dependent variable is the drug condition. The research question is basically what pattern or combination of the independent variables best classifies individuals into the actual group to which they belong. That is, can we predict actual group membership accurately on the basis of each participant's scores on the independent variables?

Some authorities describe discriminant function analysis as the reverse of MANOVA. This is a reasonable description, especially since the independent and dependent variables are reversed between MANOVA and discriminant function analysis. In MANOVA, the categories of the independent variable become the dependent variable in discriminant function analysis. The dependent variables (the score variables) in MANOVA become the independent variables in discriminant function analysis. ANOVA and multiple regression are strongly related – indeed many calculations of ANOVA use regression techniques. The strongest indication of that is the use of the term intercept (from regression) in some ANOVA analyses. Remember that also there is also a very strong relationship between MANOVA and discriminant function analysis.

Of course, what is really confusing is the use of the terms independent and dependent variables, which should not be taken to indicate that one thing causes the other. Predictor and criterion variables are another way of saying the same thing less misleadingly.

No matter, in discriminant function analysis the independent variables are the score variables whereas the dependent variable consists of the different groups of participants. So essentially in discriminant function analysis we are trying to predict which group of participants individuals belong to on the basis of a number of predictor variables. Another way of saying exactly the same thing is to suggest that discriminant function analysis seeks to find whether the different groups of participants vary in terms of their means on the independent variables. This is often expressed in terms of the means of each group on the discriminant functions. These means are called centroids. Though this sounds like a radically new concept, picture them as being merely the group mean on a discriminant function.

One thing is vital to understand. A discriminant function is basically a way of totalling or combining the scores on the independent variables. Instead of adding the scores on variables A, B, C and D as follows:

$$A + B + C + D, \text{etc.}$$

in discriminant function analysis, each score variable is given a different weight (w) so that the formula for the discriminant function is:

$$w_1A + w_2B + w_3C + w_4D, \text{etc.}$$

This is little different from the formula for multiple regression (Chapter 34), though a constant has been omitted from the above for clarity. The weights calculated ensure that the discriminant function is the one which best distinguishes between the various groups of participants. Only one discriminant function can meet this criterion. One could think of the discriminant function as simply a variable based on a weighted combination of other variables, just as factors in factor analysis are variables (see Chapter 33). Just remember that this combination variable is the one that maximises differences between the groups (conditions) in the study then you cannot go far wrong.

There can be several discriminant functions calculated for any set of data. The first discriminant function maximises the differences between the groups of participants (on that discriminant function). In other words, the discriminant function is the weighted combination of the predictor variables that maximises the difference between the groups of participants (i.e. conditions of the study). Thus it is the function (weighted combination of variables) that best discriminates the groups in the study. There may remain important variation in the data after this has been done. So a second discriminant function may sometimes be calculated based on the original data minus variation due to the first discriminant function. The process can continue to produce further discriminant functions depending on the number of groups to differentiate and the number of predictor variables (score variables). The discriminant functions are unrelated to each other – that is to say, they are independent of each other or orthogonal. Basically this means that discriminant functions from an analysis do not correlate.

Actually, discriminant function analysis does not handle more than one dependent variable at a time. This is no great problem as the main effects from the MANOVA can be dealt with one at a time (the main effects of MANOVA are independent of each other).

It is important, so as not to be flustered when you come across new terminology, to know that discriminant function analysis works largely using *canonical correlations*. These are similar to multiple correlations (see Chapter 34) which are the correlation of several variables with one other variable. Canonical correlation is the correlation of a set of several variables with another set of several variables. In discriminant function analysis there are several independent variables and also several dependent variables since there are usually several different groups. Don't worry. We have read claims that canonical analysis has the dubious distinction of being the hardest multivariate concept to understand. Actually, apart from knowing that there is such a thing as canonical correlations, there is not a great deal more that you need to know about the computer output for discriminant function analysis that you probably don't know already from other parts of this book.

There is a limit to the number of discriminant functions that can be produced for any set of data. The number of groups being discriminated minus 1 is one criterion and the number of (score) variables in the analysis is the other criterion. Whichever is the smaller of the two is the maximum number of discriminant functions.

30.2 Doing the discriminant function analysis

Table 30.2 gives the discriminant function analysis version of the data that we used in Chapter 29 to illustrate the steps in a MANOVA analysis. Chapter 29 left the MANOVA analysis incomplete since it lacked a discriminant function analysis, which adds to our ability to understand what is happening in our data. In the following discussion we concentrate solely on using discriminant function analysis to identify group membership in terms of team-building procedures. We know from MANOVA (Chapter 29) that we have a significant effect of the teamwork condition on the scores on the set of three dependent variables. In the MANOVA chapter, the fact that we had found a significant MANOVA freed us to do several ANOVAs to see which of the dependent variables (score variables) were influenced by the particular group to which participants belonged. We found that teamwork training did not seem to have an influence on the number of games played, but it did have an influence on the other two dependent variables. In other words, we already know quite a bit from the MANOVA. This is important now we are moving on a discriminant function analysis. And don't forget that when we say independent variable in discriminant function analysis we would call it a dependent variable in MANOVA and vice versa. So the group variable is labelled the dependent variable in Table 30.2 and the independent variables are the scores. Figure 30.1 gives the key steps in discriminant function analysis.

■ Step 1

Before we start a discriminant function analysis, one warning must be repeated. Avoid highly correlated score variables because of the problem of collinearity (discussed in Chapter 34). Correlations of the order of maybe .7 and above could be a problem.

Table 30.2	Data for the discriminant function analysis

Group (dependent variable)								
Team building with sports psychologist Independent variables			Team building with sports coach Independent variables			No team building controls Independent variables		
Like[a]	Gym	Game	Like	Gym	Game	Like	Gym	Game
9[b]	12	14	4	6	15	9	6	10
5	9	14	5	4	12	1	2	5
8	11	12	4	9	15	6	10	12
4	6	5	3	8	8	2	5	6
9	12	3	4	9	9	3	6	7
9	11	14	5	3	8	4	7	8
6	13	14	2	8	12	1	6	13
6	11	18	6	9	11	4	9	12
8	11	22	4	7	15	3	8	15
8	13	22	4	8	28	3	2	14
9	15	18	5	7	10	2	8	11
7	12	18	4	9	9	6	9	10
8	10	13	5	18	18	3	8	13
6	11	22	7	12	24	6	14	22

[a] Like = difference between ratings of most and least liked team members, Gym = number of gym sessions voluntarily attended and Game = number of games played.
[b] The scores are the scores on the three independent variables.

Compute the correlations between all of the score variables for such high correlations. The score variables are the independent or predictor variables in discriminant function analysis. What can be done if there are high correlations and, thus, potentially collinearity problems? High correlations between variables means that they are measuring more or

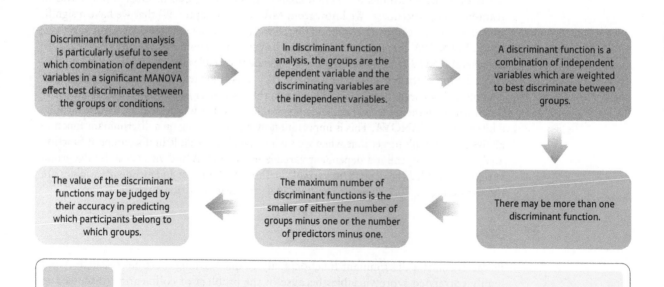

| Discriminant function analysis is particularly useful to see which combination of dependent variables in a significant MANOVA effect best discriminates between the groups or conditions. | In discriminant function analysis, the groups are the dependent variable and the discriminating variables are the independent variables. | A discriminant function is a combination of independent variables which are weighted to best discriminate between groups. |
| The value of the discriminant functions may be judged by their accuracy in predicting which participants belong to which groups. | The maximum number of discriminant functions is the smaller of either the number of groups minus one or the number of predictors minus one. | There may be more than one discriminant function. |

less the same thing. So one could reasonably do the discriminant function analysis of one of the two highly correlated variables and any others you find. This makes sense as the two variables are virtually the same so omitting does not really handicap the analysis. For your own peace of mind, you could repeat the analysis reinstating the omitted variables by leaving out the variables which correlated highly with them. Almost certainly, the two analyses would be virtually identical save for the variable names involved.

Step 2

Having run your data through SPSS or some other program which does discriminant function analysis, the next thing to do is to look for the eigenvalues in the output. Note that for our example, the maximum number of discriminant functions possible is the number of groups -1 which is $3 - 1$, which is 2 discriminant functions. (The number of variables is the other formula but this is bigger than 2 in this case, so it is ignored.) The first discriminant function is the most discriminating between the groups and the later discriminant functions are the most discriminating *after* the earlier discriminant functions have been removed from the data. Table 30.3 gives the characteristic eigenvalue information that is provided. For discriminant function 1, we can see that the eigenvalue is 0.87. This is indicative of the amount of variation in the data which is accounted for by the first discriminant function. Looking at the column for % of variance, this corresponds to 97% of the total variance. This is not the total of the variance in the data but the total of the variance *explained* by the discriminant functions. It is, in other words, the reliable variance explained and excludes error variance. Thus in this example the total of the two eigenvalues is $0.87 + 0.03 = 0.90$. Thus the proportion of variance explained $=$ $0.87 \div 0.90$, which equals .97; expressed as a percentage this becomes the figure of 97% of the total variance explained in the penultimate column in Table 30.3. Don't be misled into thinking that the research has identified a weighted set of variables (the discriminant function) which explains 97% of the variation in the data. That would be phenomenal. What it means is that the researcher has found a discriminant function that explains the reliable variance (i.e. with error variance ignored), which is much less impressive.

Table 30.3	Eigenvalues and variance explained by each discriminant function		
Function	**Eigenvalue**	**% of variance**	**Canonical correlation**
Discriminant function 1	0.87	97	.68
Discriminant function 2	0.03	3	.16

Also notice that a cumulative % of variance explained figure is given. Since the maximum number of discriminant functions possible is two where one has three groups, then it is hardly surprising that those two discriminant functions account for all of the variation that could be accounted for by the discriminant functions. It is all the reliable variance that can be explained. The final column in Table 30.3 gives the canonical correlation for the first discriminant function as being .68. If you interpret this much as you would do any correlation, it is clear that it is quite a substantial correlation and indicative of a strong relationship between the predictor (score) variables and the groups of participants. In contrast, the second discriminant function not only explains very little of the variance but the canonical correlation is fairly low at .16. Again, if this were an ordinary correlation coefficient we would regard the value as fairly low. This is exactly the same for the canonical correlation. So we are left with the impression that there is one substantial discriminant function and a rather unsubstantial second discriminant function for these data.

■ Step 3

A crucial part of the analysis is the information on Wilks' lambda (Table 30.4). The table can be a little confusing at first. What the analysis basically does is to indicate whether or not your discriminant function analysis is statistically significant. It does so by first of all giving the significance of all of your discriminant functions together. So where you see in the first column 1 through 2 this includes all of the discriminant functions in the analysis. For our example, the maximum is 2, so that row reads 1 through 2. If we had four groups then this would read 1 through 3 because 3 is the maximum number of discriminant functions with four groups (see above). The next row in our example reads just 2. This is the test for the second discriminant function *alone*. So, as we can see, discriminant functions 1 and 2 together are very significant at 0.00, but discriminant function 2 on its own is not significant. Of course, this means that the discriminant functions do not individually have to be statistically significant in order that you have a significant discriminant function analysis overall. The table for Wilks' lambda becomes more complex with increasing numbers of discriminant functions. But, despite this, the key is the first row in the table since if that is not significant then you need proceed no further in examining the output. (You probably would not have done the discriminant function analysis anyway since the MANOVA that you probably computed previously would have already indicated a lack of significance in the data.)

If the Wilks' lambda is statistically significant then this indicates that the means (centroids) of the different groups on the discriminant function(s) are statistically different. The value of lambda can range from 0 to 1. It is the amount of variation in the discriminant function which cannot be accounted for by the different groups (conditions). The value of lambda will increase as you go down the column for lambda since the discriminant functions lower down the list involve variance which cannot be explained by differences between the groups in the analysis. We know that already, since they are the discriminant functions which are poorest at differentiating the groups in the analysis.

Table 30.4	Values of Wilks' lambda			
Test of function(s)	**Wilks' lambda**	**Chi-square**	*df*	**Sig.**
Discriminant functions 1 through 2	.52	24.69	6	.00
Discriminant function 2	.97	1.01	2	.61

■ Step 4

The main point of doing the discriminant function analysis following MANOVA is to understand which of your predictor (independent) variables are associated with the discriminant functions that have been calculated. In other words, just what weights are given to the predictor variables in calculating each of the discriminant functions? Merely knowing the weights as such is not very helpful since the weights depend on the exact scale and range of scores on each variable. These may be different for each of your predictor variables, so it is better to have a standardised version of the weights (coefficients) as this then allows meaningful comparison. These standardised weights can be seen in Table 30.5.

Table 30.5	Standardised coefficients for the different discriminant functions	
Group (condition)	**Function**	
	Discriminant function 1	Discriminant function 2
Difference between ratings of most and least liked team members	.85	−.31
Number of gym sessions voluntarily attended	.30	.05
Number of games played	−.04	1.00

The big weights given to the first discriminant function are for 'difference between ratings of most and least liked team members' (.85). The number of gym sessions voluntarily attended has a smaller *relative* weight (.30). It is also notable that 'number of games played' has a near zero weight (−.04). Thus, the first discriminant function is most clearly identified with the variable concerning the most and least favourite team member, though there is also a component of the discriminant function which is associated with the voluntary attendance at gym session. The second discriminant function, which we already have seen is in itself not statistically significant, has its major weighting solely for number of games played.

Alternatively, we could look at the correlations between the predictor variables and the standardised discriminant functions (the structure matrix). Although the values of the correlations in Table 30.6 naturally differ from the weights shown in Table 30.5, the direction of the results is similar. The variable that is most highly correlated with the first standardised discriminant function in Table 30.6 is the difference between the most and least liked team members (.97). This variable also has the largest weight (.85) on the first standardised discriminant function in Table 30.5. The variable that is most highly correlated with the second discriminant function in Table 30.6 is the number of games played (.96). This variable also has the greatest weight (1.00) on the second discriminant function in Table 30.5.

So the picture seems to be that the first discriminant function consists largely of 'difference between ratings of most and least liked team members' with a smaller contribution from 'number of gym sessions voluntarily attended'. The second discriminant function is the 'number of games played', though it is fairly clear by now that this function is unimportant relative to the first discriminant function and non-significant statistically.

Although this interpretation makes sense and fits the statistical analysis, it has to be said that the discriminant function analysis does not shed a great deal of light on the

Table 30.6	Structure matrix of the correlation of the predictors and the standardised discriminant functions	
Group (condition)	**Discriminant function 1**	**Discriminant function 2**
Difference between ratings of most and least liked team member	.97	.09
Number of gym sessions voluntarily attended	.64	.38
Number of games played	.27	.96

combination of predictor variables which best discriminate between the groups. It is not like, say, exploratory factor analysis (Chapter 33) which can unveil patterns which are meaningful and informative. This is partly because that is not really the job of discriminant function analysis. More light may be shed if you have more variables than in this case. However, if you have many variables (such as where you have administered a lengthy questionnaire) then it would be wise to subject this questionnaire to factor analysis initially rather than throw all of the variables into a discriminant function analysis.

Step 5

Since the discriminant scores are variables of a special sort, it is useful to examine the mean 'scores' for each discriminant function for each group of participants. These are shown in Table 30.7. Remember that discriminant functions are just variables so each participant can be scored on each discriminant function. Thus it is possible to find the average score for each group on the discriminant functions. This tells us which groups are high and low on each discriminant function. So in terms of the first discriminant function, the teamwork talk by the sports psychologist generates the highest mean (remember that the discriminant function is largely about the 'difference between the most and least favourite team member'). The other two groups are more similar to each other on this discriminant function. The second discriminant function (number of games played was the most associated variable) seems to suggest that the teamwork talk by the team coach produced higher scores. However, this second discriminant function is to be discounted because of its lack of significance.

Table 30.7	Means (centroids) for the groups (conditions) on each discriminant function	
Group	Discriminant function 1	Discriminant function 2
Team psychologist	1.24	−0.04
Team coach	−0.42	0.21
Control	−0.83	−0.17

Step 6

Finally, we need to ask to what extent the discriminant functions can be used to accurately classify participants in terms of the group that they were in. This is done by comparing the predicted group based on the discriminant functions with the actual group membership. Examining Table 30.8, it can be seen that the accuracy of the prediction depends on which group one is considering. The discriminant functions accurately classified 78.6% of the 14 participants who underwent the team-building sessions with the psychologist, but only 28.6% of the 14 participants who had team-building sessions with the coach were correctly classified. For the control group, accuracy was 57.1% since 8 out of the 14 members of the control group were accurately classified by the discriminant functions. Fifty per cent of those allocated to the coach teamwork condition were actually misclassified as being in the control condition.

Table 30.8	Accuracy of the classification based on the discriminant functions		
Actual group membership	**Predicted group membership**		
	Psychologist teamwork	Coach teamwork	Controls
Psychologist teamwork	11 (78.6%)	2 (14.3%)	1 (7.1%)
Coach teamwork	3 (21.4%)	4 (28.6%)	7 (50.0%)
Controls	4 (28.6%)	2 (14.3%)	8 (57.1%)

Step 7

There is an alternative way of doing the discriminant function analysis – using a stepwise process. Stepwise processes are discussed in Chapter 34. In SPSS, this involves pressing one additional button. Stepwise would have advantages in terms of simplicity of the output. This is because it chooses the biggest discriminant functions and does not include any discriminant function which is not statistically significant. Thus in the above tables, only one discriminant would be mentioned because only the first discriminant function is significant. This is a considerable saving of effort, of course. Unfortunately, and this may be sufficient reason for you not to use stepwise, this is not the same model as the original MANOVA employed. In that MANOVA, essentially all discriminant functions were used as the basis of the calculation (though it would not be apparent that this was what was happening) – that is, the significant MANOVA is based on all of the discriminant functions. So there is no reason why this should change for the discriminant function analysis. But by using stepwise you are probably violating the MANOVA model. Some textbooks, nevertheless, advise the use of stepwise discriminant function analysis. In truth, it probably makes very little difference to the way you understand your analysis.

30.3 Reporting your findings

One way of summarising the results of this analysis according to the APA (2010) Publication Manual's recommendations is as follows: 'A direct discriminant analysis was carried out using the three predictors of the difference between the most and least liked team member, the number of gym sessions voluntarily attended and the number of games played to determine which of these variables best discriminate between teams built with a sports psychologist, teams built with a coach and teams built with neither of these (the control condition). Two discriminant functions were calculated, explaining about 97% and 3% of the variance, respectively. Wilks' lambda was significant for the combined functions, $\chi^2(6, N = 42) = 24.69, p < .001$ but was not significant when the first function was removed, $\chi^2(2, N = 42) = 1.01, p = .605$. The first discriminant function maximally differentiated the psychologist's teamwork training from the other two groups and correlated most highly with the difference between the most and least liked members (.97) and the number of gym sessions attended (.64). The second discriminant function maximally distinguished the coach's team from the other two groups and loaded most strongly with the number of games played (.96). SPSS gives a table called Classification Result which tabulates how accurately participants have been classified by the discriminant functions which we have not included. From this table, about 55% of the cases were correctly classified compared with 33% expected by chance. About 79% of the psychologist's team members were correctly identified with 14% misclassified as the coach's team members. Fifty-seven per cent of the control team members were correctly identified with 29% misclassified as the psychologist's team members. Twenty-nine per cent of the coach's team members were correctly identified with 50% misclassified as the control team members.'

Research examples

Discriminant function analysis

Although discriminant function analysis is included in this book largely to help with the interpretation of MANOVA, it can be used in its own right as in the examples below. However, we would recommend using logistic regression in these circumstances.

Gannon and Barrowcliffe (2012) used a group of both university students and community participants. The participants were asked to indicate confidentially whether they have ever been involved in firesetting. At intervals they were also asked to complete a new Fire Setting Scale and Fire Proclivity Scale. Eleven per cent admitted firesetting. Using discriminant function analysis an attempt was made to see whether the firesetters could be effectively discriminated from the non-firesetters using the two scales. Just one subscale from the Fire Propensity Scale known as the propensity behavioural index significantly discriminated between the two groups of participants. The overall hit rate was 91% but only 72% of the firesetters were correctly classified.

Gray, LaPlante and Shaffer (2012), using records of actual Internet gambling, were able to study a group of gamblers who had triggered an irresponsible gambling alert with a matched group of controls who had had the same amount of exposure to gambling on the internet but did not trigger concerns. Discriminant function analysis was used to differentiate the two groups. It was found that indices reflecting the intensity of the gambling activity best differentiated the two groups. These indices included the total number of bets made, the number of Euros per bet and the number of bets per betting day especially for live sports betting.

Ridenour, McCoy and Dean (1996) investigated the possibility of malingering by patients under neuropsychological assessment. One possible reason for the malingering was the involvement of an insurance claim. Some participants were asked to fake symptoms on the Neuropsychological Symptom Inventory whereas others reported honestly. The items of the Inventory were used in a discriminant function analysis in an attempt to see whether the two groups could be differentiated on the basis of their replies. Overall, participants were correctly classified according to their group membership. There were just over 2% false positives.

Key points

- Although discriminant function analysis is a general technique to assess the accuracy with which different groups can be classified on the basis of a set of score variables, it is not the best technique for doing so. It is important in relation to MANOVA since discriminant function analysis and MANOVA are based on very similar assumptions and mathematics.

- Check out logistic regression (Chapters 41 and 42) if you simply want to know which variables accurately classify groups of participants. Discriminant function analysis has drawbacks compared to logistic regression.

Only where you have a significant MANOVA do you need to consider using discriminant function analysis.

COMPUTER ANALYSIS

Discriminant function analysis using SPSS

| Data | • Name the variables in 'Variable View' of the 'Data Editor'.
• Enter the data under the appropriate variables names in 'Data View' of the 'Data Editor'. This is the same as for Chapter 29. |

| Analysis | • Select 'Analyze', 'Classify' and 'Discriminant...' (Screenshot 30.1).
• Move grouping variable to 'Grouping Variable:' box (Screenshot 30.2). |

| 2 | • Select 'Define Range'. Put the lowest group number code in the 'Minimum' box and the highest in the 'Maximum' box. Select 'Continue'. |

| 3 | • Move predictor variables to the 'Independents' box and select 'Statistics'.
• Select 'Means', 'Box's M' and 'Continue'. |

| 4 | • Select 'Classify', 'Compute from group size', 'Summary table', 'Continue' and 'OK' (Screenshot 30.3). |

| Output | • Check whether any of the Wilks' lambda for the discriminant functions are significant with a Sig(nificance) of .05 or less (Screenshot 30.4). |

| 2 | • If so check in the 'Structure Matrix' table which predictors are most highly correlated as these best discriminate the groups (Screenshot 30.5). |

| 3 | • Determine the percentage of correct classification for the groups which is given in another table. |

| FIGURE 30.2 | SPSS steps for a discriminant function analysis |

Interpreting and reporting the output

- The main task of interpreting the data is to identify how many significant discriminant functions there are from the Wilks' lambda output table. In this case there are two significant discriminant functions. The Structure Matrix then tells you how each of the variables loads on each of the discriminant functions.

- A detailed approach to reporting these findings is given in Section 30.3. This draws on additional output tables. Refer to this section to find help on how to report your findings.

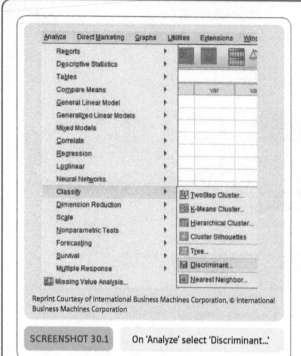

Reprint Courtesy of International Business Machines Corporation, © International Business Machines Corporation

SCREENSHOT 30.1   On 'Analyze' select 'Discriminant...'

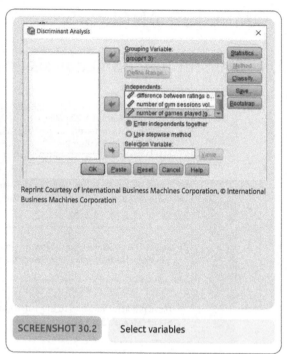

Reprint Courtesy of International Business Machines Corporation, © International Business Machines Corporation

SCREENSHOT 30.2   Select variables

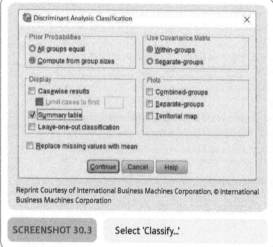

Reprint Courtesy of International Business Machines Corporation, © International Business Machines Corporation

SCREENSHOT 30.3   Select 'Classify...'

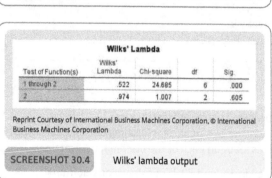

Wilks' Lambda

Test of Function(s)	Wilks' Lambda	Chi-square	df	Sig.
1 through 2	.522	24.685	6	.000
2	.974	1.007	2	.605

Reprint Courtesy of International Business Machines Corporation, © International Business Machines Corporation

SCREENSHOT 30.4   Wilks' lambda output

Structure Matrix

	Function	
	1	2
difference between ratings of most and least liked team members	.965*	-.093
number of gym sessions voluntarily attended	.635*	.378
number of games played	.265	.958*

Pooled within-groups correlations between discriminating variables and standardized canonical discriminant functions
Variables ordered by absolute size of correlation within function.

*. Largest absolute correlation between each variable and any discriminant function

Reprint Courtesy of International Business Machines Corporation, © International Business Machines Corporation

SCREENSHOT 30.5   Structure Matrix table giving correlations of each variable with the functions

Recommended further reading

Cramer, D. (2003). *Advanced quantitative data analysis* (Chapter 13). Buckingham, UK: Open University Press.

Diekhoff, G. (1992). *Statistics for the social and behavioral sciences* (Chapter 14). Dubuque, IL: Wm. C. Brown.

Hair, J. F., Jr, Anderson, R. E., Tatham, R. L., & Black, W. C. (2018). *Multivariate data analysis* (8th ed., Chapter 5). Upper Saddle River, NJ: Pearson Prentice Hall.

Tabachnick, B. G., & Fidell, L. S. (2013). *Using multivariate statistics* (6th ed., Chapter 9). Boston, MA: Allyn & Bacon.

CHAPTER 31

Statistics and analysis of experiments

Overview

- Not thinking about your statistical analysis until the last minute is not a good idea. The analysis ideally should begin at the research planning stage though many find it difficult to give it that priority.

- Try to discipline yourself to sketch out the statistical analysis as early as possible. This may help forestall analytic problems while they can be avoided.

- Choice of an appropriate statistical analysis depends on a clear statement of what the analysis is intended to achieve (e.g. the hypotheses or relationships to be tested), correctly identifying which variables are scores and which are nominal categories, and whether correlations or differences in mean scores are sought.

- Researchers often need to be creative in their analytic approach. They should feel free to manipulate the data to create new variables or develop composite measures from several items.

Preparation

Make sure that you understand hypotheses (Chapter 11) and nominal category data versus numerical score data (Chapter 2).

31.1   Introduction

Feeling jaded and listless? Don't know what stats to use to analyse your study? Make money from home. Try Professor Warburton's Patent Stats Pack. All the professional tricks revealed. Guaranteed not to fail. Gives hope where there is no hope. Professor Warburton's Stats Pack troubleshoots the troubleshooters.

Since the death of Professor Warburton in 1975, through thrombosis of the wallet, his Patent Stats Pack had been feared lost. Libraries on three continents were searched. Miraculously it was discovered after many years in Australia in a trunk under the bed of a dingo farmer. Auctioned recently at Sotheby's to an unknown buyer – reputedly a German antiquarian – it broke all records. Controversy broke out when scholars claimed that Professor Warburton was a fraud and never held an academic appointment in his life. To date, it has not been possible to refute this claim.

These are vile slurs against Professor Warburton whom many regard as the founder of the postmodernist statistics movement and the first person to deconstruct statistics. We have exclusive rights to the Patent Stats Pack, so judge for yourself.

31.2   The Patent Stats Pack

■ Principle 1

Practically nothing needs to be known about statistical calculations and theory to choose appropriate procedures to analyse your data. The characteristics of your research are the main considerations – not knowledge of statistics books.

■ Principle 2

Ideally you should not undertake research without being able to sketch out the likely features of your tables and diagrams.

■ Principle 3

You *can* make a silk purse out of a sow's ear. First catch your silk pig. . . . A common mistake is thinking that the data as they are collected are the data as they will be analysed. Sometimes, especially when the statistical analysis has not been planned prior to collecting data, you may have to make your data fit the available statistical techniques. Always remember that you may need to alter the format of your data in some way in order to make them suitable for statistical analysis or a particular analysis. These changes include:

- adding scores from several variables to get a single overall or composite variable

- separating a variable into several different components (especially where you have collected data as frequencies in nominal categories and have allowed multiple answers).

Box 31.1 | Focus on

Where to get advice

One should be wary about from where to get statistical advice. A little knowledge can be a dangerous thing and this applies to statistical advice as much as anything. Sometimes a sort of blind panic sets in whereby, for example, a student feels that they cannot cope with the demands of a quantitative analysis of their data and so becomes reliant on anyone who will listen and appears to know a little more than they do. It is easy to impress by bandying about statistical terminology and alluding to the inherent problems of various statistical techniques. None of this is particularly helpful to someone with a pressing need to get on with analysing their data. What we are trying to

say, hopefully subtly, is that in our experience students' difficulties with statistical analysis are made worse by being given wrong or impractical advice given the circumstances. Worse still, sometimes this third party advice is communicated with such conviction that the hapless student is torn between this advice and what they know about statistics in general already. Consequently, because they lack confidence in their statistical ability, this contradictory advice pushes them into a tail-spin from which it is difficult to recover. Whatever, a clear head and sufficient time are needed to sort out your statistical analysis.

31.3 | Checklist

Years of experience providing statistical advice suggest that rarely is the statistical analysis the basic problem – far more important is the inadequate conceptualisation which underlies the research design (see Box 31.1). Statistics is of some help – but limited – even where a research design was inadequate in some way. It is far better to get your research design clear before data are collected. Profound knowledge of statistical techniques is probably not the most important skill of the researcher. Instead, apparently simple skills such as being able to understand how one's research aims can be met using your chosen research questions are more important. Just what is there in the research design which allows one to answer the research question? If you can't address this satisfactorily then there is likely to be some sort of conceptual muddle which is hindering your process. If you knew virtually nothing about statistics, how could you use your data to answer your research question? For example, you might answer this question by saying draw a scattergram between this variable and that variable or the average score in one group should be higher than the average score in another group. That is, just what would you look for in your data to answer your research question?

Of course, prevention is better than cure in statistical analysis. Sometimes it is easy to see the root cause of the conceptual muddle which has resulted in someone seeking statistical advice. It is hard to be clear about concepts, and the more concepts involved in a study then the greater the capacity for muddle. It is important to be able to write your ideas down, but it is equally or even more important to be able to talk about your ideas to other people. By talking about your plans to your research supervisor, colleagues and friends then you are actively engaging with the all-important building blocks of your study. It may be embarrassing to do so, sometimes, but this might encourage a re-think if it proves problematic to communicate your ideas clearly to others. Some non-statistical steps which are important for a good statistical analysis are given in Figure 31.1.

So what can be done where the statistical analysis does not seem to flow from your research design? The following are some of the major considerations which will help you choose an appropriate statistical analysis for your data.

Make your statistical analysis part of the planning process for your research. If you do not have a clear idea about what your analysis will involve, explore the possibility that your general research strategy needs revision.   It is especially important that you understand clearly what your research question and hypotheses are early on.

Talk to anyone who will listen about your research plans. Explain to them what your research questions are. Outline your analysis. If this is not clear, then your problem is conceptual or methodological – it is not statistical. Just how does the data that you are planning address each of your research questions?

You may well find that you have great difficulty talking through your ideas with others. This is probably because your ideas are not clear enough. Try refining your research questions etc. in discussion with others and by writing them down. Beware of keeping things in your head. It is difficult to get an overall perpsective unless they are processed in some way by talking with others or writing them out in detail.

Their work my provide some ideas also about what are good measures and what sort of sample size would be optimum. Check what other researchers have done who have researched similar research questions. The analyses that they carried out may be pertinent to yours. You could start writing a draft of your report as soon as you can as this requires the active processing of your ideas and can lead to early refinement.

Classify each of the variables you measure in turn. Is it a score or is it a nominal category variable? Do you need to create dummy variables? Spend as much time as you can analyzing your data using the basic descriptive statistics from the first few chapters of this book. You will learn a lot from this. Draw as many bar charts and scattergrams as you can think of which are relevant to your research question and show relationships between pairs of variables in your study.

Work in an organized and tidy way. Piles of computer output without any system can confuse the situation enormously. Disorganized unreadable notes are just that. Remember that there are usually several ways of answering any research question using statistics. Yours might be better than others with some care. Tests of significance have their uses but they do not replace a proper examination of your data.

FIGURE 31.1   Important things in order to get your statistical analysis right

1. Write down your hypothesis. Probably the best way of doing this is to simply fill in the blanks in the following:

   '**My hypothesis is that there is a relationship between variable 1 ___
   and variable 2 ___**'

   Do not write in the names of more than two variables. There is nothing to stop you having several hypotheses. Write down as many hypotheses as seems appropriate – but only *two* variable names per hypothesis. Treat each hypothesis as a separate statistical analysis at least for now.

   If you cannot name the two variables you see as correlated then it is possible that you wish only to compare a single sample with a population. In this case check out the single-sample chi-square (Chapter 18) or the single-sample *t*-test (Screenshots 13.2 and 14.2).

2. If you cannot meet the requirements of 1 above then you are possibly confused about the purpose of the research. *Go no further until you have sorted this out* – do not blame statistics for your conceptual muddle. Writing out your hypotheses and adjusting them until they are clear may sound like a chore, but it is an important part of statistical analysis. Your first attempts may be hopelessly inadequate but they can be improved upon. You need to start from somewhere and that is on a piece of paper.

3. Classify each of the variables in your hypothesis into either of the following categories:

   a) numerical score variables

   b) nominal (category) variables – and count the number of categories.

4. Based on 3, decide which of the following statements is true of your hypothesis:

   a) I have two numerical score variables. (Yes/No)

      (if yes then go to 5)

   b) I have two nominal category variables. (Yes/No)

      (if yes then go to 6)

   c) I have one nominal category variable and one numerical score variable. (Yes/No)

      (if yes then go to 7)

5. If you answered yes to 4(a) above (i.e. you have two numerical score variables) then your statistical analysis involves the correlation coefficient. This might include Pearson correlation, Spearman correlation or regression.

6. If you answered yes to 4(b), implying that you have two nominal category variables, then your statistical analysis has to be based on contingency tables using chi-square or closely related tests. The range available to you is as follows:

   a) chi-square

   b) Fisher exact probability test for 2×2 or 2×3 contingency tables, especially if the samples are small or expected frequencies low

   c) the McNemar test if you are studying *change* in the same sample of people

   d) at the more advanced level, logistic regression (Chapters 41 and 42) and log-linear analysis (Chapter 40) may be appropriate where you have many nominal variables.

Table 31.1	Food preferences of a sample of 50 teenagers	
Food type	**Frequency**	
Vegetarian	19	
Fast food	28	
Italian	9	
Curry	8	

The only problem you are likely to experience with such tests is if you have allowed the participants in your research to give more than one answer to a question. If you have, then the solution is to turn each category into a separate variable and code each individual according to whether or not they are in that category. This is referred to as dummy coding and is covered in detail later in this book (Chapter 41). So, for example, in a frequency table such as Table 31.1 it is pretty obvious that multiple responses have been allowed since the total of the frequencies is in excess of the sample size of 50. This table could be turned into four new tables:

- Table 1: The number of vegetarians (19) versus the number of non-vegetarians (31)

- Table 2: The number of fast food preferrers (28) versus the non-fast food preferrers (22)

- Table 3: Italian preferrers (9) versus Italian non-preferrers (41)

- Table 4: Curry preferrers (8) versus non-curry preferrers (42).

7. If you answered yes to 4(c) then the nominal (category) variable is called the *independent* variable and the numerical score variable is called the *dependent* variable. The number of categories for the independent variable partly determines the statistical tests you can apply:

a) If you have two categories for the independent (nominal category) variable then:

- the *t*-test is a suitable statistic (Chapters 13 and 14)

- the one-way analysis of variance is suitable (Chapters 23 and 24).

The choice between the two is purely arbitrary as they give equivalent results. Remember to check whether your two sets of scores are independent or correlated/related. If your scores on the dependent variable are correlated then it is appropriate to use the related or correlated versions of the *t*-test (Chapter 13) and the analysis of variance (Chapter 23).

b) If you have *three or more* categories for the independent (nominal category) variable then your choice is limited to the one-way analysis of variance. Again, if your dependent variable features correlated or related scores, then the related or correlated one-way analysis of variance can be used (Chapter 24).

Sometimes you may decide that you have *two or more independent* variables for each dependent variable. Here you are getting into the complexities of the analysis of variance and you need to consult Chapters 25 and 27 for advice.

31.4 Special cases

■ Multiple items to measure the same variable

Sometimes instead of measuring a variable with a single question or with a single technique, that variable is measured in several ways. Most likely is that a questionnaire has been used containing several questions pertaining to the same thing. In these circumstances, you will probably want to combine these questions to give a single numerical score on that variable. The techniques used to do this include the use of standard scores and factor analysis (which are described in Chapters 6 and 33). Generally by combining these different indicators of a major variable together to give a single score, the reliability and validity of your research improve. The combined scores can be used as a single variable and analysed with *t*-tests or analyses of variance, for example.

■ Assessing change over time

The simplest way of studying change over time is to calculate the difference between the first testing and the second testing. This is precisely what a repeated measures *t*-test, for example, does. However, these difference scores can themselves be used in whatever way you wish. In particular, it would be possible to compare difference scores from two or more different samples in order to assess if the amount of change over time depended on gender or any other independent variable. In other words, it is not always necessary to have a complex analysis of variance design which includes time as one independent variable and gender as the other.

Key points

- Nobody ever learnt to play a musical instrument simply by reading a book and never practising. It takes time to become confident in choosing appropriate statistical analyses.

- Simple statistical analyses are not automatically inferior to complex ones.

- Table 31.2 should help you choose an appropriate statistical procedure for your experimental data as may Table 1.1. It is designed to deal only with studies in which you are comparing the means of two or more groups of scores. It is not intended to deal with correlations between variables.

Table 31.2	Aid to selecting appropriate statistical analyses for different experimental designs					
Type of data	One sample compared with known population	Two independent samples	Two related samples	Two or more independent samples	Two or more related samples	Two or more independent variables
Nominal (category) data	One-sample chi-square	Chi-square	McNemar test	Log-linear	Not in this book[a]	Chi-square
Numerical score data	One-sample t-test	Unrelated t-test, unrelated one-way ANOVA	Related t-test, related one-way ANOVA	Unrelated ANOVA	Related ANOVA	Two-way, etc. ANOVA
Numerical score data which violate assumptions of parametric tests	Not in this book[a]	Mann–Whitney U-test	Wilcoxon matched pairs test	Kruskal–Wallis (Appendix B2)	Friedman (Appendix B2)	Not in this book[a]

[a] These are fairly specific nonparametric tests which are rarely used (see Box 31.2).

Box 31.2	Focus on

Problematic data

If it becomes clear that the basic assumptions of parametric tests are violated by your data (which for all practical purposes means that the distribution of scores is very skewed), then you might wish to employ a nonparametric equivalent (Chapter 21 and Appendix B2). However, you may wish to look at bootstrapping procedures (see Box 21.1), which are not reliant on symmetrical and normally distributed data unlike many of the parametric tests. Bootstrapping makes no more assumptions about the nature of the data than can be seen from your data. The big advantage of bootstrapping procedures is that they can be applied to many conventional parametric techniques. Bootstrapping is a feature of SPSS. The use of a computer package is essential for bootstrapping procedures which involve vast numbers of samples drawn randomly from your data set (which is multiplied numerous times in order to get a large sample).

COMPUTER ANALYSIS

Selecting subsamples of your data using SPSS

You may want to investigate the statistics in a subset of your data. For example, you may want to look at the correlation between music and maths scores in the four groups of younger and older girls and boys. To do this you need to select out each group in turn and conduct the correlation. One way of doing is to use 'Select Cases' (Screenshots 31.1 and 31.2) where you specify the age and sex of the group you want to analyse as shown in Screenshot 31.3 which selects females (coded as 1) and age equal to or less than 9.

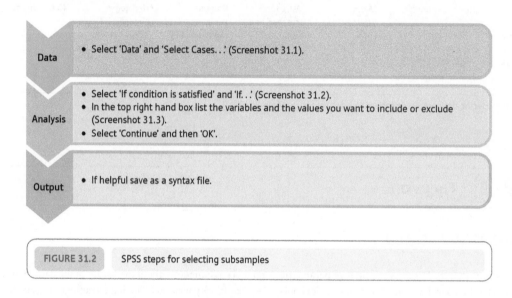

Data	• Select 'Data' and 'Select Cases...' (Screenshot 31.1).
Analysis	• Select 'If condition is satisfied' and 'If. . .' (Screenshot 31.2). • In the top right hand box list the variables and the values you want to include or exclude (Screenshot 31.3). • Select 'Continue' and then 'OK'.
Output	• If helpful save as a syntax file.

FIGURE 31.2 SPSS steps for selecting subsamples

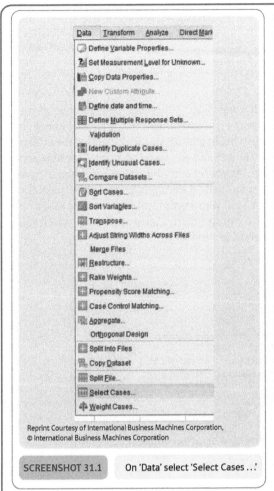

| SCREENSHOT 31.1 | On 'Data' select 'Select Cases ...' |

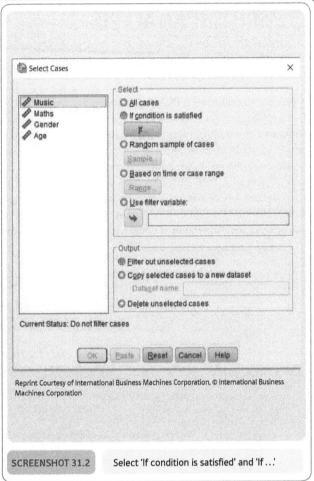

| SCREENSHOT 31.2 | Select 'If condition is satisfied' and 'If ...' |

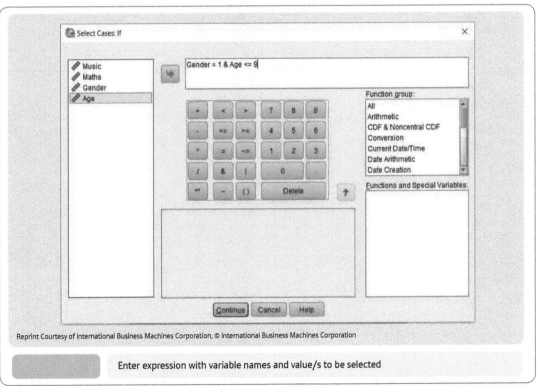

Enter expression with variable names and value/s to be selected

COMPUTER ANALYSIS

Recoding groups for multiple comparison tests using SPSS

If you have conducted a factorial analysis of variance and found a significant interaction between two of the factors, you may want to see which groups differ significantly from each other. To do this, you would need to compare the means of two groups at a time. Suppose, for example as in Chapter 25, you are looking at the effects on errors made of three levels of sleep deprivation (4, 12 and 24 hours) and two levels of alcohol (alcohol and no alcohol), you will have six groups and 15 comparisons to make. As your groups are coded according to your two variables (alcohol and sleepdep), you need to combine them to create a third group (group). Perhaps the most flexible way of doing this is to create a syntax file (Screenshot 31.4) with a set of syntax commands as shown in Screenshot 31.5 and to run this set of commands. This will give you six groups (Screenshot 31.6) which you can analyse with the multiple comparison tests of a one-way analysis of variance.

Data	• Select 'File', 'New' and 'Syntax' (Screenshot 31.4).
Analysis	• In the 'Syntax Editor' type in the following kind of commands: if old variable one = a value & old variable two = a value compute new variable = new value. (Screenshot 31.5). • Select 'Run' and 'All'.
Output	• The new variable and its values are in 'Data View' of the 'Data Editor' (Screenshot 31.6).

FIGURE 31.3   SPSS steps for recoding groups for multiple comparison tests

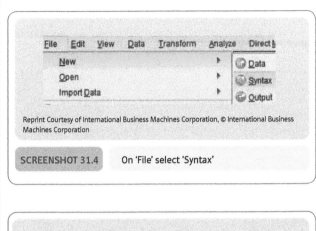

Reprint Courtesy of International Business Machines Corporation, © International Business Machines Corporation

SCREENSHOT 31.4   On 'File' select 'Syntax'

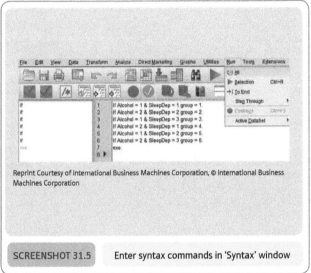

Reprint Courtesy of International Business Machines Corporation, © International Business Machines Corporation

SCREENSHOT 31.5   Enter syntax commands in 'Syntax' window

	Alcohol	SleepDep	Errors	group
1	1	1	16	1.00
2	1	1	12	1.00
3	1	1	17	1.00
4	1	2	18	5.00
5	1	2	16	5.00
6	1	2	25	5.00
7	1	3	22	3.00
8	1	3	24	3.00
9	1	3	32	3.00

Reprint Courtesy of International Business Machines Corporation, © International Business Machines Corporation

SCREENSHOT 31.6   'Data View' with the values of the new variable

PART 4

More advanced correlational statistics

CHAPTER 32

Partial correlation

Spurious correlation, third or confounding variables, suppressor variables

Overview

- Partial correlation statistically adjusts a correlation between two variables to take away the possible influence of a third (or confounding) variable or variables. These are sometimes known as control variables.

- So partial correlation deals with the third-variable problem in which additional variables may cause spurious relationships or hide (suppress) relationships.

- If one control variable is used then this is called a first-order partial correlation. Controlling two variables gives a second-order partial correlation, and so forth.

- A zero-order correlation is the original unmodified correlation between two variables.

- Partial correlation cannot definitively establish a causal relationship but may help eliminate spurious ones.

Preparation

Revise the Pearson correlation coefficient (Chapter 8) if necessary. Make sure you know what is meant by a causal relationship.

32.1 Introduction

The partial correlation coefficient is particularly useful when trying to make causal statements from field research. It is not so useful in experimental research where randomisation helps establish causal relationships. Consider the following research outlines as critically as possible:

- *Project 1* Researchers examine the published suicide rates in different geographical locations in the country. They find that there is a significant relationship between unemployment rates in these areas and suicide rates. They conclude that unemployment causes suicide.

- *Project 2* Researchers examine the relationship between shoe size and liking football matches. They find a relationship between the two but claim that it would be nonsense to suggest that liking football makes your feet grow bigger.

Although both of these pieces of research are superficially similar, the researchers draw rather different conclusions. In the first case it is suggested that unemployment causes suicide whereas in the second case the researchers are reluctant to claim that liking football makes your feet grow bigger. The researchers in both cases may be correct in their interpretation of the correlations, but should we take their interpretations at face value? The short answer is no, since correlations do not demonstrate causality in themselves (see Box 32.1).

In both cases, it is possible that the relationships obtained are spurious (or artificial) ones which occur because of the influence of other unconsidered variables. So, for example, the relationship between shoe size and liking football might be due to gender – men tend to have bigger feet than women and tend to like football more than women do. So is the relationship between shoe size and liking football really due to gender differences? The relationship between unemployment and suicide, similarly, could also be due to the influence of a third variable. In this case, the variable might be social class. If we found, for example, that being from a lower social class was associated with a greater likelihood of unemployment *and* with being more prone to suicide, this would potentially implicate social class differences in the relationship (see Box 32.2).

Partial correlation is a statistically precise way of calculating what the relationship between two variables would be if one could take away the influence of one (or more) additional variable(s). Sometimes this is referred to as controlling for a third variable or partialling out a third variable. In essence it revises the value of your correlation coefficient to take into account third variables.

Box 32.1 Key concepts

Causality

This is intended as a timely reminder of things discussed in depth earlier in this book. Partial correlation can never confirm that a causal relationship exists between two variables. The reason is that partialling out a third, fourth or fifth variable does not rule out the possibility that there is an additional variable which has not been considered which is the cause of the correlation. However, partial correlation may be useful in examining the validity of claims about specified variables which might be causing the relationship. Considerations of causality are a minor aspect of partial correlation.

32.2 | Theoretical considerations

Partial correlation can be applied to your own data if you have the necessary correlations available. It can be applied also to published research so long as they contain the necessary correlation coefficients. All it requires is that the values of the correlations between your two main variables and the possible third variable are known. It is common for these to be published in research reports, although the raw data (original scores) are rarely included.

A table of correlations between several variables is known as a correlation matrix. Table 32.1 is an example featuring the following three variables: numerical intelligence test score (which we have labelled X in the table), verbal intelligence test score (which we have labelled Y in the table) and age (which we have labelled C in the table) in a sample of 30 teenagers.

Notice that the diagonal from top left to bottom right consists of 1.00 repeated three times. This is because the correlations in the diagonal are between a set of scores and itself – a perfect relationship ($r = 1.00$). Also notice that the matrix is symmetrical around the diagonal. This is fairly obvious since the correlation of the numerical score with the verbal score has to be the same as the correlation of the verbal score with the numerical score. More often than not a researcher would report just half of Table 32.1, so the correlations would look like a triangle. It doesn't matter which triangle you choose, although it is usual to display the lower left triangle as we read from left to right.

Remember that we have used the letters X, Y and C for the different columns and rows of the matrix. The C column and C row are the column and row, respectively, for the *control* variable (age in this case).

Not only is partial correlation an important statistical tool in its own right, it also forms the basis of other techniques such as multiple regression (Chapter 34).

Table 32.1	Correlation matrix involving three variables		
	Variable X Numerical score	Variable Y Verbal score	Variable C Age in years
Variable X Numerical score	1.00	.97	.80
Variable Y Verbal score	.97	1.00	.85
Variable C Age in years	.80	.85	1.00

Box 32.2 | Key concepts

Mediator and moderator variables

The difference between moderator and mediator variables has a bearing on partial correlation. This is not a statistical issue, as such, but important in research design and methodology. Put crudely, a mediator variable is a variable which explains the relationship between two other variables (usually best expressed as the independent

→

and dependent variable). For example, imagine that there is a correlation between annual income (independent variable) and happiness (dependent variable) such that richer people are happier. Although this relationship would be interesting, it is somewhat unsatisfactory from a psychological and theoretical point of view since the psychological processes responsible for the relationship are unknown. We know from previous research that an extensive supportive social network contributes to happiness. So the reason why income is associated with happiness may be because having more money allows one to socialise more and that the more one socialises the more likely it is that one forms an extensive social network. The variable, extensiveness of social network, can be described as a mediator variable since it mediates the relationship between income and happiness.

The way that we have described this implies a causal relationship. That is, higher income (independent variable) influences social networking (the mediator variable) which then influences happiness (the dependent variable) (see Figure 32.1). Proof of this causal requires randomised studies, of course. That is, the researcher would have to randomly allocate participants to the richer and poorer conditions and study the effects of this on both the mediator variable (social networking) and the dependent variable (happiness). Without randomisation, the causal interpretation is much more tentative. For instance, it is perfectly possible that people with extensive social networks have higher incomes as a consequence of their ability to network rather than vice versa.

A moderator variable is something quite different. It is a variable which reveals that the relationship between the independent and dependent variable is not consistent throughout the data. Imagine that, once again, the researcher is investigating the relationship between income

(independent variable) and happiness (the dependent variable). However, this time the researcher is interested in whether the genders differ in terms of the size of the relationship. Imagine that for men the correlation between income and happiness is .6 but that for women the correlation is very small, only .0. This implies quite different conclusions for men and for women. In one case there is quite a substantial correlation and in the other case no correlation. In other words, gender moderates the relationship between income and happiness. How the relationship between income and happiness is understood is different for men and women. A moderator variable does not explain the relationship, of course. We would have to consider further the explanation of why the relationship is different in women and men. It could be, for example, that women's social networks are more influenced by having children and so mixing with other women with children than men's social networks. Perhaps men's social networks are more affected by having the money to go to the pub, the golf club or the yacht club, for instance. This, of course, is to begin to ask why gender moderates the relationship between income and happiness – notice that we are hinting at possible mediating variables. Moderator variables, in themselves, are not directly about establishing causal relationships so randomisation is not an issue for the research design. Chapter 38 covers moderator variables in detail.

Quite clearly, the techniques that we have described in this chapter are ways of studying moderator and mediator variables. But there are other techniques described in this book which can also contribute. For example, interactions in ANOVA (Chapter 25) can be regarded as evidence of moderator effects as explained in Chapter 38 on moderator variables. The same is true for significant loglinear interactions (Chapter 40). The appropriate statistics, as ever, depend on whether you have score or category variables or both. However, it is the research design which influences whether or not a variable is conceived as a moderator or mediator variable. For example, if a variable cannot be influenced by the independent variable, then it can only be conceived as a moderator variable. Income (independent variable) cannot affect a person's gender so gender cannot be a mediator variable between income and happiness. It can, however, be a moderator variable in the relationship between income and happiness.

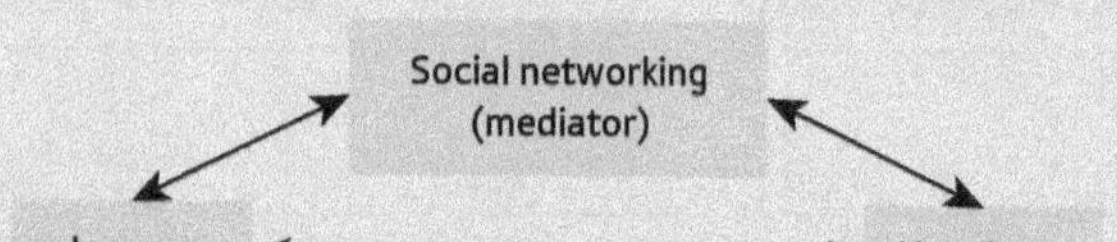

FIGURE 32.1 — Possible circumstances for partial correlation mediated by a third variable

32.3 Doing partial correlation

In order to understand partial correlation better, understanding the gist of how the calculation is done is helpful. Once you have the correlation coefficients involved, the partial correlation calculation itself takes little time. Computer programs for the partial correlation will normally calculate the correlations for you. Explaining statistics 32.1 works out the relationship between verbal and numerical scores in Table 32.1 controlling for age ($r_{XY.C}$).

Explaining statistics 32.1

How the partial correlation coefficient works

The calculation is based on the correlations found in Table 32.1. The formula is as follows:

$$r_{XY.C} = \frac{r_{XY} - (r_{XC} \times r_{YC})}{\sqrt{1 - r_{XC}^2}\ \sqrt{1 - r_{YC}^2}}$$

Where:

$r_{XY.C}$ = correlation of verbal and numerical scores with age controlled as denoted by C

r_{XY} = correlation of numerical and verbal scores (= .97)

r_{XC} = correlation of numerical scores and age (the control variable) (= .80)

r_{YC} = correlation of verbal scores and age (the control variable) (= .85).

Using the values taken from the correlation matrix in Table 32.1 we find that:

$$r_{XY.C} = \frac{.97 - (.80 \times .85)}{\sqrt{1 - .80^2}\sqrt{1 - .85^2}}$$

$$= \frac{.97 - (.68)}{\sqrt{1 - .64}\sqrt{1 - .72}}$$

$$= \frac{.29}{\sqrt{.36}\sqrt{.28}} = \frac{.29}{.60 \times .53} = \frac{.29}{.32} = .91$$

In this case, controlling for age has hardly changed the correlation coefficient – it decreases only very slightly from .97 to .91.

Interpreting the results

A section on interpretation follows. However, when interpreting a partial correlation you need to consider what the unpartialled correlation is. This is the baseline against which the partial correlation is understood. Although usually we would look to see if partialling reduces the size of the correlation, it can increase it.

Reporting the results

The following is one way of reporting this analysis: 'Since age was a correlate of both verbal and numerical ability, it was decided to investigate the effect of controlling for age on the correlation. After partialling, the correlation of .97 declined slightly to .91. However, this change is very small and so age had little or no effect on the correlation between verbal and numerical abilities.'

What does the result of Explaining statistics 32.1 mean? The original correlation between numerical and verbal scores of .97 is reduced to .91 when we control for age. This is a very small amount of change and we can say that controlling for age has no real influence on the original correlation coefficient.

The following is the original pattern of relationships between the three variables: the partial correlation essentially removes all the variation between verbal scores and age and also between numerical scores and age. This is rather like making these correlations zero. But, in this case, following partialling we still find that there is a very substantial correlation between verbal and numerical scores:

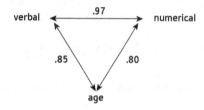

This is an important lesson. Controlling for a third variable does not always affect the correlation, despite the fact that in this case the control variable age had quite substantial relationships with both verbal and numerical ability scores. *This should be a warning that simply showing that two variables are both correlated with a third variable does not in itself establish that the third variable is responsible for the main correlation.*

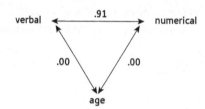

Despite this, often partialling substantially changes the size of the correlation coefficient. Of course, it is important to know that a third variable does not change the correlation value. In contrast, the example in Section 32.7 and Explaining statistics 32.3 shows a major change following partialling.

Explaining statistics 32.2

How the statistical significance of the partial correlation works

The statistical significance of a partial correlation can be found just by using tables of the significance of the Pearson correlation coefficient such as Significance Table 11.1 or the table in Appendix C. However, you will need to adjust the sample size by subtracting three. Thus if the sample size is 10 for the Pearson correlation, it is $10 - 3 = 7$ for the partial correlation coefficient with one variable controlled. So in our example in Table 32.1, which was based on a sample of 30 teenagers, we obtain the 5% significant level from the table in Appendix C by finding the 5% value for a sample size of $30 - 3 = 27$. The minimum value for statistical significance at the 5% level is .382 (two-tailed).

Interpreting the results

The statistical significance of the partial correlation coefficient is much the same as for the Pearson correlation coefficient on which it is based. A statistically significant finding means that the partial correlation coefficient is unlikely to have been drawn from a population in which the partial correlation is zero.

Reporting the results

The statistical significance of the partial correlation may be reported in exactly the same way as for any correlation coefficient. The degrees of freedom are different since they have to be adjusted for the number of control variables. If the sample size for the correlation is 10, then subtract three to give seven degrees of freedom if just one variable is being controlled for. In other words, subtract the total number of variables including the two original variables plus all of the control variables. So if there were four control variables in this example, the degrees of freedom become $10 - 2 - 4 = 4$.

32.5   Multiple control variables

It may have struck you that there might be several variables that a researcher might wish to control for at the same time. For example, a researcher might wish to control for age and social class simultaneously, or even age, social class and gender. This can be done relatively easily on SPSS but is rather cumbersome to do by hand. On SPSS it is simply a matter of adding in more control variables.

There are a number of terms that are used which are relatively simple if you know what they mean:

- *Zero-order correlation* – the correlation between your main variables (e.g. r_{XY}).

- *First-order partial correlation* – the correlation between your main variables controlling for just *one* variable (e.g. $r_{XY.C}$).

- *Second-order partial correlation* – the correlation between your main variables controlling for *two* variables at the same time (the symbol for this might be $r_{XY.CD}$).

Not surprisingly, we can extend this quite considerably; for example, a *fifth*-order partial correlation involves *five* control variables at the same time (e.g. $r_{XY.CDEFG}$). The principles remain the same no matter what order of partial correlation you are examining.

32.6   Suppressor variables

Sometimes you might find that you actually obtain a low correlation between two variables which you had expected to correlate quite substantially. In some instances this is because a third variable actually has the effect of reducing or suppressing the correlation between the two main variables. Partial correlation is useful in removing the inhibitory effect of this third variable. In other words, it can sometimes happen that controlling the

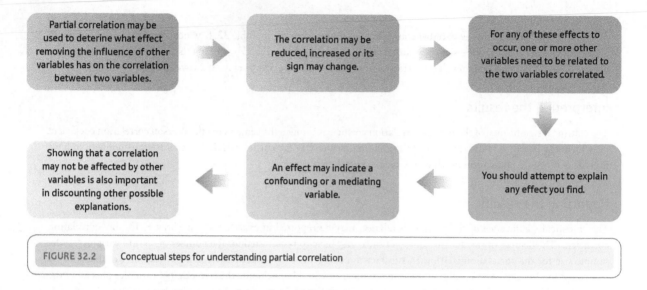

FIGURE 32.2   Conceptual steps for understanding partial correlation

influence of a third variable results in a *larger* correlation. Indeed, it is possible to find that an initially negative correlation becomes a positive correlation when the influence of a third variable is controlled. Figure 32.2 outlines the key steps in partial correlation.

32.7   Example from the research literature

Baron and Straus (1989) took the officially reported crime rates for rapes from most US states and compared these with the circulation figures for soft-core pornography in these areas. The correlation between rape rates and the amounts of pornography over these states was .53. (If this confuses you, the correlations are calculated 'pretending' that each state is like a person in calculating the correlation coefficient.) The temptation is to interpret this correlation as suggesting that pornography leads to rape. Several authors have done so.

However, Howitt and Cumberbatch (1990) took issue with this. They pointed out that the proportions of divorced men in these areas also correlated substantially with both pornography circulation rates and rape rates. The data are listed in Table 32.2.

It might be the case that rather than pornography causing rape, the apparent relationship between these two variables is merely due to the fact that divorced men are more likely to engage in these 'alternative sexual activities'. It is a simple matter to control for this third variable, as set out in Explaining statistics 32.3.

Table 32.2	Correlation between rape, pornography and divorce		
	Variable *X* Rape rates	Variable *Y* Pornography circulation	Variable *C* Proportion of divorced men
Variable *X*: Rape rates	1.00	.53	.67
Variable *Y*: Pornography circulation		1.00	.59
Variable *C*: Proportion of divorced men			1.00

Explaining statistics 32.3

Another example of how the partial correlation works

The formula is:

$$r_{XY.C} = \frac{r_{XY} - (r_{XC} \times r_{YC})}{\sqrt{1 - r_{XC}^2}\sqrt{1 - r_{YC}^2}}$$

where

$r_{XY.C}$ = correlation of rape rates with pornography controlling for proportion of divorced men

r_{XY} = correlation of rape and pornography (= .53)

r_{XC} = correlation of rape and proportion of divorced men (= .67)

r_{YC} = correlation of pornography and proportion of divorced men (= .59).

Using the values taken from the correlation matrix in Table 32.2 we find that:

$$r_{XY.C} = \frac{.53 - (.67 \times .59)}{\sqrt{1 - .67^2}\sqrt{1 - .59^2}} = .22$$

In this case, the correlation when the third variable is taken into account has changed substantially from .53 to .22 – much nearer zero. It would be reasonable to suggest that the partial correlation coefficient indicates that there is no causal relationship between pornography and rape – quite a dramatic change in interpretation from the claim that pornography causes rape. The argument is not necessarily that the proportion of divorced men directly causes rape and the purchase of pornography. However, since it is an unlikely hypothesis that rape and pornography cause divorce then the fact that partialling out divorce reduces greatly the correlation between rape and pornography means that our faith in the original 'causal' link is reduced.

32.8 Example from a student's work

It is becoming increasingly common to teach children with special educational needs in classrooms along with other children rather than in special schools. Butler (1995a) measured the number of characteristics a sample of 14 teachers possessed which have been held to be of special importance in the effective teaching of special needs children. These qualities would include 'empathy towards special needs children', 'attitude towards integrating special needs children' and about ten others.

In order to assess the quality of the learning experience, the student researcher time-sampled children's task-centred behaviour – the number of time periods during which the child was concentrating on the task in hand rather than, say, wandering around the classroom causing a nuisance. The researcher rated one special needs child and one 'normal' child from each teacher's class. She found that there was an unusually very high correlation of .96 between the number of qualities that a teacher possessed and the amount of time that the special needs children spent 'on task' ($df = 12$, $p < .01$). Interestingly, the correlation of the measure of teacher qualities with the behaviour of normal children in the class was only .23. The student used partial correlation to remove the task-oriented behaviour of the 'normal' children in order to control for the extent to which teacher qualities had a beneficial effect on ordinary teaching. This made absolutely the amount of time special needs children spent on educational tasks. In other words, the student could be confident that she had identified qualities of teachers which were especially beneficial to special needs children.

In terms of the research design there might be some worries, as the student was well aware. In particular, in an ideal research design there would be a second observer rating the behaviour of the children in order to check the consistency of the ratings among different observers.

Research examples

Partial correlation

Gotwals and colleagues (2012) argue that sport perfectionist research has not established whether or not perfectionism is adaptive or maladaptive. They distinguish between perfectionist striving and perfectionist concerns. It is clear that perfectionist concerns are maladaptive but not so for perfectionist strivings. They systematically reviewed 31 studies which contained 201 correlations of perfectionism. When normal correlations are considered the evidence was slightly in favour of the view that perfectionist strivings lead to adaptive characteristics in sport rather than maladaptive ones. However, the results of partial correlation analysis added a great deal of clarity. The researchers correlated perfectionist strivings with adaptive/maladaptive measures but controlled for perfectionist concerns. This materially altered the interpretation since perfectionist strivings were overwhelmingly associated with adaptive characteristics. That is, perfectionist strivings are a good thing especially when the negative aspect of perfectionist concerns is eliminated from the strivings measure.

Nair, Collins and Napolitano (2012) point out that in women smoking can sometimes be regarded as a maladaptive means of weight control. Indeed, they perceive benefits in smoking such as weight control, enhanced mood and anxiety, even though physical activity has much the same influence. The researchers used what they call a cue reactivity paradigm which involved looking at one's own body in a mirror and verbal accompaniments to increase body concerns. Smoking was measured using indices such as the women's urge to smoke and the latency until their first smoke after the exposure sessions using the mirror, etc. They could then engage in intense physical activity. Partial correlations controlling for body mass index, nicotine dependency, withdrawal and depressive symptoms showed that the amount of time engaging in intense physical activity was associated with a lower self-reported urge to smoke. The time to the first puff did not show this relationship.

Potter, Hartman and Ward (2009) point out that there is a role of depression and anxiety in the memory complaints of older adults. Their study explored the influence of perceived stress, life events and activity level on memory complaints made by older women in a healthy population. Fifty-four women completed self-report questionnaires dealing with these key variables. The General Frequency of Forgetting Scale was used to measure memory complaints and various reasonably well-established scales to measure the other variables. It was shown using partial correlation that high levels of perceived stress were correlated with more memory complaints after controlling for the influence of depression and anxiety. However, recent life events and activity level were not involved in memory complaints. The authors regard perceived stress as a psychological variable which affects the person's assessment of their cognitive abilities.

Key points

- If you are doing a *field* rather than a laboratory project, check your research hypotheses. If they appear to suggest that one variable *causes* another then consider using partial correlation. It can potentially enhance one's confidence about making causal interpretations if a significant correlation remains after partialling.

However, caution should still be applied since there always remains a risk that an additional variable suppresses the relationship between your two main variables.

- Do not forget that even after partialling out third variables, any causal interpretation of the correlation coefficient remaining has to be tentative. No correlation coefficient (including partial correlation coefficients) can establish causality in itself. You establish causality largely through your research design, not the statistics you apply.

- Do not overlook the possibility that you may need to control more than one variable.

- Do not assume that partial correlation has no role except in seeking causal relationships. Sometimes, for example, the researcher might wish to control for male–female influences on a correlation without wishing to establish causality. Partial correlation will reveal the strength of a non-causal relationship having controlled for a third variable. Causality is something the researcher considers; it is not something built into a correlation coefficient as such.

- Do not forget to test the statistical significance of the partial correlation – as shown above, it is very easy.

COMPUTER ANALYSIS

Partial correlation using SPSS

Data
- Name the variables in 'Variable View' of the 'Data Editor'.
- Enter the data under the appropriate variable names in Data View of the Data Editor (Screenshot 32.1).

Analysis
- Select 'Analyze', 'Correlate' and 'Partial...' (Screenshot 32.2).

2
- Move the two variables to be correlated to the 'Variables:' box and move the variables to be controlled to the 'Controlled for:' box (Screenshot 32.3).

3
- Select 'Options...' if 'Means and standard deviations', 'Zero-order correlations' or 'Exclude cases pairwise' is needed. Select 'Continue' (Screenshot 32.4).
- Select 'OK'.

Output
- Check for any difference in size and sign between the zero-order correlation and the partial correlation. These can be found in additional output (Screenshot 32.5).
- Note whether the partial correlation is significant with a Significance of .05 or less.

FIGURE 32.3   SPSS steps for partial correlation

Interpreting and reporting the output

- Usually you will wish to compare the partial correlation with the original (zero order) correlation. The output table contains the original correlations at the top and the correlations with age partialled out towards the bottom of the table.

- We could write: 'Because age was correlated with both verbal and numerical ability, age was controlled in this relationship using partial correlation. The correlation of .92 declined to .78 on partialling (Screenshot 32.5). The partial correlation was not significant at the 5% level.'

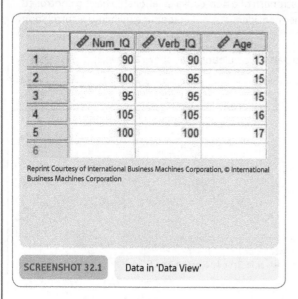

Reprint Courtesy of International Business Machines Corporation, © International Business Machines Corporation

SCREENSHOT 32.1   Data in 'Data View'

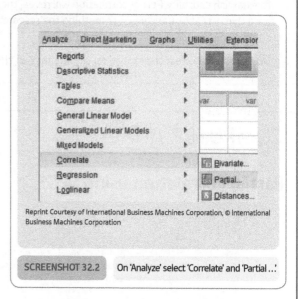

Reprint Courtesy of International Business Machines Corporation, © International Business Machines Corporation

SCREENSHOT 32.2   On 'Analyze' select 'Correlate' and 'Partial ...'

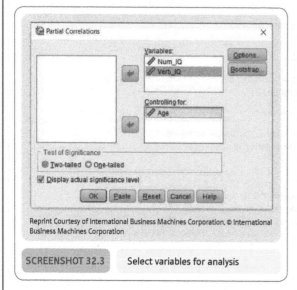

Reprint Courtesy of International Business Machines Corporation, © International Business Machines Corporation

SCREENSHOT 32.3   Select variables for analysis

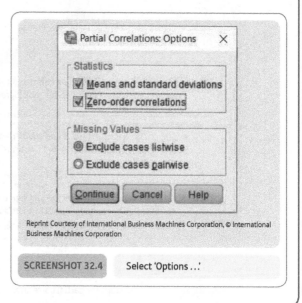

Reprint Courtesy of International Business Machines Corporation, © International Business Machines Corporation

SCREENSHOT 32.4   Select 'Options ...'

Correlations

Control Variables			Num_IQ	Verb_IQ	Age
-none-[a]	Num_IQ	Correlation	1.000	.923	.798
		Significance (2-tailed)	.	.025	.105
		df	0	3	3
	Verb_IQ	Correlation	.923	1.000	.828
		Significance (2-tailed)	.025	.	.084
		df	3	0	3
	Age	Correlation	.798	.828	1.000
		Significance (2-tailed)	.105	.084	.
		df	3	3	0
Age	Num_IQ	Correlation	1.000	.776	
		Significance (2-tailed)	.	.224	
		df	0	2	
	Verb_IQ	Correlation	.776	1.000	
		Significance (2-tailed)	.224	.	
		df	2	0	

a. Cells contain zero-order (Pearson) correlations.

SCREENSHOT 32.5 Important output

CHAPTER 33

Factor analysis

Simplifying complex data

Overview

- Factor analysis seeks to identify the basic dimensions underlying the intercorrelations of substantial numbers of variables seemingly measuring similar things. It has proven particularly useful with questionnaires though not exclusively so.

- Factor analysis reduces data involving a number of variables down to a smaller number of factors which encompass the original variables. Factors are themselves essentially variables.

- Factor loadings are the correlations of the original variables with a factor. Hence they range from −1.0 through .0 to +1.0. Factors are named by examining the original variables which correlate highly with them.

- It is important not to have too many factors. The scree plot may be used to identify those factors which are likely to be significantly different from a chance factor.

- Rotation is the procedure by which the original, mathematically defined factors are transformed into more easily interpreted ones. One procedure for achieving this is to maximise the number of large and small factor loadings while minimising the number of moderate factor loadings. Rotation is akin to twisting the axes of a scatterplot around without moving the data points. Consequently these data points have new positions in relation to those axes.

- Factor scores provide a way of treating factors like any other variable. They are similar to standard or z-scores in that they have symmetrical numbers of positive and negative values and their mean is .00. Groups made be compared in terms of their mean factor scores.

Preparation

Review variance (Chapter 4), correlation coefficient (Chapter 8) and correlation matrix (Chapter 32).

33.1 Introduction

Researchers frequently collect large amounts of data. Sometimes, speculatively, they add extra questions to a survey without any pressing reason. Having data on so many variables, it becomes difficult to make sense of the complexity. With questionnaires, one naturally seeks patterns in the correlations between questions. However, the sheer number of interrelationships makes this hard. Take the following brief questionnaire:

Item 1: It is possible to bend spoons by rubbing them.

| Agree strongly | Agree | Neither | Disagree | Disagree strongly |

Item 2: I have had 'out of body' experiences.

| Agree strongly | Agree | Neither | Disagree | Disagree strongly |

Item 3: Satanism is a true religion.

| Agree strongly | Agree | Neither | Disagree | Disagree strongly |

Item 4: Tarot cards reveal coming events.

| Agree strongly | Agree | Neither | Disagree | Disagree strongly |

Item 5: Speaking in tongues is a peak religious experience.

| Agree strongly | Agree | Neither | Disagree | Disagree strongly |

Item 6: The world was saved by visiting space beings.

| Agree strongly | Agree | Neither | Disagree | Disagree strongly |

Item 7: Most people are reincarnated.

| Agree strongly | Agree | Neither | Disagree | Disagree strongly |

Item 8: Astrology is a science, not an art.

| Agree strongly | Agree | Neither | Disagree | Disagree strongly |

Item 9: Animals have souls.

| Agree strongly | Agree | Neither | Disagree | Disagree strongly |

Item 10: Talking to plants helps them to grow.

| Agree strongly | Agree | Neither | Disagree | Disagree strongly |

Agree strongly could be scored as 1, Agree scored as 2, Neither as 3, Disagree as 4 and Disagree strongly as 5. This turns the words into numerical scores. Correlating the answers to each of these 10 questions with each of the others for 300 respondents generates a large correlation matrix (a table of all possible correlations between all of the possible pairs of questions). Ten questions will produce 10×10 or 100 correlations. Although the correlation matrix is symmetrical about the diagonal from top left to bottom right, there remain 45 *different* correlations to examine. Such a matrix might be much like the one in Table 33.1.

Table 33.1	Correlation matrix of 10 items									
	Item 1	Item 2	Item 3	Item 4	Item 5	Item 6	Item 7	Item 8	Item 9	Item 10
Item 1	1.00	.50	.72	.30	.32	.20	.70	.30	.30	.10
Item 2	.50	1.00	.40	.51	.60	.14	.17	.55	.23	.55
Item 3	.72	.40	1.00	.55	.64	.23	.12	.17	.22	.67
Item 4	.30	.51	.55	1.00	.84	.69	.47	.44	.56	.35
Item 5	.32	.60	.64	.84	1.00	.14	.77	.65	.48	.34
Item 6	.20	.14	.23	.69	.14	1.00	.58	.72	.33	.17
Item 7	.70	.17	.12	.47	.77	.58	1.00	.64	.43	.76
Item 8	.30	.55	.17	.44	.65	.72	.64	1.00	.27	.43
Item 9	.30	.23	.22	.56	.48	.33	.43	.27	1.00	.12
Item 10	.10	.55	.67	.35	.34	.17	.76	.43	.12	1.00

It is not easy to make complete sense of this even though ten items is quite a small number of items for a questionnaire. Larger matrices are even harder for our brains to comprehend. This is where factor analysis can be beneficial. It is a technique which helps you overcome the complexity of correlation matrices. In essence, it takes a matrix of correlations and generates a much smaller set of 'supervariables' which characterise the main trends in the correlation matrix. These supervariables or factors are generally much easier to understand than the original matrix.

33.2 A bit of history

Factor analysis is not a new technique – it dates back to shortly after the First World War. It originally was an invention largely of psychologists to serve a very specific purpose in the field of mental testing. There are numerous psychological tests of different sorts of intellectual ability. Initially, factor analysis was intended to uncover which sorts of mental skills tend to go together and which are distinct abilities. It has proven more generally useful and is used in the development of psychological tests and questionnaires. Personality, attitude, intelligence and aptitude tests are often based on it since it can help select which items from the tests and measures to retain. By using factors, it is possible to obtain 'purer' measures of psychological variables than subjectively deciding what can be combined with what else in order to measure something. Not surprisingly then it impacted research. The personality theories of researchers Raymond Cattell and Hans Eysenck (Cramer, 1992) were heavily dependent on factor analysis. Initially these researchers would spend weeks if not months doing the calculations by hand so factor analytic studies were not very common. Now far more complex analyses can be carried out in seconds. In the last 100 years, techniques for factor analysis have developed in many ways so the level of technical complexity can be fairly high. Despite this, the most important thing to learn is the process of interpreting factors which requires psychological knowledge and insight, combined with an ability to synthesise ideas.

33.3 Basics of factor analysis

In order to understand factor analysis, it is useful to start with a simple and highly stylised correlation matrix such as the one in Table 33.2. You can probably detect that there are *two* distinct clusters of variables. Variables *A, C* and *E* all tend to correlate with each other pretty well. Similarly, variables *B, D* and *F* all intercorrelate quite substantially. Importantly, members of the first cluster (*A, C, E*) do not correlate well with members of the second cluster (*B, D, F*) – they would not be distinct clusters if they did. In order to give meaning to the clusters, we need to check what the variables contributing to the first cluster (*A, C, E*) have in common; next we need to explore the similarities of the variables in the second cluster (*B, D, F*). Calling the variables by arbitrary letters did not help much. But if we add a little detail by identifying the variables involved more clearly and relabelling the matrix of correlations as in Table 33.3 then considerable light is shed on the meaning of the clusters.

Interpretation of the clusters is now possible. Drawing the clusters from the table we find:

First cluster
variable *A* = skill at batting
variable *C* = skill at throwing darts
variable *E* = skill at juggling

Second cluster
variable *B* = skill at doing crosswords
variable *D* = skill at doing the word game Scrabble
variable *F* = skill at spelling

Table 33.2	Stylised correlation matrix between variables A to F					
	Variable A	Variable B	Variable C	Variable D	Variable E	Variable F
Variable A	1.00	.00	.91	−.05	.96	.10
Variable B	.00	1.00	.08	.88	.02	.80
Variable C	.91	.08	1.00	−.01	.90	.29
Variable D	−.05	.88	−.01	1.00	−.08	.79
Variable E	.96	.02	.90	−.08	1.00	.11
Variable F	.10	.80	.29	.79	.11	1.00

Table 33.3	Stylised correlation matrix with variable names added					
	Batting	Crosswords	Darts	Scrabble	Juggling	Spelling
Batting	1.00	.00	.91	−.05	.96	.10
Crosswords	.00	1.00	.08	.88	.02	.80
Darts	.91	.08	1.00	−.01	.90	.29
Scrabble	−.05	.88	−.01	1.00	−.08	.79
Juggling	.96	.02	.90	−.08	1.00	.11
Spelling	.10	.80	.29	.79	.11	1.00

Once this 'fleshing out of the bones' has been done, the meaning of each cluster becomes more apparent. The first cluster seems to involve a general skill at hand–eye coordination; the second cluster seems to involve verbal skill.

This sort of interpretation is easy enough in clear-cut cases like this and with small correlation matrices. Life and statistics, however, are rarely that simple. Remember that in Chapter 32 on partial correlation, we found that a zero correlation between two variables may become a large positive or negative correlation when we take away the influence of a third variable or a suppressor variable which is hiding the true relationship between two main variables. Similar sorts of things can happen in factor analysis. Factor analysis enables us to handle such complexities which would be next to impossible by just inspecting a correlation matrix.

Factor analysis is a mathematical procedure which reduces a correlation matrix containing many variables into a much smaller number of factors or supervariables. A supervariable cannot be measured directly and its nature has to be inferred from the relationships of the original variables with the abstract supervariable. However, in identifying the clusters above we have begun to grasp the idea of factors. The abilities which made up cluster 2 were made meaningful by suggesting that they had verbal skill in common. (In factor analysis the factors are latent variables underlying variables which can be directly measured.)

The *output* from a factor analysis based on the correlation matrix presented above might look rather like Table 33.4. There are two things to understand:

- Factor 1 and factor 2 are like the clusters of variables we have seen above. They are really variables, but we are calling them supervariables because they take a large number of other variables into account. Ideally there should only be a small number of factors to consider.

- The numbers under the columns for factor 1 and factor 2 are called *factor loadings*. Really they are nothing other than correlation coefficients recycled with a different name. So the variable 'skill at batting' correlates .98 with the supervariable which is factor 1. 'Skill at batting' does not correlate at all well with the supervariable which is factor 2 (the correlation is nearly zero at −.01). Factor loadings follow all of the rules for correlation coefficients so they vary from −1.00 through .00 to +1.00.

Factor 1 is interpreted in much the same way as we interpreted the clusters earlier. We find the variables which correlate best with the supervariable or factor in question by looking at the factor loadings for each of the factors in turn. Usually you will hear phrases like 'batting, darts and juggling load highly on factor 1'. All this means is that they

Table 33.4	Factor loading matrix	
Variable	**Factor 1**	**Factor 2**
Skill at batting	.98	−.01
Skill at crosswords	.01	.93
Skill at darts	.94	.10
Skill at Scrabble	−.07	.94
Skill at juggling	.97	−.01
Skill at spelling	.15	.86

correlate highly with the supervariable, factor 1. Since we find that batting, darts and juggling all correlate well with factor 1, they must define the factor. We try to see what batting, darts and juggling have in common – once again we would suggest that hand–eye coordination is the common element. Thus the factor might be called hand–eye coordination. Obviously there is a subjective element in this since not everyone would interpret the factors identically or describe them in the exact same terms. Naming factors uses your psychological skills and is not about being a statistician.

In order to interpret the meaning of a factor we need to decide which items are the most useful in identifying what the factor is about. Although every variable may have something to contribute, those with the highest loadings on a factor probably are the most important for the interpretation. So where does one draw the line between useful factor loadings and not so useful? Generally speaking, you will not go far wrong if you take factor loadings with an absolute value of .50 and above as being important in assessing the meaning of the factor, but with a very small sample this figure could be .70. Now this is a rule of thumb and with a very big sample size then smaller factor loadings may be taken into account. Generally speaking, this is not a vital issue but it would be silly to try to interpret loadings like .2 except where the sample approaches 1000 (see Box 33.1).

When you have identified the highly loading items on the factor, write them out as a group on a piece of paper. Then peruse these items over and over again until you are able to suggest what these items seem to have in common or what it is they represent. There are no rules for doing this and, of course, different researchers may well come up with different interpretations of exactly the same list of items. This is not a problem any more than it is whenever we try to label any sort of concept.

Often a distinction is strongly made between factor analysis (of which there are several types) and principal components analysis. In many cases the 'solutions' (factor structures) which they produce are more-or-less indistinguishable. Only when the number of variables is relatively small and the communalities (see later) are small can differences occur. As it is so easy on SPSS to do both with just a few key strokes it is simple to make the comparison for yourself when you have appropriate data.

33.4   Decisions, decisions, decisions

This entire section can be ignored by the feint-hearted who are not about to carry out a factor analysis.

Now that you have an idea of how to interpret a factor loading matrix derived from a factor analysis, it is time to add a few extra complexities. These are essential when you are actually planning and carrying out a factor analysis. It cannot be stressed too much that factor analysis is more interpretative, subjective and judgemental than most statistical techniques you have studied so far. This is not solely because of the subjectivity of interpreting the meaning of factors. There are many variants of factor analysis and quite a few choices to make when you do the analysis. By and large these are easily coped with as they merely involve selecting the best options for you, leaving the computer to do the hard work. However, there are five issues that should be raised as they underlie the choices to be made.

Box 33.1	Focus on

Data issues in factor analysis

One crucial question is what sample size is appropriate for a factor analysis. There is no simple answer to this. Well, nothing straightforward anyway. Often it is suggested that for every variable in the analysis there should be several times more participants. Commonly the figure of ten times the number of variables is stipulated as an adequate sample size to yield reliable outcomes from a factor analysis. (Reliability means in this case stability of the factor structure over different studies.) However, as the advice we have seen ranges from just 2 to 20 participants per variable, you have quite a lot of discretion! The main alternative approach has been to stipulate a minimum number of participants for a factor analysis. Again, though, different sources recommend different things. We have seen sample sizes between 100 and 1000 participants recommended. For most student work, these are overwhelming numbers of participants. With the best will in the world, many student researchers would be hard pressed to obtain samples of this sort of size. Fellow students, for example, are often unwilling to spend half an hour completing yet another questionnaire for someone's student project when they have other things to do. Does this mean that students should never carry out a factor analysis?

It is not just a problem for students. Professional researchers may have problems in getting samples big enough to meet some of these criteria. This is not sloth on their part. Specific sorts of samples are notoriously difficult to obtain. How much effort would be involved in getting a sample of 100 serial killers in the United Kingdom? Again, should researchers ignore factor analysis as an analytic technique in these circumstances? There are no equally effective alternatives to factor analysis.

One can interpret all of this as implying that one should simply get as big a sample as possible given your resources bearing in mind that the more variables you include the bigger the sample size should be. Big samples lead to more stability in the analysis, but big in this case means about 500 participants, which is a substantial study. A sample size of 300 would be adequate in the eyes of most researchers. Your work is almost certain to be acceptable to most researchers if it is based on the lower figure of 300 participants. The smaller your sample size is below this, the more your work is likely to be criticised by someone. So you may need to justify your decision to use factor analysis on a smaller sample.

The important thing is to be aware of the limitations of your sample size. Discuss them in any report you write to demonstrate that you are aware of the issues. One would not claim to have obtained a reliable factor structure based on a single study so any factor structure needs more research to assess its reliability. You may find some support for your factor structure in the previous research literature. Many student projects, because of the limitations of resources, are best conceived as pilot studies not simply because of the tendency for students to use small samples. So the study is more exploratory in nature than decisive. There are a few things which you should bear in mind which help you cope better with small sample sizes or might be used to argue that your findings might be reliable despite the small sample:

- It is bad practice to simply throw any bunch of variables into a factor analysis. The axiom 'junk in, junk out' applies here. Be selective about which variables you use. The computer will cope no matter what but you are in the hot seat of having to interpret its output. Confine yourself to variables which you feel are likely to be good measures of a particular important concept. Selectivity leads to fewer variables for the factor analysis and less issues about small sample sizes.

- Be especially vigilant when you carry out your basic examination of your data using descriptive statistics prior to the factor analysis. For example, variables that have little variability; variables that produce the same response from the vast majority of participants because, for example, they are rarely agreed with; variables for which many of your participants fail to give an answer; and variables that participants have difficulty understanding may be omitted from the factor analysis. In other words, get rid of variables which are in some way problematic as they contribute junk (error) to your data. You would be well advised to do this anyway for any data. SPSS will generate a plethora of descriptive statistics to help you do this.

- The bigger the typical correlation there is between your variables, the more reliable the factor analysis is likely to be. Hence a smaller sample size might be a little more acceptable where intercorrelations are high. Similarly, the bigger the communality estimates, the smaller the sample size can be. If your communalities are all at least

.6 or greater then a small sample of around the 100 mark would be OK. Communality estimates are discussed elsewhere in this chapter.

- The more variables that you have for each factor you extract then the more stable the factor structure is likely to be.

There are other criteria that you can apply which concern the reliability of the individual factors. For example, if you have a factor with ten or more statistically significant loadings of .4 or larger with a substantial sample, that factor will tend to be reliable even with a sample of 200 or a little less (see Table 33.5 for values for statistically significant loadings).

Rotated or unrotated factors?

Factor analysis (including principal components analysis) is a mathematically based technique which has the following characteristics:

- The factors are extracted in order of magnitude from the largest to smallest in terms of the amount of variance explained by the factor. Since factors are variables they will have a certain amount of variance associated with them.

- Each of the factors explains the *maximum amount* of variance that it possibly can.

The amount of variance 'explained' by a factor is related to something called the *eigenvalue*. This is easy to calculate since it is merely the *sum* of the *squared* factor loadings of a particular factor. Thus the eigenvalue of a factor for which the factor loadings are .86, .00, .93, .00, .91 and .00 is $.86^2 + .00^2 + .93^2 + .00^2 + .91^2 + .00^2$ which equals 2.4.

But maximising each successive eigenvalue or amount of variance is a purely mathematical choice which may not offer the best factors for the purposes of understanding the conceptual underlying structure of a correlation matrix. For this reason, a number of different criteria have been suggested to determine the 'best' factors. These are collectively known as rotation or factor rotation. The way in which this is done is to adjust the factor structure in various ways. One method, Varimax, for example, involves maximising the number of high factor loadings on a factor and minimising the number of low loadings (much as in our stylised example). Quartimax, another method, seeks to minimise the number of factors needed to 'explain' each variable in the analysis. Rotation is not simple because a factor analysis generates several factors – adjustments to one factor can adversely affect the satisfactoriness of the other factors. This process is called *rotation* because in pre-computer days it involved rotating (or twisting) the axes on a series of scattergrams until a satisfactory or 'simple' (i.e. more easily interpreted) factor structure was obtained. The data points stay in the same place but the axes are rotated which means that the factor loadings on each axis (or factor) change. Nowadays we do not use graphs to obtain this simple structure since procedures such as Varimax do this for us. Principal components are the unadjusted factors which explain the greatest amounts of variance but are not always particularly easy to interpret psychologically.

These are quite abstract ideas and you may still feel a little confused as to which to use. Experimentation by statisticians suggests that the rotated factors tend to reveal underlying structures a little better than unrotated ones. We would recommend that you use rotated factors until you find a good reason not to.

Orthogonal or oblique rotation?

Routinely researchers will use *orthogonal rotations* rather than *oblique rotations*. The difference is not too difficult to grasp if you remember that factors are in essence variables, albeit supervariables:

allowed to correlate with the others. This mathematical requirement is built into the computational procedures. You can choose between Varimax, Quartimax and Equamax on SPSS. They will not give you identical outcomes because they work in different ways.

● Oblique rotation means that the factors or supervariables are allowed to correlate with each other (although they can end up uncorrelated) if this helps to simplify the interpretation of the factors. Computer procedures such as Promax and Oblimin are available on SPSS to produce correlated or oblique factor structures. The case for using oblique rotation is that there is no reason to expect that psychological constructs will be unrelated to each other. Psychological variables like depression relate to many others, for example. Since oblique rotation will not make factors correlate with each other if it is not appropriate, some researchers prefer this form of rotation. Once again, you can quickly compare oblique and orthogonal outcomes using SPSS. There may well be little difference.

In computer output you may find both a factor structure matrix and a factor pattern matrix. If your factors are orthogonal then these two matrices will be identical. The factor structure matrix consists of factor loadings in the form of correlation coefficients much as we have discussed throughout this chapter. The factor pattern matrix consists of regression coefficients. Since standardised regression weights and correlation coefficients for the same data are identical then the two matrices are the same. But oblique rotation changes things. Where there has been oblique (but not orthogonal) rotation then the pattern and a structure matrix are not the same basically because the factors correlate. The factor loadings as correlation coefficients are not the same as the regression coefficients where the factors have been allowed to correlate with each other. It is possible to use the regression weights from the factor pattern matrix to reproduce the original variables. The factor structure matrix cannot be used in this way when oblique rotation is applied. However, concentrate on the factor structure matrix as this is the one which involves factor loadings as correlation coefficients.

There is something known as *second-order factor analysis* which can be done if you have correlated factors. Since the oblique factors are supervariables which correlate with each other, it is possible to produce a correlation matrix of the correlations between factors. This matrix can then be factor analysed to produce new factors. Since second-order factors are 'factors of factors' they are very general indeed. You cannot get second-order factors from uncorrelated factors since the correlation matrix would contain only zeros. Some of the classic controversy among factor analysts is related to the use of such second-order factors.

How many factors?

We may have misled you into thinking that factor analysis reduces the number of variables that you have to consider. It can, but not automatically so, because without some intervention on your part there could be as many factors as variables in the analysis. This would not be very useful since it means that the factor matrix is as complex as the correlation matrix. Furthermore, interpreting all of the factors is not possible since the later ones tend to be junk consisting of nothing other than error variance.

The number of factors need to be limited to 'statistically significant' ones. There are no commonly used, universally accepted tests of the significance of a factor. However, one procedure is to ignore any factor for which the eigenvalue is less than 1.00 (this is the Kaiser test). The reason for this is that a factor with an eigenvalue of less than 1.00 is not receiving its 'fair share' of variance by chance. A factor with an eigenvalue under 1.00 cannot possibly be statistically significant – although an eigenvalue greater than 1.00 does not necessarily establish statistical significance. For most purposes it is a good enough criterion although skilled statisticians might have other views. Some suggest that the figure should be an eigenvalue of .7 whereas others suggest a figure above 1.0. It is best to stick with the conventional figure of 1.0.

Another procedure is the scree test. This is based simply on a graph of the amount of variance explained by successive factors in the factor analysis. The point at which the curve flattens out indicates the start of the non-significant factors. It may sound difficult to do this but almost invariably the point of flattening out is obvious. You can see an example of a scree plot produced by SPSS in Screenshot 33.5. If you are uncertain, then try the competing numbers of factors in several factor analyses (and rotations).

One final criterion for the number of factors worth trying is that of *trivial factors*. These are factors which have less than two or three variables loading above the level of significance. This cut point is a loading of .4 but varies according to sample size. You may find factors which only have bigger loadings on just one variable or they may have no loadings above the cut point. When these trivial factors start emerging in the factor structure then you have enough factors. They will be the factors with the smaller eigenvalues as they account for little variance. Some values for the statistical significance of a factor loading for different sample sizes are given in Table 33.5. More sample sizes are to be found in Pituch and Stevens (2016).

Getting the number of factors right matters most of all when rotation to a simpler structure is involved. Too many factors and the variance tends to be shared very thinly. The criteria given above for the number of factors may well give slightly different numbers. They are different criteria after all. There is nothing wrong with trying the various numbers of factors that the different criteria suggest especially as these are quickly calculated on SPSS and similar computer programs. So try the effect of varying the number of factors just to see what happens. There is generally little point in trying more factors than either the scree or eigenvalues tests suggest. A researcher's preference is usually for a factor structure which has the least possible number of factors.

Communality

Although up to this point we have said that the diagonal of a correlation matrix from top left to bottom right will consists of ones, an exception is usually made in factor analysis. The reason for this is quite simple if you compare the two correlation matrices in Tables 33.6 and 33.7.

You will notice that matrix 1 contains substantially higher correlation coefficients than matrix 2. Consequently the ones in the diagonal of matrix 2 contribute a disproportionately large amount of variance to the matrix compared to the equivalent ones in

Table 33.5	Minimum value of a factor loading to be statistically significant at various sample sizes
Sample size	Minimum factor loading
600	.2
300	.3
200	.4
100	.5

Table 33.6	Correlation matrix 1		
	Variable *A*	Variable *B*	Variable *C*
Variable *A*	1.00	.50	.40
Variable *B*	.50	1.00	.70
Variable *C*	.40	.70	1.00

Table 33.7	Correlation matrix 2		
	Variable *A*	Variable *B*	Variable *C*
Variable *A*	1.00	.12	.20
Variable *B*	.12	1.00	.30
Variable *C*	.20	.30	1.00

matrix 1 (where the rest of the correlations are quite large anyway). The factors obtained from matrix 2 would largely be devoted to variance coming from the diagonal. In other words, the factors would have to correspond more or less to variables *A*, *B* and *C*. This is hardly a satisfactory simplification of the correlation matrix. Since most psychological data tend to produce low correlations, we need to do something about the problem. The difficulty is more severe when the intercorrelations between the variables tend to be small. This is simply because the value in the diagonal is disproportionately larger than the correlations.

The solution usually adopted is to substitute different values in the diagonal of the correlation matrix in place of the ones seen above. These replacement values are called the *communalities*. Theoretically, a variable can be thought of as being made of three different types of variance:

- *Specific variance* Variance which can only be measured by that variable and is specific to that variable.

- *Common variance* Variance which a particular variable has in common with other variables.

- *Error variance* Just completely random variance which is not systematically related to any other source of variance.

A correlation of any variable with itself is exceptional in that it consists of all of these types of variance (that is why the correlation of a variable with itself is 1.00), whereas a correlation between two different variables consists only of variance that is common to the two variables (common variance).

Essentially, communality is the correlation that a variable has with itself based solely on common variance. Of course, this is a curious abstract concept. Obviously it is not possible to know the value of this correlation directly since variables do not come ready broken down into the three different types of variance. All that we can do is estimate the communality as best we can. The highest correlation that a variable has with any other variable in a correlation matrix is used as the communality. This is shown in Table 33.8.

Table 33.8	Correlation matrix 1 (communality italicised in each column)		
	Variable *A*	Variable *B*	Variable *C*
Variable *A*	1.00	.50	.40
Variable *B*	*.50*	1.00	*.70*
Variable *C*	.40	*.70*	1.00

So if we want to know the communality of variable *A* we look to see what its highest correlation with anything else is (in this case it is the .50 correlation with variable *B*). Similarly we estimate the communality of variable *B* as .70 since this is its highest correlation with any other variable in the matrix. Likewise the communality of variable *C* is also .70 since this is its highest correlation in the matrix with another variable. We then substitute these communalities in the diagonal of the matrix as shown in Table 33.9.

These initial estimates can be a little rough and ready. Normally in factor analysis, following an initial stab using methods like this, better approximations are made by using the 'significant' factor loading matrix in order to 'reconstruct' the correlation matrix. For any pair of variables, the computer multiplies their two loadings on each factor, then sums the total. Thus if part of the factor loading matrix was as shown in Table 33.10, the correlation between variables *A* and *B* is $(.50 \times .40) + (.70 \times .30) = .20 + .21 = .41$. This is not normally the correlation between variables *A* and *B* found in the original data but one based on the previously estimated communality and the significant factors. However, following such a procedure for the entire correlation matrix does provide a slightly different value for each communality compared with our original estimate. These new communality estimates can be used as part of the factor analysis. The whole process can be repeated over and over again until the best possible estimate is achieved. This is usually referred to as a process of *iteration* – successive approximations to give the best estimate.

This method of calculating communality is easily grasped and was the method that would have been used for some of the classic work of intelligence and personality in psychology. Of course there are other ways which are not so intuitive, such as by using multiple regression (Chapter 34). So if you have variables *A, B, C, D* and *E* to take a small

Table 33.9	Correlation matrix 1 but using communality estimates in the diagonal		
	Variable *A*	Variable *B*	Variable *C*
Variable *A*	.50	.50	.40
Variable *B*	.50	.70	.70
Variable *C*	.40	.70	.70

Table 33.10	Part of a factor loading matrix	
	Factor 1	Factor 2
Variable *A*	.50	.70
Variable *B*	.40	.30

illustration, it is possible to estimate the communality of variable A by using variables B, C, D and E as predictors in a multiple regression to predict A. The multiple correlation squared (multiple R^2) obtained by this calculation provides the initial estimate of the communality for variable A. Of course, SPSS and other statistical packages take care of these calculations. You do not have to use communalities. Principal components analysis does not.

■ Factor scores

We often carry out a factor analysis to determine whether we can group a larger number of variables such as questionnaire items into a smaller set of 'supervariables' or factors. For example, we may have made up 10 questions to measure the way in which people express anxiety and a further 10 questions to assess how they exhibit depression. Suppose that the results of our factor analysis show that all or almost all of the 10 questions on anxiety load most highly on one of these factors and all or almost all of the 10 questions on depression load most highly on the other factor. This result would suggest that rather than analyse each of the 20 questions separately we could combine the answers to the 10 questions on anxiety to form one measure of anxiety and combine the answers to the 10 questions on depression to form a measure of depression. In other words, rather than have 20 different measures to analyse, we now have two measures. This greatly simplifies our analysis.

The most common way of combining variables which are measured on the same scale is simply to add together the numbers which represent that scale. This is sometimes referred to as a summative scale. For example, if respondents only had to answer 'Yes' or 'No' to each of our 20 questions, then we could assign a number to an answer which indicated the greater presence (or absence) of either anxiety or depression. We could assign the number 2 to show the presence of either anxiety or depression and the number 1 to show the absence of either anxiety or depression. Alternatively, we could assign the number 1 to indicate the presence of either anxiety or depression and the number 0 to the absence of either. We would then add together the numbers for the anxiety items to form a total or overall anxiety score and do the same for the depression items. If we had assigned the number 2 to indicate the presence of either anxiety or depression, then the total score for these two variables would vary between a minimum score of 10 and a maximum score of 20. Alternatively, if we had assigned the number 1 to reflect the presence of either anxiety or depression, then the total score for these two variables would vary between a minimum score of 0 and a maximum score of 10.

Another way of assigning numbers to each of the variables or items that go to make up a factor is to use the factor score for each factor. There are various ways of producing factor scores and this is generally done with the computer program which carries out the factor analysis. A factor score may be based on all the items in the factor analysis. The items which load or correlate most highly on a factor are generally weighted the most heavily. So, for example, anxiety items which load or correlate most highly with the anxiety factor will make a larger contribution to the factor score for that factor. Factor scores may be positive or negative but will have a mean of zero. The main advantage of factor scores is that they are more closely related to the results of the factor analysis. In other words, scores represent these factors more accurately. Their disadvantage is that the results of a factor analysis of the same variables are likely to vary according to the method used and from sample to sample so that the way that the factor scores are derived is likely to vary. Unless we have access to the data, we will not know how the factor scores were calculated.

One key thing to remember about factor scores is that they allow you to use the factors as if they were like any other variable. So they can be correlated with other variables, for example, or they might be used as the dependent variable in ANOVA.

33.5   Exploratory and confirmatory factor analysis

So far, we have presented factor analysis as a means of simplifying complex data matrices. In other words, factor analysis is being used to explore the structure (and, as a consequence, the meaning) of the data. This is clearly a very useful analytical tool. Of course, the danger is that the structure obtained through these essentially mathematical procedures is assumed to be the basis for a definitive interpretation of the data. This is problematic because of the inherent variability of most psychological measurements which suggest that the factors obtained in exploratory factor analysis may themselves be subject to variability.

As a consequence, it has become increasingly common to question the extent to which exploratory factor analysis can be relied upon. One development from this is the notion of confirmatory factor analysis. Put as simply as possible, confirmatory factor analysis is a means of confirming that the factor structure obtained in exploratory factor analysis is robust and not merely the consequence of the whims of random variability in one's data. Obviously it would be silly to take the data and re-do the factor analysis. That could only serve to check for computational errors. However, one could obtain a new set of data using more or less the same measures as in the original study. Then it is possible to factor analyse these data to test the extent to which the characteristics of the original factor analysis are reproduced in the fresh factor analysis of fresh data. In this way, it may be possible to confirm the original analysis. Box 33.2 contains more information about confirmatory factor analysis. Figure 33.1 gives the key steps in exploratory factor analysis.

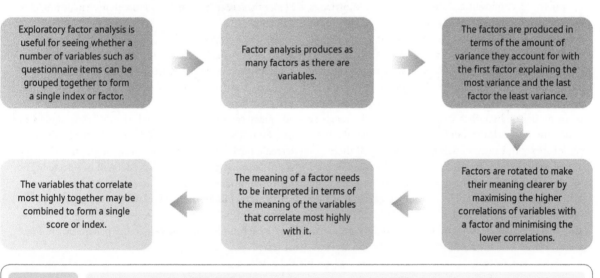

FIGURE 33.1   Conceptual steps for exploratory factor analysis

---

Box 33.2	Key concepts

Confirmatory versus exploratory factor analysis

Most of this chapter discusses factor analysis as a way of exploring data. Exploratory factor analysis is best regarded as generating hypotheses about the nature of relationships between variables than definitive evidence of the underlying structure of the data. There are a number of reasons why one should be careful about exploratory factor analysis. Sometimes we have to interpret the factors on the basis of very limited information. Also, the results of a factor analysis are somewhat dependent on the choice of method of factor analysis. This is partly why some authorities write of factor analysis as being a good hypothesis-generating rather than hypothesis-confirming tool. It is probably going too far to describe exploratory factor analysis as 'shotgun empiricism' or 'empiricism gone mad'.

So why confirmatory factor analysis? Exploratory factor analysis is generally regarded as a very powerful analytic technique. The problem lies more with the way in which it is employed. Ideally, in research, knowledge and understanding are built on previous research. Out of this previous research, 'models' or sets of variables are built up which effectively account for observed data. Frequently factor analysis is used simply to explore the data and to suggest the underlying nature of the relationships between variables. As a consequence, there is no model or hypothesis to test. It is at the stage at which there is a clear model or hypothesis that analyses can properly test such models or hypotheses. If there is a model or hypothesis available, factor analysis can be used to test it. There is a traditional approach to this employing principal axes factor analysis. The researcher would include 'indicator variables' in the data to be factor analysed. These indicator variables would have predicted relationships with the factors. For example, if a factor is

proposed to be 'feminist attitudes' an appropriate indicator variable for this might be gender since the researcher might suppose that females would be more inclined towards feminist views. Gender would load heavily on the factor if the factor and its relationship with the indicator variable were as expected by the researcher.

The modern approach uses some form of structural equation modelling such as is employed by the computer software LISREL. The researcher begins with hypotheses about the relationships between the variables and factors as well as which (if any) factors are interrelated. The hypotheses are based on theoretical and empirical resources built up from previous investigations in that research field. Typically the researcher will have an idea of how many different factors are required to account for the data which ultimately consist of a correlation matrix of relationships between variables. Of course, a number of different models will always be potentially viable for any given set of data. Hence the researcher will have more than a single model to compare.

Models are specified by the research by fixing (or freeing) certain specific characteristics of the model. This could be the number of factors or the size of the correlation between factors or any other aspect deemed appropriate. These various models are compared for their adequacy by assessing how well the different models fit the data. The best-fitting model is, of course, the preferred model – though if there is any competition then the simplest (most parsimonious) model will be selected. The fit of the models to the data is assessed by a number of statistics including the chi-square/degrees of freedom or a number of alternative statistics. Of course, there may be a better model that the researcher has not formulated or tested

---

33.6	Example of factor analysis from the literature

Butler (1995b) points out that children at school spend a lot of time looking at the work of their classmates. Although the evidence for this is clear, the reasons for their doing so are not researched. She decided to explore children's motives for looking at the work of other children and proposed a four-component model of the reasons they gave.

Some children could be concerned mainly about learning to do the task and developing their skills and mastery of a particular type of task; other children might be more concerned with the quality of the product of their work. Furthermore, a child's motivation might be to evaluate themselves (self-evaluation); on the other hand, their primary motivation might be in terms of evaluating the product of their work on the task. In other words, Butler proposed two dichotomies which might lead to a fourfold categorisation of motivations for looking at other children's work (Table 33.11).

Table 33.11	Butler's model of reasons to look at the work of others	
	Product improvement	Self-improvement
Performance oriented	Doing better than others with little effort	Comparing task skills with those of others
Mastery oriented	Wanting to learn and improve	Checking whether own work needs improving

Based on this sort of reasoning, the researcher developed a questionnaire consisting of 32 items, 'Why I looked at other children's work'. Raters allocated a number of items to each of the above categories and the best eight items in each category were chosen for this questionnaire.

An example of a question from this questionnaire is:

I wanted to see if my work is better or worse than others.

The children's answers had been coded from 1 to 5 according to their extent of agreement with the statements.

Each child was given a page of empty circles on which they drew many pictures using these circles as far as possible. When this had been completed, they answered the 'Why I looked at other children's work' questionnaire. The researcher's task was then to establish whether her questionnaire actually consisted of the four independent 'reasons' for looking at the work of other children during the activity.

An obvious approach to this questionnaire is to correlate the scores of the sample of children on the various items on the questionnaire. This produced a 32×32 correlation matrix which could be factor analysed to see whether the four categories of motives for looking at other children's work actually emerged:

Principal-components analysis[1] with oblique rotation[2] yielded five factors with eigenvalues greater than 1.0[3] which accounted for 62% of the variance[4]. . . Three factors corresponded to the mastery-oriented product improvement (MPI), performance-oriented product improvement (PPI), and performance-oriented self-evaluation (PSE) categories, but some items loaded high on more than one factor[5]. Items expected a priori to load on a mastery-oriented self-evaluation (MSE) category formed two factors. One (MSE) conformed to the original conceptualization, and the other (checking procedure [CP]) reflected concern with clarifying task demands and instructions. (Butler, 1995b, p. 350, superscripts added)

The meaning of the superscripted passages is as follows:

1. Principal components analysis was the type of factor analysis employed – it means that communalities were *not* used. Otherwise the term 'principal axes' is used where communalities have been estimated.

2. Oblique rotation means that the factors may well correlate with each other. That is, if one correlates the factor loadings on each factor with the factor loadings on each of the other factors, a correlation matrix would be produced in which the correlations may differ from zero. Orthogonal rotation would have produced a correlation matrix of the factors in which the correlation coefficients are all zero.

3. This means that there are five factors which are potentially statistically significant – the minimum value of a potentially significant eigenvalue is 1.0 although this is only a *minimum* value and no guarantee of statistical significance.

4. These five factors explain 62% of the variance, apparently. That is, the sum of the squared factor loadings on these five factors is 62% of the squared correlation coefficients in the 32 × 32 correlation matrix. Doing this is problematic for oblique rotation as the factors are correlated which means that the variance of a factor is not specific to that factor.

5. In factor analysis, some items may load on more than one factor – this implies that they are measuring aspects of more than one factor.

Table 33.12 gives an adapted version of the factor analysis table in which some items have been omitted for simplicity's sake in the presentation. You will notice that many factor loadings are missing. This is because the researcher has chosen not to report low factor loadings on each factor. This has the advantage of simplifying the factor loading matrix by emphasising the stronger relationships. The disadvantage is that the reporting of the analysis is incomplete and it is impossible for readers of the report to explore the data further. (If the original 32 × 32 correlation matrix had been included then it would be possible to reproduce the factor analysis and carry out variants on the original analysis.)

The researcher has inserted titles for the factors in the matrix. Do not forget that these titles are arbitrary and are the researcher's interpretation. Consequently, you may wish to consider the extent to which her titles are adequate. The way to do this is to examine the set of questions which load highly on each of the factors to see whether a radically different interpretation is possible. Having done this you may feel that Butler's interpretations are reasonable. Butler's difficulty is that she has five factors when her model would predict only four. While this means that she is to a degree wrong, her model is substantially correct because the four factors she predicted appear to be present in the factor analysis. The problem is that some of the questionnaire items do not appear to measure what she suggested they should measure.

Some researchers might be tempted to re-do the factor analysis with just four factors. The reason for this is that the proper number of factors to extract in factor analysis is not clear-cut. Because Butler used a minimal cut-off point for significant factors (eigenvalues of 1.0 and above), she may have included more factors than she needed. It would strengthen Butler's argument if such a re-analysis found that four factors reproduced Butler's model better. However, we should stress that factor analysis does not lead to hard-and-fast solutions and that Butler would be better confirming her claims by the analysis of a fresh study using the questionnaire.

| Table 33.12 | Butler's factor loading matrix | | | | |

Item: I wanted to see ...	Performance-oriented self-evaluation	Mastery-oriented product improvement	Checking procedures	Performance-oriented product improvement	Mastery oriented self-evaluation
Who had the most ideas	.61	–	–	−.37	–
Whose work was best	.74	–	–	–	–
If others had better ideas than me	.68	–	–	–	–
Whether there were ideas I hadn't thought of	–	.68	–	–	.34
Ideas which would help me develop my own ideas	–	.68	–	–	–
If I'd understood what to do	–	–	.85	–	–
Whether my drawings were appropriate	–	–	.86	–	–
If I was working at the appropriate speed	–	–	–	–	.63
How I was progressing on this new task	–	–	–	–	.70
I didn't want to hand in poor work	–	–	–	.67	–
I didn't want my page to be emptier than others'	–	–	–	.74	–

Factor loadings with absolute values less than .30 are not reported.
Source: Table adapted from Butler (1995b).

33.7 Reporting the results

There is no standard way of reporting the results of a factor analysis which will suffice irrespective of circumstances. However, it is essential to report the type of factor analysis, the type of rotation, how the number of factors was determined, and the relative importance of the factors in terms of variance explained or eigenvalues. Although the original author's description is given above, the following is another way of writing much the same:

A principal components factor analysis was conducted on the correlation matrix of the 32 items on the 'Why I looked at other children's work' questionnaire. Five factors were extracted which accounted for 62% of the variance overall. Three of these factors corresponded to components of the proposed model. Oblique rotation of the factors was employed which yielded the factor structure given in Table 33.12. One factor was identified as mastery-oriented product improvement (MPI), another was performance-oriented product improvement (PPI) and a third was performance-oriented self-evaluation (PSE). These are as the model predicted. The fourth category predicted by the model (mastery-oriented self-evaluation (MSE)) was also identified but some of the items expected to load on this actually formed the fifth factor, checking procedures.

Notice that some aspects of this description would be fairly general to any factor analysis, but there are other aspects which are idiosyncratic in nature and due to the distinctive characteristics and purposes of this particular study. Ideally, you should study reports of factor analyses which are similar to yours (coming from the same area of research) for more precise examples of how your work could be reported.

Research examples

Factor analysis

Gibbs and Powell (2012) studied the beliefs of teachers in the efficacy of their teaching skills in dealing with children's classroom behaviour as well as the question of whether the use of exclusion as a sanction was associated with this. Over 200 primary and nursery school teachers in the UK completed questionnaires assessing their efficacy beliefs. They used principal components factor analysis on the efficacy belief items together with a scree test to estimate the proper number of factors and were guided too by previous research findings. Promax rotation to simple structure was also applied. Three factors accounted for the teachers' individual efficacy beliefs. These were labelled a) classroom management, b) children's engagement and c) instructional strategies. For individual efficacy beliefs, none of the factors was associated with school exclusions. However, an analysis of collective efficacy beliefs showed some evidence of an association with exclusion.

Motes and colleagues (2008) discuss the research on spatial memory for moving targets. This seems to suggest that this ability is frequently based on the implied direction of momentum of the target and implied gravity. Implied gravity is illustrated by the fact that after viewing a drawing of a flowerpot on a table and then viewing a flowerpot without support then the position of the flowerpot is often judged to be lower than it actually it is – i.e. a shift in the direction of gravity. Similar effects are created by downwardly or horizontally moving targets. They set up a situation in which participants viewed targets moving horizontally in a left–right direction and then, finally disappearing. Alternatively, as a control, they were briefly shown a stationary target. Both targets disappeared. The participants in the research were then asked to show the point at which the target disappeared. The vertical (gravity) error was measured and could be negative or positive according to whether it was in the direction of gravity. The horizontal (momentum) error was measured and could be negative or positive depending on whether the error was in the direction of momentum or not. The misplacements in the location identified were subjected to a principal components factor analysis in which rows were the participants and the columns were the horizontal and vertical displacement for each target activity. Overall, the analysis indicated that two underlying dimensions account for this variability. That is, the expected implied gravity and implied direction of momentum.

Pechey and Halligan (2011) studied anomalous experiences such as hearing voices when there was nobody around. They occur in psychiatric conditions and in non-patients also. The researchers studied the distribution and relationships of self-reported anomalous experiences in a sample of 1000 UK non-clinical participants. Nearly half of the sample of the general population reported that anomalous experiences occurred sometimes or often. In order to know whether there were common underlying factors to delusional beliefs, the researchers carried out exploratory factor analysis. As an indication of the stability of the factor structure they analysed two halves of the sample separately. Principal components factor analysis was carried out. The Kaiser test which counts factors with an eigenvalue of 1.00 or more suggested two factors but a scree test indicated just one factor. So a single component solution was adopted which accounted for about a third or more of the variance explained. The experiences which loaded most highly on this single factor included 1) seen or sensed a ghost, 2) sensed when a friend or family member was in trouble, 3) seen things which other people cannot, and 4) felt that familiar objects appeared different even though they knew they hadn't changed. These had factor loadings of about .6 or greater.

Key points

- Do not be afraid to try out factor analysis on your data. It is not difficult to do if you are familiar with using simpler techniques on a computer.

- Do not panic when faced with output from a factor analysis. It can be very lengthy and confusing because it contains things that mere mortals simply do not want to know. Usually the crucial aspects of the factor analysis are to be found towards the end of the output. If in doubt, do not hesitate to contact your local expert – computer output is not always user friendly.

- Take the factor analysis slowly – it takes a while to build your skills sufficiently to be totally confident.

- Do not forget that interpreting the factors can be fairly subjective – you might not always see things as other people do and it might not be you who is wrong.

- Factor analysis can be applied only to correlations calculated using the Pearson correlation formula.

COMPUTER ANALYSIS

Principal components analysis using SPSS

Data
- Name the variables in 'Variable View' of the 'Data Editor'.
- Enter the data under the appropriate variable names in 'Data View' of the 'Data Editor' (Screenshot 33.1).

Analysis
- Select 'Analyze', 'Dimension Reduction' and 'Factor. . .' (Screenshot 33.2).
- Move the variables to be analysed to the 'Variables:' box either singly or altogether by holding down Shift and selecting all items (Screenshot 33.3).

2
- Select 'Descriptives. . .', 'Univariate descriptives' and 'Continue'.
- Select 'Extraction. . .', 'Method' of extraction if different from principal components, 'Scree test' and 'Continue'.

3
- Select 'Rotation. . .', method of rotation and 'Continue'.
- Select 'Options. . .', 'Sorted by size', 'Continue' and 'OK'.

Output
- The analysis may not complete if any variable has no variance and if the number of iterations needed is greater than the default of 25. Adjust analysis accordingly.
- Check the sample size in the 'Descriptive Statistics' table.

2
- Check the meaning of the variables correlating most highly on the rotated factors to determine the meaning of the factors (Screenshot 33.4).

3
- You may need to redo the analysis on the basis of your judgement of how many factors should be extracted. This judgement may depend on the outcome of the Scree test (Screenshot 33.5).

FIGURE 33.2   SPSS steps for exploratory factor analysis

Interpreting and reporting the output

- Factor analysis produces a lot of output on SPSS and we can only present a small amount. It is important to make sure that you obtain the 'right' number of factors which you do using the scree plot. Where the curve flattens then the factors are not significant. The interpretation of the factors is based on an examination of which variables correlate with the factor (what do these have in common?) and to a lesser extent those which do not correlate with the factor.

- You might write: 'The variables were subjected to a principal components analysis and rotated using the Varimax method. Two factors met the requirements of the scree test and these seemed to be a factor on which sensory motor skills loaded highly and another factor on which verbal skills loaded highly.'

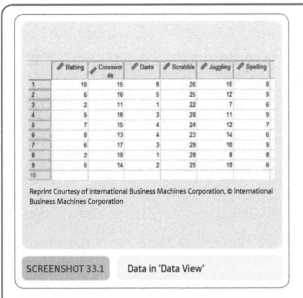

Reprint Courtesy of International Business Machines Corporation, © International Business Machines Corporation

SCREENSHOT 33.1   Data in 'Data View'

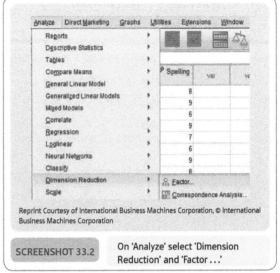

Reprint Courtesy of International Business Machines Corporation, © International Business Machines Corporation

SCREENSHOT 33.2   On 'Analyze' select 'Dimension Reduction' and 'Factor ...'

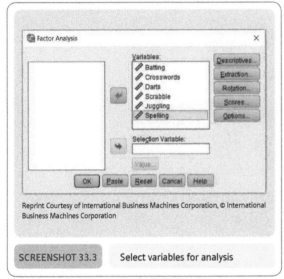

Reprint Courtesy of International Business Machines Corporation, © International Business Machines Corporation

SCREENSHOT 33.3   Select variables for analysis

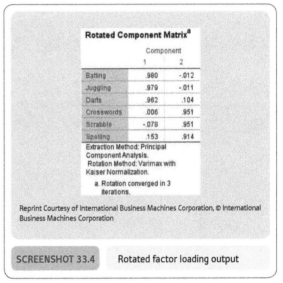

Reprint Courtesy of International Business Machines Corporation, © International Business Machines Corporation

SCREENSHOT 33.4   Rotated factor loading output

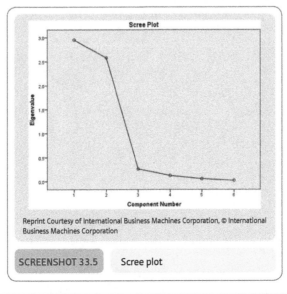

Reprint Courtesy of International Business Machines Corporation, © International Business Machines Corporation

SCREENSHOT 33.5   Scree plot

Recommended further reading

Bryman, A., & Cramer, D. (2011). *Quantitative data analysis with IBM SPSS 17, 18 and 19: A guide for social scientists* (Chapter 11). London, UK: Routledge.

Child, D. (1970). *The essentials of factor analysis. London,* UK: Holt, Rinehart & Winston.

Kline, P. (1994). *An easy guide to factor analysis.* London, UK: Routledge.

Tabachnick, B. G., & Fidell, L. S. (2013). *Using multivariate statistics* (6th ed., Chapter 13). New York, NY: Allyn & Bacon.

CHAPTER 34

Multiple regression and multiple correlation

- Up to this point, we have dealt with regression and correlation involving just two variables – variable X and variable Y. Variable X is the independent or predictor variable and variable Y the dependent or criterion variable. Causality is not implied.

- Multiple regression and correlation extend the number of X variables and identify each with a subscript $(X_1, X_2, X_3, \ldots)$. Only one Y variable is involved.

- Multiple regression and correlation show the best predictors of the Y variable. The weight to give to each predictor is calculated to yield the best prediction or correlation.

- Multiple regression has many variants which work in slightly different ways.

- Usually there are two versions of multiple regression. One works with the original scores and yields unstandardised regression or b-weights. Another version works with the scores turned into z-scores. This yields standardised regression or beta (β) weights which are essentially correlation coefficients. The advantage of standardised or beta weights is that they allow the influence of the different variables to be compared directly.

Preparation

Revise Chapter 9 on simple regression and the standard error in relation to regression. You should also be aware of standard scores from Chapter 6 and the coefficient of determination for the correlation coefficient in Chapter 8. Optimal understanding of this chapter is aided if you have insight into the basic concepts of partial correlation and zero-order correlation described in Chapter 32.

34.1 Introduction

Traditionally, psychologists assumed that the primary purpose of research is to isolate the influence of one variable on another. So they might study whether paternal absence from the family leads to poor mathematical skills in children. However, other variables might influence a child's mathematical skills. Away from the psychology laboratory, variables do not act independently of each other. The obvious alternative approach is to explore the complex pattern of variables which relate to mathematical skills such as maternal educational level, the quality of mathematical teaching at school, the child's general level of intelligence or IQ, whether or not the child went to nursery school, the gender of the child and so forth. We rarely know every factor related to important variables like mathematical skill prior to beginning our research. Consequently, we may choose to include, speculatively, variables which prove to be poor predictors of the criterion. Multiple regression helps us choose empirically the most effective set of predictors for any criterion.

Multiple regression can be carried out with scores or standardised scores (z-scores). Standardised multiple regression has the advantage of making the regression values directly analogous to correlation coefficients. This makes it easy to compare the influence of different variables. In unstandardised multiple regression the variables are left in their original form. Standardised and unstandardised multiple regression are usually computed simultaneously by computer programs including SPSS (see Box 34.1).

Box 34.1 Focus on

Standardised or unstandardised regression weights

Regression can involve the raw scores or standard scores. Computers will usually print out both sorts.

Regression involving 'standard scores' gives regression coefficients (weights) which can more readily be compared in terms of their size since they range between +1.0 and −1.0 like simple correlation coefficients (i.e. Pearson correlation). In other words, the predictor variables are comparable irrespective of the units of measurement on which they were originally based. This is just like any other standard scores (Chapter 6). The regression weights for this are usually called beta (β) weights.

Regression involving 'non-standardised scores' or raw scores is about the 'nuts and bolts' of prediction. The unstandardised regression coefficient (weight) can take, theoretically, any positive or negative value. Like our account of simple regression, it provides predicted numerical values for the criterion variable based on an individual's scores on the various predictor variables. However, the size of the regression coefficient (weight) is no indication of the importance of the unstandardised predictor since the size is dependent on the units of measurement involved. The unstandardised regression weight is usually given the symbol b.

34.2 Theoretical considerations

The techniques described in this chapter concern linear multiple regression which assumes that the relationships between variables fall approximately on a straight line.

Multiple regression is an extension of simple (or bivariate) regression (Chapter 9). In simple regression, a single dependent variable (or criterion variable) is related to a single independent variable (or predictor variable). For example, marital satisfaction may be regressed against the degree to which the partners have similar personalities. In other words, can marital satisfaction be predicted from the degree of personality similarity between partners? In multiple regression, on the other hand, the criterion is regressed against several potential predictors. For example, to what extent is marital satisfaction related to various factors such as socio-economic status of both partners, similarity in socio-economic status, religious affiliation, similarity in religious affiliation, duration of courtship, age of partners at marriage and so on? Of course, personality similarity might be included in the list of predictors studied.

Multiple regression serves two main functions:

1. To determine the minimum number of predictors needed to predict a criterion. Some of the predictors which are significantly related to the criterion may also be correlated with each other and so may not all be necessary to predict the criterion. Assume, for example, that the two predictors of attraction to one's spouse and commitment to one's marriage both correlate highly with each other. In addition, both these variables are positively related to the criterion of marital satisfaction. However, marital commitment is more strongly related to marital satisfaction than is attraction to the spouse. Since most of the variation between marital satisfaction and attraction to the spouse was also shared with marital commitment, then marital commitment alone may be sufficient to predict marital satisfaction. Another example of this would be the industrial psychologist who wished to use psychological tests to select the best applicants for a job. Obviously a lot of time and money could be saved if redundant or very overlapping tests could be weeded out, leaving just a minimum number of tests which predict worker quality.

2. To explore whether certain predictors remain significantly related to the criterion when other variables are controlled or held constant. For example, marital commitment might be partly a function of religious belief so that those who are more religious may be more satisfied with their marriage. We may be interested in determining whether marital commitment is still significantly related to marital satisfaction when strength of religious belief is controlled.

When trying to understand multiple regression, it is useful to remember the main features of simple regression. These are listed below as a quick summary of what you need to know about simple regression in order to understand multiple regression:

- Simple regression can be represented by the scatterplot in Figure 34.1 in which values of the criterion are arranged along the vertical axis and values of the predictor are arranged along the horizontal axis. For example, marital satisfaction may be the criterion and personality similarity the predictor. Each point on the scatterplot indicates the position of the criterion and predictor scores for a particular individual in the sample. The relationship between the criterion and the predictor is shown by the slope of the straight line through the points on the scattergram. This best-fitting straight line is the one which minimises the sum of the (squared) distances between the points and their position on the line. This slope is known as the regression line or the line of best fit and the slope of this line is given by the regression coefficient.

- The intercept constant is the point at which the regression line intersects or cuts the vertical axis, in other words, the value on the vertical axis when the value on the horizontal axis is zero. Confusingly, in multiple regression this is sometimes referred to as the coefficient of the intercept. It is a constant and so is not variable.

- To determine the predicted score of the criterion from a particular score of the predictor, we draw a line parallel to the vertical axis from the score on the horizontal axis to the regression line. From here we draw a second line parallel to the horizontal axis to the vertical axis, which gives us the predicted score of the criterion. More precisely, we

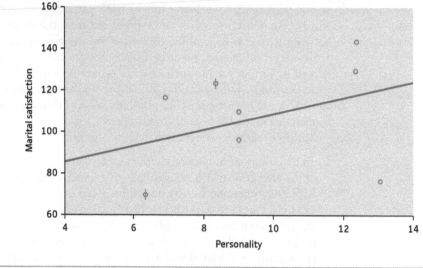

FIGURE 34.1 Simple scatterplot

can use the regression weights to make our prediction. In this, we simply multiply the regression weight by the score that we are interested in on the independent variable and add the regression weight (i.e. cut point) for the intercept. This gives us our predicted score.

● Unless there is a perfect relationship between the predictor and the criterion, the predicted score of the criterion will usually differ from the actual score for a particular case.

● Unlike the correlation coefficient, regression is dependent on the variability of the units of measurement involved. This makes regressions on different samples and different variables very difficult to compare. However, we can standardise the scores on the predictor and the criterion variables. By expressing them as standard scores (i.e. z-scores), each variable will have a mean of 0 and a standard deviation of 1. Furthermore, the intercept or intercept constant will always be 0 in these circumstances.

■ Regression equations

Simple regression is usually expressed in terms of the following regression equation as we have already mentioned in the brief notes on simple regression:

$$
\begin{array}{ccccc}
Y & = & a & + & bX
\end{array}
$$

Y		a		bX
predicted score on criterion variable		intercept constant		regression coefficient $\times$ predictor score

The equation describes the relationship between the criterion and the predictor ignoring any error variance. So to predict a particular criterion score, we multiply the particular score of the predictor by the regression coefficient and add to it the intercept constant.

When the scores of the criterion and the predictor are transformed or standardised to z-scores, the regression coefficient is the same as Pearson's correlation coefficient and ranges from +1.00 through .00 to −1.00. Regression weights standardised in this way are known as beta weights.

In multiple regression, the regression equation is the same except that there are several predictors and each predictor has its own (partial) regression coefficient (Figure 34.2):

$$Y = a + b_1X_1 + b_2X_2 + b_3X_3 + \ldots$$

A partial regression coefficient expresses the relationship between a particular predictor and the criterion controlling for, or partialling out, the relationship between that predictor and all the other predictors in the equation. This ensures that each predictor variable provides an independent contribution to the prediction.

The relationship between the criterion and the predictors is often described in terms of the percentage of variance of the criterion that is *explained* or *accounted for* by the predictors. (This is much like the coefficient of determination for the correlation coefficient.) One way of illustrating what the partial regression coefficient means is through a Venn diagram (Figure 34.3) involving the criterion Y and the two predictors X_1 and X_2. Each of the circles signifies the amount of variance of one of the three variables. The area shaded in Figure 34.3a is common only to X_1 and Y, and represents the variance of Y that it shares with variable X_1. The shaded area in Figure 34.3b is shared only by X_2 and Y, and signifies the amount of variance of Y that it shares with variable X_2. Often a phrase like 'the amount of variance explained by variable X' is used instead of 'the amount of variance shared by variable X'. Both terms signify the amount of overlapping variance.

Selection

Since multiple regression is particularly useful with a large number of predictors, such an analysis potentially would involve many regression equations. That is to say, one might stipulate a wide variety of different 'models' to examine in the multiple regression. Obviously the complexity of the analysis could be awesome. In practice, however, a researcher does not need to consider every possible regression equation when carrying out multiple regression. This involves deciding the broad analysis strategy for the multiple regression and stipulating this as part of the analysis when using a computer package. A number of different approaches are available for selecting and testing predictors. These approaches include *hierarchical* (or *blockwise*) *selection* and *stepwise selection*. Hierarchical selection enters predictors into the regression equation on some practical or theoretical consideration. Stepwise selection employs statistical criteria to choose the smallest set of predictors which best predict the variation in the criterion. In contrast to these methods, entering all predictors into the regression equation is known as *standard* or *simultaneous* multiple regression or Entry on SPSS.

a) Simple regression

b) Multiple regression

FIGURE 34.2   Simple regression and multiple regression formula

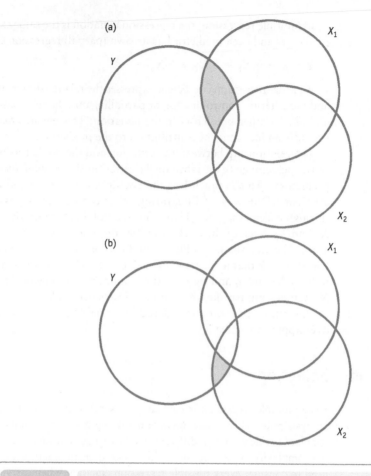

FIGURE 34.3   Venn diagrams illustrating partial regression coefficients

Finally, *setwise* regression compares all possible sets of predictors such as all predictors singly, in pairs, in trios and so on until the best set of predictors is identified.

- *Hierarchical selection* Predictors are entered singly or in blocks according to some practical or theoretical rationale. For example, potentially confounding variables such as sociodemographic factors may be statistically controlled by entering them first into the regression equation. Alternatively, similar variables may be grouped (or 'blocked') together and entered as a block, such as a block of personality variables, a block of attitude variables and so on. The computer tells us the net influence of each block in turn.

- *Stepwise selection* The predictor with the highest zero-order correlation is entered first into the regression equation if it explains a significant proportion of the variance of the criterion. The second predictor to be considered for entry is that which has the highest partial correlation with the criterion. If it explains a significant proportion of the variance of the criterion, it is entered into the equation. At this point, the predictor which was entered first is examined to see if it still explains a significant proportion of the variance of the criterion. If it no longer does so, it is dropped from the equation. The analysis continues with the predictor which has the next highest partial correlation with the criterion. The process stops when no more predictors are entered into or

Box 34.2 gives an overview of some of the possibilities for multiple regression analyses. Figure 34.4 shows the key steps in a multiple regression.

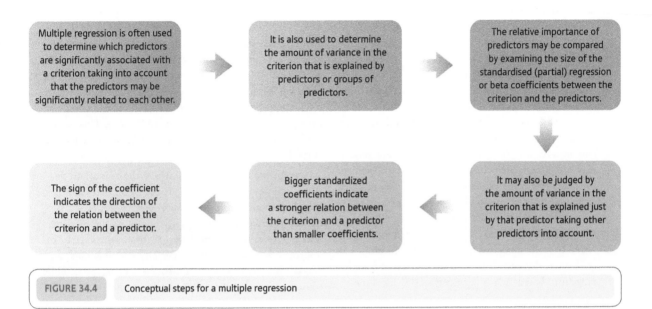

Multiple regression is often used to determine which predictors are significantly associated with a criterion taking into account that the predictors may be significantly related to each other.

It is also used to determine the amount of variance in the criterion that is explained by predictors or groups of predictors.

The relative importance of predictors may be compared by examining the size of the standardised (partial) regression or beta coefficients between the criterion and the predictors.

The sign of the coefficient indicates the direction of the relation between the criterion and a predictor.

Bigger standardized coefficients indicate a stronger relation between the criterion and a predictor than smaller coefficients.

It may also be judged by the amount of variance in the criterion that is explained just by that predictor taking other predictors into account.

FIGURE 34.4   Conceptual steps for a multiple regression

Box 34.2   Focus on

Different approaches to multiple regression

Among the choices of methods for multiple regression are the following:

- *Simultaneous:* Single-stage entry of all predictors in which all predictors are employed whether or not they are likely to be good predictors (i.e. irrespective of their potential predictive power).

- *Blocks:* There are circumstances in which the researcher does not wish to enter all of the variables at the same time. Instead, it is possible to enter the predictors in sets, one set at a time. These are sets specified by the researcher and are usually called blocks. There can be any number of variables in a block from a minimum of one. There are a number of advantages to this. Putting variables into blocks allows the variables in the block to be analysed together, either before or after other variables. One might put variables into blocks because they are similar in some way. For instance, they may be a particular type of variable (e.g. health variables,

education variables, social class variables could all form separate blocks). Another use is to 'control' for certain variables first – that is, age and social class may be entered as the first block. This is often done as a way of controlling for the influence of demographic variables. If the first block included demographic variables such as gender, age and social class, this is the equivalent of partialling them out of the analysis (see Chapter 32). Once this is done, one can compare the outcome of this block with what happens when other predictors are introduced. This is known as hierarchical multiple regression.

- *Finding best predictors:* The analysis may proceed on a stepwise basis by finding the best predictors in a set of predictors and eliminating the poor predictors. This is particularly appropriate where the main objective of the researcher is to predict with the highest possible accuracy – rather than to find explanatory models of influences on the dependent variable.

→

● *Reverse (backwards) elimination of predictors:* In this the first model is initially employed. That is, the model in our earlier example is calculated. All of the predictor variables are included. Having done that, the worst predictor is dropped. Usually this is the least significant predictor. Essentially the model is recalculated on the basis of the remaining predictors. Then the remaining worst predictor is dropped and again the model recalculated. The researcher is looking to see whether dropping a variable or variables actually substantially worsens the model. This is not simply a matter of the goodness-of-fit of the model to the data; some models may be better at predicting one value of the dependent variable rather than the other. If one is trying to avoid letting men out of prison early if they are likely to re-offend, the model which maximises the number of recidivists (re-offenders) correctly identified may be preferred over the model which misclassifies recidivists as likely to be non-recidivists. This is obviously a complex judgement based on a wide variety of considerations.

● *Mixed:* There are models which mix blocks and stepwise approaches.

In this chapter, we largely deal with individual predictors acting alone or their combined effects on the dependent variable. Following the General Linear Model (see Box 9.1), this essentially means that the analysis adds a standard amount to the prediction of the dependent variable for each increment in each of the predictor (independent) variables. In other words, the effects of the independent variables are additive. It is, however, possible to deal with interactions between predictors in multiple regression just as we do in analysis of variance (ANOVA). This is discussed in detail in Chapter 38 which deals with moderator variables.

Except for the simple case where the maximum possible accuracy of prediction is required and all variables may be entered *en masse*, the choice of approach is a matter of judgement that partly comes with experience and practice. It does no harm to try out a variety of approaches on one's data, especially if one is inexperienced with the techniques. Of course, one has to be able to justify the final choice of model.

34.3   Assumptions of multiple regression

There are a lot of assumptions underpinning the use of multiple regression which, at first sight, are rather off-putting. However, this is true of many of the techniques discussed in this book, though multiple regression tends to attract attention in this regard. You should be aware of the most important of these assumptions and requirements and take action if there is a problem. Sometimes they seem to amount to statistical overkill so we will just concentrate on the main things that a competent psychologist would be aware of and take note of:

● Linearity assumption: it is called linear regression so the expectation is that each of the predictors has a linear relationship with the dependent variable. Examining the scatterplots for the predictors against the dependent variables may suggest a non-linear relationship (that is a curved relationship). Such relationships can be made linear sometimes by transforming the variables using logarithmic and other transformations. Small deviations from the assumption of linearity do not affect the analysis much.

● It is assumed in linear regression that the residuals are normally distributed. The residuals are the difference between what the regression analysis predicts a person's score on the predicted (or outcome) variable should be and the actual score they have on that variable. It is possible to get a frequency distribution of the residuals on SPSS by selecting 'Regression' then 'Linear…' (Screenshot 34.2), 'Plots…' (Screenshot 34.3) and 'Histogram'. Check the output from this labelled Histogram. Ideally this will show an

- Outliers can be a problem with any analysis. So when you examine your data initially by doing individual scatterplots of each independent variable against the dependent variable, be on the look-out for possible outliers which would distort the analysis. Once again, it is possible to use SPSS to check by selecting 'Regression' then 'Linear...' (Screenshot 34.2), 'Statistics...' (Screenshot 34.3), 'and 'Casewise diagnostics' (Screenshot 34.4). Outliers could be dealt with by deletion, etc. if appropriate.

If your analysis violates various assumptions of linear regression, there is a relatively straightforward solution – that is, use a robust version of regression which is not based on the same assumptions. One such robust method is bootstrapping which SPSS will do for you. (See also Box 21.1 about bootstrapping.) Put simply, bootstrapping involves repeatedly randomly sampling from the available data (which is multiplied many times to yield a large population) in order to build up a sampling distribution. You might also wish to use bootstrapping to see if it produces markedly different results from the original analysis. Similarity of outcomes in reassuring. Bootstrapping is only available for Entry methods of multiple regression on SPSS including hierarchical models. Selecting 'Regression' then 'Linear...' (Screenshot 34.2), 'Enter' and 'Bootstrap...' (Screenshot 34.3), and 'Perform bootstrapping'. At this stage you should deselect anything that may remain selected under 'Statistics...', 'Plots...' and 'Save...' as these can prevent the analysis from completing. The main output table you need is the 'Bootstrap for Coefficient's' table. The regression weights remain the same, but the significance levels and confidence intervals are different. Differences between the original analysis and the bootstrap analysis usually do not alter the interpretation of the regression but they can if the assumptions of multiple regression are violated.

As with all statistics, you need to consider the appropriate sample size for a multiple regression. Obviously a bigger sample size is better than a smaller one so long as it is not too wasteful of resources. There are rules of thumb suggesting a particular ratio of participants to predictors. These ratios can vary greatly according to source from a low of $10\times$ to as much as $40\times$. Since a sample of 100 can be quite a data collection feat in student research then selectivity in the use of predictor variables is needed. The temptation is, of course, to put in as many predictor variables as you have available, which is not the best strategy. The consequence of doing so is to bump up the number of cases you need considerably. The better the fit of the model to the data the smaller can be the sample size because the error variation (residuals) is smaller. You could use G*Power (discussed in Chapter 39) to calculate the appropriate sample size especially if you know the likely effect size. The bigger the effect size the smaller the sample.

34.4 Stepwise multiple regression example

Since we will need to use standard multiple regression to carry out path analysis in the next chapter, we will illustrate stepwise multiple regression in the present chapter. There is quite a lot of hostility to stepwise multiple regression from statisticians, and some psychologists echo this. Nevertheless, it is not uncommon to see it used in studies, so you need to know about how it works. Our example asks whether a person's educational achievement (the criterion variable) can be predicted from their intellectual ability, their motivation to do well in school and their parents' interest in their education (the predictor variables). The minimum information we need to carry out a multiple regression is the number of people in the sample and the correlations between all the variables, though you would normally work with the actual scores when carrying out a multiple regression. It has been suggested that with stepwise regression it is desirable to have 40 times more cases than predictors. Since we have three predictors, we will say that we have a sample of 120 cases. (However, much reported research fails to follow this rule of thumb.) In order to interpret the results of multiple regression it is usually necessary to have more information than this, but for our purposes the fictitious correlation matrix presented in Table 34.1 is sufficient.

The calculation of multiple regression with more than two predictors is complicated and so will not be shown. However, the basic results of a stepwise multiple regression analysis are given in Table 34.2. What this simple example shows is that only two of the three 'predictors' actually explain a significant percentage of variance in educational achievement. That they are significant is assessed using a t-test. The values of t are given in Table 34.2 along with their two-tailed significance levels. A significance level of .05 or less is regarded as statistically significant.

The two significant predictor variables are intellectual ability and school motivation. The first variable to be considered for entry into the regression equation is the one with the highest zero-order correlation with educational achievement. This variable is intellectual ability. The *proportion* of variance in educational achievement explained or predicted by intellectual ability is the square of its correlation with educational achievement which is .49 ($.7^2 = .49$). The next predictor to be considered for entry into the regression equation is the variable which has the highest partial correlation with the criterion (after the variance due to the first predictor variable has been removed). These partial correlations have not been presented; however, school motivation is the predictor variable with the highest partial correlation with the criterion variable educational achievement.

The two predictors together explain .52 of the variance of educational achievement. The figure of the total proportion of variance explained is arrived at by squaring the overall R (the multiple correlation) which is $.72^2$ or .52. The multiple correlation is likely to be bigger the smaller the sample and for more predictors. Consequently, this figure is usually adjusted for the size of the sample and the number of predictors, which reduces it in size somewhat. Finally, the partial regression or beta coefficients for the regression equation containing the two predictors are also shown in Table 34.2 and are .65 for intellectual ability and .16 for school motivation. There is also a constant (usually denoted as a)

Table 34.1	Correlation matrix for a criterion (educational achievement) and three predictors		
	Educational achievement	Intellectual ability	School motivation
Intellectual ability	.70		
School motivation	.37	.34	
Parental interest	.13	.11	.34

Table 34.2	Some regression results – significant predictors only				
Predictor variables	r	b	β	t	Significance
Intellectual ability	.70	0.83	.65	9.56	.001
School motivation	.37	0.17	.16	2.42	.02
Constant $= -0.17$, $R^2 = .52$, Adjusted $R^2 = .51$, $R = .72$					

which is −.17 in this instance. The constant is the equivalent to the cut-off point described in Chapter 9. We can write this regression equation as follows:

$$\text{Educational achievement} = a + (0.83 \times \text{intellectual ability}) + (0.17 \times \text{school motivation})$$

According to our fictitious example, intellectual ability is more important than school motivation in predicting educational achievement (see Boxes 34.3 and 34.4).

Box 34.3	Key concepts

Multicollinearity

There is a concept, multicollinearity, which needs consideration when planning a multiple regression analysis. It is a problem when the researcher is using multiple regression to build psychological models in which the predictors are relevant to the theory. It is not a problem when simply using the predictors to make the best possible prediction. In terms of research design, it is a well-known phenomenon that if you measure several different variables using the same type of method then there is a tendency for the variables to intercorrelate simply because of that fact. If all of your measures are based on self-completion questionnaires or on ratings by observers then you may find strong intercorrelations as a consequence. Multicollinearity can happen for other reasons, of course. Multicollinearity mainly refers to the situation in which two predictor variables correlate very highly with each other. Correlations between any of the predictor variables bigger than $r = .8$ are indicative of multicollinearity but there can be multicollinearity without this. Most commonly, small sampling fluctuations may result in one of the two-predictor variables appearing to be a powerful predictor while the other may appear to be a relatively weak predictor. Imagine two variables, A and B, both of which predict the dependent variable, which correlate with each other at, say, $r = .9$. However, because variable A, say, has a minutely better correlation with the criterion it is selected first by the computer. Variable B consequently seems to be a far worse predictor. Multicollinearity can cause an unwary researcher confusion since, for example, known good predictors from past research suddenly do not predict or just one of them does. If multicollinearity is apparent then be very careful about claiming that one of the predictors is far better than another. Quite clearly, care should be exercised to ensure that your predictor measures do not intercorrelate highly.

SPSS can help you check for multicollinearity using the collinearity diagnostics procedure. To do this select 'Regression' then 'Linear…' (Screenshot 34.2), 'Statistics…' (Screenshot 34.3), and 'Collinearity diagnostics' (Screenshot 34.4). The relevant output can be found in the 'Coefficients' output table (Screenshot 34.5). Look for the column head VIF, which is the amount by which the variance of a regression weight is increased because the predictor is correlated with other predictors. The minimum value that it can have is 1. If you find a big value for VIF then collinearity is an issue. Different experts say different things but we have seen values for VIF between 2.5 and 10 being mentioned as the point at which collinearity rears its ugly head.

There is no need to become paralysed with fear if evidence of multicollinearity is found. Here are a few possible strategies:

- The obvious cure is simply to delete from the analysis one of the pair of variables showing a high correlation. After due consideration, you may decide that one of the predictors is conceptually more important than the other so retain that one. Of course both predictors may be important to your theoretical model so you may not wish to do this.

- Combine the highly correlated variables if it seems logical to do so. This may be as simple as adding together each person's scores on the two variables to make a single combined variable. For example, you might be using several measures of depression in which case combining them into one variable would seem quite sensible.

- You could do a principal components analysis on the predictor variables (see Chapter 33). This will give you

→

a small number of components (factors) which could replace the original predictors. The factor scores for the components would be used in the multiple regression.

- Be on the look-out for things you may have done inadvertently which resulted in the multicollinearity. If you made a predictor D by combining Variables A, B and C, then make sure that you haven't used any of Variables A, B and C as predictors in the regression analysis

as well as D. You should also be careful if you create dummy variables from a categorical predictor. The number of dummy variables at most is one less than the number of categories. If the categorical variable has three categories X, Y and Z then there are two possible dummy variables X versus not X and Y versus not Y. You would not include Z versus not Z. See Section 41.2 for a discussion of dummy variables.

Box 34.4   Focus on

Prediction in multiple regression

Prediction in regression is often not prediction at all. This can cause some confusion. In everyday language, prediction is indicating what will happen in the future on the basis of some sign in the present. Researchers, however, often use regression analysis with no intention of predicting future events. Instead, they collect data on the relation between a set of variables (let's call them X_1, X_2, and X_3,) and another variable (called Y). They think that the X variables may be correlated with Y. The data on all of these variables are available to the researcher. The analysis proceeds essentially by calculating the overall correlation of the several X variables with the Y variable. The overall correlation of a set of variables with another single variable is called multiple correlation. If there is a multiple correlation between the variables then this means that we

can use the value of this correlation together with other information to estimate the value of the Y variable from a pattern of X variables. Since the multiple correlation is rarely a perfect correlation, then our estimate of Y is bound to be a little inaccurate. Explained this way, we have not used the concept of prediction. If we know the multiple correlation between variables based on a particular sample of participants, we can use the size of the correlation to estimate the value of Y for other individuals based on knowing their pattern of scores on the X variables. That is the task of multiple regression. Prediction in multiple regression, then, is really estimating the unknown value of Y for an individual who was not part of the original research sample from that individual's known pattern of scores on the X variables.

34.5   Reporting the results

Multiple regression can be performed in a variety of ways for a variety of purposes. Consequently, there is no standard way of presenting results from a multiple regression analysis. However, there are some things which are best routinely mentioned. In particular, the reader needs to know the variables on which the analysis was conducted, the particular form of the multiple regression used, regression weights and the main pattern of predictors. Other information may be added as appropriate. By all means consult journal articles in your field of study for other indications as to style. We would say the following when reporting the simple example in Section 34.4:

A stepwise multiple regression was carried out in order to investigate the best pattern of variables for predicting educational achievement. Intellectual ability was selected for entry into the analysis first and explained 49% of the variance in educational achievement. School motivation was entered second and together with intellectual ability explained 52% of the variance in educational achievement. Greater educational attainment was associated with greater intellectual ability and school motivation. A third variable, parental interest, was not included in the analysis as it was not a significant, independent predictor of educational achievement.

34.6 Example from the published literature

Munford (1994) examined the predictors of depression in African-Americans. The research involved her administering the following measures:

1. Beck Depression Inventory.

2. Rosenberg Self-esteem Scale.

3. Hollingshead two-factor index of social position – this is a measure of the occupational social class and educational standards (i.e. a measure of social class).

4. Gender (self-reported sex) of the individual.

5. Racial Identity Attitude Scale which measures several different stages in the development of racial identity:

   1. Pre-encounter: the stage before black people become exposed to racism. It is the stage at which they accept the definitions of themselves imposed by the white racist community

   2. Encounter: the stage where identity is challenged by direct experiences of racism

   3. Immersion: the individual is learning to value his or her own race and culture

   4. Internalisation: the individual has achieved a mature and secure sense of his or her own race and identity.

As one might expect, Munford was interested in the relationship between depression as measured by the Beck Depression Inventory (the criterion variable) and the remaining variables (the predictor variables). She computed a correlation matrix between all of the variables, but as this involved 28 different correlation coefficients it is obvious that she needed a means of simplifying its complexity. She subjected her correlation matrix to a stepwise regression which yielded the outcome shown in Table 34.3.

Table 34.3	Summary of stepwise multiple regression: self-esteem, gender, social class and racial identity attitudes as predictors of depression		
Predictor	R^2 increments	R^2 (adjusted) total	Beta F
Self-esteem	.37	.37	134.10
Pre-encounter	.02	.39	8.97
Encounter	.01	.41	4.71
Gender	.01	.42	4.77

Data from Munford 1994.

As you can see, many of the predictors are not included in the table, indicating that they were not significant independent predictors of depression (thus social class and internalisation, for example, are excluded). Self-esteem is the best predictor of depression – those with the higher self-esteem tended to have lower depression scores. One cannot tell this directly from the table as it presents squared values which would have lost any negative signs. *We have to assess the direction of the relationship from the sign of the regression coefficient.* This sign is negative.

Although pre-encounter, encounter and gender all contribute something to the prediction, the increment in the amount of variation explained is quite small for each of them. Thus R^2 for pre-encounter is only .02 which means (expressed as a percentage) that the increase in variation explained is only 2% (i.e. .02 × 100%)).

Beta F in essence reports F-ratios (Chapter 23) for each of the predictor variables. All of those presented are statistically significant since otherwise the variable in question would not correlate significantly with depression.

Research examples

Multiple regression

Ang and Huan (2006) tested whether depression mediated the relation between academic stress and thoughts of killing oneself (suicidal ideation) in adolescents. Academic stress was significantly correlated with both depression and suicidal ideation. To determine whether depression mediated the relation between academic stress and suicidal ideation, they regressed suicidal ideation on both depression and academic stress. The standardised partial regression coefficient between academic stress and suicidal ideation was smaller than the correlation between them but was still significant which suggested that depression was a partial rather than a complete mediator of the relation between them.

Lounsbury and his colleagues (2003) conducted a hierarchical multiple regression to determine whether five personality factors and work drive would predict the grades students obtained on a course once intelligence had been taken into account. In the first analysis they present, intelligence was entered in the first step of the regression, the five personality variables were entered in the second step, and work drive was entered in the third step. Intelligence accounted for a significant 16% of the variance in course grades. The five personality variables accounted for a significant additional 7% of the variance and work drive a significant further 4%. As they found work drive to explain a significant percentage of the variance in course grades, they checked to see whether the five personality variables would explain a significant amount of the variance if they were entered after work drive which they did not. When work drive was entered in the second step, it explained a significant 8% of the variance with the five personality variables explaining a non-significant further 3%.

Nicholas and his colleagues (2009) were interested in which pain variables were related to depression in patients with chronic pain once age, gender and pain duration had been controlled. After entering these three variables in the first step of the regression to control for them, they carried out a forward entry multiple regression in which variables were selected in terms of their statistical significance. The first three variables of age, gender and pain duration explained a significant 5% of the variance in depression. The first variable with the highest statistical significance which was statistically significant was catastrophising, which is a tendency for patients to despair about their pain. This variable explained a significant further 39% of the variance in depression. There were four other variables which explained further significant amounts of variance and there were three which did not.

Key points

- Multiple regression is only practicable in most cases using a computer since the computations are numerous.

- Normally one does not have to compute the correlation matrix independently between variables. The computer program usually does this on the raw scores. There may be a facility for entering correlation matrices which might be useful once in a while when you are reanalysing someone else's correlation matrix.

- Choose hierarchical selection for your multiple regression if you are trying to test theoretical predictions or if you have some other rationale. One advantage of this is that you can first of all control for any social or demographic variables (gender, social class, etc.) which might influence your results. Then you can choose your remaining predictors in any order which you think best meets your needs.

- Choose stepwise selection methods in circumstances in which you simply wish to identify the best and smallest set of predictors. This would be ideal in circumstances in which you wish to dispense with time-consuming (and expensive) psychological tests, say in an industrial setting involving personnel selection. The main considerations here are entirely practical.

- Avoid construing the results of multiple regression in cause and effect terms.

COMPUTER ANALYSIS

Stepwise multiple regression using SPSS

Data
- Name the variables in 'Variable View' of the 'Data Editor'.
- Enter the data under the appropriate variable names in 'Data View' of the 'Data Editor' (Screenshot 34.1).

Analysis
- Select 'Analyze', 'Regression' and 'Linear. . .' (Screenshot 34.2).

2
- Move the criterion or dependent variable to the 'Dependent:' box and the predictors or independent variables to the 'Independent(s):' box (Screenshot 34.3).

3
- In the 'Method' box select 'Stepwise'.
- Select 'Statistics. . .' and then 'Confidence intervals', 'R squared change', 'Descriptives', 'Part and partial correlations', 'Collinearity diagnostics', 'Continue' and 'OK' (Screenshot 34.4).

Output
- Check sample size in 'Descriptive Statistics' table.
- In the 'Model Summary' table note the predictor and R Square Change in each step.
- In the 'Coefficients' table check that the Tolerance level is above 0.1 (Screenshot 34.5).

FIGURE 34.5 SPSS steps for stepwise multiple regression

Interpreting and reporting the output

- The most important part of the output is the 'Coefficients' table. This has produced a two predictor model involving Ability and Motivation as the important predictors. The *B* weights are both positive and so indicate positive relationships. Both are statistically significant. The beta weights are standardised versions of the *B* weights.

- You might write: 'The data were subjected to a stepwise multiple regression analysis in order to ascertain what were the best predictors of school achievement. A two-variable model was indicated in which Ability was found to have a *B* weight of .83 and motivation a *B* weight of .17. Intellectual ability was entered first and explained 49 per cent of the variance in educational achievement, $F(1, 118) = 113.76, p = .001$. School motivation was entered second and explained a further 2 per cent, $F(1, 117) = 5.85, p = .017$. Greater educational attainment was associated with greater intellectual ability and school motivation.'

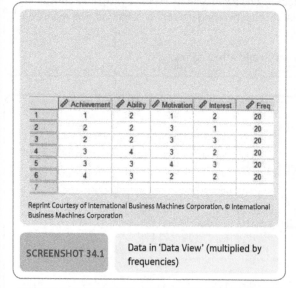

Reprint Courtesy of International Business Machines Corporation, © International Business Machines Corporation

| SCREENSHOT 34.1 | Data in 'Data View' (multiplied by frequencies) |

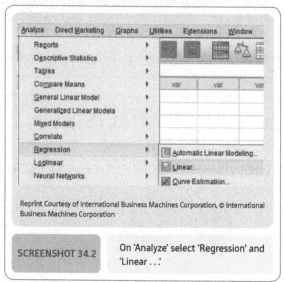

Reprint Courtesy of International Business Machines Corporation, © International Business Machines Corporation

| SCREENSHOT 34.2 | On 'Analyze' select 'Regression' and 'Linear . . .' |

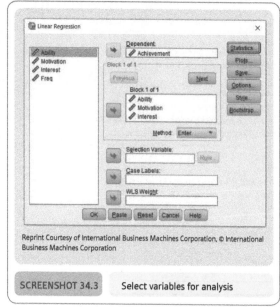

Reprint Courtesy of International Business Machines Corporation, © International Business Machines Corporation

| SCREENSHOT 34.3 | Select variables for analysis |

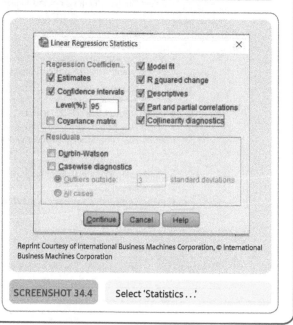

Reprint Courtesy of International Business Machines Corporation, © International Business Machines Corporation

| SCREENSHOT 34.4 | Select 'Statistics . . .' |

Coefficients[a]

Model		Unstandardized Coefficients B	Std. Error	Standardized Coefficients Beta	t	Sig.	95.0% Confidence Interval for B Lower Bound	Upper Bound	Correlations Zero-order	Partial	Part	Collinearity Statistics Tolerance	VIF
1	(Constant)	.100	.234		.428	.669	-.363	.563					
	Ability	.900	.084	.701	10.667	.000	.733	1.067	.701	.701	.701	1.000	1.000
2	(Constant)	-.167	.254		-.656	.513	-.670	.337					
	Ability	.833	.087	.649	9.561	.000	.661	1.006	.701	.662	.615	.900	1.111
	Motivation	.167	.069	.164	2.419	.017	.030	.303	.369	.218	.156	.900	1.111

a. Dependent Variable: Achievement

Reprint Courtesy of International Business Machines Corporation, © International Business Machines Corporation

SCREENSHOT 34.5   'Coefficients' table output

Recommended further reading

Cramer, D. (2003). *Advanced quantitative data analysis* (Chapters 5 and 6). Buckingham, UK: Open University Press.

Glantz, S. A., & Slinker, B. K. (1990). *Primer of applied regression and analysis of variance.* New York, NY: McGraw-Hill.

Pedhazur, E. J. (1982). *Multiple regression in behavioral research: Explanation and prediction* (2nd ed., Chapter 6). New York, NY: Holt, Rinehart & Winston.

Tabachnick, B. G., & Fidell, L. S. (2013). *Using multivariate statistics* (6th ed., Chapter 5). Boston, MA: Allyn & Bacon.

CHAPTER 35

Path analysis

Overview

- Path analysis is based on multiple regression, but it conceptualises predictors (independent variables) more complexly.

- The primary objective of path analysis is to indicate likely relationships between the independent variables as predictors of the dependent variable.

- There are numerous possible relationships among the predictor variables. Variable X_1 may affect variable X_2, or variable X_2 may affect variable X_1, or they may both affect each other (a bidirectional relationship).

- The relationships between variables in path analysis are given as path coefficients. These are essentially correlation coefficients based on the beta weights (standardised regression coefficients) calculated in multiple regression.

- Path analysis is about trying to establish a causal model of how predictor variables are combined to affect the level of the dependent variable.,

Preparation

Path analysis requires that you understand the basic principles of multiple regression (Chapter 34).

35.1 Introduction

As modern psychology has increasingly drawn from real issues and non-laboratory research methods, the ways of establishing what variables affect what other variables have changed. The methodological sophistication of laboratory experiments which establish causality by random assignment to experimental and control groups has been augmented by more statistical approaches. Causal modelling is merely a generic name for attempts to explore the patterns of interrelationships between variables in order to suggest how some variables might be causally influencing others. Of course, some suggestions might be rather better than others; some theoretical links might not fare well against actual empirical data. In path analysis, it is possible to estimate how well a particular suggested pattern of influences fits the known data. The better the model or causal pattern is supported by the actual data then the more likely we are to believe that the model is a useful theoretical development.

There is no suggestion intended that path analysis will always provide indisputable evidence strongly favouring one particular causal model over a number of other possibilities. It is not a question of showing that one model is the best model. Path analysis simply seeks to describe a particular path which explains the relationships among the variables well and precisely; the researcher may have overlooked other variables when planning the study or analysing it. Had they been included, these variables might have radically changed our understanding of what is happening in the data. Brain power is part of the process just as much as statistics, so, as an example, we can exclude some causal pathways on logical grounds. For example, a causal influence has to precede changes in the variable of interest. If it does not, it cannot be a cause. So changes in a causal influence need to precede changes in the variable being explained (the dependent variable). Thus, childhood experiences might possibly influence our adult behaviour and so it is reasonable to include childhood experiences as influences on adult behaviour. But the reverse pattern is not viable. Our childhood experiences cannot possibly be caused by things that happen to us in our adult years; the temporal sequence is wrong. In other words, some causal models are not convincing simply because they are not logically feasible whereas other models may be possible by logical criteria of this sort.

35.2 Theoretical considerations

Path analysis involves specifying the assumed causal relationships among several variables. Take, for example, the variables:

- marital satisfaction

- love between a couple and

- remaining married.

A reasonable assumption which might lead to a causal model is that couples who love one another are more likely to be satisfied with their marriage and consequently are more likely to stay together. Such a pattern of influences (or causal model) can be drawn as a path diagram such as the one in Figure 35.1. This is little more than a flow diagram indicating the direction of influence of one variable on another. In this particular model (and it clearly is just one of several possibilities), variables to the left (marital love) are thought to influence variables towards the right (marital satisfaction and remaining

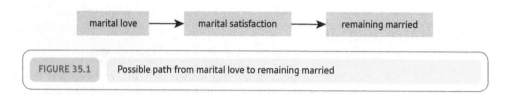

FIGURE 35.1   Possible path from marital love to remaining married

model is quite simply that marital love causes marital satisfaction which in turn is responsible for remaining married.

Of course, the temptation is simply to correlate scores on the three variables in this model. Suppose that we find that they all intercorrelate – then what? Well this might appear to be evidence in support of the suggested model, but it would also support many other models based on these three variables. The main point is that relationships between variables do not, in themselves, establish that marital love really causes marital satisfaction. Just taking two variables at a time results in four possible causal relationships:

- As suggested by our model, marital love may increase marital satisfaction.

- The opposite effect may occur with marital satisfaction heightening marital love.

- Both variables may affect each other, marital love bringing about marital satisfaction and marital satisfaction enhancing marital love. This kind of relationship is variously known as a *two-way, bidirectional, bilateral, reciprocal* or *non-recursive* relationship.

- The relationship may not really exist but may appear to exist because both variables are affected by some further confounding factor(s). For example, both marital love and marital satisfaction may be weaker in emotionally unstable people and stronger in emotionally stable people. This creates the impression that marital love and marital satisfaction are related when they are not, because emotionally unstable people are lower in both marital love and marital satisfaction while emotionally stable people are higher in both. This fourth sort of relationship is known as a *spurious relationship*.

In path analysis, a distinction is often made between *exogenous* and *endogenous* variables:

- An exogenous variable is one for which assumed causes have not been measured or tested as part of the model. In other words, it refers to those variables which do not have arrows pointing to them in a path diagram.

- An endogenous variable is one for which one or more possible causes have been measured and have been put forward in the causal model. In other words, endogenous variables have arrows pointing to them in the path diagram.

So, in the above model, marital love is an exogenous variable while marital satisfaction and remaining married are endogenous variables.

There will be some variation in endogenous variables which is unaccounted for or unexplained by causal variables in the model. This unexplained variance in an endogenous variable is indicated by vertical arrows pointing towards that variable as shown in the path diagram in Figure 35.2. For example, the variance in marital satisfaction *not* explained by marital love is represented by the vertical arrow from e_2. Similarly, the variance in remaining married unaccounted for by marital satisfaction is depicted by the vertical arrow from e_3. The e stands for *error* – the term used to describe unexplained variance. The word *residual* is sometimes used instead to refer to the variance that remains to be explained and the phrase *disturbance term* is also applied, in path analysis, to exactly the same concept. It is important to realise that e refers to the influence of unknown factors

a more complex model.

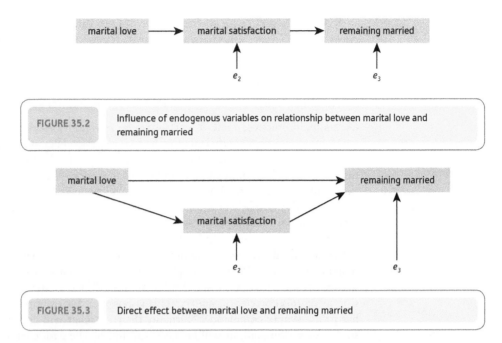

FIGURE 35.2   Influence of endogenous variables on relationship between marital love and remaining married

FIGURE 35.3   Direct effect between marital love and remaining married

In this model, marital love is assumed to have an *indirect* effect on remaining married through its effect on marital satisfaction. However, marital love may also have a *direct* effect on remaining married as shown in the path diagram of Figure 35.3.

■ Path coefficients

The values of the direct effects are expressed as *path coefficients*. They are usually the standardised beta coefficients taken from the sort of multiple regression analysis which was introduced in the previous chapter. In other words, understand them as analogous to correlation coefficients. The values of the paths reflecting error (or residual) variance are known as error or residual path coefficients.

We will use the following symbols:

- p_1 for the path coefficient for the direct effect of marital love on marital satisfaction

- p_2 for the direct effect of marital love on remaining married

- p_3 for the direct effect of marital satisfaction on remaining married

- p_4 for the path reflecting the error variance for marital satisfaction

- p_5 for the path reflecting the error variance for remaining married.

These are illustrated in Figure 35.4.

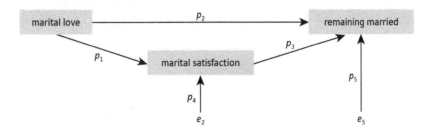

To calculate these path coefficients we need to calculate the following two regression equations, which are essentially the same as for the multiple regression discussed in the previous chapter:

marital satisfaction $= a + p_1$ marital love

remaining married $= b + p_2$ marital love $+ p_3$ marital satisfaction

(Actually, in practice, a and b will always be zero and so may be ignored. The symbols a and b are intercept coefficients for the two regression equations. Intercept coefficients are the points at which the regression lines cut the vertical axis. They are identified with different symbols in our example simply because they refer to different regression equations with different variables. However, they will always take a value of .00 if we are using standardised multiple regression as we do in path analysis. We can, therefore, omit or ignore them for present purposes.)

Suppose that the correlation between marital love and marital satisfaction is .50, between marital love and remaining married .40 and between marital satisfaction and remaining married .70 for a sample of 100 couples. These are correlations which have been made up for the purposes of this example. We have carried out our multiple regression using this correlation matrix. This is possible, for example, with SPSS though one has to use syntax commands. Normally the researcher will have the raw data available so the regression analysis will be based on this. So the path coefficients about to be discussed are based on this analysis of the correlation matrix. (Because means and standard deviations were not entered with the correlation matrix as they are unknown, the so-called unstandardised coefficients in the output will be standardised ones. This is fine as these are the only ones we are interested in.) The path coefficients are the standardised beta coefficients for these two equations which are:

marital satisfaction $= a + .50$ marital love

remaining married $= b + .07$ marital love $+ .67$ marital satisfaction

In other words, the path coefficient for p_1 is .50, for p_2, .07 and for p_3, .67 as shown in Figure 35.5.

Since there is only one predictor variable in the first regression, the standardised beta coefficient of .50 is the same as the zero-order correlation of .50 between marital love (the predictor variable) and marital satisfaction (the criterion variable). (If there are several predictors then partial regression coefficients would be involved.) Note that the path coefficient between marital love and remaining married is virtually zero (.07) and statistically not significant. This means that marital love does not directly affect remaining married. The path coefficient (.67) between marital satisfaction and remaining married differs little from the correlation (.70) between them. This indicates that the relationship between marital satisfaction and remaining married is not due to the spurious effect of marital love.

To determine an indirect effect (such as that between marital love and remaining married which is mediated by marital satisfaction), the path coefficient between marital love and marital satisfaction (.50) is multiplied by the path coefficient between marital

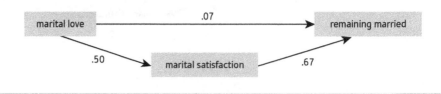

satisfaction and remaining married (.67). This gives an indirect effect of .335 (.50 × .67 = .335). To calculate the total effect of marital love on remaining married, we add the direct effect of marital love on remaining married (.07) to its indirect effect (.335) which gives a sum of .405. The total effect of one variable on another should be, within rounding error, the same as the zero-order correlation between the two variables. As we can see, the total effect of marital love on remaining married is .405, which is very close to the value of the zero-order correlation of .40. In other words, path analysis breaks down or decomposes the correlations between the endogenous and exogenous variables into their component parts, making it easier to understand or work out what might be happening. So, for example, the correlation between marital love and remaining married is decomposed into (a) the indirect effect of marital love on remaining married and (b) the direct effects of marital love on marital satisfaction and of marital satisfaction on remaining married. Doing this shows us that although the correlation between marital love and remaining married is moderately strong (.40), this relationship is largely mediated indirectly through marital satisfaction. It will always be far easier to see this by drawing up a path diagram than in the computer output.

The correlation between marital satisfaction and remaining married can also be decomposed into the direct effect we have already calculated (.67) and a spurious component due to the effect of marital love on both marital satisfaction and remaining married. This spurious component is the product of the direct effect of marital love on marital satisfaction (.50) and of marital love on remaining married (.07) which gives .035 (.50 × .07 = .035). This is clearly a small value. We can reconstitute the correlation between marital satisfaction and remaining married by summing the direct effect (.67) and the spurious component (.035) which gives a total of .67 + .035 = .705. This value is very similar to the original correlation of .70.

To calculate the proportion of variance not explained in an endogenous variable we subtract the adjusted multiple R-squared value for that variable from 1. The adjusted multiple R-squared value is .24 for marital satisfaction and .48 for remaining married. So .76 (1 − .24 = .76) or 76% of the variance in marital satisfaction is not explained, and .52 (1 − .48) or 52% of the variance in remaining married is not explained. In path analysis, it is a basic assumption that the variables representing error are unrelated to any other variables in the model (otherwise it would not be error). Consequently, the error path coefficient is the correlation between the error and the endogenous variable which can be obtained by taking the square root of the proportion of unexplained variance in the endogenous variable. In other words, the residual path coefficient is .87 for marital satisfaction and .72 for remaining married (Figure 35.6).

Where there is a relationship between two variables whose nature is not known or specified, this relationship is depicted in a path diagram by a curved double-headed arrow. Suppose, for example, the two exogenous variables of similarity in personality and similarity in physical attractiveness, which were assumed to influence marital satisfaction, were known to be related, but this relationship was thought not to be causal. This relationship would be shown in a path diagram as in Figure 35.7.

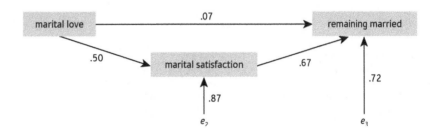

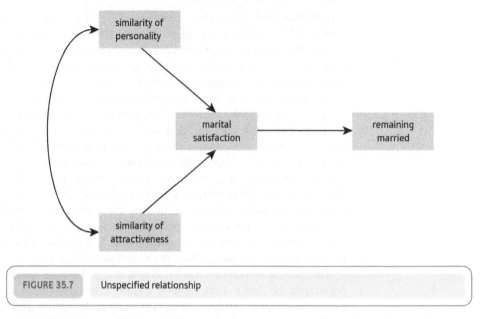

FIGURE 35.7   Unspecified relationship

The correlation between these two exogenous variables is not used in calculating the effect of these two variables on marital satisfaction and remaining married. Figure 35.8 shows the key steps in a path analysis.

■ Generalisation

To determine whether our path analysis is generalisable from the sample to the population, we calculate how well our model reflects the original correlation matrix between the variables in that model using the large sample chi-square test. This will not be described here other than to make these two points:

- If this chi-square test is statistically significant, then this means that the model does not fit the data.

- Other things being equal, the larger the sample, the more likely it is that the chi-square test is statistically significant and the model is to be rejected.

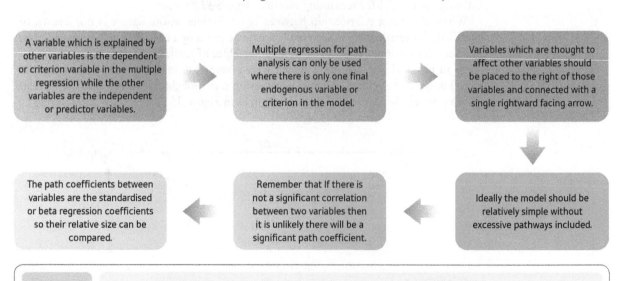

Table 35.1	Original and recomposed correlations		
Pairs of variables		**Original correlations**	**Recomposed correlations**
Marital love and marital satisfaction		.50	.500
Marital love and remaining married		.40	.405
Marital satisfaction and remaining married		.70	.705

In terms of our model in Figure 35.6, we can see that the recomposed correlations for the model are very similar to the original correlations between the three variables as shown in Table 35.1. This is not always true, as explained in Box 35.1.

Box 35.1   Key concepts

Identification

Although in Table 35.1 we give an example where the correlations between the variables and the recomposed correlations based on path analysis are very similar, not all models which emerge in path analysis demonstrate this feature. It is always true when the model is just-identified. Identification is an important concept in path analysis. There are three types of identification:

- *Just-identified* This means that all the variables in the path analysis model put forward by the researcher are connected by unidirectional paths (single-headed arrows). Actually, even with the arrows entirely reversed in direction this would still be the case. Since the standardised beta coefficients are essentially correlation coefficients, this entirely reversed model would fit our data just as well as our preferred model. In other words, the recomposed correlations for this reversed just-identified model are just the same as for the forward model. The reconstituted correlations for any just-identified model are similar to the original correlations. Consequently it is not possible to use the match between the model and the data as support for the validity of the model.

- *Under-identified* In this, there are assumed to be one or more bidirectional pathways (double-headed arrows between variables) in the model. For example, the relationship between marital love and marital satisfaction

may be thought of as being reciprocal, both variables having an influence on each other. Since it is impossible to provide an estimate of the influence of marital love on marital satisfaction which is entirely independent of the influence of marital satisfaction on marital love, it is not possible to say what the unique estimate for these pathways would be. Consequently, we would need to modify our model to avoid this. That is, we need to re-specify it as a just-identified or an over-identified model in order to deal with this problem.

- *Over-identified* In an over-identified model, it is assumed that some pairs of variables do not relate. Using our example, an over-identified model assumes that there is no relationship between two pairs of variables. For instance, take the following model which postulates that marital love does not lead directly to remaining married:

marital love → marital satisfaction → remaining married

This is over-identified because a third possible pathway between marital love and remaining married has not been suggested (that is, the direct pathway from marital love to remaining married). Thus there are more variables (three) than pathways (two).

35.3   Example from published research

Path analysis can be as simple or as complex as the researchers' theories about the inter-relationships between variables in their research. Increasing the numbers of variables under consideration rapidly accelerates the complexity in the path diagram. Not only does the analysis look more daunting if many variables are involved, but the path diagram becomes harder to draw. In this section we will discuss a path analysis by Wagner and Zick (1995) of the causes of blatant ethnic prejudice as a typical example of path analysis in psychology. It is fairly well known and established that there is a relationship between people's level of formal education and their expressions of prejudice: the more prejudiced tend to have the least formal education. This suggests that there is something about education which leads to less prejudice, but what is the mechanism involved? Does education act directly to reduce prejudice or does it do so indirectly through some mediating variable (Figure 35.9)? Thus there are two possible paths: (1) the *direct* path from formal education to blatant prejudice and (2) the *indirect* path which involves a mediating variable(s).

As we have indicated, the apparent complexity of this path diagram can be increased if several mediating variables are used rather than just one. Furthermore, if several direct variables are used instead of formal education alone, the diagram will become increasingly complex. Wagner and Zick (1995) collected information in a number of European countries on several potential mediating variables linking formal education and blatant prejudice:

● *Individual (relative) deprivation* The feeling of an individual that he or she is economically deprived compared with other people.

● *Group (relative) deprivation* The feeling that one's social group (e.g. ethnic group) has fared badly economically compared with the rest of society.

● *Perceived incongruency* The incompatibility between an ethnic group's values and those dominant in society.

● *Political conservatism* The individual's position on the political left-wing to right-wing dimension.

● *National pride* Pride in being a member of the national group (e.g. French or German).

● *Contact with foreign people* The numbers of foreign people living in one's neighbourhood.

Although this list of mediating variables far from exhausts the possibilities, it does identify a number of variables which are related to blatant ethnic prejudice according to a number of empirical studies.

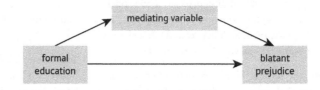

FIGURE 35.9   Path diagram of the direct and indirect influence of formal education on blatant prejudice

In addition, the researchers had other measures which they could have included in the path diagram (e.g. gender and age) but omitted because the researchers did not consider them relevant to their immediate task. However, they were used by the researchers as control variables, as we shall see. There was another variable, *social strata*, which was a measure of social class. This was included in the path diagram by the researchers as social class was actually affected by a person's level of education.

There is no mystery about the path diagram; it is merely one of several path diagrams which the researchers could have studied. Most of the possibilities were ignored and the researchers concentrated on why those with the most formal education tend to express the least blatant prejudice. Drawing the diagram is a paper-and-pencil task based on elaborating substantially the simple path diagram in Figure 35.9. One way of presenting this is shown in Figure 35.10. It includes both direct and indirect (mediated) relationships. Arrows pointing more or less towards the right are the only ones included as these indicate possible causal directions. Having drawn the elaborated diagram, the values of the relationships between the variables are added adjacent to the appropriate arrows. These are the path coefficients which can be regarded as being essentially correlation coefficients. These path coefficients were obtained, of course, using multiple regression. Arrows (pathways) are omitted when the path coefficient do not reach statistical significance. However, because the sample was big ($N = 3788$), very small values were significant at the 5% level. A correlation of .04 is statistically significant for such a massive sample, but its coefficient of determination or amount of variation shared by the two variables is tiny at $.04^2$ or .0016 or 0.16%. The square of $e = .83$ in Figure 35.10 indicates how much variation in blatant prejudice is *unexplained* by the path diagram.

The process of carrying out the path analysis involves quite substantial matrixes involving first of all the correlations of every variable in the analysis with every other. This provides a basis for making certain decisions about the actual path analysis. Table 35.2 gives part of a correlation matrix by presenting just six of the variables with each other for purposes of illustration. Of course, the analysis itself includes all of the variables including age and gender which were used as control variables. The path coefficients themselves for these six variables are to be found in Table 35.3.

Wagner and Zick (1995) carried out a simultaneous multiple regression on the correlation matrix in order to predict blatant prejudice from age, gender, formal education, social strata and the mediating variables (individual deprivation, group deprivation, etc.). Standard or simultaneous multiple regression is called the enter method on SPSS. It simply means that all of the predictor variables are included in the analysis at the same time

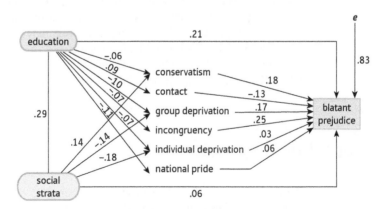

FIGURE 35.10   Significant path on blatant prejudice (from Wagner & Zick, 1995, Fig 1, p. 52)

Table 35.2	The intercorrelations of a small selection of the variables in the path analysis				
	Blatant prejudice	Education	Social Strata	Perceived Incongruency	Group Relative Deprivation
Education	−.34				
Social Strata	−.14	.27			
Perceived Incongruency	.32	−.08	−.02		
Group Relative Deprivation	.25	−.14	.17	.12	
National Pride	.18	−.15	−.02	.04	.03

All correlations are zero-order correlations.
All coefficients are statistically significant at the 1% level except those highlighted in blue which are significant at the 5% level and those highlighted in green which are not significant.

Table 35.3	The path coefficients for a small selection of the variables in the path analysis				
	Blatant prejudice	Education	Social Strata	Incongruency	Group Deprivation
Education	−.21				
Social Strata	−.06	.29			
Incongruency	.25	−.07	.00		
Group Deprivation	.17	−.10	−.14	.11	
National Pride	.06	.11	.01	.01	.04

The coefficients in the cells highlighted with **yellow** are beta coefficients from a simultaneous regression such as the enter procedure on SPSS. The coefficients in the cells highlighted in **lilac** are partial correlations in which education and social strata plus age and gender have been partialled out. They are not part of the path diagram but show the adjusted correlations between the variables in question.

rather than being entered in stepwise order, for example, such as where the variable explaining the most variance is dealt with as a priority. This is the source of the beta weights from this multiple regression are given in Table 35.3.

Table 35.3 includes some calculations which do not appear in the path diagram. These are shown highlighted in **lilac** in Table 35.3. These are partial correlation coefficients in which the effects of age, gender, education and social strata have been removed.

35.4   Reporting the results

Path analysis is a difficult procedure to apply and few students would carry out such analysis at undergraduate level. Even at the postgraduate level, novices to path analysis would probably be wise to seek some experienced support. Part of the difficulty in writing a simple way of reporting the results of a path analysis is that the reasons for this

Nevertheless, readers may find it helpful to read Wagner and Zick's description of the results of their path analysis:

> The path analysis shows that the predictors of ethnic prejudice mentioned above are determined by formal education, even though some of the direct paths from education are relatively weak. However, for individual and group relative deprivation, and for political conservatism, social strata mediates part of the determination by formal education. The influence of mediating variables means that the covariation of formal education and ethnic prejudice can be partially explained especially by variations in social strata, group deprivation, incongruency, conservatism and acceptance of contact with foreigners. In addition to this, the path analysis indicates a strong direct path from education to blatant prejudice which cannot be explained by the mediation variables measured. A chi-square analysis shows that a restricted model without the assumption of a direct path from education to prejudice is significantly worse than the full model presented (chi $-$ square $= 84.02$, $df = 1$). Thus, the path analysis demonstrates that part of the educational differences in ethnic outgroup rejection can be accounted for by the mediating psychological variables, even though a substantial proportion of the covariance of respondents' education and outgroup rejection remained unexplained.

(Wagner & Zick, 1995, pp. 53–4).

The following may help clarify the Wagner and Zick quotation:

- Education influences variables which influence blatant prejudice. Often the influences are very weak. Most studies would use far smaller sample sizes so the tiny coefficients sometimes obtained in the study would be dismissed as not significant.

- The chi-square tests whether the indirect paths model is significantly improved by adding in the direct path from formal education to blatant prejudice. The results of the analysis suggest that the direct plus indirect effects model is superior to the indirect effects alone model.

Research examples

Path analysis

Kuhnle, Hofer and Kilian (2012) describe how a number of studies have shown the importance of self-control to achieving positive outcomes in life especially in terms of learning and academic performance. They theorised that school students who manifest the highest levels of self-control 1) would be more effective at balancing their academic and leisure time satisfactorily and 2) would protect their studying from the negative influence of distractions. Nearly 700 schoolchildren with an average age of 13 completed a questionnaire measuring 1) self-control, 2) subjective life balance and 3) flow while studying as well as school grades. The same questionnaire was completed on two occasions – once at the beginning of the school year and again at its end. The analysis employed structural equation modelling. Self-control was important in predicting school grades, life balance and flow. (Flow is the experience of concentration on the task unaffected by things like other tasks to be done or negative emotions – the student can isolate themselves from distractions like phone calls and talking with other people.) The researchers argue that self-control helps young people to be prepared and coordinated in various areas of life including school.

➜

Lamoureux and colleagues (2012) explored a model in which child sexual abuse as a consequence of 1) its effect on resiliency resources (self-esteem and self-efficacy) and 2) psychological distress affects adulthood interpersonal functioning and sexual risk. A sample of nearly 700 inner-city women were interviewed twice (the interviews were six months apart). It was found that childhood sexual abuse influenced interpersonal problems via its effect on psychological distress. In contrast, child sexual abuse affected HIV/sexual risk via its effect on resiliency resources.

Maguire-Jack, Gromoske and Berger (2012) used data from the Fragile Families and Child Wellbeing national representative sample study of 3870 children in the USA. They wanted to know whether smacking children at 1 and 3 years of age leads to lower cognitive skills and worse behaviour problems at the ages of 3 and 5 years. Various correlates which did not change over time were controlled for. Path analysis showed that smacking at age 1 led to higher levels of behavioural problems in the form of externalising behaviour at the age of 5 years. The path was largely mediated through ongoing smacking at age 3. No association was found between early smacking at the age of 1 year and cognitive skills at the age of 3 and 5 years.

Key points

- Path analysis requires a degree of mastery of statistical concepts which many students will not achieve during their degree course. Anyone who is convinced that it is appropriate for their research will need to consult supplementary sources and any local expert who might be available.

- The complexity of path analysis should not be allowed to interfere with one's critical faculties. A path analysis cannot be any better than the quality of the data which go into it.

- Path analysis involves exploring data in ways which seem alien to those who feel that statistics should be a hard-and-fast discipline in which there is only one right way of doing things. It is an example of a statistical technique which is an exploratory tool rather than a fixed solution to a fixed problem.

COMPUTER ANALYSIS

Hierarchical multiple regression using SPSS

Data	• Name the variables in 'Variable View' of the 'Data Editor'. • Enter the data under the appropriate variable names in 'Data View' of the 'Data Editor' (Screenshot 35.1).
Analysis	• Select 'Analyze', 'Regression' and 'Linear. . .' (Screenshot 35.2).
2	• Move the criterion or dependent variable to the 'Dependent:' box and the other predictors or independent variables to the 'Independent(s):' box (Screenshot 35.3) .
3	• Select 'Statistics. . .', 'Confidence intervals', 'Descriptives', 'Part and partial correlations', 'Collinearity diagnostics', 'Continue' and 'OK' (Screenshot 35.4).
Output	• In the 'Correlations' table, note the size, direction and significance of the correlation coefficients (Screenshot 35.5). • In the 'Coefficients' table note the size, direction and significance of the standardised or beta coefficient for the predictors together with their tolerance value (Screenshot 35.5).

FIGURE 35.11   SPSS steps for the hierarchical or 'Enter' regression procedure

Interpreting and reporting the output

- SPSS produces a great deal of statistics. For a simple path analysis involving three variables, the correlations between these three variables need to be noted. For a mediator relation to be present, the correlations with the mediator should be significant. The standardised regression coefficient between the predictor variable and the criterion variable controlling for the mediating variable needs to be examined. If this standardised regression is substantially different from the correlation between the predictor and the criterion variable, it suggests there is a mediating effect.

- According to the American Psychological Association (2010) Publication Manual, one way of reporting the results of the analysis illustrated is as follows: 'As the relation between intellectual ability and educational achievement, $r(118) = .70$, 2-tailed $p < .001$, was little affected when school motivation was controlled, $B = .65$, $t(117) = 9.56$, 2-tailed $p < .001$, school motivation was not considered to mediate the relation between intellectual ability and educational achievement. Greater educational attainment was associated with greater intellectual ability.' These values are given in Screenshot 35.5.

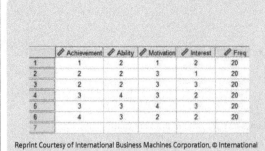

Reprint Courtesy of International Business Machines Corporation, © International Business Machines Corporation

| SCREENSHOT 35.1 | Data in 'Data View' (multiplied by frequencies) |

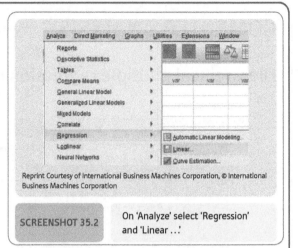

Reprint Courtesy of International Business Machines Corporation, © International Business Machines Corporation

| SCREENSHOT 35.2 | On 'Analyze' select 'Regression' and 'Linear …' |

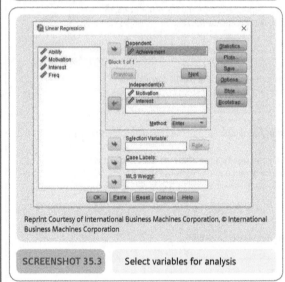

Reprint Courtesy of International Business Machines Corporation, © International Business Machines Corporation

| SCREENSHOT 35.3 | Select variables for analysis |

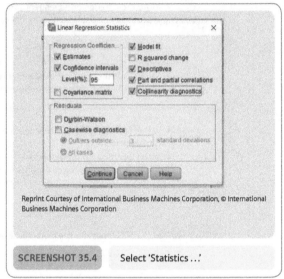

Reprint Courtesy of International Business Machines Corporation, © International Business Machines Corporation

| SCREENSHOT 35.4 | Select 'Statistics …' |

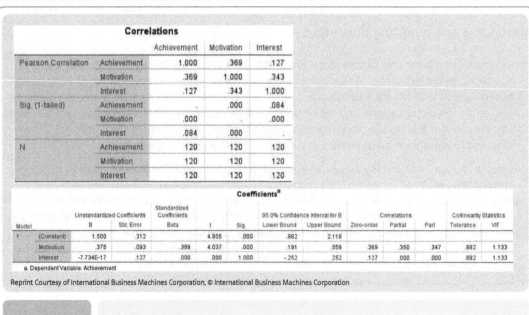

Correlations

		Achievement	Motivation	Interest
Pearson Correlation	Achievement	1.000	.369	.127
	Motivation	.369	1.000	.343
	Interest	.127	.343	1.000
Sig. (1-tailed)	Achievement	.	.000	.084
	Motivation	.000	.	.000
	Interest	.084	.000	.
N	Achievement	120	120	120
	Motivation	120	120	120
	Interest	120	120	120

Coefficients[a]

Model		Unstandardized Coefficients B	Std. Error	Standardized Coefficients Beta	t	Sig.	95.0% Confidence Interval for B Lower Bound	Upper Bound	Correlations Zero-order	Partial	Part	Collinearity Statistics Tolerance	VIF
1	(Constant)	1.500	.312		4.805	.000	.882	2.118					
	Motivation	.375	.093	.369	4.037	.000	.191	.559	.369	.350	.347	.882	1.133
	Interest	-7.734E-17	.127	.000	.000	1.000	-.252	.252	.127	.000	.000	.882	1.133

a. Dependent Variable: Achievement

Reprint Courtesy of International Business Machines Corporation, © International Business Machines Corporation

Recommended further reading

Bryman, A., & Cramer, D. (2011). *Quantitative data analysis with IBM SPSS 17, 18 & 19: A guide for social scientists* (Chapter 10). London, UK: Routledge.

Cramer, D. (2003). *Advanced quantitative data analysis* (Chapter 7). Buckingham, UK: Open University Press.

Pedhazur, E. J. (1982). *Multiple regression in behavioral research: Explanation and prediction* (2nd ed., Chapter 15). New York, NY: Holt, Rinehart & Winston.

PART 5

Assorted advanced techniques

Meta-analysis

Combining and exploring statistical findings from previous research

Overview

- Most research reports review the pertinent previous research. This can be difficult especially where there are large numbers of past research studies.

- Meta-analysis provides a way of handling this by making overall systematic statistical summaries of these previous studies.

- The findings of each study is converted into a standard measure of effect such as a Pearson correlation coefficient or Cohen's *d*. It is easy to convert the Pearson correlation to Cohen's *d* and vice versa.

- Effect sizes from several studies may be combined to give an overall effect size.

- Furthermore, studies may be coded in terms of features such as the type of study, the number of participants and even the geographic location of the study. The relationship between these variables and effect size can be calculated. The findings may suggest that, for example, laboratory studies reveal greater effects than field studies.

Preparation

Review effect size (Chapter 17). In particular, make sure that you understand the difference between statistical significance and effect size.

36.1   Introduction

Meta-analysis is a general term for statistical techniques enabling researchers to statistically analyse the pattern of findings from a variety of published and unpublished studies into a particular research question. Usually statistical analyses investigate data from a single research study. However, when reviewing the research literature, frequently a number of studies researching similar hypotheses using similar variables are found. Such studies can vary enormously in terms of the method they employ (for example, field studies versus laboratory studies) or the populations they sample (for example, students versus the general population). Sometimes a number of studies may find positive evidence in favour of the hypothesis whereas others support the reverse trend or even no trend. So meta-analysis's main objectives include:

- Assessing the strength of relationships over a range of studies and, if possible, combining these into a single overall indicator of the relationship.

- Assessing the influence of various characteristics of pertinent studies (the type of sample, the type of method, etc.) on the strength of the relationship found.

Meta-analysis is a highly organised literature review process. There is another very structured review process known as the systematic review. The objective is to structure literature reviews such that they are freed from the influence of the whims of the researcher. It employs expertise in database searches. There is considerable overlap between the database searching procedures of both meta-analyses and systematic reviews. It is not unusual, as a consequence, for a research team to carry out both more or less simultaneously. Systematic reviews are discussed in Howitt and Cramer (2020).

Meta-analysis involves some new concepts. Although relatively rare in student work, a meta-analysis is a feasible proposition where time and resources are available for a thorough literature search. To date, meta-analysis has not routinely been applied to these reviews although some elements of it would be easy to incorporate. Usually a meta-analysis is carried out as an independent exercise because it is very resource demanding:

- Because meta-analysis is a study of studies, it is necessary to obtain copies of relevant reports and publications dealing with the statistical analysis of the particular research question. Sometimes these may have to be obtained, say, from other libraries (or from the researchers themselves if the study has been recently published). Obtaining research reports costs time. Since there may be a bias towards the publishing of significant research findings, ideally meta-analysis should include unpublished research. This can be very difficult to track down.

- The meta-analyst needs to be somewhat expert with computerised database searches. Unless a variety of databases are searched using a variety of appropriate keywords, important research studies may be overlooked. Published articles and books may be sources of additional studies which have not been found using the databases.

- There is inconsistency in the reporting of research findings. Sometimes important pieces of information are missing especially in older studies. Fortunately meta-analysis can be done with minimal information – sample size and significance level are all that are required. If effect size were routinely reported for every research study there would be no problem and, increasingly, journals are requiring this.

Meta-analysts sometimes need a range of formulae to transpose published findings into measures of effect size.

- There is a good deal of non-computer work involved in meta-analysis. Meta-analysis is not available on any of the standard statistical packages. However, much of the work is computationally easy with just a few simple hand calculations. Computers can be useful in later stages of the analysis, but they are far from essential.

- Meta-analysis involves defining the variables and types of study of interest with some precision. This requires some understanding of the field of study which is difficult to achieve within the timescale of student projects.

Don't be deterred by the above comments. After all, they simply imply diligence, planning, hard work and understanding of the chosen research field. These are reasonable targets for any researcher whether or not using meta-analysis.

Criticisms of meta-analysis usually apply equally to conventional reviews of the empirical studies. So, for example, problems of retrieval of studies, biases favouring the publication of statistically significant findings in research publications, glossing over details in particular studies and similar issues are common to both meta-analytic and other attempts to synthesise the literature.

This chapter provides a practical introduction to meta-analysis which should be sufficient to guide students through its major features. It is not exhaustive. Figure 36.1 gives the key steps to consider in understanding meta-analysis.

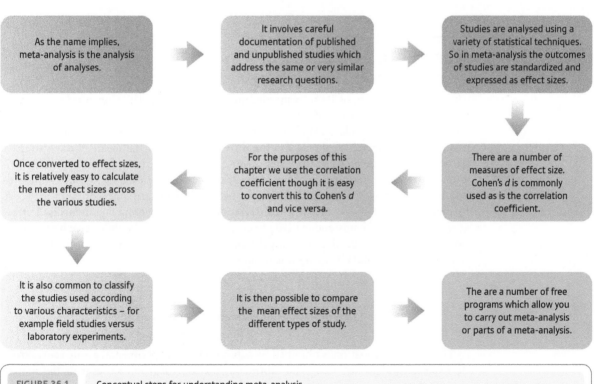

FIGURE 36.1   Conceptual steps for understanding meta-analysis

36.2 Pearson correlation coefficient as the effect size

Effect size is the central concept in meta-analysis. It means exactly what it says – the size of the effect of one variable on a second. In other words, in meta-analysis the effect size is the strength of the relationship between one variable and another variable – expressed in a standardised way. Ultimately, and largely for practical reasons, the most convenient measure of effect size is the Pearson correlation coefficient between the two variables (say the independent variable and the dependent variable). In Chapter 17, the correlation coefficient was used as a measure of effect size (i.e. the strength of the relationship between the two variables). Effect size is not the same as statistical significance, which is about generalising from a sample to a population. The larger the correlation coefficient between two variables, the larger the effect of one variable on the other. This is nothing to do with cause and effect.

Chapter 17 also showed just how easy it is to convert a number of different statistical tests such as the *t*-test and chi-square into a Pearson correlation coefficient. It is the ease of such conversions that ensures the Pearson correlation coefficient's practical utility as a measure of effect size. Irrespective of the nature of the statistical analysis reported by the researcher in the primary report, it is highly likely that a correlation coefficient can be obtained from this information. The minimum information required, remember, is merely the significance level and sample size.

Meta-analysis can be used in virtually any type of study. Also, bear in mind that the techniques can be useful even when combining the results of just two studies.

36.3 Other measures of effect size

There are other, perhaps more common, measures of effect size. Cohen's *d* is probably the most common measure of effect size reported. Its major disadvantage is that it can be more difficult to calculate from the statistical analyses usually presented in reports of psychological research. Cohen's *d* is the difference between the mean of one group of participants and the mean of the other group adjusted by dividing by the standard deviation of the scores. In other words, it is the difference between the two groups standardised by dividing by the standard deviation. Just as we can turn any score into a *z*-score by dividing the score by the standard deviation, we can generate a standardised effect score by dividing the unstandardised effect size (for example, the difference between the experimental and control group) by the size of the standard deviation of the scores. Expressed as a formula, Cohen's *d* is usually given as:

$$\text{Cohen's } d = \frac{\text{mean of Group A} - \text{mean of Group B}}{\text{standard deviations of both groups of scores pooled together}}$$

The standard deviation is obtained by subtracting the experimental group scores from the experimental group's mean and subtracting the control group scores from the control group's mean. These difference scores are then pooled (combined) as a first step in computing their standard deviation. Actually, this is not Cohen's formulation since he simply recommended using the standard deviation of one of the populations on the assumption that both populations should have the same standard deviation. It is possible to find on the Web a number of programs and applets which will calculate Cohen's *d* for you.

G*Power (discussed in Chapter 39) can do this as part of power analysis. (See the Computer Analysis section at the end of this chapter.) Although there is a similarity, it is not true to say that Cohen's d is the same as the t-test despite overlaps in their calculation. In the t-test, the division is by the standard error of the difference between the sample means; in Cohen's d, the division is by the standard deviation of the pooled groups of scores. (In essence the two standard deviations are combined arithmetically.)

Although Cohen's d is commonly used in meta-analysis, it is not quite as flexible in use as the Pearson correlation coefficient. Most importantly, it is much easier to estimate the Pearson correlation coefficient from the minimal information that researchers sometimes supply. We saw in Chapter 17 how we can calculate a correlation coefficient from a range of tests of significance. This is not so easy with Cohen's d. Furthermore, the conversion of a correlation coefficient to Cohen's d is easy using the table we provide later in this chapter. Consequently, it is probably easier to work with correlation coefficients and then convert them to Cohen's d should this seem appropriate.

36.4 Effects of different characteristics of studies

Modern meta-analyses are not simply about determining the effect size over a range of studies. They also try to estimate what characteristics of studies may be responsible for large effect sizes and what characteristics of studies may be responsible for smaller effect sizes. It is usual to select a range of possible study variables which may be related to effect size. These may include:

- size of the study
- quality of the study as rated by a panel of psychologists or from the prestige of the journal in which the study was published
- whether the study was a laboratory experiment or field study
- which research team carried out the study

Study variable selection depends on knowledge, skill and a degree of insight. These are much the same characteristics that are required by any researcher. Basic procedures for investigating study variable effects on effect size are very simple. So if a meta-analyst wished to investigate the effect size for studies of female participants compared with those for males, the following effect sizes could be calculated:

- Overall (combined) effect size for relevant studies irrespective of the gender of the participants.
- Overall (combined) effect size for female participant studies.
- Overall (combined) effect size for male participant studies.

The overall effect size may be essentially similar irrespective of gender. However, they could be very different. A more complex analysis would be involved in order to compare the effect sizes for young males, young females, older males and older females. This would involve the calculation of effect sizes for the four different age/gender combinations (see Table 36.1).

Not all meta-analyses investigate the influence of study characteristics. Only do so if it is relevant to your research purposes and there is sufficient variety in the types of study available in the research literature.

Table 36.1	Meta-analysis table for different age and gender combinations	
	Young	**Older**
Males	$r = .32$	$r = .13$
	$r = .45$	$r = .03$
	$r = .35$	$r = -.04$
Females	$r = .22$	$r = .05$
	$r = .12$	$r = .15$
	$r = .15$	$r = .11$

36.5   First steps in meta-analysis

◼ Step 1: Define the variables of interest to you

Decide which two variables you are investigating in your meta-analysis. (Other pairs of variables can also be considered and treated in the same way in parallel.) This is in essence deciding the nature of the research hypothesis to be tested.

◼ Step 2: Plan your database search

Plan your search for relevant studies involving your chosen variables. This search should involve a computer search of the relevant databases. Perusing studies referred to in relevant research publications may generate additions to your list of relevant studies. Of course, you may wish to omit certain types of study because they are not relevant or do not meet other criteria. It is important to do this using stipulated criteria rather than on whims. If possible, seek out unpublished studies.

◼ Step 3: Obtain research reports

Obtain copies of research reports containing the statistical analyses of the relevant studies. These may be available in your local university or college library in hard copy or digital form. Sometimes they may have to be ordered from elsewhere. Consider contacting the authors of recently published studies by mail or email for copies of all of their relevant work. Databases usually contain an adequate address for the senior author and email address for the corresponding authors. Remember that at the very minimum, you need a significance level and sample size to calculate an effect size.

Previous meta-analytic studies may include details of otherwise unobtainable studies. Effect sizes might be found which are usable in your meta-analysis. Cohen's d is easily converted to r (and vice versa) by using Table 36.2. This table also serves as a ready reference to compare effect sizes expressed as r with those given as Cohen's d.

Table 36.2	Equivalent effect sizes expressed as Cohen's *d* and Pearson correlation coefficient

Pearson *r*	Cohen's *d*	Pearson *r*	Cohen's *d*	Pearson *r*	Cohen's *d*	Pearson *r*	Cohen's *d*	Pearson *r*	Cohen's *d*
.00	0.00	.20	0.41	.40	0.87	.60	1.50	.80	2.67
.01	0.02	.21	0.43	.41	0.90	.61	1.54	.81	2.76
.02	0.04	.22	0.45	.42	0.93	.62	1.58	.82	2.87
.03	0.06	.23	0.47	.43	0.95	.63	1.62	.83	2.98
.04	0.08	.24	0.49	.44	0.98	.64	1.67	.84	3.10
.05	0.10	.25	0.52	.45	1.01	.65	1.71	.85	3.23
.06	0.12	.26	0.54	.46	1.04	.66	1.76	.86	3.37
.07	0.14	.27	0.56	.47	1.06	.67	1.81	.87	3.53
.08	0.16	.28	0.58	.48	1.09	.68	1.85	.88	3.71
.09	0.18	.29	0.61	.49	1.12	.69	1.91	.89	3.90
.10	0.20	.30	063	.50	1.15	.70	1.96	.90	4.13
.11	0.22	.31	0.65	.51	1.19	.71	2.02	.91	4.39
.12	0.24	.32	0.68	.52	1.22	.72	2.08	.92	4.69
.13	0.26	.33	0.70	.53	1.25	.73	2.14	.93	5.06
.14	0.28	.34	0.72	.54	1.28	.74	2.20	.94	5.51
.15	0.30	.35	0.75	.55	1.32	.75	2.27	.95	6.08
.16	0.32	.37	0.77	.56	1.35	.76	2.34	.96	6.86
.17	0.35	.37	0.80	.57	1.39	.77	2.41	.97	7.98
.18	0.37	.38	0.82	.58	1.42	.78	2.49	.98	9.85
.19	0.39	.39	0.85	.59	1.46	.79	2.58	.99	14.04

Step 4: Calculating effect sizes for each study

A standard measure of effect size should be calculated for each of the relationships between the variables for each study reviewed. Our chosen measure of effect size is the Pearson correlation coefficient or *r*. Some studies may report this value or some other measure of effect size, but usually they do not. Where effect sizes are not reported they need to be calculated by the meta-analyst.

It is usually possible to use the test of significance reported in the original analysis to calculate the effect size *r*. Table 36.3 gives this conversion for common tests of significance. We have already seen some of these in Chapter 17.

However, sometimes this information is missing from the primary source. This is less of a problem with modern research publications but it is nevertheless useful to know what to do when even minimum information is missing. If you know the sample size and the significance level, then the following formula can be used to approximate the effect size irrespective of the particular test of significance involved. The significance levels should be converted to their one-tailed equivalents if they are given as two-tailed probabilities because the absolute value of *z* refers to one tail of the standard normal distribution. The sign of the *z*-score needs to be noted.

$$r = \frac{z}{\sqrt{N}}$$

Table 36.3	Converting various tests of significance to a correlation coefficient	
Statistic	**Formula for converting to Pearson correlation**	**Notes**
t-test	$r_{bis} = \sqrt{\dfrac{t^2}{t^2 + df}}$	Can be used for a related or unrelated *t*-test
chi-square	$r = \sqrt{\dfrac{chi\text{-}square}{N}}$	Only use this formula for a 2 × 2 chi-square
Cohen's *d*	Convert to *r* using Table 36.2	Useful if no source of data from a study is available other than another meta-analysis
Nonparametric test	$r = \dfrac{z}{\sqrt{N}}$	Alternatively convert to parametric equivalent and substitute this value in formula (see Section 17.4)
Pearson correlation coefficient and variants	No conversion necessary	These are already the value of the effect size
Most common tests of significance and when only significance level and sample size given	$r = \dfrac{z}{\sqrt{N}}$	Convert the significance level to *z* using Table 36.4. Then divide by the square root of the sample size involved

The value of *z* for the significance level is obtained by consulting Table 36.4. So, if the significance level for a particular study is 0.7% (i.e. the probability is .007), then the value of *z* obtained from Table 36.4 is 2.326. Assuming that the one-tailed significance level is based on 40 participants, the effect size is:

$$r = \frac{2.326}{\sqrt{40}} = \frac{2.326}{6.325} = .37$$

This is a good approximation given the limited information required. The formula has obvious advantages for use with uncommon tests of significance or those for which a conversion formula to *r* is not available. It can also be used to convert *non*parametric significance levels to effect sizes. Of course, significance levels are not always reported very precisely, which may cause problems especially when the findings are *not* significant at the 5% level. Just what is the effect size for this? Some authors report it as an effect size of zero, though clearly this is not likely to be the case. Others take it as the 50% or .5 level of significance. In these circumstances, it would be better to estimate the effect size from the formulae in Table 36.3 if at all possible.

At the end of this step, you should have values or estimated values of the effect size for each of the studies you are using in your meta-analysis. If you are unable to give an effect size because of incomplete information in the original report of a study or because the report was unobtainable, it will have to be omitted. This omission should be mentioned in your report of your meta-analysis.

Step 5: Combining effect sizes over a number of studies

One aim of meta-analysis is to combine the findings of several studies (or a selected subset of studies such as those involving female participants) into a single composite effect size. The obvious way of doing this is to average the effect sizes. However, the simple numerical average of the effect sizes can give a distorted value, particularly when some of the values of the correlation coefficients are large. Instead, we average

Table 36.4		z-distribution for converting one-tailed probability levels to z-scores									

p	z	p	z	p	z	p	z	p	z	p	z
.000 01	4.265	.19	0.878	.40	0.253	.61	− 0.279	.82	− 0.915		
.00 01	3.719	.20	0.842	.41	0.228	.62	− 0.306	.83	− 0.954		
.001	3.090	.21	0.806	.42	0.202	.63	− 0.332	.84	− 0.995		
.01	2.326	.22	0.772	.43	0.176	.64	− 0.359	.85	− 1.036		
.02	2.054	.23	0.739	.44	0.151	.65	− 0.385	.86	− 1.080		
.03	1.881	.24	0.706	.45	0.126	.66	− 0.413	.87	− 1.126		
.04	1.751	.25	0.675	.46	0.100	.67	− 0.440	.88	− 1.175		
.05	1.645	.26	0.643	.47	0.075	.68	− 0.468	.89	− 1.227		
.06	1.555	.27	0.613	.48	0.050	.69	− 0.496	.90	− 1.282		
.07	1.476	.28	0.583	.49	0.025	.70	− 0.524	.91	− 1.341		
.08	1.405	.29	0.553	.50	0.000	.71	− 0.553	.92	− 1.405		
.09	1.341	.30	0.524	.51	− 0.025	.72	− 0.583	.93	− 1.476		
.10	1.282	.31	0.496	.52	− 0.050	.73	− 0.613	.94	− 1.555		
.11	1.227	.32	0.468	.53	− 0.075	.74	− 0.643	.95	− 1.645		
.12	1.175	.33	0.440	.54	− 0.100	.75	− 0.675	.96	− 1.751		
.13	1.126	.34	0.413	.55	− 0.126	.76	− 0.706	.97	− 1.881		
.14	1.080	.35	0.385	.56	− 0.151	.77	− 0.739	.98	− 2.054		
.15	1.036	.36	0.359	.57	− 0.176	.78	− 0.772	.99	− 2.326		
.16	0.995	.37	0.332	.58	− 0.202	.79	− 0.806				
.17	0.954	.38	0.306	.59	− 0.228	.80	− 0.842				
.18	0.915	.39	0.279	.60	− 0.253	.81	− 0.878				

Find the appropriate significance or probability level p-value from the table, the required z-score is adjacent to the right.
Reverse this process if you wish to convert your z-score back to a significance or probability level.
Remember that a probability needs to be multiplied by 100% to get the percentage probability.

the effect sizes by converting each r into a z-score (z_r) for the correlation coefficient using Table 36.5. This table is of the correlation coefficient expressed as a normal distribution. It is different from the z-distribution so take care. You need the purple columns to find your value of the correlation coefficient r and the required value of z_r is to the right of this in the blue column. The several values of z_r are then summed and averaged by dividing by the number of values. This average can then be turned back into the combined effect size by using Table 36.5 in the reverse mode. (That is, you look for your value of the combined z_r in the right-hand side (blue) of the pairs of columns and find the value of r to the left of this.)

Thus if we wish to calculate the average effect size from three studies with the following effect sizes:

study A: $r = .3$

study B: $r = .7$

study C: $r = .5$

We convert each to their z_r by using Table 36.5. These values are 0.310, 0.867 and 0.549, respectively. The numerical average of these is

| Table 36.5 | | Extended table of Fisher's z_r transformation of the correlation coefficient | | | | | | | | | | | |

r	z_r	r	z_r	r	z_r	r	z_r	r	z^r	r	z^r	r	z^r
.01	0.10	.41	0.436	.801	1.101	.841	1.225	.881	1.380	.921	1.596	.961	1.959
.02	0.020	.42	0.448	.802	1.104	.842	1.228	.882	1.385	.922	1.602	.962	1.972
.03	0.030	.43	0.460	.803	1.107	.843	1.231	.883	1.389	.923	1.609	.963	1.986
.04	0.040	.44	0.472	.804	1.110	.844	1.235	.884	1.394	.924	1.616	.964	2.000
.05	0.050	.45	0.485	.805	1.113	.845	1.238	.885	1.398	.925	1.623	.965	2.014
.06	0.060	.46	0.497	.806	1.116	.846	1.242	.886	1.403	.926	1.630	.966	2.029
.07	0.070	.47	0.510	.807	1.118	.847	1.245	.887	1.408	.927	1.637	.967	2.044
.08	0.080	.48	0.523	.808	1.121	.848	1.249	.888	1.412	.928	1.644	.968	2.060
.09	0.090	.49	0.536	.809	1.124	.849	1.253	.889	1.417	.929	1.651	.969	2.076
.10	0.100	.50	0.549	.810	1.127	.850	1.256	.890	1.422	.930	1.658	.970	2.092
.11	0.110	.51	0.563	.811	1.130	.851	1.260	.891	1.427	.931	1.666	.971	2.110
.12	0.121	.52	0.576	.812	1.133	.852	1.263	.892	1.432	.932	1.673	.972	2.127
.13	0.131	.53	0.590	.813	1.136	.853	1.267	.893	1.437	.933	1.681	.973	2.146
.14	0.141	.54	0.604	.814	1.139	.854	1.271	.894	1.442	.934	1.689	.974	2.165
.15	0.151	.55	0.618	.815	1.142	.855	1.274	.895	1.447	.935	1.697	.975	2.185
.16	0.161	.56	0.633	.816	1.145	.856	1.278	.896	1.452	.936	1.705	.976	2.205
.17	0.172	.57	0.648	.817	1.148	.857	1.282	.897	1.457	.937	1.713	.977	2.227
.18	0.182	.58	0.663	.818	1.151	.858	1.286	.898	1.462	.938	1.721	.978	2.249
.19	0.192	.59	0.678	.819	1.154	.859	1.290	.899	1.467	.939	1.730	.979	2.273
.20	0.203	.60	0.693	.820	1.157	.860	1.293	.900	1.472	.940	1.738	.980	2.298
.21	0.213	.61	0.709	.821	1.160	.861	1.297	.901	1.478	.941	1.747	.981	2.323
.22	0.224	.62	0.725	.822	1.163	.862	1.301	.902	1.483	.942	1.756	.982	2.351
.23	0.234	.63	0.741	.823	1.166	.863	1.305	.903	1.488	.943	1.764	.983	2.380
.24	0.245	.64	0.758	.824	1.169	.864	1.309	.904	1.494	.944	1.774	.984	2.410
.25	0.255	.65	0.775	.825	1.172	.865	1.313	.905	1.499	.945	1.783	.985	2.443
.26	0.266	.66	0.793	.826	1.175	.866	1.317	.906	1.505	.946	1.792	.986	2.477
.27	0.277	.67	0.811	.827	1.179	.867	1.321	.907	1.510	.947	1.802	.987	2.515
.28	0.288	.68	0.829	.828	1.182	.868	1.325	.908	1.516	.948	1.812	.988	2.555
.29	0.299	.69	0.848	.829	1.185	.869	1.329	.909	1.522	.949	1.822	.989	2.599
.30	0.310	.70	0.867	.830	1.188	.870	1.333	.910	1.528	.950	1.832	.990	2.647
.31	0.321	.71	0.887	.831	1.191	.871	1.337	.911	1.533	.951	1.842	.991	2.700
.32	0.332	.72	0.908	.832	1.195	.872	1.341	.912	1.539	.952	1.853	.992	2.759
.33	0.343	.73	0.929	.833	1.198	.873	1.346	.913	1.545	.953	1.863	.993	2.826
.34	0.354	.74	0.951	.834	1.201	.874	1.350	.914	1.551	.954	1.875	.994	2.903
.35	0.365	.75	0.973	.835	1.204	.875	1.354	.915	1.557	.955	1.886	.995	2.995
.36	0.377	.76	0.996	.836	1.208	.876	1.358	.916	1.564	.956	1.897	.996	3.106
.37	0.388	.77	1.020	.837	1.211	.877	1.363	.917	1.570	.957	1.909	.997	3.250
.38	0.400	.78	1.045	.838	1.214	.878	1.367	.918	1.576	.958	1.921	.998	3.453
.39	0.412	.79	1.071	.839	1.218	.879	1.371	.919	1.583	.959	1.933	.999	3.800
.40	0.424	.80	1.098	.840	1.221	.880	1.376	.920	1.589	.960	1.946		

But this is the average z_r. We can then reconvert this value to an overall effect size by using Table 36.5 in reverse. The effect size r for the three studies combined is therefore .52.

It is possible that a particular study has findings in the reverse direction from those of the majority. In this case, its effect size is given a negative value. Thus the overall effect size will be reduced.

Step 6: Statistical significance of the combined studies

The significance level of the combined studies can also be assessed. Once again, the simple numerical average of the probability levels is misleading. Intuitively we may appreciate that this simple average makes no allowance for the greatly increased effective sample size obtained by combining studies. There are numerous different ways of combining significance levels from a range of studies to give an overall significance level, each having different advantages or disadvantages. The simplest and one of the most satisfactory methods is to convert each significance level into a z-score using Table 36.4. Rather than divide by the number of z-scores to obtain the average, the sum of the z-scores is divided by the square root of the number of z-scores:

$$\bar{z} = \frac{\sum z}{\sqrt{N}}$$

Thus if the significance levels from a set of studies are .08, .15 and .02, each of these is converted to a z-score using Table 36.4. This gives us z-scores of 1.405, 1.036 and 2.054, respectively. These z-scores are summed and divided by the square root of the number of z-scores:

$$\bar{z} = \frac{1.405 + 1.036 + 2.054}{\sqrt{3}} = \frac{4.495}{1.732} = 2.595$$

This average z is converted back into a significance level using Table 36.4. In this case, this gives a combined significance level of .001 (or 1.0%).

Note that if the findings of a study are in the *reverse* direction from those of the majority, the corresponding z-score is given a negative sign. Once again, this tends to reduce the overall significance level.

Step 7: Comparing effect sizes from studies with different characteristics

Finally, what if one wished to compare effect sizes between studies with different characteristics? For example, what if one wanted to know whether studies involving female participants differed from those involving male participants in terms of their effect size? The easiest way of doing this is to turn your data into a table like Table 36.6. In this table, the effect sizes for the male and female studies are listed in separate columns. It is then a relatively simple matter to compare these two sets of effect-size 'scores' using the Mann–Whitney U-test (Explaining statistics 21.3) or the t-test (Explaining statistics 14.1). This is an approximate procedure in the eyes of some experts since all studies are considered equal although they may differ in terms of the sample size. Despite criticisms of such an approach, it uses familiar statistics and may well be sufficiently powerful for most purposes.

There is a significant difference between these two groups as assessed by either the Mann–Whitney U-test or the unrelated t-test. Thus the effect sizes are greater in studies which involved female participants than in studies involving male participants. If you choose the t-test, it might be advantageous to convert your effect sizes to z_r values since this will reduce the undue influence of extreme values a little.

Table 36.6	Illustrating the comparison of effect sizes for different study characteristics
Effect sizes of studies of males	**Effect sizes of studies of females**
.27	.41
.15	.52
.22	.43
.29	.47
Mean = .23	Mean = .46

36.6   Illustrative example

There is evidence that men's physiological responses to sexually explicit pictures may differentiate sex offenders from non-offenders and non-sex offenders. Physiological response in these studies is assessed by plethysmographs which measure either changes in the volume of the penis or changes in the circumference of the penis. The latter measure is generally not well regarded. The data reported are fictitious but help to illustrate the processes involved in meta-analysis.

■ Step 1: Define the variables of interest to you

In this case, the researchers wished to review the available studies which might indicate whether physiological responses to sexual images could be used to differentiate sex offenders from other men. Consequently the independent variable was sex offender versus non-offender or non-sex offender and the dependent variable was measured by scores on a plethysmograph assessment of the men's response to erotic pictures.

■ Step 2: Plan your database search

The researchers searched the psychological abstract database (PsycINFO – this database is discussed in Chapter 5 of Howitt and Cramer, 2020) and also the medical science database using the keywords plethysmograph, sex offender, rapist, paedophile and molester. Additionally, as the field is relatively small, the researchers chose to write to one hundred researchers in the field requesting relevant research reports, either published or unpublished.

Step 3: Obtain research reports

The researchers found nine studies from their database search to be obtained from their own or other university libraries. These are listed in column 1 of Table 36.7 but they also received two additional unpublished studies from their request to key researchers. Table 36.7 also includes information relevant to calculating the effect size gleaned from these reports and information about possible study variables.

Step 4: Calculating an effect size for each study

Table 36.7 lists the information obtained from each study relevant to calculating the effect size. The formula (or table) used is mentioned and the final column provides effect sizes expressed as r for each of the studies. Edwards's study, however, is so lacking in the statistical detail provided that it has been deleted from this meta-analysis.

Step 5: Combining effect sizes over a number of studies

The meta-analyst combined the effect sizes for all of the studies by converting each effect r into a z_r, averaging these and finally converting back to an effect size. This involves turning each effect size correlation into a Fisher z_r using Table 36.5. The effect sizes in order are .24, .54, .52, .37, .19, .34, .49, .34, .22 and .50 according to Table 36.7.

Remember that the final study has been discarded from the analysis. The average of the corresponding z_r is:

average z_r

$$= \frac{0.245+0.604+0.576+0.388+0.192+0.354+0.536+0.354+0.224+0.549}{10}$$

$$= \frac{4.022}{10} = 0.4022$$

This value of z_r according to Table 36.5 corresponds to an average of the effect sizes of .38 (this is obtained by looking for the average z_r of 0.4022 in the body of Table 36.5 and reading off the value of r which corresponds to this value of the averaged z_r).

This process could be repeated to obtain, say, the overall effect size of the volume measure and the circumference measure separately.

Step 6: Statistical significance of the combined studies

The overall significance of the combined studies is obtained by turning each significance level into the corresponding z-score using Table 36.4. The various z-scores are then summed and divided by the square root of the number (N) of significance levels employed. Note that for two studies the significance level is not reported or is not precise enough. Thus the calculation is based on just nine studies. The formula for z is:

$$z = \frac{\sum z}{\sqrt{N}}$$

Table 36.7　Illustrative summary of studies and the conversion of statistics to effect sizes

Study (fictitious)	Effect-size information	Significance	Plethysmograph measure	Control group	Effect-size formula	Effect size r
Brown (1976)	chi-square value given as 4.06 with 1 degree of freedom based on N of 73 cases	.05	circumference	prisoners	$r = \sqrt{\dfrac{\text{chi-square}}{N}}$	.24
Grey (1998)	gives effect size as r = .54	?	volume	prisoners	none needed	.54
Black (1983)	F given as significant at .01 with 20 cases	.01	circumference	prisoners	$r = \dfrac{z}{\sqrt{N}}$	.52
White (1995)	t-value given as 2.31 with 34 cases (i.e. df = 32)	.025	volume	non-prisoners	$r_{bis} = \sqrt{\dfrac{t^2}{t^2 + df}}$	.37
Jones (1966)	t-test reported as 1.45, df = 54	.10	circumference	non-prisoners	$r_{bis} = \sqrt{\dfrac{t^2}{t^2 + df}}$	.19
Williams (1987)	Mann–Whitney U significant at 1% level based on 47 cases	.01	circumference	non-prisoners	$r = \dfrac{z}{\sqrt{N}}$	.34
Parton (unpublished)	related t = 2.53, df = 10, this was a matched design in which prisoners served as own control	.025	volume	prisoners	$r_{bis} = \sqrt{\dfrac{t^2}{t^2 + df}}$ (This formula works with related t-tests)	.49
Carter (unpublished)	t = 1.67 with total N = 23	.075	circumference	prisoners	$r_{bis} = \sqrt{\dfrac{t^2}{t^2 + df}}$	.34
Elliot (1999)	Cohen's d given as .45	.001	circumference	prisoners	convert to r with Table 36.2	.22
Smith (1989)	F reported as significant at .03 with df = 1, 54 (i.e. N = 56)	.03	volume	non-prisoners	$r = \dfrac{z}{\sqrt{N}}$	.50
Edwards (1953)	t-value not reported. Findings not significant at 5% level with sample size = 14	> .05 or set at p = .50	circumference	prisoners	use of formula too crude because of uncertainty about exact significance and no other statistics (alternatively r could be set at .00)	study ignored

This gives:

$$= \frac{1.645 + 2.326 + 1.960 + 1.282 + 2.326 + 1.960 + 1.440 + 3.090 + 1.881}{\sqrt{9}}$$

$$= \frac{17.908}{3} = 5.97$$

Remember that this is the value of z which has to be converted back to a significance level using Table 36.4. Thus the combined significance level is .000 01 or 0.001%.

■ Step 7: Comparing effect sizes from studies with different characteristics

Because there is some question whether the circumference measure is as good as the volume measure, the overall effect sizes were calculated for the circumference measure studies and the volume measure studies separately. This yielded the data in Table 36.8.

Comparing these overall effect sizes, it would seem that there are grounds for thinking that circumference studies produce the smallest effect size, implying that they are inferior at identifying sex offenders from other men. This comparison is significant at only the .067 level with a Mann–Whitney test but significant at .04 with the unrelated t-test. Using z_r instead of the effect size made no substantial difference to the outcome. This seems reasonably strong evidence that the volume measure tends to produce greater effects than the circumference measures.

A similar analysis comparing the effect of having a prisoner versus a non-prisoner control group showed no significant difference in terms of effect size using the same tests of significance.

Table 36.8	Effect size data for volume measures and circumference penile measures compared
Effect sizes of studies involving volume measure	**Effect sizes of studies involving circumference measure**
.54	.24
.37	.52
.49	.19
.50	.34
	.34
	.22
Mean = .48	Mean = .31

36.7 Comparing a study with a previous study

Meta-analysis is useful when you are replicating another researcher's study as it provides a method of combining the results of the two studies. Furthermore, you can test to see if your effect size is significantly different from that found in the previous research. The formula involves converting each effect size to   using Table 36.5 and then subtracting one from the other and making other calculations involving N (the sample sizes) as in the following formula:

$$z = \frac{r_1 - r_2}{\sqrt{\dfrac{1}{N_1 - 3} + \dfrac{1}{N_2 - 3}}}$$

Thus if the effect sizes under consideration are .43 (with $N = 25$) and .62 (with $N = 47$) then these are first converted to z_r using Table 36.5. This gives us values of .460 and .725. The calculation is then:

$$z = \frac{0.460 - 0.725}{\sqrt{\dfrac{1}{25 - 3} + \dfrac{1}{47 - 3}}}$$

$$= \frac{- 0.265}{\sqrt{\dfrac{1}{22} + \dfrac{1}{44}}}$$

$$= \frac{- 0.265}{\sqrt{0.0455 + 0.0227}}$$

$$= \frac{- 0.265}{\sqrt{0.0682}}$$

$$= \frac{- 0.265}{0.261}$$

$$= - 1.015$$

This value of z (not z_r) is turned into a significance level by using Table 36.4. This gives a probability value of .15 (or 15%) which is not statistically significant. Our conclusion in this case would be that the effect sizes of the two studies are similar and certainly not significantly different from each other. We could go on to report the effect size of the combined studies and the combined significance levels using the methods described above.

Of course, this formula can be used to compare any two correlation coefficients with each other to see whether they are significantly different.

36.8 Reporting the results

Meta-analytic studies are almost always substantial research studies in their own right. Consequently, many of the requirements of reporting a meta-analytic study are the very same requirements that one would require when writing a substantial report such as a journal article. You may find the detailed account of writing psychological reports in the authors' companion volume (Howitt & Cramer, 2020) invaluable in reporting a meta-analysis as a consequence. Because there may be details of a large number of studies to tabulate, then special care may be required in generating the tables using, say, Excel or

Word. SPSS would not be particularly helpful in this regard. Since any meta-analysis needs to make reference to previous relevant meta-analytic studies, often there is a model already available for one to consult to get an idea of the sort of style to adopt.

None of this should be a deterrent to using meta-analytic techniques as part of the literature review, say, for any study you are writing up. As we have seen, many of the calculations are relatively simple and straightforward by hand. It is perfectly feasible to, say, add in effect sizes for the findings of relevant previous research as you report them. Not only would this be good practice but it would also change the emphasis from statistical significance to that of effect size.

Research examples

Meta-analysis

Freund and Kasten (2012) explain that we have perceptions of our cognitive abilities which are involved in the self-concept because they relate our abilities to the abilities of other people. This process of self- and other-evaluation may be regarded as a continuous feature of our lives and is employed in formal settings too (e.g. the careers guidance setting where psychometric measurements are available). The researchers performed a meta-analysis based on 41 published studies of the relationship between self-estimated and psychometrically assessed cognitive abilities. This involved 41 published studies and a total of 154 effect sizes obtained from them. The overall relationship between the self-estimated and psychometric cognitive abilities was a correlation of .33. Among other things, the analysis also showed that the relationship was greater when mathematical abilities were the focus as opposed to more global cognitive abilities.

Sedlmeier and co-workers (2012) carried out a meta-analysis of the psychological effects of meditation. Their main focus was on nonclinical groups of people using meditation, i.e. psychologically healthy adults. But there were problems since a big proportion (75%) of the studies they identified were excluded for reasons such as psychological measures were not used or that the study did not involve nonclinical samples. So the study itself was based on the remaining 163 studies which met the study criteria. The average effect size was $r = .28$. Taking the 125 studies which were published in reviewed journals the average effect size remained much the same at $r = .27$. The effects of meditation were large for emotionality and relationship problems with smaller effects for measures of attention and smaller still for cognitive variables. The details of the findings varied for different approaches (transcendental meditation, mindfulness meditation, etc.). The authors tried a number of possible mediating variables such as length of time doing meditation and age but little of sufficient clarity to draw conclusions emerged from this.

Taylor, Rastle and Davis (2013) point out that reading in many language systems depends on both knowledge of the word (e.g. sew) and a knowledge of how to generate sounds from spellings such as when pseudowords are read (e.g. gew). The neural basis for these skills has been discussed by researchers but Taylor et al. propose that such skills depend on a) the degree of engagement of a brain region brought about by the stimulus word and b) the amount of effort involved in processing that stimulus. Predictions from this were assessed with a meta-analysis of neuroimaging studies of reading. Among other things, the meta-analysis of the studies revealed that real words compared with pseudowords led to the activation of the left anterior fusiform gyrus of the brain. Pseudowords compared to words generated activity in a more anterior part of the left fusiform gyrus and the occipitotemporal cortex.

Key points

- This account of meta-analysis should convince you of the importance of reporting effect sizes for all studies you carry out. The most useful effect size formula is simply the Pearson's correlation coefficient between two variables.

- When carrying out a literature review, it is a positive advantage to report the effect sizes for all of the important studies. This is more important than reporting statistical significance alone.

- Experience will show that the difference between significant and non-significant findings can be very small indeed when their effect sizes are compared. Consequently, you need to consider near-significant results carefully when evaluating the research literature.

COMPUTER ANALYSIS

Some meta-analysis software

The basic calculations for meta-analysis are essentially straightforward and well within the capabilities of anyone prepared to give this chapter careful study. Although some of the calculations can benefit from computer assistance, the common statistical computer packages will only be of occasional help with a meta-analysis. SPSS does not deal with meta-analysis. Generally speaking, this program provides no particular help in relation to meta-analysis. There are a number of commercial software options available to help with meta-analysis though these may or may not be available to you at your university or college, for example.

Of more immediate practical help may be the following free meta-analytic software:

- *Meta-Stat – A tool for the meta-analysis of research studies* by Lawrence M. Rudner, Gene V. Glass, David L. Evartt and Patrick J. Emery. This is documented and can be downloaded at echo.edres.org:8080/meta/metastat.htm

- *Statistics software for meta-analysis* by Ralf Schwarzer. This is documented and can be downloaded at userpage.fu-berlin.de/health/meta_e.htm

- *The meta-analysis calculator.* This can be used as an applet at www.lyonsmorris.com/lyons/metaAnalysis/index.cfm

- *The MIX program for meta-analysis* which uses Microsoft's Excel spreadsheet.

Of course, a search of the Internet will find others. Try https://toptipbio.com/free-meta-analysis-software/ for a longer list of free meta-analysis software.

Screenshots 36.1 to 36.3 illustrate the calculation of effect sizes using the Meta Analysis Calculator. G*Power is discussed in more detail in Chapter 39. The steps are fairly intuitive but for more information see Chapter 39 and the G*Power documentation referred to there.

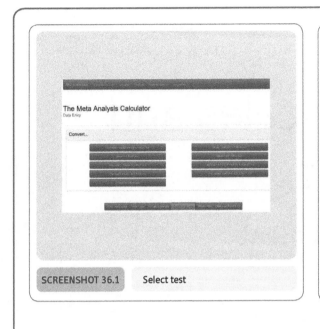

SCREENSHOT 36.1   Select test

SCREENSHOT 36.2   Enter test statistics

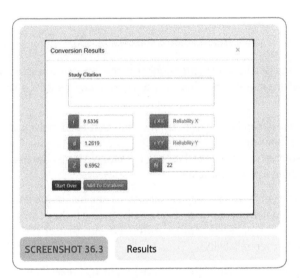

SCREENSHOT 36.3   Results

Recommended further reading

Howitt, D., & Cramer, D. (2020). *Introduction to research methods in psychology* (Chapter 5). Harlow, UK: Pearson.

Rosenthal, R. (1991). *Meta-analytic procedures for social research*. Newbury Park, CA: Sage (especially Chapters 1–4).

CHAPTER 37

Reliability in scales and measurement

Consistency and agreement

Overview

- Reliability as discussed in this chapter concerns the internal consistency of a psychological scale or similar measurements. That is, do all components of the scale measure similar things?

- Internal consistency can be achieved by ensuring that each individual item correlates with the sum of the items on the scale. This is known as item analysis. Any items which do not correlate substantially with the total (of all of the items) is deleted because it is not measuring the same thing as the total score.

- Split-half reliability involves correlating the total of one half of the items and the total of the other half. The two halves are measuring the same thing if they correlate highly. Sometimes the sum of the odd-numbered items is correlated with that of the even-numbered items. This is called odd-even reliability.

- Alpha reliability is the average of every possible split-half reliability that could be calculated on a scale. This overcomes the influence of the particular selection of items chosen for each half on split-half reliability.

- Kappa is a measurement of the agreement between raters or observers. That is, it assesses inter-rater or inter-observer agreement.

Preparation

The concept of correlation (Chapter 8) is an essential prerequisite to understanding the assessment of reliability. Chapter 24 on the correlated scores analysis of variance and Chapter 33 on factor analysis may also help with particular sections of this chapter.

37.1   Introduction

Statistics plays an important role in constructing good scales and measures. Usually in psychology, but not always, measures consist of several different components added together to give a total score on that measure. Thus many attitude and personality tests consist of a large number of questionnaire items which are combined to give a total score on some attitude or personality dimension. Although the analysis of such scales using factor analysis (Chapter 33) is generally part of modern psychological test and measure construction, there are other approaches. A researcher may wish to develop a fairly general measure of a particular psychological variable for which simple methods may suffice. So, for example, a questionnaire designed to measure 'love' for one's partner might consist of several questions each about different aspects of the concept. The extent to which the items measure much the same thing (love) is obviously important. Generally speaking, if they intercorrelate to a reasonable degree then we can assume that they are probably measuring different aspects of love. However, since it is the overall or total score on the measure of love which matters to the researcher, we would expect that:

- scores on each item correlate with the total score (this is item–total or item–whole correlation)

- scores based on half of the items of the scale would correlate with scores based on the remainder of the scale (this is called split-half reliability which can be elaborated into Cronbach's coefficient alpha).

The procedures described in this chapter are about the *internal consistency* of psychological measures. Internal consistency is the extent to which all of the items constituting a measure are measuring much the same thing. If they are measuring similar things, each item should correlate with the other items in the measure. Although this is referred to as reliability, it is a very different matter from reliability across two different points in time, for example. Figure 37.1 gives the key steps in understanding reliability.

37.2   Item-analysis using item–total correlation

Look at Table 37.1. It contains scores on four different items for ten different participants. There is also a total score given in the total column consisting of the scores on each of item 1, item 2, item 3 and item 4. So the second participant has a total score of $2 + 1 + 1 + 2 = 6$. The correlations between the scores of the ten participants for item 1 and the total score can be calculated with the Pearson correlation formula (Explaining statistics 8.1) or using a computer package, of course. The value of the correlation is .74 which suggests that item 1 is a fairly good measure of what the total score on the measure is measuring. The other items may be treated in the same way in order to see whether this is true of all of them.

Generally speaking, we would be happy with this scale given the relatively high item–total or item–whole correlations.

When an item is excluded from the total score, its correlation with this adjusted total score is reduced. Thus, in Table 37.2 the correlation of item 1 with the total score (based on summing items 2, 3 and 4) is .49 as opposed to a correlation of .74 when all items are included. This more refined analysis does nothing to revise our opinion of the scale. Generally speaking, the items which seem to be the poorest are items 1 and 4 which have the lowest item–total correlations with the item removed from the total.

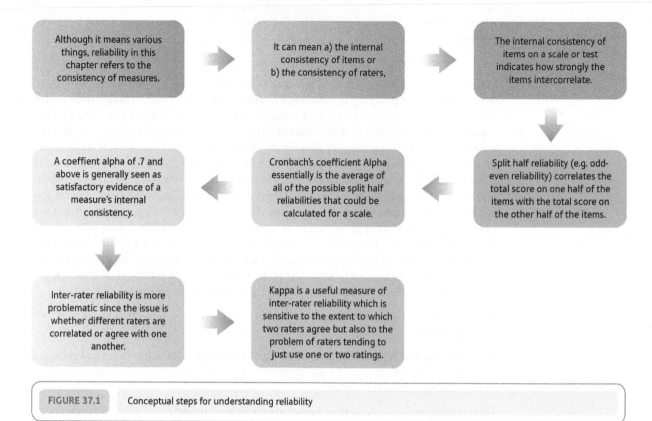

FIGURE 37.1 Conceptual steps for understanding reliability

Table 37.1	Data from ten cases from a four-item questionnaire				
Person	Item 1	Item 2	Item 3	Item 4	Total score
1	1	3	5	6	15
2	2	1	1	2	6
3	1	1	1	1	4
4	5	2	4	2	13
5	6	4	3	2	15
6	5	4	5	6	20
7	4	5	3	2	14
8	2	1	2	1	6
9	1	2	1	1	5
10	1	1	2	2	6

Of course, four-item scales are unusual in psychological research. Normally we have many items. If we had a lot more items, we might be inclined to try to shorten the scale a little, perhaps to make it more appealing to participants. The technique for doing this is simple. Delete the lowest-correlating items and re-do the analysis based on the shortened scale. Although our example is a short scale, if we wanted to reduce its length then we would probably wish to delete item 1 since it has the lowest correlation with the total score.

Table 37.2	Correlations of items with the total score on the scale	
	Correlation with total score	Correlation with total score excluding item in question
Item 1	.74	.49
Item 2	.84	.71
Item 3	.91	.84
Item 4	.76	.55

Table 37.3	Correlations of shortened-scale items with the total score on that scale	
	Correlation with total score	Correlation with total score excluding item in question
Item 2	.77	.56
Item 3	.94	.87
Item 4	.90	.73

Table 37.3 gives the outcome of shortening the scale in this way. You will see that compared with the correlations in Table 37.2, the shortened scale has increased item–total correlations. In this sense, a better scale has been achieved by shortening it. The difficulty is that we can carry on deleting items and improving the internal consistency of the items but this may result in a shorter scale than we want. Usually it is best to exclude only the poorest of items. By doing so we leave a scale which covers a wide range of the aspects of the thing being measured. The appropriate scale length involves a degree of judgement.

A standard statistical package such as SPSS reduces the work in calculating item–total (item–whole) correlations of various sorts and makes reducing the number of items in the scale easy.

The results of this analysis can be written up as follows: 'An item–whole analysis was carried out on the items on the scale. As can be seen from Table 37.2, each item had a satisfactory correlation with the total score on all of the items combined. After the item–whole correlations had been recalculated with the item removed from the total score, there was a decline in the item–whole correlations. However, the relationships remained substantial and it was decided not to shorten the scale given that it consists of just four items.'

37.3 Split-half reliability

A computationally less demanding way of assessing the internal structure of a questionnaire is split-half reliability. Remember that internal reliability refers to the extent to which all of the items in a questionnaire (or similar measure) are assessing much the same thing. Split-half reliability simply involves computing a score based on half of the items and a score based on the other half. The correlation between the scores for these two halves is the split-half reliability (more or less, but read on).

There are no rules for deciding which of the items should be in which half. There are common practices, however. Odd–even reliability is based on taking the odd-numbered items (1, 3, 5, etc.) as one set and the even-numbered items (2, 4, 6, etc.) as the other set. Alternatively, the first half of the items could be correlated with the second half. But there would be nothing against selecting the halves at random.

Explaining statistics 37.1

How the split-half reliability works

Taking the data in Table 37.1, we could sum items 1 and 2 for the total of the first half and sum items 3 and 4 for the total of the second half. The correlation between the two halves is .477.

There is a further step. The difficulty is that we are correlating a scale half the length of our original scale with another scale half the length of our scale. Because of this, the reliability will be lower than for the full length scale. Fortunately, it is quite easy to compute the reliability of a full scale from the reliability of half of the scale using the following formula:

$$\text{full scale reliability} = \frac{n \times \text{known reliability}}{1 + [(n - 1) \times \text{known reliability}]}$$

where n is the ratio by which the number of items is to be increased or decreased.

Since we know the reliability of the half scale (r_{hh}) is .477, the full scale reliability is:

$$\text{full scale reliability} = \frac{2 \times .477}{1 + .477} = \frac{0.954}{1.477} = .65$$

Thus the value of the split-half reliability is .65 when corrected to the full scale length. Standard computer statistics packages such as SPSS can do most of the hard work for you.

Reporting the results

The results of this analysis may be written up as follows: 'The split-half reliability of the scale was found to be .65. This is a somewhat low value but given the exploratory nature of this research, the scale was nevertheless employed.' (As a rule of thumb, a value of about .7 or above would generally be seen as adequate evidence of reliability for general use.)

37.4   Alpha reliability

There is a problem with split-half reliability – its value will depend on which items are selected for each half. The odd–even reliability will not be the same as that found by comparing the first half of the items with the second half, for example. There is an obvious solution: calculate every possible split-half reliability having every possible combination of items in each half and then simply take the average of these. The average of all possible split-half reliabilities from a scale is known as *coefficient alpha*. We will calculate this from first principles and an alternative approach based on the analysis of variance.

Table 37.4 contains all of the possible ways of splitting four items into two halves. There are only three different ways of doing this with our short scale:

● The total of items 1 and 2 compared with the total of items 3 and 4.

● The total of items 1 and 3 compared with the total of items 2 and 4.

● The total of items 1 and 4 compared with the total of items 2 and 3.

The reliability coefficients for these three different possibilities are to be found in Table 37.5. The average of the split-half coefficients corrected (adjusted) for length is coefficient alpha. So the average of .642 + .844 + .946 (or coefficient alpha) is .81. It is generally accepted that a coefficient alpha of .7 or above is satisfactory for psychological research.

This calculation may be feasible with a short scale of four items and a sample of ten individuals, but what, say, if the scale consisted of 100 items? The number of ways of sorting these 100 items into two separate sets of 50 is huge. Obviously the conceptually correct approach given so far would take too much computation time. The alternative hand-computation method is not quite so cumbersome but still time-consuming. One simply carries out a one-way ANOVA for correlated scores on the data shown in Table 37.6.

Table 37.4	Scores for all possible split-halves from four items					
Person	Split-half version 1		Split-half version 2		Split-half version 3	
	Items 1 + 2	Items 3 + 4	Items 1 + 3	Items 2 + 4	Items 1 + 4	Items 2 + 3
1	4	11	6	9	7	8
2	3	3	3	3	4	2
3	2	2	2	2	2	2
4	7	6	9	4	7	6
5	10	5	9	6	8	7
6	9	11	10	10	11	9
7	9	5	7	7	6	8
8	3	3	4	2	3	3
9	3	2	2	3	2	3
10	2	4	3	3	3	3

Table 37.5	Correlations between split-halves and with corrections for shortened length	
	Pearson correlation	Corrected for scale length
Items 1 + 2 with items 3 + 4	.477	.642
Items 1 + 3 with items 2 + 4	.730	.844
Items 1 + 4 with items 2 + 3	.898	.946

Table 37.6	Data on four-item questionnaire for ten cases arranged as for correlated one-way ANOVA			
Person	**Item 1**	**Item 2**	**Item 3**	**Item 4**
1	1	3	5	6
2	2	1	1	2
3	1	1	1	1
4	5	2	4	2
5	6	4	3	2
6	5	4	5	6
7	4	5	3	2
8	2	1	2	1
9	1	2	1	1
10	1	1	2	2
Cell mean	2.8	2.4	2.7	2.5

Table 37.7	ANOVA summary table on four-item questionnaire data				
Source of variation	**Sum of squares**	**Degrees of freedom**	**Mean square (or variance estimate)**	**_F_-ratio**	**Significance**
Between treatments (i.e. between items)	1.00	3	not needed	not needed	not needed
Between people (i.e. individual differences)	70.60	9	7.84		
Error (i.e. residual)	40.00	27	1.48		

This yields the ANOVA summary table (Table 37.7). It is a simple matter then of substituting the appropriate values from this summary table into the following formula for coefficient alpha:

$$\text{coefficient alpha} = \frac{\text{between-people variance} - \text{error variance}}{\text{between-people variance}}$$

$$= \frac{7.84 - 1.48}{7.84} = \frac{6.36}{7.84} = .81$$

This would be generally accepted as evidence of a satisfactory level of internal consistency since coefficients alpha above .7 are regarded as sufficient. The results of this analysis may be written up as follows: 'Coefficient alpha was calculated for the scale and found to be .81 which is generally accepted to be satisfactory.'

It need hardly be said that the use of a computer package such as SPSS which includes coefficient alpha is highly recommended.

37.5 Agreement among raters

Not all research involves psychological scales. Some research involves ratings by a pair of judges or even a panel of judges or assessors. Sometimes rating is used because it is felt that self-completion questionnaires might be inappropriate. Let us take the concept of dangerousness, i.e. the risk posed to members of the public by the release of sex offenders or psychiatric hospital patients. One might be very unhappy about using self-completion questionnaires in these circumstances. It might be considered preferable to have expert clinical psychologists, forensic psychologists and psychiatrists interview the sex offenders or patients to assess the dangerousness of these people on release into the community. Let us assume that we have one clinical psychologist, one forensic psychologist and one psychiatrist who are used in a study of 12 sex offenders. Having interviewed each offender, read all case notes and obtained any further information they required, each of the three professionals rates each offender on a three-point dangerousness index:

- a rating of 1 means that there is no risk to the public
- a rating of 2 means that there is a moderate risk to the public
- a rating of 3 means that there is a high risk to the public.

Their ratings of the 12 offenders are shown in Table 37.8.

Table 37.9 shows the Pearson correlations between the ratings of the three professionals. They suggest that the relationship between the forensic psychologist's and the psychiatrist's ratings is close. A correlation of .83 is, after all, very strong. The difficulty with this only becomes apparent when we examine Table 37.10 which gives agreements between the forensic psychologist and the psychiatrist. This is constructed by tabulating the forensic psychologist's ratings against those of the psychiatrist. The frequencies in the diagonal represent agreements, all other frequencies represent a degree of disagreement.

Table 37.8	Data from the three professionals for each of the 12 sex offenders		
	Clinical psychologist	Forensic psychologist	Psychiatrist
Offender 1	2	3	3
Offender 2	3	3	3
Offender 3	3	3	3
Offender 4	1	1	1
Offender 5	2	1	2
Offender 6	3	3	3
Offender 7	1	2	3
Offender 8	1	3	3
Offender 9	2	2	3
Offender 10	3	3	3
Offender 11	3	3	3
Offender 12	2	3	3

Table 37.9	Correlations between the ratings of various professions	
	Forensic psychologist	**Psychiatrist**
Clinical psychologist	.55	.44
Forensic psychologist	–	.83

Table 37.10	Agreements and disagreements between the forensic psychologist and the psychiatrist on ratings of sex offenders		
Forensic psychologist's ratings	**Psychiatrist's ratings**		
	1	2	3
1	1	1	0
2	0	0	2
3	0	0	8

At first sight it still might appear that there is strong agreement between the two sets of ratings. A total of 9 out of the 12 ratings suggest perfect agreement. So what is the problem? A closer examination of Table 37.10 suggests that virtually all of the agreement occurs when the two experts rate the sex offender as a high risk to the public (rating 3). For the other two ratings they agree only one time out of four. This is a much lower level of agreement. Of course, if the experts rated all of the offenders as a high risk to the public then the agreement would be perfect – although they would not appear to be discriminating between levels of risk. If it were decided to release only sex offenders rated as a low risk to the public, only one sex offender would be released on the basis of the combined ratings of the psychiatrist and forensic psychologist. In other words, correlation coefficients are not very helpful when the exact agreement of raters is required.

The index of agreement between raters needs to have the following characteristics:

● It provides an index of the extent of overlap of ratings.

● It should be sensitive to the problem that agreement is rather meaningless if both raters are using only one rating and do not vary their ratings.

Kappa is a useful index of agreement between a pair of raters since it is responsive to both of these things. The kappa coefficient is calculated from the following formula:

$$\text{kappa} = \frac{\text{total frequency of agreement} - \text{expected total frequency of agreement by chance}}{\text{number of things rated} - \text{expected total frequency of agreement by chance}}$$

Kappa can take negative values if the raters agree at less than chance level. It is zero if there is no agreement greater or lesser than chance. Coefficients approaching +1.00 indicate very good agreement between the raters.

Explaining statistics 37.2

How kappa coefficient works

The above data on the ratings of the forensic psychologist and the psychiatrist will be used to calculate kappa for their ratings.

Step 1 Draw up a crosstabulation table of the data for the two raters and insert the marginal totals (i.e. the sum of frequencies for each row, the sum of frequencies for each column and the overall sum). This is shown in Table 37.11.

Table 37.11	Agreements and disagreements between the forensic psychologist and the psychiatrist on ratings of sex offenders with marginal totals added				
	Forensic psychologist's ratings	Psychiatrist's ratings			Marginal totals
		1	2	3	
	1	1	1	0	2
	2	0	0	2	2
	3	0	0	8	8
Marginal totals		1	1	10	Total = 12

Step 2 Calculate the frequencies of agreement. These are the frequencies in the diagonal of Table 37.11. They have been given in bold. So the frequency of agreements is $1 + 0 + 8 = 9$.

Step 3 Calculate the expected frequency of agreement by firstly calculating the following for each of the diagonals:

$$\text{expected frequency} = \frac{\text{column total} \times \text{row total}}{\text{total}}$$

Thus the expected frequency of agreement for ratings of 3 is the product of the column total of 10 and the row total of 8 divided by the overall total of 12. This is $80 \div 12$ or 6.667. Table 37.12 gives the results of these calculations.

Table 37.12	Expected frequencies for agreement				
	Forensic psychologist's ratings	Psychiatrist's ratings			Marginal totals
		1	2	3	
	1	0.167			2
	2		0.167		2
	3			6.667	8
Marginal totals		1	1	10	Total = 12

Step 4   The expected total frequency of agreement by chance is therefore:

$$0.167 + 0.167 + 6.667 = 7.001.$$

Step 5   We can then substitute our calculated values in the formula:

$$\text{kappa} = \frac{\text{total frequency of agreement} - \text{expected total frequency of agreement by chance}}{\text{number of thing rated} - \text{expected total frequency of agreement by chance}}$$

$$= \frac{9 - 7.001}{12 - 7.001} = \frac{1.999}{4.999} = .40$$

Reporting the results

The results of this analysis can be written up as follows: 'Coefficient kappa was calculated on the relationship between the forensic psychologist's and the psychiatrist's ratings of dangerousness. Despite there being a high level of agreement overall, it was found that kappa was only .40, suggesting that much of the apparent agreement was in fact due to both professionals using the highest dangerousness rating much of the time.'

Interpreting the results

Notice that although the actual agreement seems high at 9 of the 12 ratings, coefficient kappa implies fairly low agreement. This reflects the relative lack of variability in the experts' ratings and the tendency for both to rate the offenders as 3 rather than any other value. Consequently, we can appreciate that coefficient kappa is superior to the simple proportion of agreement in assessing the reliability of ratings.

Research examples

Reliability using Cronbach's alpha and kappa

Ingravallo and co-workers (2008) discuss impairment of job performance due to narcolepsy and indicate that there is a lack of accepted criteria for its assessment. Narcolepsy is a chronic neurological condition in which the brain cannot maintain day-time–night-time sleep cycles properly and sleepiness can occur frequently in circumstances not conducive to employment. In Italy there are benefits available but in order for the sufferer to receive them their case has to go through a medical commission. Fifteen narcolepsy claimees were assessed by four different commissions in simulated assessments. The different commissions were unaware of the decision making of the other commissions in the study. Inter-observer reliability using kappa ranged from .10 to .35 for decisions concerning disability benefits. The raw agreement levels for the pairs of medical commissions ranged from 20.0% to 53.4%. The lack of agreed criteria for identifying narcolepsy is an obvious problem.

Laaksonen and colleagues (2012) report work on an interview-based scale concerning suitability for psychotherapy which was intended to assess suitability for long- and short-term therapy. The scale was used with 326 psychiatric outpatients to obtain baseline measures. The usefulness of the Suitability for Psychotherapy Scale to assess changes in symptoms at a one year follow-up was also measured. Kappa coefficient was used to measure the extent of agreement between interviewers and a reference decision. In general, the agreement level was in the range of fair to good. Mostly the kappa coefficients ranged from .41 to .62 between interviewers and between interviewers and the reference.

Vassari and Crosby (2008) were concerned about the internal consistency reliability of the well-established UCLA Loneliness Scale (Revised). This scale has been widely used and it is associated with several distressing or negative psychological states. The authors were interested in knowing the reliability of this measure over a wide range of studies using the Loneliness Scale. Eighty studies were found which reported Cronbach alpha reliability coefficients. They used a variety of meta-analysis known as Reliability Generalisation to do this. The mean internal consistency reliability coefficient across all of the samples in the studies was .87 indicating a good level of internal consistency. However, the variability of alpha was quite considerable over studies and ranged from .53 to .95. Further analysis suggested that coefficient alphas varied according to 1) type of article, 2) where the report was published and 3) the standard deviations involved.

Key points

- Although the methods employed in calculating internal reliability are straightforward, great care is needed to differentiate between internal reliability as assessed by the methods described in this chapter and measures of external reliability which are very different. External reliability includes the correlation between scores on a measure at two different points in time (i.e. test–retest reliability).

- The difference between a correlation between scores and agreement between scores is very important. Remember that there can be a strong correlation between two variables with absolutely no match in the scores.

COMPUTER ANALYSIS

Cronbach's alpha and kappa using SPSS

Data
- Name the variables in 'Variable View' of the 'Data Editor'.
- Enter the data under the appropriate variable names in 'Data View' of the 'Data Editor' (Screenshot 37.1).

Analysis
- For alpha reliability, select 'Analyze', 'Scale' and 'Reliability Analysis...' (Screenshot 37.2).
- Move items to the 'Items:' box either singly or altogether by holding down Shift, Control and selecting all items (Screenshot 37.3).

2
- Select 'Statistics...', 'Scale if item deleted', 'Continue' and 'OK' (Screenshot 37.4).

3
- For kappa, select 'Analyze', 'Descriptive Statistic's and 'Crosstabs...'.
- Move one rater to 'Row(s):' box and the other rater to the 'Column(s):' box.

4
- Select 'Statistics...', 'Kappa', 'Continue' and 'OK'.

Output
- For alpha reliability, check number of cases and whether deleting an item substantially improves reliability (Screenshots 37.5 and 37.6).

2
- For kappa, check the distribution of ratings.

| FIGURE 37.2 | SPSS steps for Cronbach's alpha internal reliability and kappa |

Interpreting and reporting the output

- It is generally accepted that a value of alpha of about .7 or larger indicates that a scale has satisfactory reliability. See main text of chapter for more on item analysis using item-total statistics.

- We would write something like: 'The alpha reliability of the scale was .81 which indicates satisfactory internal reliability for the scale.'

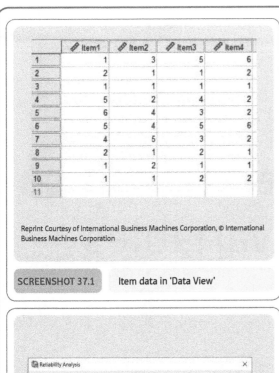

Reprint Courtesy of International Business Machines Corporation, © International Business Machines Corporation

SCREENSHOT 37.1   Item data in 'Data View'

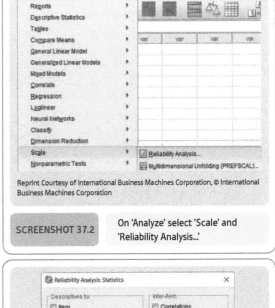

Reprint Courtesy of International Business Machines Corporation, © International Business Machines Corporation

SCREENSHOT 37.2   On 'Analyze' select 'Scale' and 'Reliability Analysis...'

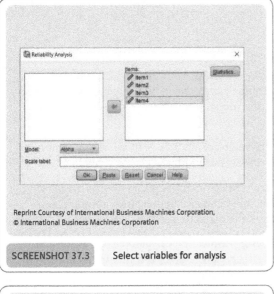

Reprint Courtesy of International Business Machines Corporation, © International Business Machines Corporation

SCREENSHOT 37.3   Select variables for analysis

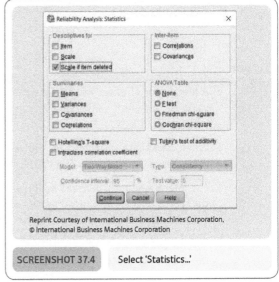

Reprint Courtesy of International Business Machines Corporation, © International Business Machines Corporation

SCREENSHOT 37.4   Select 'Statistics...'

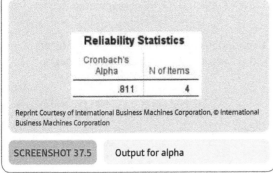

Reliability Statistics

Cronbach's Alpha	N of Items
.811	4

Reprint Courtesy of International Business Machines Corporation, © International Business Machines Corporation

SCREENSHOT 37.5   Output for alpha

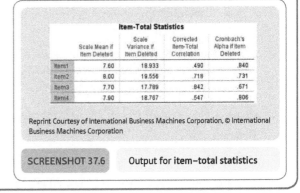

Item-Total Statistics

	Scale Mean if Item Deleted	Scale Variance if Item Deleted	Corrected Item-Total Correlation	Cronbach's Alpha if Item Deleted
Item1	7.60	18.933	.490	.840
Item2	8.00	19.556	.718	.731
Item3	7.70	17.789	.842	.671
Item4	7.90	18.767	.547	.806

Reprint Courtesy of International Business Machines Corporation, © International Business Machines Corporation

SCREENSHOT 37.6   Output for item–total statistics

Recommended further reading

Journal of Counseling Psychology, 22, 358–376.

CHAPTER 38

Influence of moderator variables on relationships between two variables

Overview

- A moderator effect is where the size of the relationship between two variables is not the same for different values of a third variable. The moderating effect is also known as an interaction effect.

- When only score variables are involved, then hierarchical multiple regression can identify interactions (moderator) effects. This method makes full use of available information.

- The interaction term involves multiplying the two predictors together. Ideally the means of the two predictors should be transformed to zero by standardising them (i.e. centring them). This reduces the size of the correlations between the predictors and the interaction.

- The two predictors are entered in step 1 (block 1) of the hierarchical multiple regression and the interaction in step 2 (block 2). A moderator effect is indicated by the interaction explaining a significant proportion of the variance in the criterion.

- To interpret the interaction, values of the criterion are predicted for widely separated values of the two predictors.

- Moderator effects of categorical variables on a continuous or score variable can be tested with the analysis of variance (ANOVA). An interaction between the independent and moderator variables indicates a moderator effect.

Preparation

You should have a working knowledge of *z*-scores (Chapter 6), simple regression (Chapter 9), two-way analysis of variance (Chapter 25) and multiple regression (Chapter 34).

38.1 Introduction

There are various circumstances in which a relationship between two variables is in some way affected by a third variable. Two types of third variables are mediator and moderator variables. We discussed mediating variables in Chapters 32 and 35, but the essentials are worth repeating. Take a look at Figure 38.1. It shows a relationship between the level of stress experienced by an individual and how depressed they feel. The more stress, the more depression. A mediating variable is a third variable which is responsible for the relationship between the main variables – stress and depression in this case. Stress might lead to depression because stress reduces one's available time to engage in close social relationships with friends and family and that it is the absence of close relationships which leads to depression as shown in Figure 38.2. In other words, stress in our example does not directly lead to depression but it causes changes in a third variable (social relationships) which then affects depression. In this case, social relationships would be a mediator variable for the relationship between stress and depression.

This chapter deals with the other type of third variable – moderator variables. These are conceptually quite distinct from mediator variables, though a variable which is a moderator variable may also be a mediating variable in another context. How do you know whether a variable is a moderator variable? Quite simply, if the main relationship you are interested in is different for different values of the third variable then this third variable is having a moderating effect – and so it is a moderator variable. A simple example of a moderator might be gender if it were found to be the case, say, that there is no relationship between stress and depression in women but a strong relationship between the two in men. Gender is moderating the relationship between stress and depression.

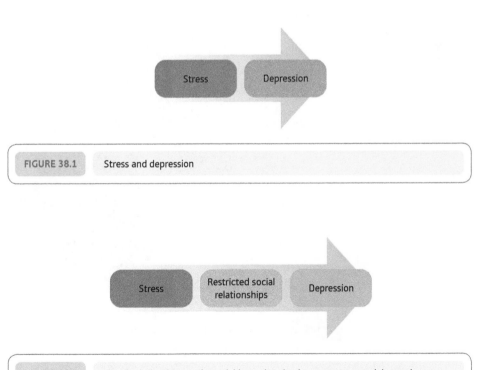

FIGURE 38.1   Stress and depression

FIGURE 38.2   Social relationships as the variable moderating between stress and depression

Another possible moderator variable for the relationship between stress and depression might be the variable social support – this refers to the extent to which an individual has family and friends which provide them with a warm, supportive social environment. Figure 38.3 illustrates the interrelationships between stress and depression and social support. Stress, depression and social support, we shall assume, have each been measured using a psychological scale so each variable consists of scores.

But just what is the nature of the relationships involved? There are several possible options:

- stress leads directly to depression

- depression leads to stress

- both of these are true

- stress leads the individual to be more isolated (lack social support) and this lack of social support leads to depression

- depression leads the individual to be more isolated (lack social support) which makes them susceptible to stress.

It is very difficult to decide which of the first three might be the case. However, the last two options are examples of mediating variables – that is, the reason why stress leads to depression is because stress affects social support, which then leads to depression. Or a similar argument might apply in which depression affects social support which then leaves the individual susceptible to stress. Partial correlation (Chapter 32) and other statistical techniques (Chapter 35) can help you decide whether social support is mediating the relationship between stress and depression.

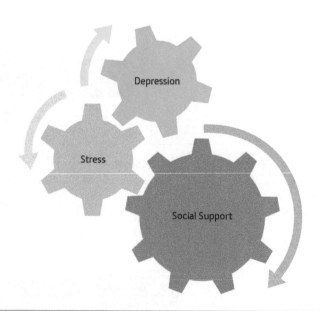

FIGURE 38.3   Stress, social support and depression

However, remember that *moderator* variables are very different from mediating variables, though they are easily confused semantically unless one is very careful. One would say that social support is a moderating variable if the extent of the relationship between stress and depression is not the same for people with excellent social support networks, people with moderate social support networks and people whose social support networks are poor – they have few friends and family who they can turn to in time of difficulty. This is illustrated in Figure 38.4. As you can see, for that group of individuals who have poor social support there is a strong relationship between stress and depression. If social support is moderate or excellent, then there is little or no relationship between stress and depression. In other words, then, the relationship between stress and depression depends on the level of social support (excellent, moderate or poor) experienced by participants in the study. In this example, individuals who lack social support seem to be vulnerable to depression when under stress. Those who have moderate or excellent social support networks seem not to be vulnerable to depression when they are stressed. That is, social support has a sort of cushioning effect preventing stress leading to depression. This is perfectly sensible since social support is associated with helping with problems and preventing difficulties from getting worse. So social support as a moderating variable in the relationship between stress and depression would seem to make good psychological sense.

Another way of visualising this situation is in terms of Table 38.1. This table indicates that where there is a high level of stress but poor social support then the mean of the depression score is very high. In all other cells the level of depression is much the same. In other words, only where social support is poor do high levels of stress lead to high levels of depression. Of course, the outcome could be more complex than this. Nevertheless, this is the basic situation which leads to the suggestion that there is a moderator variable, social support, different levels of which lead to different relationships between stress and depression. In this example, there is no relationship between stress and depression except in circumstances in which social support is poor.

Of course, there may well be other potential moderator variables which could be included in the analysis – we simply need to work out what they may be, measure them

MAIN RELATIONSHIP Stress leads to depression?	POSSIBLE MODERATOR VARIABLE: Social support	SIZE OF RELATIONSHIP AT DIFFERENT LEVELS OF THE MODERATOR VARIABLE
STRESS	Excellent social support	Little or no relationship
	Moderate social support	Little or no relationship
DEPRESSION	Low social support	Strong relationship

FIGURE 38.4   Social support as a moderator variable in the relationship between stress and depression

Table 38.1	Mean depression scores for groups formed on the basis of level of social support and level of stress		
	Poor social support	Moderate social support	Excellent social support
Low level of stress	6.20	5.60	5.65
Medium level of stress	6.10	4.60	5.30
High level of stress	12.25	5.60	6.25

and then establish that they do play this sort of role. But this does rely on the researcher having bright ideas about likely moderator variables. We may also look for moderator variables (interactions) in circumstances where we expect variable *A* to be related to variable *B* but nevertheless find that in reality the relationship between the two variables is weak. It is appropriate in these circumstances to think of the sorts of reasons why we would expect a stronger relation than the one we found. We have mentioned simple instances of this, but gender, age group, occupational group and so forth might be considered. What is a possibility really depends on what is being studied – and perhaps some insight on the part of the researcher. Figure 38.5 gives the key steps to consider in understanding moderator variables.

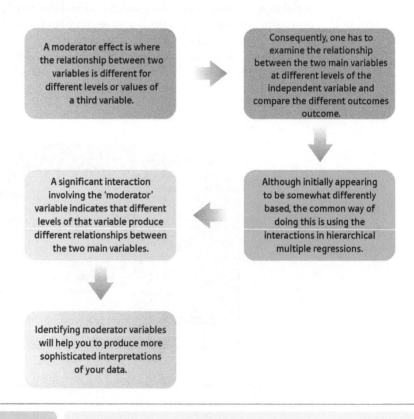

A moderator effect is where the relationship between two variables is different for different levels or values of a third variable.

Consequently, one has to examine the relationship between the two main variables at different levels of the independent variable and compare the different outcomes outcome.

Although initially appearing to be somewhat differently based, the common way of doing this is using the interactions in hierarchical multiple regressions.

A significant interaction involving the 'moderator' variable indicates that different levels of that variable produce different relationships between the two main variables.

Identifying moderator variables will help you to produce more sophisticated interpretations of your data.

FIGURE 38.5   Conceptual steps for understanding moderator variables

38.2   Statistical approaches to finding moderator effects

You may have spotted something – that is, surely what is being referred to as a moderator variable here is part of what we called an interaction in analysis of variance (ANOVA). This is absolutely correct. It also suggests one way of examining one's data to see if there is a moderator variable – that is, simply carry out a two-way analysis of variance on the data of a sort which resulted in Table 38.1. If there is a significant interaction then there is a moderator effect. Chapter 25 discusses a two-way independent samples ANOVA design which corresponds to Table 38.1. However, it should be noted that if the stress and social support categories are based on score data, then there is information in the data which is being lost by simply classifying the scores into high, medium and low categories. (That is to say, for example, that although the people in the high category would have different scores, this information about order is lost when they have been classified into the high social support category.) This is bad form in statistical analysis. However, if the study had involved variables measured in terms of nominal categories rather than scores, then the ANOVA method is the accepted approach. Since the data which psychologists collect are usually in the form of scores rather than nominal categories, then a different form of analysis would be preferred in most cases. The alternative method – the one used where the independent variable (e.g. stress) and the moderator variable (social support) are score variables – is based on hierarchical multiple regression which is presented in Chapter 34. In other words, both the ANOVA approach and the hierarchical multiple regression approaches are substantially the analyses described in other chapters. The big difference is that the way in which we are conceptualising the analysis.

To summarise:

● If all of your variables are score variables then the best way to look for moderator effects is to use the hierarchical multiple regression approach.

● If your predictor and moderator variables are measured using a nominal (i.e. category or categorical) classification scheme but your dependent variable is a score, then you can use the ANOVA approach.

However, you might wish to take note of the following:

● Sometimes researchers use the ANOVA approach where all of their variables are scores. They merely categorise the moderator and the independent variables into high, medium and low categories. You may find this approach intuitively more appealing.

● You might be wondering what you can do if all of your variables are nominal category ones. Well you can't apply the two approaches described in this data for the obvious reason that the dependent variable is also a nominal category. You might wish to check out Chapter 40 on log-linear analysis since this can help you deal with these circumstances.

We will discuss the hierarchical multiple regression approach first and then go on to the ANOVA method.

38.3   Hierarchical multiple regression approach to identifying moderator effects (or interactions)

So the multiple regression approach to identifying moderator variables involves many of the ideas discussed in Chapter 34 on multiple regression and multiple correlation and, to a lesser extent, Chapter 35 on path analysis. If you have read those chapters then there should be few nasty surprises in what follows. However, there are new things in this section, particularly a) the use of standardisation of variables and b) the introduction of a new predictor variable – the interaction. The interaction is where the moderator effect reveals itself (see Box 38.1). So standardisation and interaction are given particular attention in the following discussion.

We did not standardise variables for the multiple regressions described in Chapters 34 and 35, so why do we need to now? In statistics, standardisation usually means turning scores into z-scores and this applies in this case. That is, for each of our variables every score is turned into a z-score (using the methods described in Chapter 6, though we will describe the process again in this chapter). There is a technical reason for this standardisation which boils down to the fact that if this is not done, then the chances of detecting a moderator effect where one exists are reduced. A more detailed explanation depends on understanding how the regression calculation is actually done, so read the following explanation at your peril. In multiple regression where there are two or more predictors, the regression weights or regression coefficients are calculated setting the value of the other predictor variable at 0. For the raw scores, depending on what is being measured, the value of 0 could be anywhere in the distribution – i.e. it could represent a very big, a medium or a very low score. So it makes sense to involve the more typical scores in the middle of the distribution. So if we have ensured that a score of 0 is equivalent to the middle value of the distribution of scores by using z-scores where the middle of the distribution is 0, then we have ensured that the value of the 'other' variable is set at the mid-point of the distribution.

The other new thing in this chapter is the use of the interaction term in multiple regression. Although interactions have been discussed in Chapter 25 in relation to the analysis of variance (ANOVA), we have not previously discussed them in relation to multiple regression. It has to be said that there is a far closer relationship between ANOVA and multiple regression than appears on the surface. And if you understood interaction in terms of ANOVA then this should help you with it in relation to multiple regression. Essentially, the

---

Box 38.1	Key concepts

Interaction in multiple regression

Interaction can be seen as a multiplicative effect in multiple regression. That is, different levels of the predictor variables have an effect on the scores which is greater than can be understood in terms of the individual effects of the predictor variables. This is much as we described interactions in ANOVA in Chapter 25. The individual predictor variables have an additive effect on the dependent variable – that is, each predictor variable has a certain influence on the dependent variable and their combined influence is simply the sum of their separate influences. Of course, it is possible that the relationship between two variables is not a simple linear (and therefore additive) one. So sometimes, but rarely, you will find other relationships explored – the square of the scores on one variable in relation to the square of the scores on another variable, for example.

However, it is possible that the influence of the predictor variable is not simply additive (or even based on a squared or quadrupled relationship) but multiplicative instead. That is, the effects of the predictor variables are multiplied together and not simply added together. As a consequence, when we seek to understand the influence of the predictor variables on the dependent variable in multiple regression, we look for the additive effects and also the multiplicative or interaction effects. That is why, quite simply, to get the interaction in multiple regression we multiply the scores on the independent variables together. Of course, the interaction is partly predictable from the independent variables which went to make up the interaction, but not entirely so. So if the simple effects of the independent variables are removed first, then we have the 'pure' multiplicative effect. This is precisely what happens in the calculations – the main effects of the variables acting individually are removed, which leaves a 'pure' interaction effect.

Table 38.2	Correlations between the variables and their interaction in raw scores and in standardised form			
	Raw scores		**Standardised scores**	
	Social support	Stress	Social support	Stress
Stress	−.26		−.26	
Interaction	.29	.83	−.00	.02

interaction term is created as a new computed variable simply by multiplying the score on one variable (stress) and the score on the moderator variable (social support). The interaction is really a new variable and is treated as such in multiple regression.

The following may help you understand why standardisation is used in this context. Table 38.2 gives the correlations between the three raw variables involved in the multiple regression and then, separately, between the three standardised versions of the same variables for our data. It can be seen that the correlations between the two predictor variables and the interaction of the two predictor variables are larger for the raw scores than for the standardised versions of the same variables and their interaction. The correlation between stress and social support for the raw scores is −.26 and exactly the same for the standardised scores. This is not surprising since these correlations are based on exactly the same data apart from the fact that they have been standardised in one case. What is more interesting is that the correlations between the interaction and the predictor variable change substantially from the raw scores to the standardised scores. The correlations with the interactions are much lower for the standardised scores than for the raw scores. This means that the problem of multicollinearity has been virtually eliminated by using standardised scores rather than the original unstandardised raw scores. The correlations of social support and stress with the interaction are .29 and .83 for the raw data, but in the standardised scores these correlations decline to −.00 and .02 – essentially zero correlations in both cases. The reduction in multicollinearity means that the interaction of the two predictor variables (which indicates a moderator effect) is more likely to be identified.

In hierarchical multiple regression, as with any form of regression, the basic task is to assess the extent to which a set of predictor variables (independent variables if you prefer) is related to the criterion (or dependent variable). In our example, stress and social support would be independent or predictor variables and depression would be the dependent or criterion variable. Although social support is believed to be a moderator variable in this research, it is also a predictor variable for the purposes of the hierarchical multiple regression. The interaction, as we have seen, is obtained simply by multiplying the scores for the two independent variables (stress and social support). An interaction would normally be indicated by the term stress × social support or whatever is appropriate. The interaction term is essentially treated as an additional predictor variable – which is precisely what it is. However, in the multiple regression the interaction is dealt with after the effects of the independent and moderator variables acting independently have been taken into account.

The hierarchical multiple regression procedure is essentially as illustrated in Figure 38.6. The basic principles of the hierarchical multiple regression process are as follows:

- The independent or predictor variables are entered in blocks.

- The first block is used in the analysis first and the second, third, etc. in strict order following that. In our example, there are only two blocks.

There has to be a minimum of one independent variable in each block.

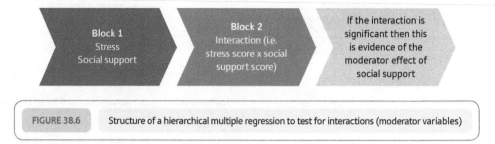

FIGURE 38.6   Structure of a hierarchical multiple regression to test for interactions (moderator variables)

So there are priorities in hierarchical multiple regression which are determined by the order of blocks of variables. Each block may have just one independent variable in it, but it may have more according to the researcher's choices for their analysis. As Figure 38.6 indicates, the first block includes both the stress and the social support variables. The second block involves the interaction of the two variables – that is, the interaction term or, in other words, a predictor variable which is created from the multiplication of the stress and social support scores. By multiplying stress and social support together we get a new variable which is normally referred to as the interaction of stress with social support. If the interaction is statistically significant in the multiple regression analysis then we have a moderator effect; otherwise there is no moderator effect.

To reiterate, in our example, the first block comprises both the stress and the social support variables. This stage of the analysis seeks to find out what influence stress and social support, acting separately, have on the dependent variable – i.e. depression. By analysing these in the first block, their influence on the interaction term is taken into account just as the main effects are taken into account first in ANOVA. The second block is the interaction of stress and social support. This is calculated by multiplying each individual's score on the stress variable by their score on the social support variable. In our example, we have just one potential moderator variable, but we could have two or three if we so wished. The problem with multiple moderators is that there are multiple interactions and the number of potential interactions increases disproportionately the more moderator variables there are. This is reminiscent of what happens in ANOVA when you have too many independent variables. In a phrase, the result is information overload. So be parsimonious in terms of the number of moderator variables you include in your analysis.

If the hierarchical multiple regression does produce a significant interaction then this is indicative of a moderator effect. Unfortunately, it does not tell us just what the moderator effect is. To see what the form of the interaction is, it is necessary to carry out further analyses. It is suggested by some statisticians that this is done by predicting the scores on the dependent or criterion variable (i.e. depression) for low, medium and high scores on the independent variable and the moderator variable using the unstandardised regression coefficients (Aitken & West, 1991). The advantage of this method is that it takes into account particular scores when determining the significance of the interaction term (i.e. moderator effect) and does not bundle together participants into somewhat arbitrarily defined groups.

Multiple regression assumes that the relationship between the criterion and the interaction can be represented by a straight line although nonlinear relations can sometimes be tested if an appropriate transformation method is available for turning the nonlinear relationships into linear ones (Aitken & West, 1991). However, this is beyond the scope of this chapter and you should consult Aitken and West if you need more information.

Explaining statistics 38.1

Identifying moderator variables using the hierarchical multiple regression approach

The amount of data needed to study moderator variables is large. So instead of presenting the data in a table we have provided an SPSS file of the data on the website for this book. The steps in hierarchical multiple regression for moderator variables are summarised in Figure 38.7.

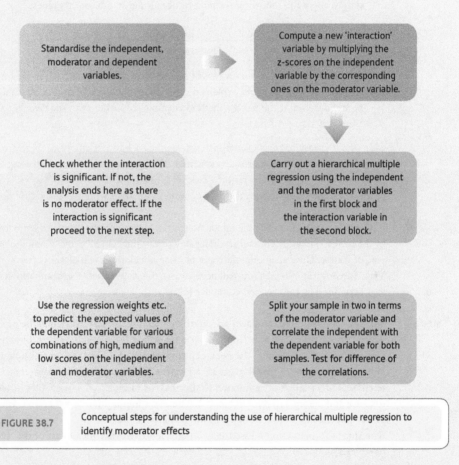

FIGURE 38.7   Conceptual steps for understanding the use of hierarchical multiple regression to identify moderator effects

Step 1   When using hierarchical multiple regression to identify moderator variables, the usual practice is to standardise each of the variables (the independent variable, the dependent variable and the moderator variable). The interaction is based on the standardised independent and moderator variables. Multicollinearity problems are likely to occur if one uses the raw scores to calculate the interaction term and these are likely to reduce the statistical significance of the interaction and risk making it non-significant. In general, it is less likely that a moderator effect will be detected if there are multicollinearity problems.

In the approach to moderating variables used in this chapter, standard scores are used in order to eliminate collinearity influences. However, there are two possible methods for dealing with collinearity:

→

1. Instead of using the raw scores, the scores are 'centred' to make 0 the mean value of the variables. This can be done simply by taking the mean score on the variable away from each score. This needs to be carried out for both the moderator and the independent variables, but it is not necessary for the dependent variable. The formula for centring is:

   centred score = individual score − mean score

2. The alternative to this uses standardised scores (i.e. z-scores). This ensures that the mean score on each variable is 0.00, just as the previous method. This is regarded as the preferred approach (e.g. Aitken & West, 1991). It is the method we describe in this chapter. Essentially the standard scores approach adds an extra stage to the calculation in that each centred score is divided by the standard deviation of the scores. This gives us the standardised score or z-score. We calculated z-scores in Chapter 6 if you need to refresh yourself on these. Thus to standardise scores on each variable we simply apply the following formula to obtain the standardised values:

$$z - score = \frac{individual\ score - mean\ score}{standard\ deviation\ of\ scores}$$

Scores standardised in this way will have a mean of 0.00 and a standard deviation of 1.00 (this is always true of z-scores as explained in Chapter 6). The criterion or dependent variable should also be standardised if the z-score method is employed rather than the centring approach (e.g. Aitken & West, 1991).

Although it is easy to turn a score into a z-score by a hand calculation, there are many such calculations to be done so a computer package is essential. Turning scores into standard scores is easy with a computer program like SPSS – it merely requires ticking a box in the 'Descriptive' analysis routine. The new variable based on z-scores will appear as a new column in the data with a slightly different variable name.

Step 2 It is equally easy to calculate the interaction variable by multiplying each z-score for the moderator variable by the corresponding z-score for the independent variable. On SPSS the 'Compute' procedure will do this for you, of course. Once again, the outcome of these calculations will be shown as a new variable on the 'Data View' spreadsheet of SPSS. You will need to give this new variable a meaningful name. Otherwise it is easy to get confused by the eventual computer output.

Step 3 So, now we have three standardised variables – the independent variable, the moderator variable and the dependent variable – plus the interaction term which is essentially a variable created by multiplying the first two variables together. The next step is to carry out a hierarchical multiple regression on these variables. The structure of this analysis is summarised in Figure 38.6. In hierarchical multiple regression different sets of variables are entered into the analysis in blocks. The variables in block 1 will be dealt with together and before variables in block 2. There is a minimum of one variable in each block. The point of this is that the interaction term needs to be analysed after the two independent variables have been dealt with since the interaction is essentially what is left over after the effects of the two independent variables have been 'removed'.

Given the general advice that a large sample size is needed when looking for moderator effects it is probably wise to use a computer package to do this calculation too.

Step 4 Table 38.3 summarises the outcome of running a hierarchical multiple regression analysis on the data. From this table you can obtain values for the intercept, the regression weights for each variable and their statistical significance. Since we are mainly interested in moderator effects, the significance level of the interaction term in Table 38.3 is most important since it tells us whether or not we have a significant moderator effect. However, the table also has the values of the regression weights needed for us to identify just what the nature of the moderator effect is. It is clear that all of the regression weights are statistically significant in this example (except for the intercept which can be ignored).

Table 38.3	Regression summary table		
	B (regression weight)	t	Sig.
Intercept (constant)	−0.05	0.69	.49
Stress (standardised)	0.21	2.86	.01
Social support (standardised)	−0.21	2.87	.01
Interaction	−0.19	2.86	.01

The dependent variable is depression.

The most important thing in Table 38.3 is the statistical significance of the interaction. The interaction is what indicates the presence or not of a moderator effect. If the interaction is not statistically significant, then there is no moderator effect – i.e. social support is not a moderator variable for these data. However, if there is a significant interaction then you do have a moderator effect. Unfortunately, this does not tell us precisely what the nature of this moderator effect is. (This is analogous to the situation in ANOVA where a significant ANOVA does not tell you just where the differences between the cell means lie.) So there is another step that needs to be carried out.

Step 5   The problem at this point is that the output from the hierarchical multiple regression merely gives us regression weights and their significance levels. What it does not tell us is just what parts of the data show markedly different trends from the other parts of the data differentiated by different levels of the moderator variable. The solution adopted is to choose a high score, a medium score and a low score on both the independent variable (stress) and the moderator variable (social support). This gives us nine possible combinations of high, medium and low stress and high, medium and low social support. So in other words, some fairly arbitrary values for the high, medium and low scores are chosen. The high, medium and low scores are defined simply as the score one standard deviation above the mean, a score at the mean and a score one standard deviation below the mean. Of course, expressed as standard scores (z-scores) these are $+1$, 0 and -1, respectively. Don't forget that scores on the independent, dependent and moderator variables have been turned into z-scores at an earlier stage. So the score corresponding to a high score is already $+1$, a medium score is already 0 and a low score is already -1.

What happens next is the regression weights shown in Table 38.3 are used to predict the most likely score on the dependent variable, depression, for each of the nine combinations of high, medium and low stress scores with high, medium and low social support scores. We will look at the formula for calculating the estimated depression scores in the next paragraph. However, it is important to understand that these nine predicted depression scores are examined to find out just where the interaction effect is. That is, one is looking for just where exceptionally large or small predicted scores are to be found. Having found these, then one has identified the location of the moderator effect – that is, what combination of high, medium or low scores on stress and high, medium and low predicted scores on social support are associated with these exceptionally high or low predicted scores on depression?

In order to predict the depression score from the independent variable (X), the moderator variable (M) and the interaction (XM), we simply apply the following formula (which is an extension of what we saw in Chapter 34):

$$\hat{Y} = a + b_1 X + b_2 M + b_3 XM$$

That is, we multiply the relevant X, M and XM scores by the relevant regression weight from Table 38.3 plus the constant or intercept and this gives us the best prediction of the depression score based on our predictors.

The following lists the elements of the above formula for clarity:

$\hat{Y}$ = the predicted score on the dependent variable

a = the intercept (cut-point) for the regression line – it is a constant for any particular analysis so is the same in every case

b_1 = the regression weight for the predictor (independent variable)

X = the score (z-score) on the predictor variable (i.e. +1, 0 or −1)

b_2 = the regression weight for the moderator variable

M = the score (z-score) on the moderator variable (i.e. +1, 0 or −1)

b_3 = the regression weight for the interaction

XM = the interaction of the independent and moderator variables – this is not a z-score though it is the product of the two z-scores

So, in order to work out the predicted value of the dependent variable for each of the nine combinations of high, medium and low scores for the two variables, we calculate the above equation nine times which gives nine estimated scores on the dependent variable (depression) for each of the possible combinations of the high, medium and low scores for the independent variable (stress) and the moderator variable (social support).

Well, that is what we do in theory, but there is a problem using the above formula. The problem basically is that we do not know precisely what the interaction term means. We do not know which scores it is made up from. For example, for a particular interaction value – say 2.00 – there are many different values of the moderator and the independent variable which multiplied together would give a value of 2.00. So it could be, for example, 1 on the moderator variable and 2 on the independent variable – but equally it could be 2 on the moderator variable and 1 on the independent variable. Both of these give a value of 2.00. Fortunately, it is possible to rewrite the equation so that it does not involve the use of the interaction term. The formula for regression given above can be rearranged (by anyone clever enough) to yield the following version of that original formula:

$$a + (b_1 + b_3 M)X + b_2 M$$

This formula is the one which is actually used in the calculation as you can see in Table 38.4.

The nine calculations are illustrated in the nine cells of Table 38.4. As you can see:

- The prediction formula is the same in each cell, of course.

- The constant or intercept a is the same throughout for this particular analysis (it is −0.05).

- The various regression weights are the same throughout.

- Only M (the value of the moderator variable) and X (the value of the independent variable) vary in the formulae. They will be +1, 0 or −1 according to the particular cell in question. The scores are entered as appropriate depending on the row and column of the cell in question. The value that goes into the calculation can be found at the top of the relevant row and the top of the relevant column.

The predicted mean depression scores can be plotted on a graph (Figure 38.8) in order to illustrate the predicted score's relationship to different levels of stress and social support. It is quite obvious that the slopes in Figure 38.8 are very different. The blue slope for low social support is quite steep whereas the red slope for high social support is quite flat. It is clear that the graph indicates that for individuals

Table 38.4	Illustrating the three levels of the predictor and moderator variable and the calculation of the expected mean on the dependent variable

High score on predictor variable (X) (i.e. score at $+1$ standard deviation)	$a + (b_1 + b_3M)X + b_2M$ $= -0.05 + (0.21$ $+ -0.19 \times 1) \times 1$ $+ -0.21 \times 1$ $= -.24$	$a + (b_1 + b_3M)X + b_2M$ $= -0.05 + (0.21$ $+ -0.19 \times 0) \times 1$ $+ -0.21 \times 0$ $= -.16$	$a + (b_1 + b_3M)X + b_2M$ $= -0.05 + (0.21$ $+ -0.19 \times -1) \times 1$ $+ -0.21 \times -1$ $= -.56$
Medium score on predictor variable (X) (i.e. score at mean)	$a + (b_1 + b_3M)X + b_2M$ $= -0.05 + (0.21$ $+ -0.19 \times 1) \times 0$ $+ -0.21 \times 1$ $= -.26$	$a + (b_1 + b_3M)X + b_2M$ $= -0.05 + (0.21$ $+ -0.19 \times 0) \times 0$ $+ -0.21 \times 0$ $= -.05$	$a + (b_1 + b_3M)X + b_2M$ $= -0.05 + (0.21$ $+ -0.19 \times -1) \times 0$ $+ -0.21 \times -1$ $= -.16$
Low score on predictor variable (X) (i.e. score at -1 standard deviation)	$a + (b_1 + b_3M)X + b_2M$ $= -0.05 + (0.21$ $+ -0.19 \times 1) \times -1$ $+ -0.21 \times 1$ $= -.28$	$a + (b_1 + b_3M)X + b_2M$ $= -0.05 + (0.21$ $+ -0.19 \times 0) \times -1$ $+ -0.21 \times 0$ $= -.26$	$a + (b_1 + b_3M)X + b_2M$ $= -0.05 + (0.21$ $+ -0.19 \times -1) \times -1$ $+ -0.21 \times -1$ $= -.24$

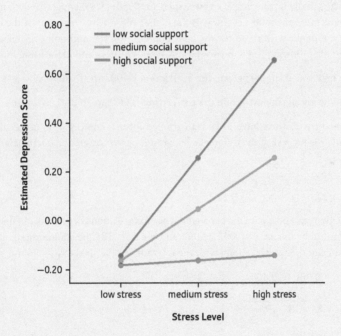

FIGURE 38.8	Plot of predicted depression scores based on output from hierarchical multiple regression

with high levels of social support, the level of stress made no difference to the level of depression. On the other hand, for those who have low social support, it is clear that as stress levels increase then so does depression. The lines are straight lines because they represent a linear (straight line) relationship between stress and depression. Although it is possible to calculate a numerical value for each slope, unfortunately there is no statistical test to establish whether the slopes of these lines differ significantly. In order to carry the analysis further then we adopt the procedure described in Step 6. However, it is important to point

→

out that what our eyes see in Figure 38.8 should convince us that the interaction or moderator effect is largely to do with low levels of social support.

Step 6

Although one might expect to be able to test statistically whether the slopes in Figure 38.8 differ from each other, actually there are no available statistical techniques to differentiate these slope coefficients (e.g. Cohen et al., 2003). Hence we did not calculate these coefficients as there is no point in doing so. One solution to this problem involves dividing the sample into two approximately equal sized groups in terms of the moderator variable. So there is a high (above the mean) and low (below the mean) group on the moderator variable. Basically the idea is to see whether the correlations between the independent variable and the dependent variable are different for the high and low groups. In Section 36.7 we discuss how to test for significant differences between correlations. So it is, first of all, simply a matter of dividing your data into two groups on the basis of being high or low on the moderator variable (social support). This can be done on SPSS by using the 'Recode' procedure to divide the social support scores into two groups. The correlation between the independent variable and the dependent variable is then calculated for the high group followed by the low group. Finally, the formula for the significance of the difference between two correlation coefficients can be applied. This is not available on SPSS though applets for doing the calculation are available on the web.

However, it is not too complicated to calculate the significance of the difference between two correlation coefficients. The test is a variant of the z-test and it is also discussed in Chapter 36. Although the usual advice is to divide the sample to give equal sized groups, you might wish to modify this if you think that the moderator effect occurs towards the higher end or the lower end of the moderator variable. In this case, you might wish to adjust the split point. Using the mid-point of the social support variable resulting in the following Pearson correlations between stress and depression:

- for the high social support group the correlation is .002 ($p = .989$, $N = 84$)

- for the low social support group the correlation is .375 ($p = .001$, $N = 96$).

These two correlations have to be transformed into standardised (z) correlations using Table 36.5. The formula for the test of the difference between the two correlation coefficients is as follows:

$$z = \frac{z_{r1} - z_{r2}}{\sqrt{\dfrac{1}{N_1 - 3} + \dfrac{1}{N_2 - 3}}}$$

In this equation, z_{r1} and z_{r2} are the two standardised correlation coefficients obtained by using Table 36.5. The standardised value of $r = .002$ is .000 and for $r = .375$ the standardised value is .400. These can be substituted in the formula along with the relevant sample sizes ($N_1 = 84$, $N_2 = 96$):

$$z = \frac{0.000 - 0.400}{\sqrt{\dfrac{1}{84 - 3} + \dfrac{1}{96 - 3}}}$$

$$= \frac{-0.400}{\sqrt{\dfrac{1}{81} + \dfrac{1}{93}}}$$

$$= \frac{-0.400}{\sqrt{0.012 + 0.011}}$$

$$= \frac{-0.400}{\sqrt{0.023}}$$

$$= \frac{-0.400}{0.152}$$

$$= -2.63$$

Interpreting the results

z must equal ± 1.96 or more to be statistically significant at the .05 level with a two-tailed test of significance (1.65 or more for the one-tailed test of significance – refer to Significance Table 6.1). In other words, this analysis confirms that there is a significant difference between the correlations for high scorers on social support and low scorers on social support. The low social support group shows a strong correlation between stress and depression whereas there is a virtually zero correlation for the group high on social support.

One disadvantage of this method is that it involves dividing the sample into two smaller samples, which means that the correlations and the difference between them are less likely to be statistically significant. Of course, if you wanted a quick assessment of your data in terms of possible moderator effects, the approach taken in this step would give you a good indication of any moderator effects though it is not as powerful as going through the full process including the hierarchical multiple regression.

Reporting the results

One way of reporting the multiple regression results is as follows: 'Baron and Kenny (1986) have suggested that a moderator effect is most appropriately tested with multiple regression. Such an effect is indicated if the interaction of the two predictor variables explains a significant increment in the variance of the criterion variable while the two predictor variables are controlled. Aitken and West (1991) recommended that the criterion and the two predictor variables be standardised. Following these recommendations, a significant proportion of the variance in depression was accounted for by the interaction of stress and social support after the individual variables comprising the interaction were controlled, R^2 change $= .04$, $p < .01$. To interpret the significant interaction three separate unstandardised regression lines were plotted between standardised stress, standardised social support and the standardised level of depression at the mean and at one standard deviation above and below the mean of standardised stress and standardised social support. The relation between stress and depression was strongest at low levels of social support.'

38.4   ANOVA approach to identifying moderator effects (i.e. interactions)

The ANOVA approach is used where the independent variable and the moderator variable are in the form of nominal categories. Sometimes it is used to analyse data which have been collected in the form of scores. In this case, the scores have to be divided into three separate groups indicating high, medium and low scores for both the independent variable and the moderator variable. It is best to use three groups of scores since non-linear relationships can be identified whereas they cannot with only two groups. This grouping system can be seen in Table 38.1 which is simply a table of mean scores on depression for high, medium and low scoring groups of the independent and moderator variables. Generally speaking, it is best not to do this since information is lost from the data. On the other hand, the ANOVA approach does have some advantages in terms of being clearer and less complex.

Explaining statistics 38.2

Identifying moderator effects using the ANOVA approach for nominal independent and moderator variables

Step 1 This calculation is based on the example already discussed in the previous section. However, the essential features of the analysis of this study can be seen in Table 38.1. Unless one or more of your predictor variables is qualitative in nature – that is, a nominal/category variable – then you need to categorise the scores on your variable as being in the high, medium and low categories in terms of their size. Although you could use just two categories – such as high and low scores – this is inadvisable if you have a substantial sample size though you may need to try it if not. It is possible to use the 'Recode' procedure on SPSS to categorise a score variable into groups.

Step 2 The next step is to run the ANOVA calculation. We have a 3 × 3 ANOVA design of the sort described in Chapter 25. Chapter 25 includes an explanation of the procedure and instructions on how to carry out the analysis by hand. However, we will not repeat these instructions for this particular example. Instead, we will present the results of a computer analysis as outlined in Figure 38.9 since testing for moderator effects tends to involve substantial sample sizes.

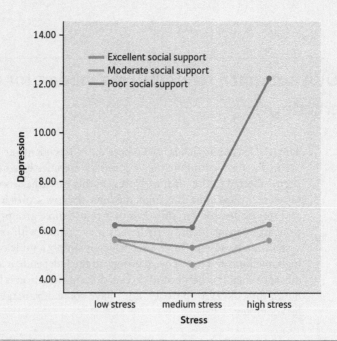

FIGURE 38.9   Plot of means of depression scores for the stress and social support groups

Step 3

The mean scores for each of the cells of the ANOVA analysis can be found in Table 38.1. However, it is generally easier to interpret the meaning of the mean scores in a significant interaction by plotting them in a graph where the dependent variable is represented by the vertical axis: one of the predictors is indicated by relatively widely separated points on the horizontal axis and the other predictor is shown by different coloured lines. This kind of graph is shown in Figure 38.9 where the horizontal axis represents the three levels of stress and the separate lines represent the three levels of social support. Figure 38.9 plots the mean depression scores of the nine groups formed on the basis of the three levels of stress and the three levels of social support. What seems clear from this plot is that there is one group – high stress and poor social support – which has a particularly high mean score on depression. The other eight groups, although their means do vary a little, have similar means. To anyone familiar with ANOVA, this pattern is very suggestive of a strong interaction between stress and social support. Differences in stress level alone and differences in social support level alone do not have much bearing on depression – in general, the depression is more or less the same for each of the stress and each of the social support groups. The exception, as we have seen, is the one group with high stress but poor social support. In other words, Figure 38.9 demonstrates a clear moderator effect.

Step 4

You also need to check out the analysis of variance (ANOVA) summary table based on this analysis (Table 38.5). The significance levels for the variables stress and social support and the interaction between them are all statistically significant. However, it is the interaction which shows whether or not there is a moderator effect. A significant interaction effect indicates the presence of a moderator effect. You will see that the row for the interaction of stress and social support is statistically significant at the .00 level, which indicates strongly the presence of a moderator effect. In this case, this is clear and unproblematic. However, note that the main effects for stress and social support are also both statistically significant. On the face of things, this seems to suggest that stress and social support, acting separately, each have an effect. This is a case where one should be somewhat cautious in the light of what Figure 38.9 suggests about the group means in general – that most of the means are about the same with the one exception. It is important to remember that ANOVA adopts a particular model for analysing data in which main effects such as stress and social support take precedence in the analysis to any interactions. So what is happening here is that some of the variation due to the interaction is being misleadingly allocated to the main effects. Despite this, in this particular case there is no doubt that there is a significant moderator effect which is what you need to know. A problem would arise if the main effects had been significant and the interaction non-significant – the plot of means as in Figure 38.9 is clearly the key to identifying the risk of assuming erroneously that there is no interaction and, hence, no moderator effect. The way in which ANOVA favours main effects was explained in Chapter 25.

Table 38.5	ANOVA summary table giving significance levels for the effects of stress and social support on depression				
Source of variance	**Sum of squares**	**Degrees of freedom**	**Mean square**	**F-ratio**	**Sig.**
Stress	248.74	2	124.37	13.67	.00
Social support	294.54	2	147.27	16.19	.00
Interaction	270.06	4	67.51	7.42	.00
Error	1555.65	171	9.10		

→

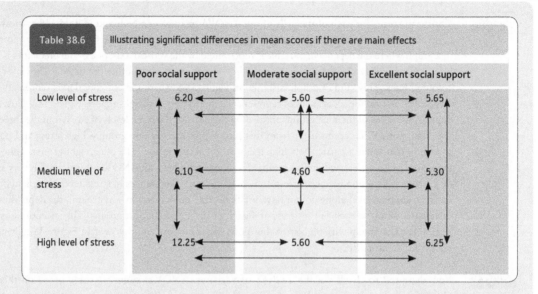

Table 38.6	Illustrating significant differences in mean scores if there are main effects		
	Poor social support	**Moderate social support**	**Excellent social support**
Low level of stress	6.20	5.60	5.65
Medium level of stress	6.10	4.60	5.30
High level of stress	12.25	5.60	6.25

Step 5 One relatively simple way of checking whether there truly are main effects is to compare appropriate pairs of cells in the ANOVA table. Remember that a main effect should apply to all pairs of cells in Table 38.1. So if there is a main effect of stress, then the group with excellent social support should have significantly different depression in the low stress condition from the medium stress condition and so forth. That is, the main effect of stress should apply at each different level of social support. Table 38.6 illustrates this. The vertical arrows indicate the cells which should be different from each other if there is a main effect of stress. The horizontal arrows indicate the cells which should be different from each other if there is a main effect of social support. Of course, this is the perfect scenario and, of course, in reality things will not be so perfect. One quick and simple way of checking is to run a *post hoc* multiple comparison test such as the Scheffé test on all of the cells. To do this, you need to turn the ANOVA into a one-way ANOVA with, in this case, nine separate cells. On a computer, one could simply add another column indicating which of the nine groups each score of the dependent variable (depression) belonged to. That is, a code of 1 to 9 is added to the data to indicate which of the nine groups each score is from. When this analysis is carried out on this data, the outcome is simple. None of the cell means differs from each other except for the high level of stress with poor social support. The mean of this cell is significantly higher than all other means in the table, just as we would expect from the plots in Figure 38.9. In other words, there are no main effects – just the interaction demonstrating that social support is, indeed, a moderator variable. This is exactly what one would expect from the pattern of means. Of course, this is, in part, a matter of judgement about the data, but ANOVA analyses can need interpretation if misleading conclusions are to be avoided.

Reporting the results

One way of reporting the ANOVA results is as follows: 'ANOVA was used to seek for moderator effects in the data. A moderator effect is indicated by a significant interaction in the ANOVA. The 3×3 ANOVA on the data indicated main effects on depression for stress, $F(2, 171)3 = 13.67$, $p < .001$, $\eta_p^2 = .14$, and social support, $F(2, 171) = 16.19$, $p < .001$, $\eta_p^2 = .16$, were statistically significant. However, more importantly in this context, it was found that the interaction of stress and social support was also statistically significant, $F(4, 171) = 67.51$, $p < .001$, $\eta_p^2 = .15$. This interaction effect indicates that social support moderates the relationship between stress and depression. In order to identify more precisely the nature of the moderator effect, multiple comparison tests were made between the means of the nine groups. It became clear that the relationship between stress and depression was strong only for participants who lacked social support.'

Research examples

Moderator variables

Sprung, Sliter and Jex (2012) examined spirituality as a moderator of the relation between being aggressive at work and various outcomes. Spirituality was partly defined as finding meaning in one's life. They found that spirituality moderated the relation between physical aggression and workplace stress. The positive relation between physical aggression and workplace stress was greater in those with higher spirituality than those with lower spirituality which was contrary to what they had hypothesised.

Warren and colleagues (2012) determined whether stress would moderate the positive relationship of talk about being too fat to body dissatisfaction and drive for thinness. They found that stress did moderate these relationships. Contrary to what they had predicted these positive relationships were stronger in those with less stress than those with more stress.

Ziegler and Britta Diehl (2012) investigated whether job ambivalence moderates the positive relation between job satisfaction and job performance. Job ambivalence was defined as having positive and negative feelings about one's job. They found that job ambivalence moderated the relation between job satisfaction and job performance. The positive relation between job satisfaction and job performance was stronger in managers who were less rather than more ambivalent about their job.

Key points

- The most appropriate way of determining whether there is a moderating or interaction effect between two continuous (score) variables is a hierarchical multiple regression.

- This analysis involves the standardisation of the measures into z-scores which overcomes some technical problems raised by using raw data.

- Another name for moderator effect is interaction, and the assessment of moderator effects is based on the identification of interactions through either multiple regression or ANOVA.

- It is not possible to do the calculations in their entirety just using a standard computer package such as SPSS. There is a certain amount of hand calculations to do or doing computations on SPSS using the 'Compute' procedure, for example.

- To interpret the interaction from a multiple regression, it is recommended that the slope or regression coefficient of the criterion on one of the predictors is calculated for three widely separated values of the other predictor such as its mean and one standard deviation above and below the mean.

COMPUTER ANALYSIS

Regression moderator analysis using SPSS

Data
- Name the variables in 'Variable View' of the 'Data Editor'.
- Enter the data under the appropriate variable names in 'Data View' of the 'Data Editor' (Screenshot 38.1).
- Standardise the variables and compute the interaction term (Screenshot 38.1).

Analysis
- Select 'Analyze', 'Regression' and 'Linear...' (Screenshot 38.2).
- In the 'Method' box check 'Enter' has been selected (Screenshot 38.3).

2
- Move the standardised criterion or dependent variable to the 'Dependent:' box and the two standardised predictors or independent variables to the 'Independent(s):' box (Screenshot 38.3).
- Select 'Next' and move the interaction term to the 'Independent(s):' box (Screenshot 38.3).
- Select 'Statistics...' and then 'Confidence intervals', 'R squared change', 'Descriptives', 'Part and partial correlations', 'Collinearity diagnostics', 'Continue' and then 'OK' (Screenshot 38.4).

Output
- In the 'Model summary' table note whether the F-ratio for the moderator or interaction effect is significant (Screenshot 38.5).
- If the *F*-ratio is not significant, the analysis stops. If it is significant, plot the predicted values on a graph for high, medium and low values.

FIGURE 38.10   SPSS steps for a moderator analysis with hierarchical multiple regression

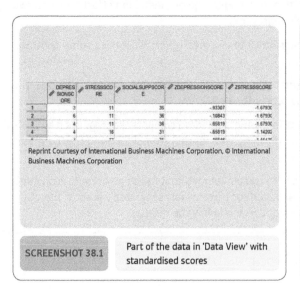

Reprint Courtesy of International Business Machines Corporation, © International Business Machines Corporation

SCREENSHOT 38.1   Part of the data in 'Data View' with standardised scores

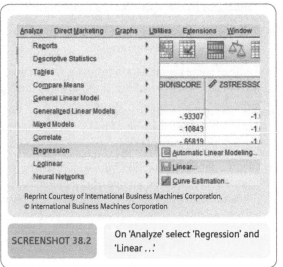

Reprint Courtesy of International Business Machines Corporation, © International Business Machines Corporation

SCREENSHOT 38.2   On 'Analyze' select 'Regression' and 'Linear ...'

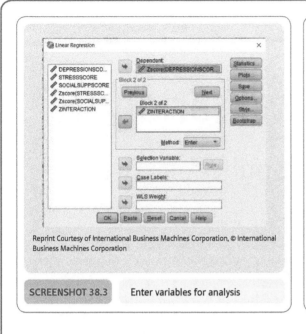

Reprint Courtesy of International Business Machines Corporation, © International Business Machines Corporation

SCREENSHOT 38.3   Enter variables for analysis

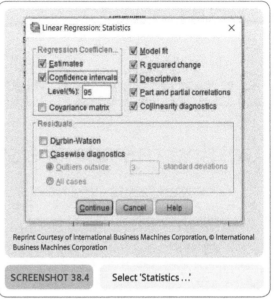

Reprint Courtesy of International Business Machines Corporation, © International Business Machines Corporation

SCREENSHOT 38.4   Select 'Statistics ...'

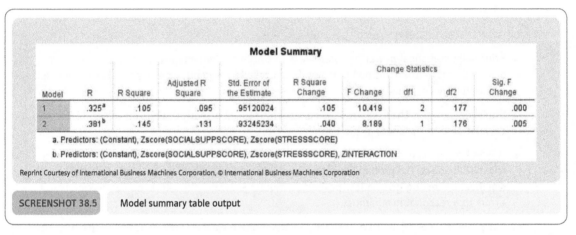

Model Summary

Model	R	R Square	Adjusted R Square	Std. Error of the Estimate	Change Statistics				
					R Square Change	F Change	df1	df2	Sig. F Change
1	.325[a]	.105	.095	.95120024	.105	10.419	2	177	.000
2	.381[b]	.145	.131	.93245234	.040	8.189	1	176	.005

a. Predictors: (Constant), Zscore(SOCIALSUPPSCORE), Zscore(STRESSSCORE)

b. Predictors: (Constant), Zscore(SOCIALSUPPSCORE), Zscore(STRESSSCORE), ZINTERACTION

Reprint Courtesy of International Business Machines Corporation, © International Business Machines Corporation

SCREENSHOT 38.5   Model summary table output

Recommended further reading

Aitken, L. S., & West, S. G. (1991). *Multiple regression: Testing and interpreting interactions.* Newbury Park, CA: Sage.

Cohen, J., Cohen, P., West, S. G., & Aitken, L. S. (2003). *Applied multiple regression/correlation analysis for the behavioral sciences* (3rd ed.). Hillsdale, NJ: Lawrence Erlbaum Associates.

CHAPTER 39

Statistical power analysis

Getting the sample size right

Overview

- Principally, statistical power analysis seeks to optimise the sample size(s) used in research such that it is neither so small that significant results are impossible nor so large resources are used unnecessarily.

- Statistical power is the likelihood that a research study correctly detects an effect (i.e. trend, correlation or difference) in the data.

- A Type 1 error occurs when the data seems to indicate that there is an effect when in reality there is no effect. The probability of this error is usually given the symbol alpha (α). Statistical significance testing gives a low probability figure – usually .05 – to keep the risk of Type I errors to a reasonable minimum.

- The probability of failing to detect an effect when one exists is known as the Type II error. It is usually designated as beta (β).

- Statistical power is, therefore, simply $1 - \beta$. Usually a figure of .80 is regarded as very satisfactory.

- Statistical power is interrelated with three things: a) the standardised effect size (such as Cohen's d or the correlation coefficient), b) the alpha (α) or significance level and c) the sample(s) size involved in the study. The larger that any of these values is, the more power there is in the study. It is possible, though a little complex, to calculate statistical power if these three things are known or can be estimated rationally.

- Furthermore, the researcher can calculate the required sample size(s) based on the required or estimated statistical power, the expected effect size and the significance level required. These calculations are best carried out using programs available on the web for ease.

- Statistical power calculations carried out before the main study is conducted are regarded as valuable. Questions have been asked, however, about using statistical power calculations after the data have been analysed. That is, statistical power analysis is largely uncontroversial in terms of planning a study but more controversial as part of the analysis of the data.

- Conceptually, statistical power analysis is quite sophisticated and relies on a mature understanding of decision-making in research and the applicability of research findings. It requires the researcher to shed some faith in the significance testing model in favour of understanding decision-making in research and its application.

Preparation

This is a relatively advanced technique which can only be built on a thorough understanding of the use of statistics in research. You need a thorough understanding of the statistical tests that you will use in your research together with knowledge of sampling distributions and sampling error.

39.1 Introduction

One of the most common questions asked by students planning research is 'What sample size do I need? Would 25 be enough?' Such questions are probably motivated by a number of factors:

- Keeping the amount of work on data collection to a minimum since time is at a premium and data collection can consume time. Often there seems little reward for time spent on collecting data compared to, say, time spent reviewing the research literature or working on the report.

- Desiring to obtain statistically significant outcomes which are more valued. This even applies to professional research where it is well known and documented that it is easier to publish research based on statistically significant findings than non-significant ones.

Though these are good enough reasons for asking the sample size question, this question may fail to receive a completely satisfactory answer from psychologists. Likely answers include:

- Get as big a sample as you can.

- You can probably get away with 50 (or some other number) participants.

- It is impossible to say – depends on too many things.

Each of these is inadequate in its own way. The reasons why this is so for each of the above follow in turn:

- *Get as big a sample as you can* Using the largest possible sample is wasteful at best. Although student research generally involves mainly time costs, professional research is a surprisingly costly activity. The financial cost for each additional participant may run to several hundred pounds or dollars. The researcher's time is expensive, in the first place, but there may well be substantial additional costs in terms of things like travel, transcription, equipment usage and so forth. Such expenditure is justifiable if

Imagine that you were the chair of a research committee allocating research funds to eager researchers: you would have many responsibilities. You would need to be satisfied that the research your committee funds is feasible and of potential value, that the research design, etc. is optimal and so forth. Furthermore, the research should not cost more than is necessary. Hence you would expect a reasoned explanation for the researcher's chosen sample size so as not to waste money. Clearly, the sample size should be as big as necessary to address the research question effectively. Basically the researcher should not choose a sample size too small to establish statistical significance or too large that unnecessary expense is involved in data collection. The optimum is dependent on various factors including the size of the effect in the study. Ordinary statistics such as the correlation coefficient and the *t*-test are indicative of the size of the effect – we are discussing the size of the correlation coefficient and the value of the *t*-test here *not* their statistical significance. But it is also dependent on the extent to which a researcher is prepared to risk making Type I and Type II errors (Chapter 11). A Type I error is accepting the hypothesis when it is, in fact, false and a Type II error is rejecting the hypothesis when it is, in fact, true. These are dealt with in Figure 39.1. The concept of power (as in the title of this chapter) simply refers to the probability of *not* making a Type II error – if there is actually a trend or difference in reality.

There is another reason why aiming for the largest sample size possible is regarded as unsatisfactory. This is because with very large sample sizes, the slightest relationship or trend in the data is likely to be statistically significant. Now if statistical significance is a researcher's sole criterion of importance, extremely unimpressive trends (effects) in the data will be given status that they do not warrant. For example, although a correlation of .70 is needed to be significant at the 5% level with a sample of 10, it only takes a correlation of .20 to be significant with 100 participants and a correlation of .06 to be significant with 1000 participants. In other words, a very small relationship in the data may achieve statistical significance and all that entails *if* the sample size is sufficiently large. Of course, a good researcher will modify their estimation of the value of their data in the light of these and other considerations.

It is probably worth mentioning at this stage that there is a view among statisticians that the null hypothesis is unlikely to be exactly true, so a study with an extremely large sample size is very likely to produce a statistically significant trend. Obviously, such statistically significant but relatively minuscule trends are unlikely to be of much real interest to most researchers.

● *You can probably get away with 50 (or some other number) participants* What about the second suggestion that there is a sample size which is likely to 'do the trick'? This has some merit in that it implies that there is a sample size likely to detect 'statistically significant effects' where they exist and that it does not demand that the researcher samples beyond what is necessary. However, just where has the proposed sample size come from?

Type 1 Errors	● A Type I Error is where a trend is detected in the data due to chance. There is no such trend in reality.
	● Statistical Significance refers to the chance of a trend being the result of chance. This is usually expressed in the phrase "The findings were statistically significant at the .05 (or .01) level."

Type 2 Errors	● A Type II Error is where in reality there is a trend but the study fails to detect the trend.
	● It is NOT simply the opposite of statistical significance.
	● Power is related to Type 2 Errors since power is the probability of NOT making a Type 2 Error.

If it is based on considerable experience in the particular area of research in question then it is probably of some value as it is based on inside information about what sample size 'works' in a particular field of research. For example, a student who is carrying out a research project in a field of research in which their supervisor is expert might well get useful advice on sample size from them. Similarly, if a student is carrying out research which is very similar to that already published then there may be a case for considering using a similar sample size. This approach may seem a little rough and ready but, failing anything else, it is informative. The trouble is that it is only worth considering if it is based on relevant experience. The central problem is that the optimum sample size which is just big enough to meet the requirements of a) being big enough to potentially produce statistical significant outcomes and b) not being unnecessarily large depends on quite sophisticated statistical ideas which do not readily lend themselves to 'plucking' numbers out of the air. Of course, such suggestions about sample size may be based on rather different considerations – the idea that a certain sample size demonstrates that the student or researcher has put in sufficient effort to achieve satisfactory outcomes. This is an irrational emotional approach which is, therefore, difficult to justify in this context.

● *It is impossible to say – depends on too many things* We can turn now to the final suggestion that optimum sample size depends on too many factors, many of which are unknown to the researcher, and so cannot be estimated. This runs counter to everything that you will learn about in this chapter. While the proper estimation of appropriate sample size is not as common in psychological research as perhaps it should be, it is not too difficult to estimate this though this involves some of the sort of intelligent guesswork (i.e. inference and estimation) for which statistics is infamous.

One reason why you need to know about statistical power analysis is that it is increasingly expected in terms of professional level research. For one thing, journals are increasingly demanding that researchers include power as part of the statistical analyses submitted for publication. For another, as we have hinted, those funding research are also increasingly likely to ask for estimates of the optimum sample size based on power calculations for reasons of economy and the viability of a study. There are other reasons too. If a researcher is carrying out research into the effectiveness of a particular form of psychotherapy using a control group, this means that some people participating in the research will *not* receive the treatment because they have been allocated to the control group. So using a sample size which is unnecessarily big will mean that if the treatment is shown to be effective then some people in the control group do not get treatment unnecessarily. Consequently, they may suffer a distressing condition for much longer than necessary. So research which goes on beyond what is really needed in terms of sample size can be counterproductive.

Statistical power is simply the likelihood that a study will detect a trend (or effect) in the data when, in reality, there is a trend. The concept of power is reviewed in Box 39.1. Remember that research deals with samples so reality, in this case, refers to the actual trend in the population which can be regarded as the baseline of truth or reality. Of course, this is largely an abstract concept since the researcher only knows about their sample(s) of data, not what is actually happening in the population. So we are talking estimation and inference once again. There are two basic risks in research which are taught to students very early on in their statistics courses. They are so important that we will repeat them. The most familiar is the idea that the sample(s) of data collected for the study sometimes will show a trend or a relationship when in reality there is no trend or relationship in the population from which the data were collected. This is known as a Type I error and is illustrated in Figure 39.2. Significance testing tries to minimise the risk of the Type I error by imposing the .05 or .01 significance criterion which refers to the level of risk of a Type I error that the researcher is prepared to take. Type I error is involved in power analysis because power depends partly on the significance level you choose for your study. The other risk is that of making a Type

trend or relationship. The Type II error is also illustrated in Figure 39.2.

	In reality (which is unknown to the researcher), there is NO trend in the data (i.e. H_0, the null hypothesis, is correct)	In reality (which is unknown to the researcher), there is a trend in the data (i.e. H_1, the hypothesis, is correct)
The researcher decides that there is a trend in the data (i.e. H_1, the hypothesis, is correct)	This is a TYPE 1 ERROR. The researcher's decision is incorrect. This is the situation that significance testing tries to avoid. The probability of this is alpha (α)	The researcher's decision is correct. This is the situation that statistical power concentrates on. The probability of this is $1 - \beta$ (see cell below)
The researcher decides that there is NO trend in the data (i.e. H_0, the null hypothesis, is correct)	The researcher's decision is correct. The probability of this is $1 - \alpha$	This is a TYPE 2 ERROR. The researcher's decision is incorrect. Statistical power analysis tries to keep Type 2 errors to a minimum. The probability of a Type 2 error is beta (β)

FIGURE 39.2   Possible correct and incorrect (errors) decisions that a researcher can make based on their data

This somewhat formal account also involves H_0, which is the null hypothesis, and H_1, which is the alternative hypothesis. You can regard the null hypothesis and alternative hypothesis in the way that they are discussed in experimental design, but they are simply the situation in which there is no trend at all in the data and the situation where there is a trend in the data. You implicitly consider Type I error every time you carry out a significance test. On the other hand, Type II error is likely to be much less familiar as its importance is often neglected. Indeed, this chapter is probably the first occasion when understanding it is of crucial importance. The concept of statistical power is essentially the opposite of that of the Type II error. Thus statistical power is the probability of *not* making Type II error if there is a trend or relationship in the data. If the probability of making a Type II error is .15 then the power of the analysis (or the probability of *not* making a Type II error) is $1.00 - .15 = .85$.

There is one important point that needs to be stressed. Power is calculated on the basis that the hypothesis (H_1) is true – in other words it only concerns the circumstances in which it is assumed that there is a relationship or trend in the population. So statistical power is the likelihood of detecting a trend or relationship in circumstances in which there is in reality a trend or a relationship exists. If you think about it, much the same applies for the Type I error – the probabilities are in terms of the likelihood of making an error if in reality the null hypothesis is true.

Statistical power is affected by other aspects of the research, most of which should be very familiar to you by now. You might find it easier to think about the factors which will reduce the likelihood of making a Type II error and consequently increase the power of the analysis. These factors can all be seen in Figure 39.3, which lists things that will affect statistical power (and the risk of making a Type II error). Most of these you could probably guess were involved anyway:

- The bigger the sample size then the greater the power of your study (and the less likely it is that a Type II error will be made), all other things being equal. This makes intuitive sense since a study with bigger samples is more likely to detect trends or relationships where they exist than one using smaller samples. One reason is that the bigger the sample then the

| Box 39.1 | Key concepts |

Statistical power

The concept of statistical power is not quite what it seems. It is very much a conceptual matter which require an appreciation of the basic concepts of statistical testing. Having reached this chapter, you probably will know some of the essential ideas. It is not true to say that the more power there is the better. Research is essentially about finding trends in fields of interest. Psychological research is traditionally conducted by measuring the size of the correlation between two variables or the difference between group means, for example. Crucially, the researcher then assesses the likelihood that the trends found could merely be the result of sampling fluctuations. This is known as significance testing. Usually a relatively arbitrary probability level of .05 or .01 is used when deciding whether or not to declare statistical significance. Sometimes this is expressed as the 5% level of significance or the 1% level of significance. A significant finding means that the data shows a trend which is unlikely to occur by chance if in reality there is no relationship in the population from which the samples come. The level of significance (.05, .01) simply represents the extreme uncharacteristic samples which will be found due to sampling fluctuations despite the reality that there is no correlation or difference. Certain things should be mentioned about significance testing:

- Discussion of the concept of Type I error is fairly commonplace in analyses of research data especially in relation to statistical significance. A Type I error is where the researcher accepts that there is a trend (correlation or difference) based on what can be seen in their data though this is an erroneous decision. The .05 and .01 levels of significance are probabilities that the researcher may have made a Type I error – if there is in reality no correlation or difference. If the researcher chooses the .01 level of significance then this means that there is less chance of making a Type I error than if they had chosen the .05 level of significance. In this sense, the .01 level of significance can be seen as more stringent. Avoiding Type 1 errors dominates psychological statistics as if statistical significance is the gold standard for research.

- Every psychology student will know that statistical significance is related to such things as sample size (the bigger the sample size the more likely a trend in the data is to be statistically significant – all other things being equal) and the size of the correlation or difference (the bigger the trend in the data the more likely one is to obtain statistical significance – all other things being equal).

All of this should be very familiar. Nevertheless, statistical power is about something related but very different. Statistical power is more about a part of decision-making in research which is commonly taught but overwhelmed by the quest for statistical significance.

All psychology students are taught about Type 1 errors which tends to stick in their minds. They are also taught about Type II errors, though many do not incorporate this concept into their decision making in research. Type II error is the likelihood that no trend is found in the data despite there being one in reality. Sampling error is responsible for Type II errors just as it is for Type I errors. However, it is the sampling distribution of the population in which there is a real trend, i.e. not of the hypothetical population distribution of the null hypothesis of no trends. So a Type II error is where the sample(s) on which a research study was based do not seem to show the trend which actually exists in reality.

Now both Type I and Type II errors are bad news in research for very different but feasible reasons. The concentration on Type I errors is unfortunate, but statistics is a complex discipline and inevitably things will get simplified if their importance is not understood. Research is largely about establishing that there are trends and relationships in whatever is being studied rather than showing that there are no trends. Rarely do researchers set out to establish that there is no trend or relationship in their data. Quite the reverse – they are usually keen to show them in their data. If you make a Type II error you are essentially claiming that there is no relationship when there is one. Given that this is simply not what researchers want (no matter how objective and dispassionate some claim to be), clarity about the implications of Type II errors seems essential.

Statistical power is essentially the opposite side of the coin to the Type II error. Statistical power concerns the ability of a research study to detect a relationship when there is indeed, in reality, a relationship. A Type II error is, in contrast, the likelihood of failing to detect a relationship where one exists in reality. So statistical power is really the extent to which the researcher is likely not to be making a Type II error – but remember that the phrase 'if the hypothesis suggests that there is a relationship in reality' always needs to be appended to the definitions of both power and Type II errors.

So statistical power = 1 − the probability of making a Type II error. If the probability of making a Type II error in a particular study is .20, the power of the study to detect a real trend or difference is 1.00 − .20 = .80. Remember that 1.00 in probability theory (Chapter 19) refers to a single event or instance. So in this case the 1.00 refers to a single instance of a researcher's decision to decide either that there is a trend or that there is not a trend in the data. The .80, therefore, is the probability that this decision has been in favour of concluding that there is a trend or difference when one actually exists in reality outside of the researcher's study.

The Type II error and power both depend on the distribution of samples taken at random from the population in which there is a trend or difference. Some of these samples will depart quite markedly from what is happening in the population from which the samples were taken. Any of these samples which are in the range of the non-statistically significant samples according to the null hypothesis of zero differences or correlations would be erroneously identified as coming from the population where the null hypothesis is true. The amount of overlap between the two sampling distributions will obviously affect the size of the Type II error and the statistical power. This can be seen in Figure 39.3.

This boils down to the following. Statistical power reflects the risk that the researcher will fail to show the relationship or difference which was the real purpose of the research. Imagine that the researcher was searching for a cure for cancer – accepting the null hypothesis erroneously might lead to the abandonment of this line of research which might have led to a cure for cancer. This would be an extremely serious consequence – some might say much more serious than mistakenly thinking that one had found a potential cure for cancer when, in truth, your treatment did not work. These are clearly complex arguments which are far more socially important than dry discussions of Type I and Type II errors.

- The bigger the significance level (i.e. alpha or α) you choose for your test of significance, the greater the power of your study (and once again the less likely it is that you will make a Type II error) all other things being equal. Now alpha is the significance level that you choose when assessing the statistical significance of the trend or relationship in your data. If you select an alpha of .05 then this is bigger than an alpha of .01. Thus an analysis using the .05 level of significance has more power than one using the .01 level of significance – all other things being equal. It is important, though, to remember that the significance level does not have to be .05 and can vary depending on a range of circumstances associated with the research, although it is a sound fall-back choice. Also remember that the significance level is the probability of identifying a trend or relationship in the data when there is no trend or relationship in reality due to sampling fluctuations (i.e. the risk of a Type I error). It is fairly obvious that where the researcher accepts a greater risk of

Effect size	Alpha level
The size of the trend in the data usually expressed as a correlation coefficient or Cohen's *d*.	The statistical probability of wrongly accepting the hypothesis on the basis of chance. Usually .05 or .01 is chosen by the researcher.

Components of statistical power analysis

Sample size	Power
The numbers of participants, cases, etc. in the study. Too small a sample and the null hypothesis cannot be rejected, too large a sample and uninterestingly small trends in the data may be detected.	The likelihood that a study will detect an effect when there really is one. So power is 1 minus the probability of rejecting the hypothesis when it is true in reality. Often a somewhat arbitrary criterion of .80 is set for satisfactory power.

FIGURE 39.3   Components of statistical power calculations

making a Type I error (finding a trend where there isn't one) then the risk of Type II error will be lower as a consequence. But we will return to this shortly.

● The bigger the size of the effect in a study (i.e. the stronger the relationship or the greater the trend or the bigger the difference between the mean scores for each group) then the greater the power your study has (and the lower the risk of making a Type II error) – all other things being equal. If you consider that the size of the effect in a study is indicated by the size of the correlation or the size of the *t*-statistic, for example, then once again this should not surprise you. A correlation of .6 is more likely to be statistically significant than one of .3, for example, for a given sample size. This means that the researcher is more likely to accept that there is a relationship or trend in the data. Since power is the likelihood of identifying a trend or relationship in a study when one exists in reality, it is not unexpected that sample size relates to power. It is usual in power calculations to use a standardised measure of effect size, most commonly Cohen's *d*, but sometimes a correlation coefficient is used as this is standardised too. See Box 39.2 for a more detailed discussion of measures of effect size.

Other things influence power, in particular the variability in the data. The greater the variability in the data, however, the lower the power in the study. This is because increased variability reduces the chance that your findings will be statistically significant. Remember that power is the likelihood of detecting a relationship or trend in your study when there is one in reality. Thus if the possibility of significant findings is reduced because of higher variability in the data then the power is reduced because the trend or relationship will not be detected even though in reality there is one. However, this is not necessarily an important feature of power calculations since the standardised measures of effect size (e.g. the Pearson correlation coefficient and Cohen's *d*) which are used in power analysis take this into account in their calculation. Nevertheless, the variability in the data is something which the researcher can often do something about – anything that can be done to reduce this variability increases the power of the analysis. For example, the researcher can standardise their methods of conducting the research and also use well-constructed tests and other measures as both these things will reduce variability and consequently increase power. That is, reduce, if they can, any unwanted source of variability in the study.

All of these aspects intertwine in a study to produce the power of your analysis. Furthermore, the analysis is different for different statistical procedures (tests of significance), which means that the calculation of statistical power can be a little complex. There are two main ways to deal with this and make statistical power accessible to researchers: a) produce tables for every test of significance which results in numerous tables to consult and b) use computer programs in which the researcher enters key aspects of their study (sample size, effect size and the significance level [i.e. alpha level] involved) and the calculation is left to the computer. Of course, alternative c) is to do the calculations yourself by hand though this is not a particularly helpful option.

Figure 39.4 is important. It shows the (theoretical) distribution of samples taken from the population. The curve on the left, in red, is the distribution of differences between sample means (of a given size) if the null hypothesis that there is no trend in the data is correct. It is therefore the sampling distribution according to the null hypothesis:

● Notice that the mean or midpoint of this curve is 0.0 as you would expect if the null hypothesis is true since there should be no difference between the samples except that due to sampling error.

● The pink area is the portion of this curve selected to be the significance level for testing the hypothesis. The pink area is bigger for a .05 significance test than for a .01 significance test. That is, the vertical green line will be further to the left for .05 significance than for .01 significance.

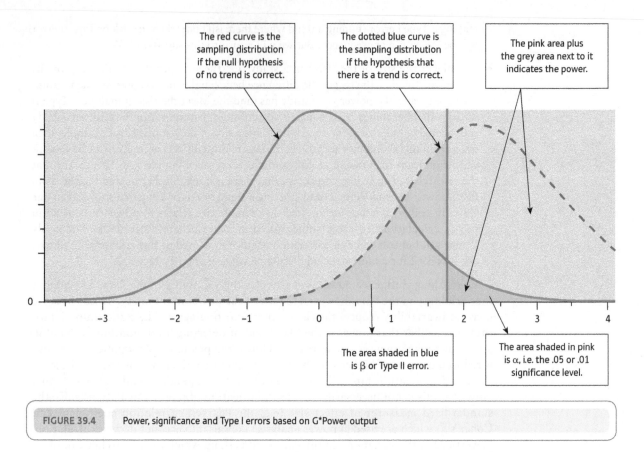

The red curve is the sampling distribution if the null hypothesis of no trend is correct.

The dotted blue curve is the sampling distribution if the hypothesis that there is a trend is correct.

The pink area plus the grey area next to it indicates the power.

The area shaded in blue is β or Type II error.

The area shaded in pink is α, i.e. the .05 or .01 significance level.

FIGURE 39.4   Power, significance and Type I errors based on G*Power output

The curve with the dotted blue line is not so familiar. It is the distribution of differences between sample means if the hypothesis is true – that is, if in reality there is a trend in the data. The mean of the dotted blue curve is about 2.3; that is, the effect of being in one group compared to the other. If this is standardised then it is an effect size.

There are a number of things that may be obvious from Figure 39.4:

- The part of the blue dotted curve which is shaded in blue to the left of the pink shaded area indicates the extent of Type II error in this particular study. The power of this particular study is indicated by the remainder of the blue dotted curve. This includes the area of statistical significance for the red curve.

- If the size of the effect of the study is increased (i.e. by mentally moving the blue dotted curve to the right) the power would increase as there would be less of the blue dotted curve to the left of the pink alpha area. Move the curve to the left and the power would decrease.

- If variability in the study were to be reduced, then the curves would have less spread and power would increase as a consequence.

- If the significance level changes then the pink alpha area will be bigger or smaller. It is smaller if the significance level is .01, which will have the effect of increasing the Type II error and so decreasing the power of the analysis. It is larger if the significance level is .05 which means that the Type II error will be smaller and the power greater, as a consequence.

What cannot be seen from Figure 39.4 is the influence of sample size on power. However, if you remember (from Chapter 10) that the sampling distribution for larger samples is

power by reducing the spread of the sampling distribution, all other things being equal.

> Box 39.2   Key concepts

Effect size

An effect size is the extent of the trend demonstrated by a study. Effect is a slightly odd word in the context of most research since it implies the influence or impact of one variable on another variable. However, effect size is really about the relationship between two variables rather than anything to do with cause and effect. It refers essentially to two things:

- *The size of the relationship (i.e. correlation) between two variables* The most familiar measure of this is the Pearson correlation coefficient which can be used as a measure of the effect size. In Chapter 36 the Pearson correlation coefficient is used as the measure of effect size for meta-analysis as we are very familiar with it. The Pearson correlation coefficient is a standardised measure of the relationship between two variables. That is, one can meaningfully compare correlation coefficients even when they are taken from different studies. The bigger the correlation between two variables the bigger the effect size.

- *The difference between the mean scores of different groups of scores* For example, this could be the difference between the mean of the experimental and control group. Although such differences do indicate the actual effect, it is not used as a measure of effect size because it is dependent on the variation in the data. In other words, differences in themselves are not standardised measures.

If the difference between two means is used as a measure of effect size, that difference needs to be standardised to allow comparisons between studies. Standardisation in this context involves adjusting the effect by the variability in the data. The commonest way of doing this is to use Cohen's d as a measure of effect size. Cohen's d is simply the difference between the two mean scores $(\overline{X}_1 - \overline{X}_2)$ divided by the standard deviation of the population:

$$\text{Cohen's } d = \frac{\overline{X}_1 - \overline{X}_2}{\text{standard deviation of population}}$$

Cohen originally suggested dividing by the standard deviation based on one or other group of scores assuming that these standard deviations would be approximately the same. But, in practice, often they turn out very different. Consequently, it is more usual to pool (combine) the two standard deviations when calculating Cohen's d, much as we do when calculating the value of t for a t-test. Unfortunately, there are various formulae for combining the two standard deviations which is less than ideal. The commonest formula for Cohen's d which involves pooling standard deviations is as follows:

$$\frac{\overline{X}_1 - \overline{X}_2}{\sqrt{\dfrac{(n_1 - 1)s_1^2 + (n_1 - 1)s_2^2}{n_1 + n_2}}}$$

The two standard deviations are listed as s_1 and s_2 in the above and their respective sample sizes are given as n_1 and n_2.

Should you wish to calculate the effects size for your study then there a number of effect size calculators available free on the Web. These involve entering some information based on your data which is number crunched to give the effect size. Simply type the words 'effect size calculator' into your favourite search engine to find suitable websites. G*Power, which is used in this chapter to calculate power, will also calculate the appropriate measure of effect size for the particular test of significance that you are using. The information required is readily available from the output of the t-test on programs such as SPSS. Alternatively, you could calculate the effect size as a correlation coefficient (using SPSS or any other statistics program). The dependent variable of the study is one variable in the calculation and the other variable is the group to which the participant in question belongs which is coded 1 for the control group and coded 2 for the experimental group, etc. If you want the effect size as a value of Cohen's d then Table 39.1 could be used to convert the resulting correlation coefficient to the equivalent value of Cohen's d as explained in the next paragraph.

There is a close relationship between Cohen's d and the Pearson correlation coefficient. This is to be seen in Table 39.1. This allows a value of Cohen's d effect size to be converted to a Pearson correlation coefficient and vice versa. In Table 39.1 the left hand columns contain values of the

→

Table 39.1	Equivalent effect sizes expressed as Cohen's *d* and Pearson correlation coefficient

Pearson	Cohen's	Pearson	Cohen's	Pearson	Cohen's	Pearson	Cohen's	Pearson	Cohen's
r	*d*	*r*	*d*	*r*	*D*	*r*	*d*	*r*	*d*
.00 ←→ 0.00		.20 ←→ 0.41		.40 ←→ 0.87		.60 ←→ 1.50		.80 ←→ 2.67	
.01	0.02	.21	0.43	.41	0.90	.61	1.54	.81	2.76
.02	0.04	.22	0.45	.42	0.93	.62	1.58	.82	2.87
.03	0.06	.23	0.47	.43	0.95	.63	1.62	.83	2.98
.04	0.08	.24	0.49	.44	0.98	.64	1.67	.84	3.10
.05	0.10	.25	0.52	.45	1.01	.65	1.71	.85	3.23
.06	0.12	.26	0.54	.46	1.04	.66	1.76	.86	3.37
.07	0.14	.27	0.56	.47	1.06	.67	1.81	.87	3.53
.08	0.16	.28	0.58	.48	1.09	.68	1.85	.88	3.71
.09	0.18	.29	0.61	.49	1.12	.69	1.91	.89	3.90
.10	0.20	.30	0.63	.50	1.15	.70	1.96	.90	4.13
.11	0.22	.31	0.65	.51	1.19	.71	2.02	.91	4.39
.12	0.24	.32	0.68	.52	1.22	.72	2.08	.92	4.69
.13	0.26	.33	0.70	.53	1.25	.73	2.14	.93	5.06
.14	0.28	.34	0.72	.54	1.28	.74 ←→ 2.20		.94	5.51
.15	0.30	.35	0.75	.55	1.32	.75	2.27	.95	6.08
.16	0.32	.36	0.77	.56	1.35	.76	2.34	.96	6.86
.17	0.35	.37	0.80	.57	1.39	.77	2.41	.97	7.98
.18	0.37	.38	0.82	.58	1.42	.78	2.49	.98	9.85
.19	0.39	.39	0.85	.59	1.46	.79	2.58	.99	14.04

Pearson correlation coefficient (Pearson *r*) and the right hand columns contain the values of Cohen's *d*. If you wish to find the equivalent Cohen's *d* for a Pearson *r* of .40, simply find the .40 in the columns and look to its right in that row. You will find that a Pearson *r* of .40 corresponds to a Cohen's *d* of 0.87. If you have a Cohen's *d* of 2.20 then you look at the column to the left of this where you will find that the corresponding Pearson *r* value is .74. If you have values which go to more than two decimal places then you will need to round down to two decimal places before you use the table. If the precise value is not in the table then use the nearest value instead. Such a conversion from Cohen's *d* to a correlation coefficient is useful if you are not very familiar with Cohen's *d*. Correlation coefficients make more immediate sense because we are familiar with them.

There are other measures of effect size when comparing two groups (Glass's Δ and Hedges's *g*) though Cohen's *d* tends to be the most commonly used. There are also other measures of effect size to deal with analysis of variance (ANOVA) designs.

39.2   Types of statistical power analysis and their limitations

There are a number of ways in which statistical power is used in research. These divide into a) the prospective (*a priori*) use which is part of the planning of a research study and b) the retrospective (*post hoc*) use where statistical power is calculated as part of the

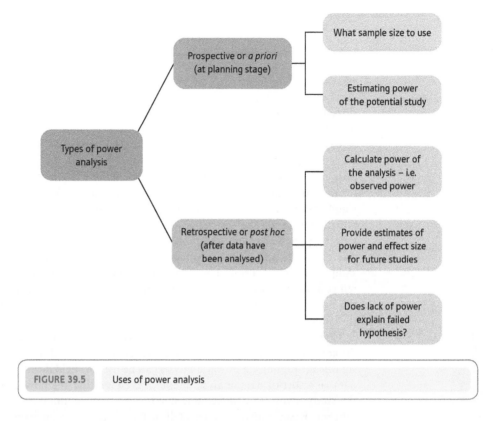

| FIGURE 39.5 | Uses of power analysis |

opinion is divided on the value of different aspects of power analysis. Most statisticians acknowledge that the prospective uses of statistical power are of value when planning substantial research projects. On the other hand, some question the value of retrospective power analyses. Some of the arguments are quite vehement.

The argument for the prospective use of power analysis as part of the planning of a research study has largely been made earlier in this chapter. However, one argument might be particularly difficult for those trained in psychological research. Psychologists tend to stress the importance of finding statistically significant differences or relationships, often forgetting other considerations. In brief, it is good to get statistically significant results. Certainly, there is a view that significant research findings are easier to get published. Statistical power analysis puts a very different gloss on the research and basically argues that only relationships or differences of a certain magnitude are important and worthy of consideration and that sample size, in particular, should be geared to making it likely that significant trends will be found in the data where they exist in reality. In other words, for a particular area of research or a particular research study, what is the size of effect which the researcher is warranted in searching for? And, given this, what is the size of sample(s) which can detect an effect of this magnitude? If a researcher's sole criterion for effective research is that statistically significant findings are obtained then very large sample sizes should normally do the trick. What emerges, though, is likely to be of trivial or no value. There is an argument in the statistical literature that null hypotheses are never (or hardly ever) true – take a large enough sample and a statistically significant difference or correlation will be found even if it involves sampling thousands of cases. Unfortunately, this is a fairly accurate caricature of some research in psychology though it is essentially mindless. Of course, statistics textbooks often inadvertently and unintentionally reinforce the view that statistical significance is a holy grail in research. Planning research should be a much more thoughtful process than this implies.

Another prospective use of power analysis is where a pilot study has been carried

procedures of the study work well enough to encourage the researcher to consider a later larger-scale study. In all likelihood, the researcher can use information about effect size from this pilot study to decide the optimal sample size for the subsequent large-scale study. This is a thoughtful intelligent approach to planning research which should be encouraged.

The argument about the retrospective use of statistical power analysis is, as mentioned, somewhat more controversial and acrimoniously presented. It boils down to the question of what value such retrospective power analyses are to the researcher. This retrospective power analysis is known as *observed power* and is calculated as part of some of the statistical routines on SPSS, for example. Quite obviously, if your study produces statistically significant findings then the study had sufficient statistical power for the particular sample size used – otherwise you would not have obtained statistically significant results. It might also be of some interest to quantify the power of your study when considering the effect size. For example, you might find that your study had a very large power value. This suggests that you may have used a far too large sample size given the effect size. In other words, any future studies could involve a smaller sample size which brings consequent economies to the research. Power analysis could tell you the size of sample that future similar studies require. This, though, is rather like the case of using pilot studies discussed above and amounts to good practice for much the same reasons.

Controversy arises when retrospective power analysis has been used to make a rather different sort of argument. Some researchers have argued that if a study fails to obtain significant findings, a power analysis can be used to help decide what is going on in the data as a sort of data analysis method. Imagine that the power analysis suggests that the study involves adequate statistical power yet the findings are not statistically significant. Basic statistics courses tell us that in these circumstances where we have not obtained statistical significance we reject the hypothesis and accept the null hypothesis of no difference or no relationship. Now retrospective power analysis (observed power) is sometimes used to suggest that where a) there is no evidence in support of the hypothesis and, consequently, b) the null hypothesis should be accepted then if the observed power is low then this suggests that the evidence in support of the null hypothesis should be regarded as weak. That is, the argument goes that the study was incapable of rejecting the null hypothesis because of its low power. The problem with this argument is that there is a direct relationship between the observed power and the probability (significance) level found using a test of significance. In other words, discussing observed power is a long-winded way of saying things which the significance level already indicates. One further criticism of using observed power (erroneously) in this way is that there are acceptable methods of testing the strength of the null hypothesis. For example, it is possible to test whether two group means are statistically equivalent rather than simply 'not significantly different' as in the case of conventional significance testing (Hoenig & Heisey, 2001). The controversy, in summary, is about whether observed power statistics add anything to the interpretation of non-significant research findings. Nevertheless, psychology journals are increasingly likely to require the reporting of observed power statistics.

The message from this seems to be clear. Power analysis as part of the planning process for a research study is generally regarded favourably by both researchers and statisticians as an important tool. It helps ensure clarity about what is an adequate effect size for a particular study but also encourages consideration of what would be an adequate sample size. In contrast, however, retrospective power analysis should be used with great caution because it is only of very limited value and is not a tool for data analysis as such. Indeed, the retrospective use of power analysis is most acceptable in circumstances where it potentially contributes to the planning of further research studies – but that is the case for prospective power analysis.

39.3 Doing power analysis

The following are interdependent:

- statistical power
- sample size
- effect size
- statistical significance.

If three of these four things are known for a particular test of significance then it is possible to calculate the fourth. Usually it is statistical power or sample size which is calculated from the other three using power analysis programs. Although it is feasible to do these calculations without the aid of a computer, there is little point in spending time on this when one has better things to do with one's time. Type the words power analysis calculator into your preferred internet search engine and any number of resources for doing particular aspects of power analysis will be listed. Mostly they will do what you need, though some have a more specialised function than others. You can download G*Power from the Web, which is our preferred program, but there are others available. Some other programs are in the form of applets on web pages so you do the calculation on screen but the program is not downloaded on your computer.

You will probably have noticed a stumbling block. What are the values of statistical power, effect size and statistical significance if I want to calculate the appropriate sample size using statistical power analysis? Where can these be found? The answer is, in general, that you can't find them but you will have to rationally decide what the appropriate values for each of these are. Let us go through the different aspects of the power calculation in turn:

- The level of statistical significance is traditionally set at .05 in psychology. This is often described as an arbitrary value and it is. There is no logic in choosing it except that it stipulates a pretty low value of probability that the researcher will choose to accept the hypothesis erroneously when the null hypothesis of no trend is in reality true. That is, there is only a 1 in 20 chance (5%) of accepting the hypothesis when it is, in fact, false in reality. But is this value always an adequate criterion? What if the research was about a cure for hay fever and a decision whether or not to spend a very large amount of money on research and development rested on the outcome of the study? In these circumstances, would it not be wiser to adopt a more stringent significance level (e.g. .01) in place of .05? The answer is probably yes. On the other hand, if the planned research is more exploratory and in a field where there is little previous research, then maybe a less stringent significance level of .10 might be adopted. For example, if the study was being carried out on a shoestring then surely the risk of prematurely abandoning research on this topic (because the study fails to obtain significant results) might be more serious than the consequences of reaching by chance the erroneous conclusion that the hypothesis was true. Quite clearly, these are not really statistical decisions but ones, nevertheless, of some importance to the researcher.

    Of course, it is possible to explore the effect on sample size of the various possible levels of significance to see if it makes any practical difference to your research. (It should be added that one does not always have to calculate significance against the usual zero effect model of the null hypothesis. Instead statistical significance can be calculated in comparison to a low level size of effect which is of no practical interest to the researcher. For example, if it is known that an inexpensive drug such as aspirin has a particular size of effect then this effect might be set as the baseline against which to evaluate a new much more expensive drug. Such procedures are discussed in Murphy and Myors, 2004.)

- The required level of the effect size must be estimated for your proposed study. This can be based on one of several sources of information:

  - If there have been similar studies using the measures that you are planning to use, then the effect sizes from these previous studies may be used. Obviously the more similar the other study(ies) to yours the better this estimate is likely to be.

  - Alternatively, a more general approach could be used. For example, Lipsey and Wilson (1993) collated effect sizes from a range of different sizes of study. They found that treatment programmes for juvenile delinquents in terms of future delinquency, worksite anti-smoking programmes in terms of rates of quitting smoking and small versus large school class sizes in terms of measures of achievement typically had small effect sizes of Cohen's d values of .20 or less. On the other hand, behaviour therapy compared to placebo controls on various outcome measures and enrichment programmes for gifted children in terms of cognitive, creativity and affective outcomes had effect sizes of .5 or so – that is medium size effect sizes. Finally, psychotherapy in terms of various outcomes and positive reinforcement in the classroom had effect sizes of .85 or more – that is, large effect sizes. Cohen (1988) stipulated a small effect as a Cohen's d of .20, a medium effect as a Cohen's d of .50 and a large effect as a Cohen's d of .80. So if a particular type of research is known to generally produce a particular effect size then this could be used.

  - One could simply look at the consequences of using Cohen's three levels of effect size in terms of sample size. It may be that each of them indicates a sample size which is feasible in terms of the proposed research. Otherwise, the conservative approach would be to take a Cohen's d of .20 (the smallest of his effect sizes) as the basis for the sample size calculation.

- The level of power required needs to be at a minimum .50 – otherwise the study is likely not to reject the null hypothesis. There is, of course, very little point in designing a study which is more than likely to support the null hypothesis. It is conventional – and no more than that – to regard a power of .80 or greater as adequate. This means that if there is truly a trend or difference in the data that it has an 80% chance of being identified by the researcher using a particular significance level and sample size(s). There is no reason why a higher level of power cannot be chosen, if this is considered appropriate by the researcher.

39.4   Calculating power

Since one cannot use SPSS to carry out most aspects of statistical power analysis we will use G*Power, which is a free-to-download and flexible program that carries out a variety of statistical power analysis calculations. Of course, SPSS output does contain relevant information to be entered into these additional programs. The SPSS company does have a power analysis program SamplePower® 3.0, but this is not generally available at universities, etc. in the way SPSS is and it is quite expensive to purchase. So it is just as well to turn to other software which is available in some variety. Many of the programs have to be purchased and so it makes sense to opt for the free resources available on the Web. G*Power is a serious competitor for commercially available software and it is well regarded. It is also flexible in terms of the number of different research designs that it can deal with. Figure 39.6 illustrates the active interface of G*Power, but expect slight variations according to circumstances.

G*Power does a wide variety of power analyses for a variety of statistical tests which are organised into 'Test families' such as those based on the *t*-test and those based on the *F*-distribution. The term 'Test family' can be seen immediately under the big white box in the screenshot (Figure 39.6). Select the 'Test family' you require from the drop-down list which appears when you hover your mouse cursor over this box. Then select the 'Statistical test' you require from the drop-down menu. Finally select the 'Type of power analysis' again from a drop-down menu. Since these drop-down menus each offer a variety of options, it is worthwhile checking out what is available by trying out a number of these options. So, as you can see in Figure 39.6, the following have been selected but, of course, the choices made depend on the design of the study:

- Test family: *t*-test

- Statistical test: Means: difference between two independent means (two-groups)

- Type of power analysis: *A priori*: Compute required sample size – given α, power and effect size.

These particular selections indicate the following: The analysis corresponds to an unrelated *t*-test comparing the difference between two means. The power analysis is intended for planning a new study (i.e. *a priori*) and it is required that the optimum sample size is computed based on the significance level (α), required level of power and the effect size. This would be a reasonable standard option for statistical power analysis when comparing, say, an experimental group with a control group – or for comparing the means of any two groups, for that matter.

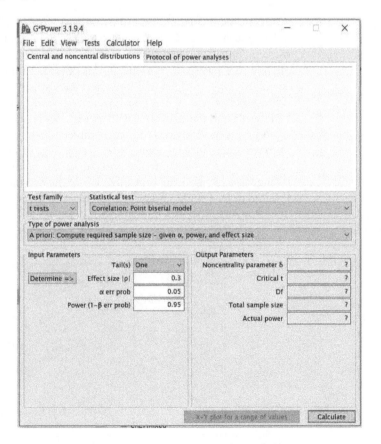

FIGURE 39.6   Screenshot of the G*Power interface

It is obvious that you then need to enter (overwrite) the 'Input Parameters' in the white boxes. We will return to the question of just what you need to enter into each of the input boxes a little later, but we need to concentrate on the box labelled 'Effect size' first of all as this is the most complex. There are various different measures of effect size to deal with different research designs. However, once you have selected the 'Test family', 'Statistical test' and 'Type of power analysis', G*Power indicates what measure of 'Effect size' is to be used. If you have relevant data, 'Effect size' can be calculated from this. G*Power will calculate the relevant type of 'Effect size' for you if you ask it to do so. However, this calculation is not based on the raw data but on things like the sample means and standard deviations (depending on the research design that you are dealing with). Consequently, this information needs to be calculated by you before you can enter it into G*Power.

Figure 39.7 shows the side-menu or drawer revealed on screen when you click on the 'Determine ⇒' button next to 'Effect size *d*'. In this screenshot, the information has already been entered into the appropriate boxes. Notice, however, that you need to select different options according to whether your sample sizes are equal or different. Although the calculation of these figures could be carried out by hand, it is probably more convenient to obtain them using SPSS or some other statistical analysis program. For example, to calculate the effect size for two independent groups using Cohen's *d,* you need to enter the means and standard deviations for the two samples into G*Power. These are part of the output of SPSS for the unrelated *t*-test. The means and standard deviations (*SD*) have been entered using SPSS *t*-test output. You probably will wish to click on the 'Calculate and transfer to main window' button as it saves you copying it yourself into the 'Input Parameters'.

Of course, it is more likely that you have no data from which to calculate effect size unless you have conducted a pilot study. Consequently, you might be well advised to examine previous research studies to see if a typical effect size can be identified. Meta-analyses are particularly useful in this regard. Failing that, you may wish to use the 'standard' high, medium and low effect sizes which have been recommended by Cohen (1988) and others. When you hover your mouse cursor over the 'Effect size' box in G*Power these standard sizes will appear on screen.

So that is one important 'Input Parameter' dealt with. The following are suggestions as to what goes into the input boxes seen in Figure 39.6. The calculation is based on the study we used to illustrate the unrelated *t*-test in Chapter 14. If the researcher has no strong basis for predicting the direction of the outcome of the research, a two-tailed test is selected. One could select a one-tailed test if this were appropriate.

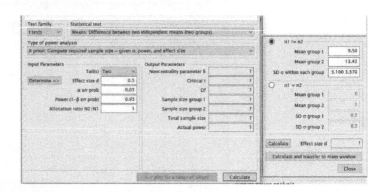

FIGURE 39.7   Effect size calculator side-menu on G*Power

- The effect size has been entered as a Cohen's *d* of 1.2645161 in Figure 39.6. This is a calculated value based on the data in the study that we are using. If no such calculation is possible then you could enter other values according to whether you expect a small (0.2), medium (0.5) or large effect (0.8). Alternatively, if this were possible, the effect size could be based on data such as when a pilot study has been carried out or the typical effect size for similar research.

- The significance level ('α err prob') is the conventional significance level of .05 though, of course, another value could be selected if there were reasons to be more or less stringent about avoiding rejecting the null hypothesis.

- The required power has been set at .80 which is a realistic but nevertheless high requirement and difficult to exceed in practice in psychological research. Consequently it is generally accepted as a reasonable level to choose. Of course it could be lower but not below .50 as explained earlier.

- The 'Allocation ratio' is simply the ratio of the two sample sizes. If you want these to be equal then the allocation ratio is 1. But, say, you wanted one group bigger than the other then you would have to juggle with this ratio. Probably there is little point in doing so for most research though sometimes researchers prefer to have small control groups relative to the experimental group.

Once your Input Parameters have been inserted in the relevant boxes, then press the 'Calculate' button. The interface will change to something like you see in the screenshot in Figure 39.8. The interface also includes a graphical representation of the power analysis. We discussed a similar graphical representation earlier (Figure 39.4) so refer to this discussion if you need clarification (p. 566).

Remember that Figure 39.8 refers to the *t*-test analysis reported in Explaining statistics 14.1. The most important thing is that it suggests that a sample size of 22 could generate the .80 level of power that we stipulated. That is, 11 in each group. The 'Actual power' simply is the consequence of turning the sample sizes into whole numbers whereas the calculation would produce decimals. So the 'Actual power' is the power based on a total sample size of 22 rather than the 'Input Parameters' that we entered, which can result in fractions for the sample sizes. One of the main reasons why the required sample size is quite low at 22 (11 in each group) is because the effect size (Cohen's *d* = 1.26) is so large. It corresponds to a correlation of .53 between the independent and dependent variable. Now if this really were a pilot study then the implications are obviously very clear – however, this is data made up for the purpose of demonstrating the unrelated *t*-test so we should not get too excited. Pretending that it was a real pilot study then the researcher could be excused for feeling delighted. The effect is a very strong one requiring a sample size of only 22 in total to detect it with a power requirement of .80. This is about as good as it gets. Even if we increased the required power to .95 and made the significance level more stringent at .01, then G*Power tells us that a total sample size of only 50 is needed. That is to say, with just about the most demanding criteria for a power analysis, the required sample size is relatively small in this case. Try for yourself the effects of a low effect size of, say, .2 on the required sample size. You will find that the required sample size is massive to obtain the statistical significance at the required power.

Power analysis encourages more careful thought in planning research and requires the researcher to evaluate what sorts of research outcomes have practical implications for decision-making following the completion of the proposed study. This is a very different sort of approach from that of relying solely on significance testing as the holy grail of research. Obviously, power analysis forces the researcher into considering the bigger picture of research, especially when important decisions about social interventions, therapy and so forth are contingent on the outcome of the research.

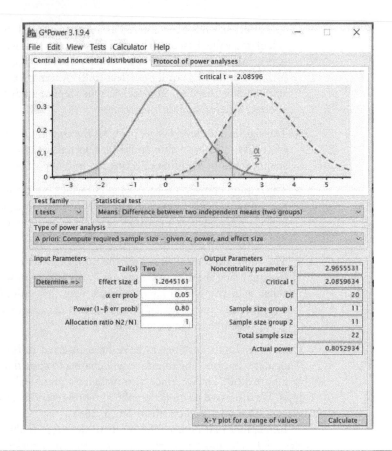

FIGURE 39.8   G*Power interface showing the output parameters and graph

39.5   Reporting the results

Research examples

Statistical power

Schimmack (2012) takes note of the evidence that despite numerous warnings about the statistical power of research in psychology, the typical statistical power of studies has not improved as a consequence. What has changed, however, over the years is the number of separate studies reported in a single paper. One possible implication of this is that multiple studies of modest statistical power result in a high probability of non-significant findings because the power of an analysis decreases the more significance tests that are applied. The statistically unacceptable but common practices employed by some researchers may be partially responsible. For example, HARKing (hypothesising after the results are known) can be involved in the problem. Because research is very expensive and because non-significant findings are difficult or impossible to publish, researchers design very complex studies which are capable of testing multiple hypotheses. There is a good chance that one of these hypotheses will appear to be supported but only because Type I error increases but is ignored. Thus something publishable may come out of the research even though it has little value otherwise. Schimmack provides information on the total number of participants required in multiple study articles to achieve 80% statistical power and to produce significant results in all of the studies. The study design involved in this exercise was a simple between-subjects experiment. These details do not matter so much as the fact that for a small effect size (Cohen's $d = .2$) then for one study the total sample size would need to be 788, for five studies 6750 and for ten studies 15 820. One doesn't need to know much about psychological research to realise that these numbers of participants would be remarkable.

Simpson and Karageorghis (2006) carried out a study of the motivating effect and otherwise on athletic performance. Of significance here, they conducted a power analysis in order to decide a satisfactory sample size for their experimental group. Using alpha at .05, a two-tailed significance test, power set at .70, and an expected effect size in the moderate range, the appropriate sample size was calculated at 35.

Woods and colleagues (2006) point out the possible problems of the statistical power of studies using novel neuropsychological interventions with clinical populations such as Parkinsonism sufferers. Such studies often have rather limited sample sizes. They examined the literature of the cognitive consequences of deep brain stimulation of the subthalamic nucleus. Using the findings of 30 different studies of this, they found that the studies only had adequate statistical power to detect real trends where the effect size was very large. However, for small, medium and large effect sizes there was too little power in the studies to detect real trends in the population. In other words, there was a significant risk of Type II errors.

Key points

- Statistical power analysis is best used to inform the planning of research studies. It is less useful after data have been collected as part of the data analysis.

- Different statistical tests require power calculations to be done differently. In particular, the measure of (standardised) effect size will differ.

- Statistical power analysis includes assumptions and estimates which cannot be standardised for all circumstances as this would defeat its purpose. So reporting a power analysis may involve justifying the estimates and decisions that you have taken.

COMPUTER ANALYSIS

Power analysis with G*Power

SPSS does compute some power values, but it is not very helpful for the bulk of the analyses outlined in this chapter. Exceptionally, this chapter contains a detailed illustration of using G*Power to calculate statistical power. Nevertheless, you may find the quick summary in Figure 39.9 a useful memory aid. Please check the following link for updates on G*Power and further documentation: www.gpower.hhu.de/. Although G*Power is free, its authors would appreciate that you cite one or both of the following papers in any published papers you produce using it in your research:

- Faul, F., Erdfelder, E., Buchner, A., & Lang, A.-G. (2009). Statistical power analyses using G*Power 3.1: Tests for correlation and regression analyses. *Behavior Research Methods, 41,* 1149–1160.

- Faul, F., Erdfelder, E., Lang, A.-G., & Buchner, A. (2007). G*Power 3: A flexible statistical power analysis program for the social, behavioral, and biomedical sciences. *Behavior Research Methods, 39,* 175–191.

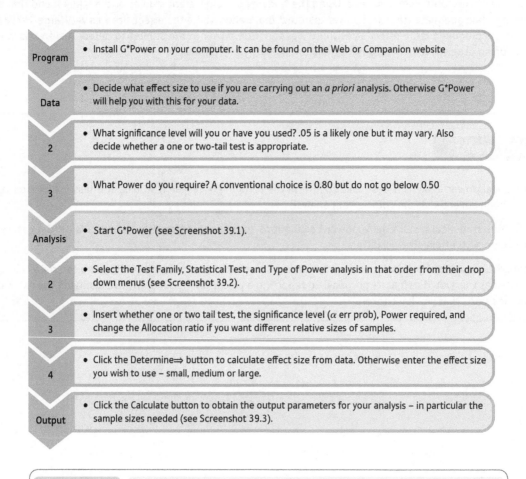

Program
- Install G*Power on your computer. It can be found on the Web or Companion website

Data
- Decide what effect size to use if you are carrying out an *a priori* analysis. Otherwise G*Power will help you with this for your data.

2
- What significance level will you or have you used? .05 is a likely one but it may vary. Also decide whether a one or two-tail test is appropriate.

3
- What Power do you require? A conventional choice is 0.80 but do not go below 0.50

Analysis
- Start G*Power (see Screenshot 39.1).

2
- Select the Test Family, Statistical Test, and Type of Power analysis in that order from their drop down menus (see Screenshot 39.2).

3
- Insert whether one or two tail test, the significance level (α err prob), Power required, and change the Allocation ratio if you want different relative sizes of samples.

4
- Click the Determine⇒ button to calculate effect size from data. Otherwise enter the effect size you wish to use – small, medium or large.

Output
- Click the Calculate button to obtain the output parameters for your analysis – in particular the sample sizes needed (see Screenshot 39.3).

| FIGURE 39.9 | Computer steps for power analysis using G*Power |

Interpreting and reporting the output

- Although this is often not done, ideally we need to carry out a power analysis to determine the size of the sample we need.

- The results of this power analysis are reported in the 'Method' section of your write-up or report where you are discussing the sample. We might write something like: 'Statistical power analysis was used to estimate an appropriate sample size. Because of the lack of previous research in this field, it was decided to use Cohen's high, medium and low effect sizes in order to explore the consequences of this on the appropriate sample size. It was decided that the significance (alpha) level would be kept high at 10% as would the power at 90%. It was felt to be much more important for this study to avoid Type II errors because of the risks of falsely accepting the null hypothesis.'

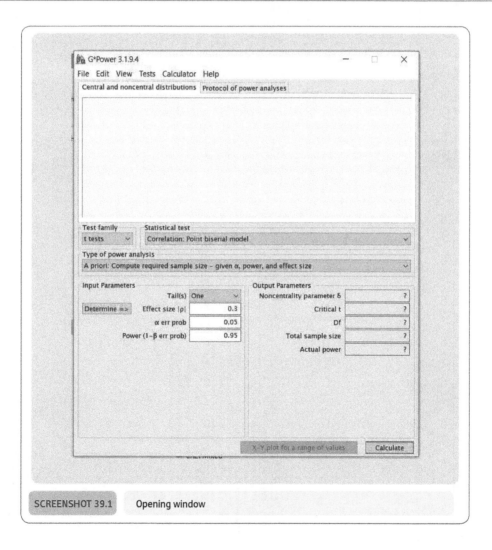

SCREENSHOT 39.1   Opening window

SCREENSHOT 39.2 Select tests and values

SCREENSHOT 39.3 Output for sample sizes needed

PART 6

Advanced qualitative or nominal techniques

Log-linear methods

Analysis of complex contingency tables

Overview

- The analysis of nominal (category) data using chi-square is severely limited since a maximum of only two variables can be used in any one analysis.

- Log-linear can be conceived as an extension of chi-square to cover greater numbers of variables.

- Log-linear uses the likelihood ratio chi-square (rather than the Pearson chi-square we are familiar with from Chapter 18). This involves natural or Napierian logarithms.

- The analysis essentially examines the adequacy of the various possible models. The simplest model merely involves the overall mean frequency – that is, the model does not involve any influence of the variables either acting individually or interactively in combination. The most complex models involve the individual effects of the variables (main effects) as well as all levels of interactions between variables. If there are three variables, there would be three main effects, plus several two-way interactions plus one three-way interaction.

- A saturated model is the most complex model and involves all of the possible components. As a consequence, the saturated model always explains the data completely, but at the price of not being the simplest model to fit the actual data. It is essentially a conceptual and computational device.

Preparation

If you are hazy about contingency tables then look back to the discussion in Chapter 7. Also revise chi-square (Chapter 18) since it is involved in log-linear analyses. Log-linear shares concepts such as main effect and interaction with ANOVA which ought to be reviewed as general preparation (especially Chapter 25).

40.1   Introduction

In essence, log-linear methods are used for the analysis of complex contingency (or cross-tabulation) tables. Data in Chapter 18 which were analysed using chi-square could be subjected to log-linear procedures instead although with no particular benefits. Log-linear comes into its own when dealing with three or more variables. Log-linear analysis identifies how the variables acting alone or in combination influence the frequencies in the cells of the contingency table. The frequencies can be regarded as if they are the dependent variable.

Some basic ideas need to be mentioned:

- *Interactions* Like analysis of variance (ANOVA), log-linear analysis uses the concept of interactions between two or more variables. Interaction refers to the effects of the variables that cannot be explained by the effects of these variables acting separately. Interactions involve variables acting in combination. Much of this chapter is devoted to explaining the concept in more detail.

- *Models* A model in log-linear analysis is a statement (which can be expressed as a formula) which explains how the variables such as gender, age and social class result in the cell frequencies found in the contingency table. For example, one model might suggest that the pattern of frequencies in the contingency table is the result of the independent influences of the variable gender and the variable age. There are probably other contending models for all but the simplest cases. An alternative model for this example is that the data are the result of the influence of variable social class plus the influence of variable gender *plus* the combined influence of variable gender interacting with the variable age. Table 40.1 gives the components of models for different numbers of variables in the contingency table. We will return to this later, but notice how the components include a constant (or the average frequency) *plus* the main effects of the variables *plus* interactive effects of the variables. Log-linear analysis helps a researcher to decide which of the possible models (i.e. which selection of the components in Table 40.1) is the best for the actual data. These different components will become clearer as we progress through this chapter. Model building can serve different purposes. Unless you have theoretical reasons for being interested in a particular model, then log-linear methods allow you to build up the model purely empirically.

- *Goodness-of-fit* This is simply the degree of match between the actual data and those values predicted on the basis of the model. Chi-square is a common measure of goodness-of-fit. Chi-square is zero if the observed data are exactly the same as the expected (or predicted) data. The bigger the value of chi-square, the greater the *misfit* between obtained and expected values. In Chapter 18, a significant value of chi-square caused us to reject the 'model' specified by the null hypothesis. A good-fitting model would have a chi-square value approximating zero whereas a badly fitting model would have a large chi-square value.

- *Pearson chi-square* This is the version of chi-square used in Chapter 18 although common practice is simply to call it chi-square. The formula for the Pearson chi-square is:

$$\text{Pearson chi-square} = \sum \frac{(\text{observed} - \text{expected})^2}{\text{expected}}$$

Component of model	1	2	3	4	5
Table 40.1 Possible model components for different sizes of contingency table					
Overall mean (equal frequencies)	yes	yes	yes	yes	yes
Main effects	A	$A + B$	$A + B + C$	$A + B + C + D$	$A + B + C + D + E$
Two-way interactions	–	$A*B$	$A*B$	$A*B$	$A*B$
			$A*C$	$A*C$	$A*C$
			$B*C$	$A*D$	$A*D$
				$B*C$	$A*E$
				$B*D$	$B*C$
				$C*D$	$B*D$
					$B*E$
					$C*D$
					$C*E$
Three-way interactions			$A*B*C$	$A*B*C$	$A*B*C$
				$A*B*D$	$A*B*D$
				$A*C*D$	$A*B*E$
				$B*C*D$	$A*C*D$
					$A*C*E$
					$A*D*E$
					$B*C*D$
					$B*C*E$
					$B*D*E$
					$C*D*E$
Four-way interactions				$A*B*C*D$	$A*B*C*D$
					$A*B*C*E$
					$A*B*D*E$
					$B*C*D*E$

- *Likelihood ratio chi-square* This is the more common formula when doing log-linear analysis:

$$\text{Likelihood ratio chi-square} = 2 \times \sum \text{observed frequency} \times \ln \text{of} \frac{\text{observed frequency}}{\text{expected frequency}}$$

The term ln is a symbol for *natural logarithm*. Don't worry if you know nothing about natural logarithms. Although tables of natural logarithms are available, it is easier to obtain them from a scientific calculator (or the calculator built into Windows, for instance). Observed frequency refers to the obtained data and expected frequency refers to the values expected according to the particular model being tested.

- *Differences between Pearson and likelihood ratio chi-square* The formulae give slightly different values of chi-square for small sample sizes but converge as the sample sizes get large. Both formulae are often computed as measures of goodness-of-fit by computer programs for log-linear analysis. Nevertheless, it is best to concentrate on likelihood ratio chi-square in log-linear analysis because of its *additive* properties. This means that different components of chi-square can be added together to give the combined effect of different components of the chosen model. The Pearson chi-square does not act additively so

40.2 Two-variable example

The distinctive approach of log-linear analysis can take a little time to absorb. Its characteristic logic is probably best explained by re-analysing an example from Chapter 18. The study of favourite types of television programme of males and females (Explaining statistics 18.1) will be presented using the log-linear perspective. The data are given in Table 40.2, but they are exactly the same as the data in Table 18.8. The two variables were gender and favourite type of programme. In the (Pearson) chi-square analysis (Explaining statistics 18.1) there is a gender difference in favourite type of television programme. Another way of putting this is that there is an interaction between a person's gender and their favourite type of television programme. (In Chapter 18, it was found that gender and favourite type of programme acting separately were insufficient to account for the data. The expected frequencies in that chapter are the frequencies expected on the basis of gender and programme effects having separate and unrelated effects. Also in Chapter 18, a significant value of chi-square meant that the distribution of cell frequencies could not be explained on the basis of this independent influence of gender and favourite programme type. The different genders had different preferences. This would be an interaction in terms of log-linear analysis.)

A log-linear analysis of the data in Table 40.2 would examine possible underlying models (combinations of the variables) which might predict the obtained data. Theoretically, there are a number of possibilities according to log-linear analysis:

- *Equal frequencies model* This suggests that the observed cell frequencies are merely the total of cell frequencies divided equally between the cells. Since there are 119 observations in Table 40.2 and six cells then we would *expect* a frequency of $119 \div 6 = 19.833$ in each cell. Obviously this model, even if it fits the data best, is virtually a non-model.

- *Main effects model* This suggests that the observed cell frequencies are the consequence of the separate effects of the variables which add together to give their overall effect. Although this might seem an important possibility if you recall main effects for ANOVA, in log-linear analysis, main effects are often trivial. The object of log-linear analysis is to account for the pattern of observed frequencies in the data. In Table 40.2 note that there are slightly unequal numbers of males and females (60 males and 59 females) but, more importantly, the choices of the different programme types are unequal. That is, the different values of gender (male and female) and favourite television programme (soap opera, crime drama and neither) are not equally represented. For the main effect of gender, the inequality is small (60 males versus 59 females), but it is somewhat larger for the main effect of favourite television programme (44 choosing soap operas, 47 choosing crime dramas and 28 choosing neither). The main effects merely refer to these inequalities which may be uninteresting in terms of the primary purpose of the analysis. In our example, a researcher is likely not to be particularly interested in these main effects but much more interested if the interaction between

Table 40.2	Data to be modelled using log-linear analysis		
	Soap opera	Crime drama	Neither
Males	observed = 27	observed = 14	observed = 19
Females	observed = 17	observed = 33	observed = 9

gender and favourite programme type explains the data. In order for there to be *no* main effects, each of the categories of each of the variables would have to have the same frequency. This is rare in research.

● *The interaction(s)* An interaction is the effect of the interrelationship between the variables. In the present example, because we have only two variables, there is just one interaction which can be described as the gender × favourite TV programme interaction. You will see from Table 40.1 that had there been more variables there would be more interactions to investigate. The number of interactions escalates with increasing numbers of variables (much as it does for ANOVA). Interactions interest researchers because they indicate the associations or correlations between variables.

The interactions and main effects are combined in log-linear analysis in order to see what main effects and what interactions are necessary to best account for (fit with) the observed data.

Log-linear analysis for this simple example involves the consideration of several different models.

Step 1: Equal frequencies model

In a manner of speaking, this is the no-model model. It tests the idea that the cell frequencies require no explanation since they are equally distributed. This is *not* the same as the null hypothesis predictions made in Chapter 18 since these predicted not equal frequencies but *proportionate* frequencies according to the marginal totals. The equal frequencies model simply assumes that all of the cells of the contingency table have equal frequencies. Since we have a total frequency of 119 in the six cells of our analysis, the equal frequencies model predicts (expects) that there should be 119 ÷ 6 or 19.833 in each cell as shown in Table 40.3. The likelihood ratio chi-square applied to this table is calculated in Table 40.4. Remember that the natural logarithms are obtained from a scientific calculator or one you find as a program on your computer. The use of natural logarithms is only important for understanding the basic calculation of log-linear.

The fit of the equal frequencies model to the data is poor. The likelihood ratio chi-square is 19.418. This is the amount of misfit of that particular model to the data. (It is also the amount by which the main effects and the interactions can increase the fit of the best model to the data.)

The differences between the values expected according to the model and what is actually found in the data are known as the *residuals*. The residuals can be used to assess the fit of the model to the data in addition to the likelihood ratio chi-squares. Often, residuals are standardised so that comparisons can be made easily between the different cells, in which case they are known as standardised or adjusted residuals. The smaller the residuals the better the fit of the model to the data.

Table 40.3	Contingency table for testing the equal frequencies model, i.e. the expected frequencies			
	Soap opera	**Crime drama**	**Neither**	**Total**
Males	observed = 27	observed = 14	observed = 19	
	expected = 19.833	expected = 19.833	expected = 19.833	
Females	observed = 17	observed = 33	observed = 9	
	expected = 19.833	expected = 19.833	expected = 19.833	
Total				119

Table 40.4	Calculation of the fit of the equal frequencies model			
Observed frequency	Expected frequency according to equal frequencies model	Observed ÷ expected	Natural logarithm of Observed ÷ expected	Observed frequency ÷ natural logarithm of Observed ÷ expected
27	19.833	1.361	0.308	8.329
14	19.833	0.706	−0.348	−4.876
19	19.833	0.958	−0.043	−0.815
17	19.833	0.857	−0.154	−2.620
33	19.833	1.664	0.509	16.802
9	19.833	0.454	−0.790	−7.111
				Total = 9.709

Likelihood ratio chi-square = 2 × total = 2 × 9.709 = 19.418

■ Step 2: Saturated model

The log-linear analysis of these data could be carried out in a number of ways since there are a variety of different models that could be tested. In general, we will concentrate on the procedures which would commonly be employed when using computer programs such as SPSS. Often these compute the *saturated model* for you. A saturated model is one which includes all of the possible components as shown in Table 40.1 which, consequently, accounts perfectly for the data. That is, the values predicted by the saturated model are exactly the same as the data. Any model based on all of the components by definition accounts for the data perfectly. Since there is always a perfect correspondence or fit between the observed data and the predictions based on the likelihood ratio chi-square for the saturated model, this chi-square is always zero for the saturated model.

Table 40.5 gives the data and the expected frequencies for the saturated model. Notice, as we have already indicated, that the observed and expected frequencies for any cell of the contingency table are identical for this model. We will not bother to do this calculation. It is worth noting that computer programs often routinely increase the observed values by 0.5. This is done to avoid undesirable divisions by zero in the calculation while making very little difference to the calculation otherwise.

Table 40.5	Contingency table for testing the saturated model			
	Soap opera	Crime drama	Neither	Total
Males	observed = 27 expected = 27.000	observed = 14 expected = 14.000	observed = 19 expected = 19.000	
Females	observed = 17 expected = 17.000	observed = 33 expected = 33.000	observed = 9 expected = 9.000	
Total				119

■ Step 3: Preparing to test for the main effects components of the model

The perfectly fitting model of the data (the saturated model) involves all possible components. It is not quite as impressive as the perfect fit suggests. We do not know what it is about our model which caused such a good fit. It could be the effects of gender, the effects of the type of programme, or the effects of the interaction of gender with type of programme, or any combination of these three possibilities. It could even mean that the equal frequencies model is correct if we had not already rejected that possibility. Further exploration is necessary to assess which of these components are contributing to the goodness-of-fit of the data to that predicted by the model. Any component of the model which does not increase the goodness-of-fit of the model to the data is superfluous since it does nothing to explain the data. (To anticipate a common practice in log-linear analysis, the corollary of this is also true: components are only retained if they *decrease* the fit of the model when they are *removed*.)

(Usually in the initial stages of log-linear analyses using a computer, similar components of the model are dealt with collectively. That is, the main effects of gender and favourite programme type are dealt with as if they were a unit of analysis. Had there been more than one interaction, these would also be dealt with collectively. At a later stage, it is usual to extend the analysis to deal with the combined components individually. That is, the data are explored in more detail in order to assess what main effects are actually influencing the data.)

To reiterate what we have already achieved we can say that we have examined two extremes of the model-building process: the saturated model and the equal frequencies model. We have established that the equal frequencies model is a poor fit to the data on this occasion (the saturated model is always a perfect fit). The misfit of the equal frequencies model to the data (likelihood ratio chi-square = 19.418) is the amount of improvement in fit achieved by the saturated model.

■ Step 4: TV programme type main effect

Main effects are one level of components in the saturated model. Understanding their calculation is fairly simple. Let us take the main effect of programme type. In order to predict the frequencies in the data based solely on the effects of the different programme type we simply replace each cell by the average of the frequencies in cells referring to that programme type. This in effect means that for our example we combine the data frequencies for the males and females who prefer soap operas and average this total by the number of cells involved (i.e. two cells). Twenty-seven males and 17 females claim to prefer soap operas so the total is 44, which is divided between the two cells involved in this case. This gives us a predicted frequency on the basis of the main effects model for programme type of 22.00 in each of the soap opera cells. This is shown in Table 40.6. The predicted value for crime drama is 14 + 33 divided by 2 which equals 23.50. The predicted value for the neither category is 19 + 9 divided by 2 = 14.00. Again these can be seen in Table 40.6.

Now one can calculate the goodness-of-fit of this model simply by calculating the likelihood ratio chi-square for the data in Table 40.6. Just follow the model of the calculation in Table 40.4. The value of the likelihood ratio chi-square is 13.849. Compare this with the misfit based on the equal frequencies model (likelihood ratio chi-square = 19.418).

Table 40.6	Table of data and expected frequencies based solely on the main effect of programme type			
	Soap opera	Crime drama	Neither	Total
Males	observed = 27	observed = 14	observed = 19	
	expected = 22.000	expected = 23.500	expected = 14.000	
Females	observed = 17	observed = 33	observed = 9	
	expected = 22.000	expected = 23.500	expected = 14.000	
Total	44	47	28	119

It seems that there has been an improvement of $19.418 - 13.849 = 5.569$ in the fit due to the programme main effect. (Remember that the bigger the likelihood ratio chi-square then the poorer the fit of the model to the data.) Because the likelihood ratio chi-square has additive properties, this difference of 5.569 is the contribution of the main effect of programme type.

■ Step 5: Gender main effect

Because the frequencies of males and females in the data are nearly equal, there clearly is a minimal main effect due to the variable gender in this case. Nevertheless, this minimal value needs to be calculated. A similar procedure is adopted to calculate the main effects of gender. This time we need to sum the frequencies over the three different programme types for each gender separately and average this total frequency by the three programme types. Thus the sum of the observed frequencies for males in each of the three different programme type conditions is $(27 + 14 + 19) \div 3 = 60 \div 3 = 20$. This gives a predicted value per male cell of 20. This is entered in Table 40.7. Similarly, the calculation for females is to sum the three observed frequencies and divide by the number of female cells. This is $(17 + 33 + 9) \div 3 = 59 \div 3 = 19.667$. Again these values are entered in Table 40.7.

The likelihood ratio chi-square for the main effect of gender in Table 40.7 is 19.405. Compared with the value of 19.418 for the equal frequencies model, there is virtually no change, indicating the smallness of the gender difference in row frequencies. The improvement in fit due to gender alone is only 0.013.

Table 40.7	Table of data and expected frequencies based on the main effect of gender type			
	Soap opera	Crime drama	Neither	
Males	observed = 27	observed = 14	observed = 19	60
	expected = 20.000	expected = 20.000	expected = 20.000	
Females	observed = 17	observed = 33	observed = 9	59
	expected = 19.667	expected = 19.667	expected = 19.667	
Total				119

▪ Step 6: Main effects of programme type plus gender

This can now be obtained. It involves taking each cell in turn and working out the effect on the frequencies of the programme type and the gender concerned. This is done relative to the frequencies from the equal frequencies model (that is, 119 ÷ 6 = 19.833 in every case). So, looking at Table 40.6, the expected frequency for soap operas is 22.000. This means that being a soap opera cell increases the frequency by 22.000 − 19.833 = 2.167 as shown in Table 40.8. It may sound banal, but in order to add in the effect of being a soap opera cell we have to add 2.167 to the expected frequencies under the equal frequencies model. Similarly, being a crime drama cell increases the frequency to 23.500 from our baseline equal frequencies expectation of 19.833. Being a crime drama cell increases the frequency by 23.500 − 19.833 = 3.667.

In contrast, being in the neither category tends to decrease the frequencies in the cell compared with the equal frequencies expectation of 19.833. From Table 40.6 we can see that the expected frequencies in the neither column due to programme type are 14.000, which is below the equal frequencies expectation of 19.833 as shown in Table 40.8. Thus, being a neither cell changes frequencies by 14.000 − 19.833 = −5.833. That is, being neither decreases frequencies by −5.833. In order to adjust the equal frequencies expectations for the programme type main effect, we have to add 2.167 to the soap opera cells, add 3.667 to the crime drama cells and subtract 5.833 from (that is add −5.833 to) the neither cells. This can be seen in Table 40.8.

We also need to make similar adjustments for the main effect of gender although these are much smaller. Compared with the equal frequencies value of 19.833, the male cells have an expected frequency of 20.000 which is an increase of 0.167. In order to adjust the equal frequencies baseline of 19.833 for a cell being male we therefore have to add 0.167. This can be seen in Table 40.8. For female cells, the expected frequency is 19.667, a reduction of 0.166. In short, we add −0.166 for a cell being female. This is also shown in Table 40.8. (Of course, the additions and subtractions for the males and females should be identical, which they are within the limits of calculation rounding.)

At this point there is a big problem. That is, the values of the expected frequencies based on the main effects model give the wrong answers according to computer output. For that matter, it does not give the same expected frequencies as given in the equivalent Pearson chi-square calculation we did in Chapter 18. Actually, the computer prints our expected frequencies which are the same as those calculated in Chapter 18. The problem is that we

Table 40.8	Table of expected (predicted) frequencies based on adding the main effects of programme type and gender to the equal frequencies expectation			
	Soap opera	**Crime drama**	**Neither**	**Total**
Males	observed = 27	observed = 14	observed = 19	60
	expected = 19.833	expected = 19.833 + 3.667	expected = 19.833 + −5.833	
	+ 2.167 + 0.167 = 22.167[a]	+ 0.167 = 23.667[a]	+ 0.167 = 14.167[a]	
Females	observed = 17	observed = 33	observed = 9	59
	expected = 19.833 + 2.167	expected = 19.833 + 3.667	expected = 19.833 + −5.833	
	+ −0.166 = 21.834[a]	+ −0.166 = 23.334[a]	+ −0.166 = 13.834[a]	
Total				119

[a]These hand-calculated values are very approximate and do not correspond to the best values for reasons discussed in the text.

Table 40.9	Table of expected (predicted) frequencies based on adding the main effects of programme type and gender to the equal frequencies expectation as obtained by the iterative computer process			
	Soap opera	**Crime drama**	**Neither**	**Total**
Males	observed = 27	observed = 14	observed = 19	60
	expected = 22.18	expected = 23.70	expected = 14.72	
Females	observed = 17	observed = 33	observed = 9	59
	expected = 21.82	expected = 23.30	expected = 13.88	
Total	44	47	28	119

are not actually doing what the computer is doing. Think back to the two-way analysis of variance. These calculations worked as long as you have equal numbers of scores in each of the cells. Once you have unequal numbers, then the calculations have to be done a different way (and best of all by computer). This is because you are not adding effects proportionately once you have different cell frequencies. In log-linear analysis, the problem arises because the marginal totals are usually unequal for each variable. This inequality means that simple linear additions and subtractions of main effects such as we have just done do not give the best estimates. That is in essence why a computer program is vital in log-linear analysis. Better estimates of expected frequencies are made using an iterative process. This means that an approximation is calculated but then refined by re-entering the approximation in recalculations. This is done repeatedly until a minimum criterion of change is found between calculations (i.e. between iterations). Computer programs allow you to decide on the size of this change and even the maximum number of iterations.

Now that we have some idea of how the adjustments are made for the main effects, even though we must rely on the computer for a bit of finesse, we will use the computer-generated values to finish off our explanation. Table 40.9 contains the observed and expected values due to the influence of the main effects as calculated by the computer's iterative process.

The value of the likelihood ratio chi-square for the data in Table 40.9 is, according to the computer, 13.841 (which is significant at .001 with $df = 2$, and is slightly different to the hand-calculated value which involves rounding errors). At this point, we can obtain the value of the gender*programme type interaction. We now know the following:

- The fit of the saturated model which includes main effects plus the interaction is 0.000.

- The fit of the model based on the two main effects is 13.841.

- The fit of the model based on the equal frequencies model is 19.418.

It becomes a simple matter of subtraction to work out the improvement in fit due to the different components. Thus:

The increase in fit due to the two main effects = 19.418 − 13.841 = 5.577

The increase in fit due to the interaction = 13.841 − 0.000 = 13.841

These numerical values are likelihood ratio chi-squares. Only the interaction is statistically significant out of these major components. The main effect of programme type taken on its own would be statistically significant as it includes fewer degrees of freedom and has nearly the same likelihood ratio chi-square value. (Degrees of freedom are explained in detail in Box 40.1.) This is of no real interest as it merely shows that different proportions of people were choosing the different programme types as their favourites. In short, the

> ## Box 40.1 Focus on
>
> # Degrees of freedom
>
> Using the computer means that you never need to actually calculate the degrees of freedom. However, if you understand their calculation from chi-square in Chapter 18, then you should have few problems with their calculation for log-linear. When reading degrees of freedom in tables, they will often include extra degrees of freedom for lower-level interactions or main effects. Adjustments may have to be made. Here are a few examples:
>
> - Total degrees of freedom are always the number of cells −1.
>
> - Degrees of freedom for the equal frequencies model = 1.
> - Degrees of freedom for a main effect
>
> $$= \frac{\text{total degrees of freedom}}{\text{number of different categories of the main effect}}$$
>
> - Degrees of freedom for the saturated model = 0.
>
> Remember that the degrees of freedom for all of the main effects, for example, are not the same as the degrees of freedom for any of the main effects taken separately.

interesting part of the model is the interaction which is statistically significant. Formally, this model is expressed simply as:

constant (i.e. equal frequency cell mean) + programme main effect + A*B interaction

As the interaction is fairly simple, it is readily interpreted with the help of Table 40.8. So we can conclude that in order to model the data effectively we need the two-variable interaction. This we did in essence in Chapter 18 when interpreting the Pearson chi-square analysis of those data. Remember that the interaction is based on the residuals in that table (i.e. the differences between the observed and expected frequencies). As can be clearly seen, males are less inclined to choose crime dramas than women but are more inclined to choose soap operas.

40.3 Three-variable example

Interactions become a little more difficult to understand. In any case, only when there are three or more variables does log-linear analysis achieve much more than the Pearson chi-square described in Chapter 18. Consequently it is important to study one of these more complex examples. Even though log-linear analysis usually requires the use of a computer using the iterative procedures, quite a lot can be achieved by trying to understand approximately what the computer is doing when it is calculating several second-order and higher-order interactions when the data have three or more variables.

Table 40.1 gives the possible model components of any log-linear analysis for one to five variables. It is very unlikely that anyone would wish to use log-linear analysis when they have just one variable, but it is useful to start from there just so that the patterns build up more clearly in the table. Computer programs can handle more variables than five, but we are constrained by space and, moreover, log-linear analyses of ten variables are both atypical of psychological research designs and call for a great deal of statistical sophistication – especially experience with simpler log-linear analyses.

Basically, the more variables you have the more components there will be to the model. All models consist of main effects plus interactions. The variables involved in model-building are those which might possibly cause differences between the frequencies in the different cells. These variables have to be measurable by the researcher too for them to be in the analysis. Also note that the more variables in a model, the more complex the interactions.

Our example involves three variables. If you look in the column for three variables in Table 40.1 you will find listed all of the possible components of the model for these data. In this column there are three main effects (one for each of the variables), three two-way interactions between all possible distinct pairs taken from the three variables and one three-way interaction. The analysis is much the same as for our earlier two-variable example, but there are more components to add in. In particular, the meaning of the interactions needs to be clarified as there are now four of them rather than just one. Remember that it is usual to take similar levels of the model together for the initial model fitting. Thus all the main effects are combined; all of the second-order interactions (two-variable interactions) together; all of the third-order (three-variable interactions) together and so forth. Only when this analysis is done is it usual to see precisely which combinations at which levels of the model are having an effect.

Our example involves the relationship between gender, sexual abuse and physical abuse in a sample of psychiatric patients. The data are to be found in Table 40.10 which gives the three-way crosstabulation or contingency table for our example. This would be described as a three-way contingency table because it involves three variables. The numbers in the cells are *frequencies*. Each of the variables has been coded as a dichotomy: a) female or male, b) sexually abused or not and c) physically abused or not. (Variables can have more than two categories, but this is not the case for these particular data.) The researchers are interested in explaining the frequencies in the table on the basis of the three *variables* – gender, sexual abuse and physical abuse – acting individually (main effects) or in combination (interactions). It is worthwhile remembering that the more variables and the more categories of each variable the greater the sample size needs to be in order to have sufficient frequencies in each cell.

Two of the possible models are easily tested. They are the equal frequencies and the saturated models, which are the extreme possibilities in log-linear analyses. The equal frequencies model simply involves the first row of Table 40.10 and no other influences. The saturated model includes all sources of influence in the table for the column for three variables.

Table 40.10	Three-way contingency showing the relationship between gender, sexual abuse and physical abuse in a sample of psychiatric hospital patients			
Variable B	**Variable C**	**Variable A Gender**		**Margin totals**
Sexual abuse	**Physical abuse**	**Female**	**Male**	
Sexually abused	Yes	45	55	100
	No	40	60	100
Not sexually abused	Yes	55	45	100
	No	80	20	100
Margin totals		220	180	400

Step 1: Equal frequencies model

The equal frequencies model is, in a sense, the worst-fit scenario for a model. It is what the data would look like if none of the variables in isolation or combination was needed to explain the data. The equal frequencies model merely describes what the data would look like if the frequencies were equally distributed through the cells of the table. As there are eight cells and a total of 400 observations, under the equal frequencies model it would be expected that each cell contains $400 \div 8 = 50$ cases. This model and the calculation of its fit with the observed data for which we are developing a model are shown in Table 40.11.

Just a reminder – the likelihood ratio chi-square is zero if the model fits the data exactly and increasingly bigger with greater amounts of misfit between the data and the data as predicted by the model. The chi-square value for the equal frequencies model is an indication of how much the variables and their interaction have to explain. The value of 44.58 obtained for the likelihood ratio chi-square on the equal frequencies model indicates that the data are poorly explained by that model. That is, there is a lot of variation in the frequencies which remains to be explained by models other than the equal frequencies model. Notice that the equal frequencies model only contains the mean frequency which is one of the potential components of all models. The equal frequencies value is sometimes called the constant. If it is zero or nearly zero then the equal frequencies model fits the data well. Do not get too excited if the equal frequencies model fits badly since the variation in frequencies between the cells might be explained by the main effects. To reiterate, main effects in the log-linear analysis are often of very little interest to psychologists. Only rarely will real-life data have no main effects in log-linear analysis since main effects occur when the categories of a variable are unequally distributed. In our data in Table 40.10, the marginal totals for physical abuse and sexual abuse are the same since equal numbers had been abused as had not been abused. Nevertheless, there is a possible main effect for gender since there are more females in the study than males. Whether or not this gender difference is significant has yet to be tested. So whatever the final model we select, it has already been clearly established that there is plenty of variation in the cell means to be explained by the main effects acting independently and the two-way interactions of pairs of these variables plus the three-way interaction of all of the variables.

Table 40.11	Calculation of the likelihood ratio chi-square for the equal frequencies model			
Observed frequency	Expected frequency according to the equal frequencies model	Observed ÷ expected	Natural logarithm of Observed ÷ expected	Observed frequency ÷ natural logarithm of Observed ÷ expected
45	50.0	0.90	−0.1054	−4.743
40	50.0	0.80	−0.2231	−8.924
55	50.0	1.10	0.0953	5.242
80	50.0	1.60	0.4700	37.600
55	50.0	1.10	0.0953	5.242
60	50.0	1.20	0.1823	10.938
45	50.0	0.90	−0.1054	−4.741
20	50.0	0.40	−0.9163	−18.326
				Total = 22.290

Likelihood ratio chi-square = 2 × sum of final column = 2 × 22.290 = 44.580

◼ Step 2: Saturated model

This model involves all of the possible variables acting separately and in combination. It includes all components given in Table 40.1 for a given number of variables. For a three-way contingency table the saturated model includes the mean frequency per cell (i.e. constant) plus the main effects plus the three two-variable interactions plus the three-variable interaction. Predictions based on the saturated model are exactly the same as the data themselves – they have to be since the saturated model includes every possible component of the model and so there is no other possible source of variation.

It is hardly worth computing the saturated model as it has to be a perfect fit to the data thus giving a likelihood ratio chi-square of 0.000. A zero value like this indicates a perfect fit between the observed data and the expectations (predictions) based on the model. Remember that for the saturated model, most computer programs will automatically add 0.5 to the observed frequencies to avoid divisions by zero, which are unhelpful mathematically. This addition of 0.5 to each of the frequencies is not always necessary so some computer programs will give you the choice of not using it. Its influence is so negligible that the analysis is hardly affected.

◼ Step 3: Building up the main-effects model

The process of building up a model in log-linear analysis is fairly straightforward once the basic principles are understood, as we have seen. The stumbling block is the calculation of expected frequencies when marginal frequencies are unequal. They are unequal most of the time in real data. In these circumstances, only an approximate explanation can be given of what the computer is doing. Fortunately, as we have already seen, we can go a long way using simple maths.

Table 40.12 contains the expected frequencies based on different components of the model. Remember that the expected frequencies are those based on a particular model or component of the model. The first column contains the data (which are exactly the same as the predictions based on the saturated model already discussed). The fifth column gives the expected frequencies based on the equal frequencies model. This has already been discussed – the frequencies are merely the total frequencies averaged over the number of cells.

The next three cells have the major heading 'Main effects', and there are separate columns for the main effect of gender, the main effect of sexual abuse and the main effect of physical abuse. The fourth column headed 'All' is for the added effect of these three main effects. How are these expected (predicted) values calculated? They are simply the averages of the appropriate cells. Thus for females, the four cells in Table 40.12 are 45, 40, 55 and 80, which totals 220. Thus if the cells in the female column reflect only the effects of being female then we would expect all four female cells to contain $220 \div 4 = 55.00$ cases. In Table 40.12, the expected frequencies under gender for the four female cells are all 55.00. Similarly for the four remaining cells in that column which all involve males, the total male frequency is 180 so we would expect $180 \div 4$ or 45.00 in each of the male cells.

Exactly the same process is applied to the sexual abuse column. Two hundred of the cases were sexually abused in childhood whereas 200 were not. Thus we average the 200 sexually abused cases over the four cells in Table 40.12 which involve sexually abused individuals (i.e. $200 \div 4 = 50.00$). Then we average the 200 non-sexually abused individuals over the four cells containing non-sexually abused individuals (i.e. $200 \div 4 = 50.00$). Because there are equal numbers of sexually and non-sexually abused individuals, no main effect of sexual abuse is present and all of the values in the sexual abuse column are 50.00.

Table 40.12 Expected (or predicted) frequencies based on separate components of the model

Data	Details of cell			Equal frequencies model	Main effects			All	Two-way interactions			All
	Gender	Sexual abuse	Physical abuse		Gender	Sexual abuse	Physical abuse		Gender *Sexual	Gender *Physical	Sexual *Physical	
45	female	yes	yes	50.00	55.00	50.00	50.00	55.00	42.50	50.00	50.00	37.23
40	female	yes	no	50.00	55.00	50.00	50.00	55.00	42.50	60.00	50.00	47.77
55	female	no	yes	50.00	55.00	50.00	50.00	55.00	67.50	50.00	50.00	62.77
80	female	no	no	50.00	55.00	50.00	50.00	55.00	67.50	60.00	50.00	72.33
55	male	yes	yes	50.00	45.00	50.00	50.00	45.00	57.50	50.00	50.00	62.77
60	male	yes	no	50.00	45.00	50.00	50.00	45.00	57.50	40.00	50.00	52.23
45	male	no	yes	50.00	45.00	50.00	50.00	45.00	32.50	50.00	50.00	37.23
20	male	no	no	50.00	45.00	50.00	50.00	45.00	32.50	40.00	50.00	27.77

* Between two or more variable names is one way of indicating interactions.

Given that there are also 200 physically abused and 200 non-physically abused cases, it is not surprising to find that all of the expected frequencies are 50.00 in the physical abuse column too. The reasoning is exactly the same as for sexual abuse in the previous paragraph.

The combined main effects column labelled 'All' is easily computed for our example. It is simply the combined individual effects of the three separate main effects. So it is the effect of gender plus sexual abuse plus physical abuse. Thus being female adds a frequency of five compared with the equal frequencies model figure of 50.00, being sexually abused adds zero and being physically abused adds zero. For example, for the first row which consists of 45 females who had been sexually abused and physically abused, we take the equal frequencies frequency of 50.00 and add 5 for being female, +0 for being sexually abused and +0 for being physically abused. This gives the expected figure of 55.00 under the all main effects column.

To give another example, take the fifth row down where the data give a frequency of 55. This row refers to males who had been sexually abused and physically abused. Being male subtracts 5.00 from the equal frequency value, being sexually abused adds nothing and being physically abused also adds nothing. So our expected value is $50 - 5 + 0 + 0 = 45$, the expected value for all of the main effects added together.

■ Step 4: Two-variable interactions

The two-way interactions are not difficult to estimate either. The two-way interaction for gender*sexual abuse is obtained by combining the physical abuse categories. In our example, there are some who have been physically abused and some who have not among the females who had been sexually abused. Of these sexually abused females, 45 had been physically abused and 40 had not been physically abused. Combining these two frequencies and averaging them across the two relevant cells gives us:

$$\frac{45 + 40}{2} = \frac{85}{2} = 42.5$$

This is the value that you see under the gender*sexual abuse interaction for the first two rows.

If you need another example, take the last two rows which have values in the data column of 45 and 20. These rows consist of the males who had not been sexually abused. One row is those who had been physically abused and the other those who had not been physically abused. The two-way interaction of gender*sexual abuse is obtained by adding together the two different physical abuse categories and entering the average of these into the last two rows. So the frequencies are 45 and 20 which equals 65, which divided between the two relevant cells gives us 32.5. This is the value that you see for the gender*sexual abuse interaction for the final two rows.

What about the next interaction – gender*physical abuse? The calculation is basically the same. The only difficulty is that the rows corresponding to the cells we are interested in are physically further apart in the table. The gender*physical abuse interaction is obtained by combining the sexual abuse categories (i.e. the sexually abused and non-sexually abused). Let us take the females who had not been physically abused. These are the second and fourth rows. If we look at the observed values in the data these are frequencies of 40 and 80. The average of these is 60, and this is the value you find in the second and fourth rows of the gender*physical abuse interaction.

The sexual abuse*physical abuse interaction is calculated in a similar way – this time we combine the male and female groups for each of the four sexual abuse*physical abuse combinations. Take the sexually *and* physically abused individuals. These are to be found in rows 1 and 5. The data (observed) values for these rows are 45 and 55. This averages at 50.00 – the value of the entry for this two-way interaction in the first and fifth rows. (Actually all of the rows for this particular column have the same value indicating a lack of a sexual abuse*physical abuse interaction.)

The combined effects of the three two-way interactions cannot be seen directly from the table. This is because the values are based on an iterative process which involves several computational stages which are best done by a computer. The values in the last column of Table 40.12 are taken from SPSS computer output. Although we will not be showing this calculation here because of its complexity, we can show the essential logic although, as you will see, it gives slightly the wrong answers. All effects in log-linear analysis are additive so we should be able to combine the three two-way interactions in order to obtain the sum of the three two-way interactions.

This is quite simple. Compared with the equal frequencies mean frequency of 50.00 for each cell, what is the effect of each interaction? Taking the first row, we can see that the gender*sexual abuse interaction changes the score by −7.50 (i.e. 42.5 − 50.00), the gender*physical abuse interaction changes the score by 0.00 (i.e. 50.00 − 50.00) and the sexual abuse*physical abuse interaction changes the score by 0.00 (50.00 − 50.00). Adding these separate effects to the equal frequencies mean frequency of 50.00 we get:

$$50.00 + (-7.50) + 0.00 + 0.00 = 42.50$$

This at first sight is the wrong answer since it is nowhere near the 37.23 obtained from the computer.

What we have not allowed for is the fact that these interactions also include the effect of the main effects. The main effects for this row combined to give a prediction of 55.00 compared with the equal frequencies mean of 50.00. That is to say, the main effects are increasing the prediction for this row by 5.00. This would have to be taken away from the prediction based on the interaction to leave the pure effects of the two-way interactions. So our value 42.50 contains 5.00 due to the main effects; getting rid of the main effects gives us the prediction of 37.50 based on the two-way interactions. This is pretty close to the 37.23 predicted by the model, but not sufficiently so. The unequal marginal totals necessitate the adjustments made automatically by the iterative computer program. Had our marginal totals been a lot more unequal then our fit to the computer's value would have been much poorer. Simple methods are only suitable as ways of understanding the basics of the process.

If you would like another example of how the entries are computed, look at the final row of Table 40.12. The predicted value based on all the two-way interactions is 27.77. How is that value achieved? Notice that the two-way gender*sexual abuse interaction prediction is 32.50, which is 17.50 less than that according to the equal frequencies model prediction of 50.00; the gender*physical abuse prediction is 40.00, which is 10.00 less and the sexual abuse*physical abuse prediction is 50.00, exactly the same. So to get the prediction based on the three two-way interactions together, the calculation is the equal frequencies mean (50.00) + (−17.50) + (−10.00) + 0.00 = 22.50, but then we need to take away the influence of all the main effects, which involves adding 5.00 this time. Thus we end up with a prediction of 27.50. Again this is not precisely the computer predicted value but it is close enough for purposes of explanation. Remember, it is only close because the main effects are small or zero.

What is the normal output of a computer program such as SPSS? The important point to remember is that it is usual to explore the model first of all as combined effects – the sum of the interactions, the sum of the main effects – rather than the individual components in the first analysis. For the data in Table 40.10 we obtained the information in Tables 40.13 and 40.14 from the computer by stipulating a saturated model.

What do Tables 40.13 and 40.14 tell us? Remember that when we assessed the fit of the data based on the equal frequencies model we obtained a likelihood ratio chi-square value of 44.580. This large value indicates a large misfit of the model to the data. (The smaller the size of chi-square the better the fit.) Notice that this value of chi-square is exactly the same (within the errors of rounding) as the chi-square value in Table 40.13 for the contribution of the main effects, two-way interactions and three-way interactions. Thus 44.580 is the improvement in the fit of the model created by including the three different levels of effect *together*.

If we take just the two-way and three-way interactions (omitting the main effects from the model), the improvement is a little less at 40.573 according to Table 40.13. Remember that the likelihood ratio chi-square is linear, so you can add and subtract values. Consequently, the improvement in fit due to the main effects is 44.579 − 40.573 = 4.006. Within the limits of rounding error, this is the same value as for the sum of all of the main effects in Table 40.14 (i.e. 4.007).

If we take only the three-way interaction in Table 40.13 (i.e. omitting the two-way interaction and main effects from the model), we get a value of 10.713 for the amount of misfit. This is the value given in Table 40.14.

Where does the value for the two-way interactions come from? We have just found that the value for the main effect is 4.006 and the value for the three-way interaction is 10.713. If we take these away from the chi-square of 44.580 we get 44.580 − 4.006 − 10.713 = 29.861 for the contribution of the two-way interactions to the fit (exactly as can be found in Table 40.14 within the limits of rounding error).

It looks as if a good model for the data can exclude the main effects which are failing to contribute significantly to the goodness-of-fit even though the value of the likelihood

Table 40.13	Tests of the increase in fit for the main effects and higher-order effects			
Level of effects	Types of effect involved	Degrees of freedom	Likelihood ratio chi-square	Probability
3	three-way interaction	1	10.713	.0011
2 (and above)	all the two-way interactions + the three-way interaction	4	40.573	.0000
1 (and above)	all the main effects + the two-way interaction + the three-way interaction only	7	44.579	.0000

Table 40.14	Tests that the levels of effect are zero			
Level of effects	Types of effect involved	Degrees of freedom	Likelihood ratio chi-square	Probability
1	all the main effects only	3	4.007	.2607
2	all the two-way interactions only	3	29.860	.0000
3	three-way interaction only	1	10.713	.0011

ratio chi-square is 4.007. Thus a model based on the two-way and three-way interactions accounts for the data well.

◼ Step 5: Which components account for the data?

This analysis has demonstrated the substantial contributions of the two-way and three-way interactions to the model's fit to the data. Since there is only one three-way interaction in this case, then there is no question what interaction is causing this three-way effect. There are three different two-way interactions for this model, not all of which are necessarily contributing to the fit to the data. The way of checking for the relative influence of the different two-way interactions is to repeat the analysis but omitting one of the two-way interactions. This is easy to do on most computer programs. Doing this for the data in Table 40.10, we obtain the following:

- Based solely on gender*sexual abuse: chi-square = 15.036, $df = 4$, $p = .005$.

- Based solely on gender*physical abuse: chi-square = 36.526, $df = 4$, $p = .000$.

- Based solely on sexual abuse*physical abuse: chi-square = 44.579, $df = 4$, $p = .000$.

Working backwards, compared with the value of 44.580 for the misfit between the data and the equal frequencies model, there is no improvement in the fit by adding in the sexual abuse*physical abuse interaction since the value of the likelihood ratio chi-square does not change (significantly) from that value of 44.580. This means that the sexual abuse*physical abuse interaction contributes nothing to the model fit and can be dropped from the model.

Considering solely the gender*physical abuse interaction, there is a moderate improvement in fit. The maximum misfit of 44.580 as assessed by the likelihood ratio chi-square reduces to 36.526 when the gender*physical abuse interaction is included. This suggests that this interaction is quite important in the model and should be retained.

Finally, using solely the gender*sexual abuse interaction, the likelihood ratio chi-square value declines to 15.036 from the maximum of 44.579, suggesting that the gender*sexual abuse interaction has a substantial influence and improves the fit of the model substantially.

It should be remembered that there is a main effect for gender in all of the above two-way interactions except for the sexual abuse*physical abuse interaction where it is not present. (Check the marginal totals for the expected frequencies to see this.) In order to understand just how much change in fit is due to the two-way interaction, we need to adjust for the main effect of gender which we have already calculated as a likelihood ratio chi-square of 4.007. So to calculate the likelihood ratio chi-square of the gender*physical abuse interaction we have to take 36.526 from 44.580, which gives a value for the improvement in fit of 8.055. This value is the improvement in fit due to the gender main effect and the gender*physical abuse interaction. So for the improvement in fit due to the gender*physical abuse interaction only, we take 8.055 and subtract 4.007 to give a value of 4.048. This value is only roughly correct because of the unequal marginals involved, which means that a better approximation will be achieved through an iterative process.

Table 40.15 gives the results of an analysis starting with the saturated model and gradually removing components. If a removed component is having an effect on the fit there will be a non-zero value for the chi-square change for that row which needs to be tested for significance. The saturated model is a perfect fit (i.e. chi-square = 0.000), but taking away the three-way interaction increases the misfit to 10.713. This change (10.713 − 0.000) is the influence of the three-way interaction on the degree of fit. Taking away the interaction of gender*sexual abuse gives a chi-square change of 25.812 which indicates that the gender*sexual abuse interaction is having a big effect on the fit of the model.

Table 40.15	Amounts of fit due to different components of the model				
Model	Likelihood ratio chi-square	Degrees of freedom	Prob.	Chi-square change
Saturated	0.000			–
All two-way interactions + all main effects (i.e. minus three-way interaction)	10.713	1	.001	10.713[a]
Previous row less gender*sexual abuse	36.526	2	.000	25.812[a]
Previous row less sexual abuse*physical abuse	36.526	3	.000	0.000
Previous row less gender*physical abuse	40.573	4	.000	4.048
Previous row less sexual abuse	40.573	5	.000	0.000
Previous row less gender	44.579	6	.000	4.006
Previous row less physical abuse	44.579	7	.000	0.000

[a] Change significant at the 5% level.

When we take away sexual abuse*physical abuse there is a 0.000 chi-square change. This indicates that this interaction is doing nothing to improve the fit of the model. Consequently, the sexual abuse*physical abuse interaction may be dropped from the model.

Similarly, the row of Table 40.15 where the main effect of sexual abuse is dropped has a zero likelihood ratio chi-square, indicating that the main effect of sexual abuse can be dropped from the model. Also the final row where the main effect of physical abuse is dropped also shows no change, implying that this main effect can be dropped from the model. Actually, only two of the components are statistically significant at the 5% level so that the model could be built on these solely. Our model then becomes:

mean frequency (i.e. equal frequencies mean) + gender*sexual abuse interaction + gender*sexual abuse*physical abuse interaction.

■ Step 6: More on the interpretation of log-linear analysis

By this stage, it should be possible to attempt fitting a log-linear model. Of course, a little practice will be necessary with your chosen computer in order to familiarise yourself with its procedures. This is not too technical in practice with careful organisation and the creation of systematic tables to record the computer output. If these things are not done, the sheer quantity of frequently redundant computer output will cause confusion.

Specifying the best-fitting model using likelihood ratio chi-squares is *not* a complete interpretation of the model. This is much as the value of Pearson chi-square in Chapter 18 is insufficient without careful examination of the data. An important concept in this respect is that of residuals. A residual is merely the difference between the data and the data predicted on the basis of the model. These can be expressed merely as the data value minus the modelled value. So residuals may take positive or negative values and there is one residual per cell. Not only this, since in a log-linear analysis you may be comparing one or more components of the model with the data then several sets of residuals will have to be computed, and so you may be calculating different residuals for different components of the model or different models. Residuals can be standardised so that values are more easily compared one with another.

The good news is twofold. There is no difficulty in calculating simple residuals, and computers generally do it for you anyway as part of calculating the model fit. If you look back to Table 40.12, you can easily calculate the residuals by subtracting any of the predicted model values from the actual data. The residuals for the saturated model are all zero, of course, indicating a perfect fit. The residuals for the equal frequencies model are -5.00, -10.00, 5.00, 30.00, 5.00, 10.00, -5.00 and -30.00; that is, the value of the frequency for that cell in the data -50.000 in each case.

The other helpful thing when interpreting log-linear models is the estimated cell frequencies based on different components of the model. Remember that not only can you calculate these fairly directly but they are usually generated for you by the computer. The important thing about these estimated cell frequencies is that they tell you the trends in the data caused by, say, the interactions. For example, look at Table 40.12 and the column for the gender*sexual abuse interaction. You can see there that there are relatively few females who had been sexually abused and relatively more males who had been sexually abused in these data. It is best to compare these frequencies with the ones for the effects of the three main effects since the interaction figures actually include the effects of the main effects. Thus this comparison removes the main effects from the interaction. Figure 40.1 gives the key steps in log-linear analysis.

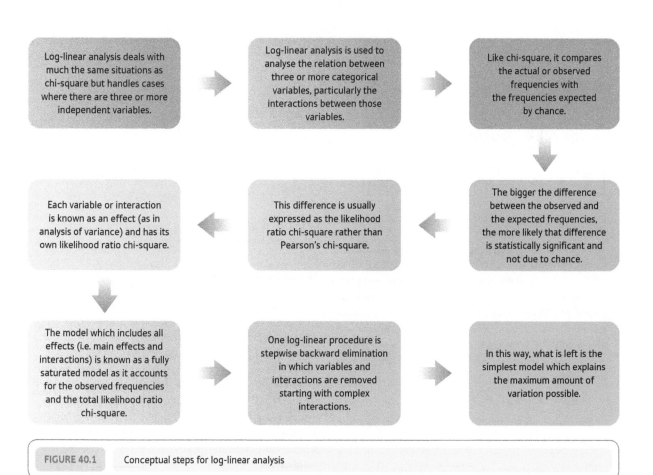

| FIGURE 40.1 | Conceptual steps for log-linear analysis |

40.4   Reporting the results

With something as complex as a log-linear analysis, you might expect that writing up the results of the analysis will be complex. Indeed it can be, and expect to write much more about your analysis than you would, for example, writing up the results of a correlation coefficient or a *t*-test. The purposes of log-linear analysis can be very varied, stretching from a fairly empirical examination of the data of the sort described earlier to testing the fit of a theoretical model to the actual data. Obviously there is no single sentence that can be usefully employed for describing the outcome of a log-linear analysis. Nevertheless certain things are very important. They are:

- A table giving the data and the residuals for each of the models that you examine. Without this, the reader cannot assess precisely the form of the fit of the models to the data. Table 40.12 would be a useful format for doing this.

- A table giving indications of the improvement in fit due to each component of the model. This will almost invariably be the likelihood ratio chi-square. Table 40.15 could be adapted to your particular data.

The text should discuss the final model which you have selected on the basis of your log-linear analysis. This model could be expressed in terms of the components of the model which contribute significantly to the fit or, alternatively, as the lambda values mentioned in Box 40.2. Earlier in this chapter we indicated the models for our two examples in a simple form.

Box 40.2   Focus on

Lambda and hierarchical models

Lambda

Often in log-linear analysis, the models are specified in terms of lambda (λ). This is simply the natural log of the influence of each of the different sorts of component of the cell frequencies. Thus a model may be built up from a succession of lambdas. These are given superscripts to denote what type of effect is involved: λ^A is the main effect of variable A and λ^{A*B} is the effect of the interaction of variables A and B. So an equation involving these and other components might be:

$$\text{Model} = \lambda + \lambda^A + \lambda^B + \lambda^{A*B}$$

This simply means that we add to the natural logarithm of the equal-cell mean or constant (λ), the natural logarithm of the main effects of the variable A (remember that this has positive and negative values), the natural logarithm of the main effects of the variable B and the natural logarithm of the interaction of the variables $A*B$.

Hierarchical models

Hierarchical models imply lower-order components and do not specify what these lower-order components are. Thus a hierarchical model may specify a four-variable interaction $A*B*C*D$. Any component involving A, B, C and D is assumed to be a component of that model. So the main effects A, B, C and D, the two-way interactions $A*B$, $A*C$, $A*D$, $B*C$, $B*D$ and $C*D$, and the three-way interactions $A*B*C$, $A*B*D$, $A*C*D$ and $B*C*D$ are automatically specified as possible components in a hierarchical model. Notice that our examples employ a hierarchical approach.

Research examples

Log-linear methods

Ahrens and colleagues (2007) conducted qualitative interviews with over 100 female rape survivors. However, the researchers felt that a quantitative analysis would be helpful in this case and chose to use log-linear analysis to help them better understand what happens when victims decide to report the events to their informal social network rather than a formal social network for victims. They analysed the sort of support provider, the victim's reasons for disclosure, social reactions to the disclosure and the impact of the disclosure on the survivor. Positive rather than negative reactions were commonest with help from informal support providers but negative reactions were most common following help from formal support providers. However, this was not the case when the formal support providers initiated the support provision themselves. In this case, exclusively positive reactions were experienced by the victims.

Bridges and colleagues (2001) used a variation of Milgram's famous lost letter technique in which letters are deliberately lost in the street in order to see whether details of the addressee affect return rates. They compared an 'emotive' address (Advocates for Battered and Abused Lesbians) with non-emotive ones. Hierarchical log-linear analysis was used to analyse the variables of 1) returned versus not, 2) geographical location, 3) community size (city versus town) and 4) emotive versus non-emotive addressees. The findings showed complex relationships. Return rates were higher for Ohio than Florida/Alabama, higher for city than town and higher for the control addressees than the 'emotive' addressee.

Tracey and colleagues (1984) presented a random sample of university students with one of eight different descriptions of workshop programmes. The programs varied according to 1) whether the workshop dealt with exam or relationship skills, 2) whether the workshop was about skills enhancement or skills deficit reduction and 3) whether the orientation was towards self-change or changing the external environment for oneself (this the authors term 'focus of effect'). Log-linear analysis was used in several ways. For example, information requests versus no requests were accounted for by a model which involved the interaction of gender*focus of effect.

Key points

- It is recommended that before analysing your own data with log-linear, you reproduce our analyses in order to become familiar with the characteristics of your chosen computer program.

- Confine yourself to small numbers of variables when first using log-linear analysis. Although computers may handle, say, ten variables, you may find it difficult without a lot of experience.

- Log-linear analysis can include score variables if these are treated as frequencies.

- Log-linear analysis is not as commonly used in psychological research as it is in other disciplines. The reason is the preference of psychologists for using score rather than categorical variables.

COMPUTER ANALYSIS

Log-linear analysis using SPSS

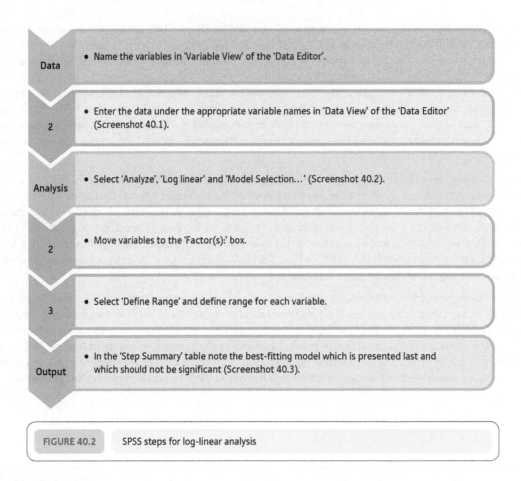

Data	• Name the variables in 'Variable View' of the 'Data Editor'.
2	• Enter the data under the appropriate variable names in 'Data View' of the 'Data Editor' (Screenshot 40.1).
Analysis	• Select 'Analyze', 'Log linear' and 'Model Selection...' (Screenshot 40.2).
2	• Move variables to the 'Factor(s):' box.
3	• Select 'Define Range' and define range for each variable.
Output	• In the 'Step Summary' table note the best-fitting model which is presented last and which should not be significant (Screenshot 40.3).

FIGURE 40.2   SPSS steps for log-linear analysis

Interpreting and reporting the output

- Log-linear analysis is not the most familiar statistical technique in psychology and understanding it needs care and effort. The main text for this chapter goes through the process of understanding log-linear output in some detail. It helps if you ignore most of the Step Summary table and concentrate on its final row as this gives the final model.

- There is no standard way of presenting the result of a log-linear analysis but you could, for example, write something like 'A log-linear analysis was carried out to determine the best model to fit the data. The interactions of physical abuse with gender and sexual abuse were the components which best accounted for the data. Their removal significantly affected the fit of the model to the data.'

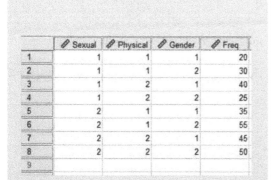

| SCREENSHOT 40.1 | Data in 'Data View' (arranged in frequencies) |

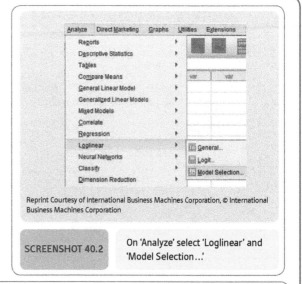

| SCREENSHOT 40.2 | On 'Analyze' select 'Loglinear' and 'Model Selection…' |

Backward Elimination Statistics

Step Summary

Step[a]		Effects	Chi-Square[c]	df	Sig.	Number of Iterations
0	Generating Class[b]	Sexual*Physical*Gender	.000	0	.	
	Deleted Effect 1	Sexual*Physical*Gender	1.185	1	.276	3
1	Generating Class[b]	Sexual*Physical, Sexual*Gender, Physical*Gender	1.185	1	.276	
	Deleted Effect 1	Sexual*Physical	.454	1	.501	2
	2	Sexual*Gender	1.963	1	.161	2
	3	Physical*Gender	5.461	1	.019	2
2	Generating Class[b]	Sexual*Gender, Physical*Gender	1.638	2	.441	
	Deleted Effect 1	Sexual*Gender	2.272	1	.132	2
	2	Physical*Gender	5.770	1	.016	2
3	Generating Class[b]	Physical*Gender, Sexual	3.910	3	.271	
	Deleted Effect 1	Physical*Gender	5.770	1	.016	2
	2	Sexual	16.485	1	.000	2
4	Generating Class[b]	Physical*Gender, Sexual	3.910	3	.271	

a. At each step, the effect with the largest significance level for the Likelihood Ratio Change is deleted, provided the significance level is larger than .050.

b. Statistics are displayed for the best model at each step after step 0.

c. For 'Deleted Effect', this is the change in the Chi-Square after the effect is deleted from the model.

| SCREENSHOT 40.3 | Main output |

Recommended further reading

Agresti, A. (1996). *An introduction to categorical data analysis* (Chapters 1–4). New York, NY: Wiley.

Anderson, E. B. (1997). *Introduction to the statistical analysis of categorical data* (Chapters 2–4). Berlin, Germany: Springer.

CHAPTER 41

Multinomial logistic regression

Distinguishing between several different categories or groups

Overview

- Multinomial logistic regression is a form of multiple regression in which a number of predictors are used to predict values of a single nominal dependent or criterion variable.

- There may be any number of values (categories) of the dependent variable with a minimum of 3. It can be used with just two categories but binomial logistic regression (Chapter 42) would be more appropriate in these circumstances.

- It is used to assess the most likely group (category) to which a case belongs on the basis of a number of predictor variables. That is, the objective is to find the pattern of predictor variables that identify of which category an individual is most likely to be a member.

- Multinomial logistic regression uses nominal or category variables as the criterion or dependent variable. The independent or predictor variables may be score variables or nominal (dichotomised) variables. In this chapter we concentrate on nominal variables as predictors.

- The concept of the dummy variable is crucial in multinomial logistic regression. A dummy variable is a way of dichotomising a nominal category variable with three or more different values. A new variable is computed for each category (just one!) and participants coded as having that characteristic or not. The code for belonging to the category is normally 1 and the code for belonging to any of the other categories is normally 0.

- Multinomial logistic regression produces B-weights and constants just as in the case of other forms of regression. However, the complication is that these are applied to the logit. A logit is the natural (or Napierian) logarithm of the odds ratio (a close relative of probability). This allows the computation of the likelihood that an individual is in a particular category of the dependent or criterion variable given their pattern on the predictor variables.

- A classification table is produced which basically describes the accuracy of the predictors in placing participants correctly in the category or group to which they actually belong.

Preparation

Make sure you are familiar with Chapter 18 on chi-square and Chapters 9 and 34 on regression.

41.1 Introduction

A simple example should clarify the purpose of multinomial logistic regression. Professionals who work with sex offenders would find it helpful to identify the patterns of characteristics which differentiate between three types – rapists, incestuous child abusers and paedophiles. The key variable would be type of sex offence, and rapists, incestuous child abusers and paedophiles would be the three different values (categories) of this nominal (category) variable. In a regression, type of sex offender would be called the dependent variable or the criterion or the predicted variable. Just what is different between the three groups of offenders – that is, what differentiates the groups defined by the different values of the dependent variable? The researcher would collect a number of measures (variables) from each of the participants in the study in addition to their offence type. These measures are really predictor variables since the researcher wants to know whether it is possible to assess which sort of offender an individual is on the basis of information about these aspects of their background. Such predictors are also known as independent variables in regression.

Imagine the researcher has information on the following independent variables (predictor variables). They are all nominal/category variables in this example, but it is possible to use score variables or a mixture of score and nominal/category variables as predictors. The dependent variable has to be a nominal/category variable (see Box 41.1):

- age of offender (younger versus older; i.e. 30 plus)

- physically abused when a child

- sexually abused when a child

- depression (low depression versus high depression) measured on the DASS (Depression Anxiety Stress Scale)

- offender spent a period of childhood in children's homes

- mother's hostility as assessed by a family experiences scale (mother not hostile versus mother hostile)

- father's hostility as assessed by a family experiences scale (father not hostile versus father hostile).

Box 41.1   Focus on

Using score variables in logistic regression

Although we concentrate on nominal or category variables as the independent or predictor variables in logistic regression in this chapter, this is because it is conceptually harder to deal with them than score variables as independent variables. So for pedagogic reasons, we have not considered score variables directly in this chapter. However, score variables can be used as the independent or predictor variables and can be mixed with nominal/category variables in logistic regression. Conceptually, you should have no difficulty going on to using score variables in this way once you have mastered the material in this chapter and Chapter 42. You may have more difficulty running the analyses on SPSS since it uses somewhat idiosyncratic terminology to refer to the two types of variable and it is not even consistent between the binomial logistic regression and multinomial logistic regression.

These data could be analysed in a number of ways. One very obvious choice would be to carry out a succession of chi-square tests. The type of offender could be one of the variables and any of the variables in the above list could be the predictor variable. An example of this is shown in Table 41.1. If we turn the numbers in the table into percentages, proportionately fewer rapists but more paedophiles had a hostile father. Similar analyses could be carried out for each of the predictor variables in the list.

There is not a great deal wrong with this approach – it would readily identify the specific variables on which the three offender groups differ (and those on which they did not differ). One could also examine how any of the three offender groups differed from the others on any of the predictor variables. Since the analysis is based on chi-square, then partitioning would help to test which groups differ from the others (Chapter 18) in terms of any of the predictors.

The obvious problem with the chi-square approach is that it handles a set of predictors one by one. This is fine if we only have one predictor, but we have *several* predictor variables. A method of handling all of the predictor variables at the same time would have obvious advantages. Predictor variables are often correlated and this overlap also needs to be taken into account (as it is with multiple regression – see Chapters 34 and 35). That is, ideally the *pattern* of variables that best predicts group membership should be identified.

In many ways, multinomial logistic regression is the more general case of binomial logistic regression described in Chapter 42. The dependent variable in multinomial logistic regression can have one of several (not just two) nominal values. Nevertheless the two

Table 41.1	Example of how the offender groups could be compared on the predictors		
	Rapists	Incestuous offender	Paedophile
Father hostile to offender as a child	30	50	40
Father not hostile to offender	40	30	10

forms of logistic regression share many essential characteristics. For example, the dependent variable is membership of a category (e.g. group) in both cases. However, not all of the sophisticated regression procedures which are available for binomial logistic regression can be used in multinomial logistic regression. Because of this, multinomial logistic regression is actually easier than binomial logistic regression. Nevertheless, there is a disadvantage for the more advanced user since there are few model-building options (no stepwise, no forward selection, no backward selection). This makes multinomial logistic regression simpler. Sometimes multinomial logistic regression is described as being rather like doing two or more binomial logistic regressions on the data. It could replace binomial logistic regression for the dichotomous category case – that is, when the dependent variable consists of just two categories.

41.2 Dummy variables

A key to understanding multinomial logistic regression lies in the concept of dummy variables. In our example, there are three values of the dependent variable, category *A*, category *B* and category *C*. These three values could be converted into *two* dichotomous variables and these dichotomous variables are known as dummy variables:

- *Dummy variable 1* Category *A* versus categories *B* and *C*.

- *Dummy variable 2* Category *B* versus categories *A* and *C*.

Dummy variables are as simple as that. The two values of each dummy variable are normally coded 1 and 0.

What about the comparison of category *C* with categories *A* and *B*? Well, no such dummy variable is used. The reason is simple. All of the information that distinguishes category *C* from categories *A* and *B* has already been provided by the first two dummy variables. The first dummy variable explains how to distinguish category *C* from category *A*, and the second dummy variable explains how to distinguish category *C* from category *B*. The third dummy variable is not used because it would overlap completely with the variation explained by the first two dummy variables. This would cause something called multicollinearity, which means that some predictors intercorrelate highly with each other. So, in our example, only two of the dummy variables can be used. Multicollinearity should be avoided in any form of regression as it is the cause of a great deal of confusion in the interpretation of the findings.

The choice of which dummy variable to omit in dummy coding is arbitrary. The outcome is the same in terms of prediction and classification whatever variable is omitted.

If you are struggling with dummy variables and collinearity consider the following. Imagine the variable gender which consists of just two values – male and female. Try to change gender into dummy variables. One dummy variable would be 'male or not' and the other dummy variable would be 'female or not'. There would be a perfect negative correlation between these two dummy variables – they are simply different ways of measuring the same thing. So one dummy variable has to be dropped since it has already been accounted for by the other dummy variable. If there are more than two dummy variables then the same logic applies although the dropped dummy variable is accounted for by several dummy variables, not just one.

41.3   What can multinomial logistic regression do?

Multinomial logistic regression can help:

- identify a small number of variables which effectively distinguish between groups or categories of the dependent variable

- identify the other variables which are ineffective in terms of distinguishing between groups or categories of the dependent variable

- make actual predictions of which group an individual will be a member (i.e. what category of the dependent variable) on the basis of their known values on the predictor variables.

What are we hoping to achieve with our multinomial logistic regression? The main things are:

- whether our predictors actually predict the offence categories at better than the chance level

- the constants and regression weights that need to be applied to the predictors to optimally allocate the offenders to the actual offending group

- a classification table that indicates how accurately the classification is based on the predictors compared to the known category of offence

- to identify the pattern of predictor variables which classifies the offenders into their offence category most accurately.

This list is more or less the same as would be applied to any form of regression.

Some researchers would use a different technique (discriminant analysis or discriminant function analysis) to analyse our data (see Box 41.2). However, multinomial logistic regression does an arguably better job since it makes fewer (unattainable?) assumptions about the characteristics of the data. More often than not, there will be little difference between the two in terms of your findings. In those rare circumstances when substantially different outcomes emerge, the multinomial logistic regression is preferred because of its relative lack of restrictive assumptions about the data. In other words, there is no advantage in using discriminant function analysis but there are disadvantages.

Figure 41.1 outlines the key steps in multinomial logistic regression.

Box 41.2   Key concepts

Difference between discriminant function analysis and logistic regression

Discriminant function analysis is very similar in its application to multinomial logistic regression. There is no particular advantage of discriminant function analysis which is in some circumstances inferior to multinomial logistic regression. It could be used for the data in this chapter on different types of sex offenders. However, it is more characteristically used when the independent variables are score variables. It would help us to find what the really

→

important factors are in differentiating between the three groups of sex offenders. The dependent variable in discriminant function analysis consists of the various categories or groups which we want to differentiate.

The discriminant function is a weighted combination of predictors which maximise the differentiation between the various groups which make up the dependent variable. So the formula for a discriminant function might be as follows:

Discriminant (function) score
$$= \text{constant} + b_1x_1 + b_2x_2 + b_3x_3 + b_4x_4 + b_5x_5 + b_6x_6$$

The bs in the formula above are merely regression weights (just like in multiple regression) and x_1, etc. are an individual's scores on each of the predictor variables. As with multiple regressions, regression weights may be expressed in unstandardised or standardised form. When expressed in standardised form, the relative impact of the different predictors is more accurately indicated. In our example, there will be two discriminant functions because

there are three groups to differentiate. The number of discriminant functions is generally one less than the number of groups. However, if the number of predictors is less than the number of discriminant functions, the number of discriminant functions may be reduced.

The *centroid* is the average score on the discriminant function of a person who is classified as belonging to one of the groups. For a two-group discriminant function analysis there are two centroids. Cut-off points are provided which help the researcher identify to which group an individual belongs. This cut-off point lies halfway between the two centroids if both groups are equal in size. The cut-off point is weighted towards one of the centroids in the case of unequal group size. A classification table (in this context also known as a confusion matrix or prediction table) indicates how good the discrimination between the groups is in practice. Such a table gives the known distribution of groups compared to how the discriminant function analysis categorises the individuals. Chapter 30 covers discriminant function analysis in relation to MANOVA.

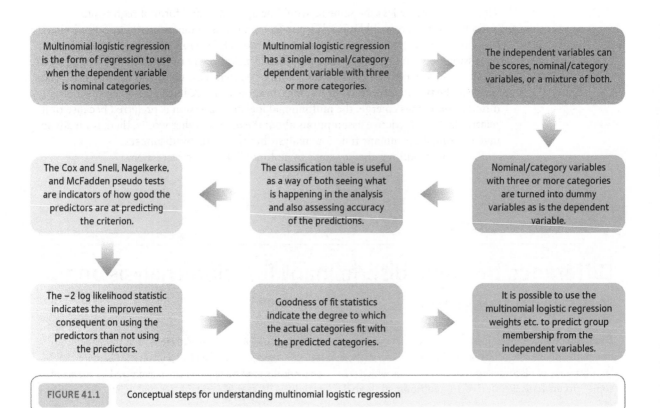

FIGURE 41.1   Conceptual steps for understanding multinomial logistic regression

41.4 Worked example

The data used are shown in Table 41.2. To make the output realistic, these 20 cases have been entered ten times to give a total sample of 200 cases. This is strictly improper as a statistical technique, of course, but helpful for pedagogic reasons.

It is not feasible to calculate multinomial logistic regression by hand. Inevitably a computer program has to be used. Consequently, the discussion refers to a computer analysis rather than to computational steps to be followed. Figure 41.2 reminds us of the basic task in multinomial logistic regression. The predictors are scores and/or nominal variables. The criterion being predicted is always a nominal variable but one with more than two categories or values. Since nominal variables have no underlying scale by definition, the several nominal categories are essentially re-coded individually as present or absent. In this way, each value is compared with *all* of the other values. It does not matter which comparison is left out and, of course, computer programs largely make the choices for you. Figure 41.3 takes the basic structure and applies it directly to our study of offenders in order to make things concrete. Remember that one dummy variable is not used in the analysis.

Our list of independent or predictor variables actually only includes two-value variables (binary or dichotomous variables). We could use more complex nominal variables as predictors. However, they would have to be made into several dummy variables just as the dependent variable is turned into several dummy variables. Score variables can also be used as independent variables though we have not done so.

Table 41.2	Data for the multinomial logistic regression							
	Age	DASS	Mother hostile	Father hostile	Children's home	Physical abuse	Sexual abuse	Type of offence
1	younger	low	high	low	no	yes	no	rapist
2	younger	low	high	low	no	yes	yes	rapist
3	older	low	high	low	no	yes	yes	rapist
4	older	high	high	high	yes	no	no	incest
5	older	high	high	high	yes	yes	yes	rapist
6	younger	low	high	low	no	no	no	rapist
7	older	high	low	high	no	yes	yes	rapist
8	older	high	low	high	yes	no	no	incest
9	younger	low	low	high	yes	no	yes	incest
10	older	high	high	low	no	yes	yes	incest
11	older	high	low	low	yes	no	yes	incest
12	younger	high	low	high	no	yes	no	rapist
13	older	high	low	high	yes	no	yes	incest
14	older	high	high	low	yes	yes	yes	incest
15	older	low	high	high	no	yes	yes	incest
16	younger	high	high	low	yes	no	no	paedophile
17	older	high	low	high	yes	no	yes	paedophile
18	older	low	high	high	no	no	yes	paedophile
19	younger	high	low	high	yes	yes	yes	paedophile
20	older	low	low	high	yes	no	no	paedophile
etc.								

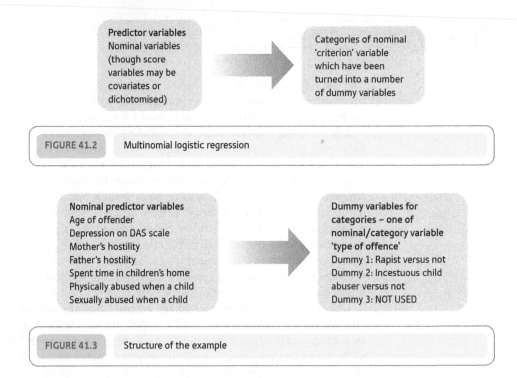

FIGURE 41.2   Multinomial logistic regression

FIGURE 41.3   Structure of the example

Remember that the dependent variable in this case is the type of offence. There are three different types, categories or values of sex offender in the study. Hence there are two dummy variables listed (out of the maximum of three possible). Dummy variable 1 is rapist versus not (not implies the offender is an incestuous child abuser or a paedophile). Dummy variable 2 is incestuous child abuser versus not (not implies the offender is a rapist or a paedophile). The choice of which dummy variable to leave out of the analysis is purely arbitrary, makes no difference to the outcome and, typically, is automatically chosen by the computer program.

41.5   Accuracy of the prediction

Once the analysis has been run through an appropriate computer program, a useful starting point is the classification table (that is, an accuracy assessment). Sometimes this is an option that you will have to select rather than something automatically produced by the program. The classification table is a crosstabulation (or contingency) table which compares the predicted allocation of the offenders to the three offender groups to which they are known to belong. Usually, such tables include percentage figures to indicate the degree of accuracy of the prediction. Classification tables make a lot of sense intuitively and help clarify what the analysis is achieving. Table 41.3 is such a classification table for our data. We have yet to look at the calculation steps that allow this table to be generated. This comes later.

For the rapists, the analysis is rather accurate. Indeed, the overwhelming majority of rapists have been correctly identified as being rapists. Hence the row percentage correctly classified for rapists is 85.7%. This calculation is simply the number of correctly identified rapists (60) expressed as a percentage of the number of rapists in total (70). So the accuracy for the prediction for rapists is $60 \div 70 \times 100\% = 0.857 \times 100\% = 85.7\%$. None of

Table 41.3	Predicted versus actual offence category of offenders			
Observed	Predicted to be rapist offender	Predicted to be incestuous	Predicted to be a paedophile	Percentage correct for row
Actually a rapist	60	10	0	85.7%
Actually an incestuous offender	20	50	10	62.5%
Actually a paedophile	0	30	20	40.0%
Column percentage	40.0%	45.0%	15.0%	Overall percentage correct = 65%

the rapists was predicted to be a paedophile though some were predicted to be incestuous offenders. The other two categories of offender were not differentiated to the same level of accuracy. For the incestuous offenders, 62.5% were correctly identified as being incestuous offenders. The paedophiles were relatively poorly predicted – only 40% of paedophiles were correctly identified. Interestingly, the paedophiles are only ever wrongly classified as being incestuous offenders; they are never wrongly classified as rapists.

So it would appear that the model (pattern of predictors of offence category) is reasonably successful at distinguishing the offender types. Nevertheless, the identification of incestuous offenders and paedophiles is not particularly good. Obviously, if we were to persist in our research then we would seek to include further predictor variables that were better at differentiating the incestuous and paedophile groups.

41.6   How good are the predictors?

Calculating multinomial logistic regression using a computer program generates a variety of statistical analyses apart from the classification table discussed so far. We need to turn to other aspects of this multinomial logistic regression output in order to identify just how successful each predictor is and what predictors should be included in the model. The classification table gives no indication of this since it does not deal with the individual predictor variables.

Is the prediction better than chance? At some point in the analysis, there should be a table or tables including output referring to, say, 'Cox and Snell' or 'Nagelkerke' or 'McFadden' or to several of these. These may be described as pseudo R-square statistics. They refer to the amount of variation in the dependent variable which is predicted by the predictor variables collectively. The maximum value of this, in theory, is 1.00 if the relationship is perfect; it will be 0.00 if there is no relationship. They are pseudo-statistics because they appear to be like R-square (which is the square of the multiple correlation between the independent and dependent variable – see p. 476) but they are only actually analogous to it. One simply cannot compute a Pearson correlation involving a nominal variable with more than two values (categories). The nearer the pseudo-statistic is to a perfect relationship of 1.00 the better the prediction (just as it would be with a proper R-square). The value for 'Cox and Snell' is .546, the value for Nagelkerke is .617 and the value for McFadden is .365. So the relationship between the predictors and the criterion is moderate (see Table 41.4). We would interpret these values more or less as if they were analogous to a squared Pearson correlation coefficient.

Table 41.4	Pseudo *R*-square statistics	
		Pseudo-statistic
	Cox and Snell	.546
	Nagelkerke	.617
	McFadden	.365

Table 41.5	Model fitting information indicating whether the prediction actually changes significantly from the values if the predictors were not used				
Model components	**− 2 log likelihood statistic[a]**	**Chi-square for change**	**Degrees of freedom**	**Significance**
Intercept (i.e. constant) only	407.957			
Final model	248.734	159.224	14	.001

[a] See Box 41.3 for a discussion of this statistic.

Another table will be found in the computer output to indicate how well the model improves fit over using *no* model at all (Table 41.5). This is also an indication of whether the set of predictors actually contributes to the classification process over and above what random allocation would achieve. This is known as the model fit (but really is whether the modelled predictions are different from purely random predictions). This involves a statistic called −2 log likelihood which is discussed in Box 41.3. Often the value for the intercept is given (remember this is a regression so there is a constant of some fixed value). Table 41.5 illustrates this aspect of the output. The chi-square value is calculated using the −2 log likelihood statistic. This amounts to a measure of the amount of change due to using the predictors versus not using the predictors. As can be seen, there is a significant change, so it is worthwhile using the model. (It is significant at the .001 level. That is, it is a change in predictive power which is significant at better than the 5% level or .05 level.)

There is yet another statistic that is worth considering – the goodness-of-fit of the model to the data. The model is not merely intended to be better than no model at all but, ideally, it will fit or predict the actual data fairly precisely. A chi-square test can be performed comparing the fit of the predicted data to the actual data. In this case, of course, the ideal outcome is no significant difference between the actual data and those predicted from the model. This would indicate that it is pointless searching for additional predictors to fit the model – assuming that the sample is fairly large so sampling fluctuations may not be too much of a problem. In this example, the model makes predictions which are significantly different from the obtained classification of the offender. The incomplete match between the data and the predicted data is not surprising given the classification table (Table 41.3). This does not mean that the model is no good, merely that it could be better. Table 41.6 gives the goodness-of-fit statistics. Probably in psychology and the social sciences, it is unrealistic to expect any model to predict the actual data perfectly. Moderate levels of fit would be acceptable.

So which are the best predictors? It was clear from Table 41.5 that the predictors improve the accuracy of the classification. However, this is for *all* of the predictors. It does not tell us which predictors (components of the model) are actually responsible for this

Table 41.6	Goodness-of-fit of the actual offence category to the predicted offence category		
	Chi-square	Degrees of freedom	Significance
Pearson goodness-of-fit statistic	228.010	22	.001

Box 41.3   Key concepts

Change in the −2 log likelihood

Logistic regression uses a statistic called −2 log likelihood. This statistic is used to indicate a) how well both the model (the pattern of predictors) actually fits the obtained data, b) the change in fit of the model to the obtained data if a predictor is removed from the model and c) the extent to which using the model is an improvement on *not* using the model. These uses are different although the same statistic is used in assessing them.

There is a similarity, however. All of them involve the closeness of fit between different versions of the classification table. Earlier in studying statistics, we would have used chi-square in order to assess the significance of these discrepancies between one classification table and another. Actually that is more or less what we are doing when we use the −2 log likelihood statistic. This statistic is distributed like the chi-square statistic. Hence, you will find reference to chi-square values close to where the −2 log likelihood statistic is reported. The −2 is there because it ensures that the log likelihood is distributed according to the chi-square distribution. It is merely a pragmatic adjustment.

Just like chi-square, then, a 0 value of the −2 log likelihood is indicative that the two contingency tables involved fit each other perfectly. That is, the model fits the data perfectly, dropping a predictor makes no difference to the predictive power of the analysis, or the model is no different from a purely chance pattern. All of these are more similar than they might at first appear. Similarly, the bigger the value of the −2 log likelihood statistic, the more likely is there to be a significant difference between the versions of the contingency table. That is, the model is less than perfect in that it does not reproduce the data exactly (though it may be a fairly useful model); the variable which has been dropped from the model should not be dropped since it makes a useful contribution to understanding the data; or the model is better than a chance distribution – that is, makes a useful contribution to understanding the pattern of the data on the dependent variable.

The statistic usually reported is the *change* in the −2 log likelihood. The calculation of the degrees of freedom is a little less straightforward than for chi-square. It is dependent on the change in the number of predictors associated with the change in the −2 log likelihood.

improvement. To address that issue, it is necessary to examine the outcomes of a number of likelihood ratio tests. Once again these use the −2 log likelihood calculation, but the strategy is different. There is a succession of such tests that examine the effect of removing one predictor from the model (set of potential predictors). The change in the −2 log likelihood statistic consequent on doing this is distributed like the chi-square distribution. Table 41.7 shows such a set of calculations for our data. Notice that in general little changes (i.e. the chi-square values are small) in a number of cases – DASS anxiety and hostility of the mother. Removing these variables one at a time makes *no* difference of any importance in the model's ability to predict. In other words, neither DASS anxiety nor hostility of the mother is a useful predictor.

Other predictors can be seen to be effective predictors simply because removing them individually makes a significant difference to the power of the model. That is, the model

Table 41.7	Likelihood ratio tests			
Predictor	− 2 log likelihood of reduced model; i.e. without the predictor to the left	Chi-square	Degrees of freedom	Significance
Intercept (constant)	248.734			
Age	267.272	18.538	2	.000
DASS	249.454	0.721	2	.697
Mother's hostility	248.932	0.199	2	.905
Father's hostility	256.089	7.355	2	.025
Children's home	259.677	10.943	2	.004
Physical abuse	287.304	38.571	2	.000
Sexual abuse	263.914	15.181	2	.001

with any of these predictors taken away is a worse fit to the data than when the predictor is included (i.e. the full model). Although we have identified the good predictors, this is not the end of the story since we cannot say what each of the good predictors is good at predicting – remember that we have several (two in this example) dummy variables to predict. The predictors may be good for some of the dummy variables but not for others.

41.7   Prediction

So how do we predict to which group an offender is likely to belong given his particular pattern on the predictor variables? This is very much the same question as asking which of the predictor variables have predictive power. It is done in exactly the same way that we would make the prediction in any sort of regression. That is, we multiply each of the 'scores' by its regression weight, add up all of these products and, finally, add the intercept (i.e. constant) (see Chapter 34 for this sort of calculation). In logistic regression we are actually predicting category membership or, in other words, which value of the dependent or criterion variable the offender has. Is he a rapist, incestuous offender or paedophile? This is done mathematically by calculating something known as 'the logit' (see also Chapter 42 on binomial logistic regression). The logit is the natural logarithm of something known as the odds ratio. The odds ratio relates very closely and simply to the probability that an offender is in one category rather than the others (see Box 42.1). A key thing to note is that multinomial logistic regression, like multiple regression (Chapter 34), actually calculates a set of regression weights (B) which are applied to the logit. It also calculates a constant or cut-point as in any other form of regression.

Table 41.8 gives the regression values calculated for our data. There are a number of things to bear in mind:

- The table is in two parts because there is more than one dependent variable to predict – that is, there are two dummy variables. If there were three dummy variables then this table would be in three parts and so forth.

- The dichotomous variables are each given a regression weight (B) value for each value. The value coded 1 has a numerical value which may be positive or negative. The other value is given a regression weight of 0 every time. That is, by multiplying the numerical

Table 41.8	Constants and regression weights for predictors used					
Category	**Predictor**	**B**	**Standard error**	**Wald**	**Degrees of freedom**	**Sig.**
Rapist – not	Intercept	−0.260	1.158	0.050	1	.822
	Age (younger)	−0.159	0.678	0.055	1	.814
	Age (older)	0			0	
	DASS (lower)	0.575	0.735	0.612	1	.434
	DASS (higher)	0			0	
	Mother's hostility (lower)	−0.328	0.791	0.171	1	.679
	Mother's hostility (higher)	0			0	
	Father's hostility (lower)	0.838	0.863	0.943	1	.332
	Father's hostility (higher)	0			0	
	Children's home (yes)	−1.576	0.815	3.739	1	.053*
	Children's home (no)	0			0	
	Physically abused (yes)	20.540	0.713	830.866	1	.000*
	Physically abused (no)	0			0	
	Sexually abused (yes)	−18.570	0.000	∞	1	
	Sexually abused (no)	0			0	
Incestuous child abuser – not	Intercept	−0.314	0.813	0.150	1	.699
	Age (younger)	−1.970	0.542	13.187	1	.000*
	Age (older)	0			0	
	DASS (lower)	0.086	0.562	0.024	1	.878
	DASS (higher)	0			0	
	Mother's hostility (lower)	−0.014	0.505	0.01	1	.977
	Mother's hostility (higher)	0			0	
	Father's hostility (lower)	1.486	0.615	5.836	1	.016*
	Father's hostility (higher)	0			0	
	Children's home (yes)	0.479	0.704	0.463	1	.496
	Children's home (no)	0			0	
	Physically abused (yes)	0.652	0.582	1.255	1	.263
	Physically abused (no)	0			0	
	Sexually abused (yes)	0.498	0.498	1.003	1	.317
	Sexually abused (no)	0			0	

* Wald test is significant at better than .05 level.

value by 0 we are always going to get 0. In other words, one of the values of a dichotomous predictor has no effect on the calculation.

- There is a statistic called the Wald statistic in Table 41.8. This statistic is based on the ratio between the B-weight and the standard error and these values are computed in Screenshot 41.5. Thus for the first dummy variable it is 0.055. This is not statistically significant ($p = .814$). Sometimes the output will be a little misleading since if the standard error is 0.00 then it is not possible to calculate the Wald statistic as it is an infinitely large value. Any value divided by 0 is infinitely large. An infinitely large value is statistically significant, but its significance value cannot be calculated. The significance values of the Wald statistic indicate which of our predictors is statistically significant.

41.8   Interpreting the results

It is fairly self-evident that the features which distinguish the three groups of offenders are as follows:

- Rapists (as opposed to incestuous and paedophile offenders) are less likely to have been in a children's home ($B = -1.576$, the minus sign meaning that the reverse of spending some time in a children's home is true). This is significant at .053 which is just about significant. The rapists were also more likely to have been physically abused ($B = 20.540$ and the sign is positive). This is much more statistically significant and the best predictor of all. Finally, the rapists were less likely to have been sexually abused. There is no significance level reported for this because the standard error is 0.000 which makes the Wald statistic infinitely large. Hence a significance level cannot be calculated but really it is extremely statistically significant.

- Incestuous abusers (as opposed to rapists and paedophile offenders) are more likely to be in the young group and to have a father low on hostility.

The findings are presented in Table 41.9. There were two dummy variables so there are two dimensions to the table. This table probably will help you to understand why only two dummy variables are needed to account for the differences between three groups.

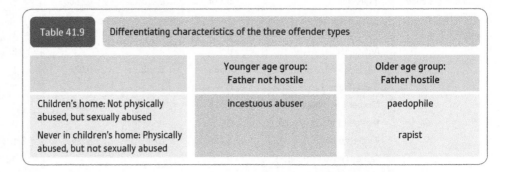

Table 41.9	Differentiating characteristics of the three offender types	
	Younger age group: Father not hostile	Older age group: Father hostile
Children's home: Not physically abused, but sexually abused	incestuous abuser	paedophile
Never in children's home: Physically abused, but not sexually abused		rapist

41.9   Reporting the results

As with some other more advanced statistical procedures, there is no standard way of presenting the outcome of a multinomial logistic regression. One way of reporting the broad findings of the analysis would be as follows:

A multinomial logistic regression was conducted using six dichotomous predictors to predict classification on the multinomial dependent variable offence type (paedophile, incestuous offender, rapist). The predictors were capable of identifying the offender group at better than the chance level. Two regression patterns were identified – one for rapists versus the other **two** groups, the second for incestuous offenders versus the other two groups. The $pseudo - r^2$ (Cox and Snell) was .55, indicating a moderate fit between the total model and data although the fit was less than perfect. Rapists were differentiated from the other two groups by not having spent time in a children's home, being physically abused but not being sexually abused. Incestuous offenders were significantly differentiated from the other two groups by being in the younger age group and their father not being hostile to them as children. Rapists were correctly identified with a high degree of accuracy (85.7% correct). Incestuous offenders were less accurately identified (62.5% correct). Paedophiles were more likely to be wrongly classified (accuracy 40.0% correct) but as incestuous offenders rather than rapists. The regression weights are to be found in Table 41.8.

Research examples

Multinomial logistic regression

Griffin and Hesketh (2008) asked what factors predict post-retirement work intentions. They used multinomial logistic regression to predict membership of various – 1) not work, voluntary work, 2) part-time paid employment and 3) voluntary work plus part-time work. The predictors included the participants' evaluations of pre-retirement work, attitudes to retirement, demographics and so forth. Positive evaluations of pre-retirement work predicted both volunteer work and paid-work post retirement. The variables gender, health, and retirement satisfaction were associated with volunteer work and higher levels of education were predictive of paid work.

Huisman, van Houwelingen and Kerkhof (2010) were interested in whether patients with particular psychiatric diagnoses were more likely to kill themselves with a particular method. They found that psychiatric diagnosis, gender and the status of patients as in- or out-patient were significantly related to the method of suicide used. They used multinomial logistic regression to determine which of these variables were related to suicide method when examined together. The dependent variable was suicide method with the four categories of 1) self-poisoning, 2) jumping before a train, 3) jumping from a high place and 4) all other methods apart from hanging, which as the most common method was chosen to be the reference category. They reported a number of significant findings. For example, 'compared to suicide by hanging, patients who poisoned themselves were more likely to have a substance-related disorder (OR = 4.13), to be in outpatient treatment (OR = 3.22) and less likely to be male (OR = 0.23)' (p. 96). OR is odds ratio.

Kogan (2004) examined the factors that predicted disclosure in women who had unwanted sexual experiences in their childhood or adolescence. The dependent variables were the timing of disclosure and the person disclosed to. Timing of disclosure consisted of the three categories of 1) immediate, 2) delayed and 3) non-disclosure, with immediate disclosure being the reference category. Person disclosed to contained the three categories of adult, peers only and non-disclosure, with adult being the reference category. Multinomial logistic regressions were carried out on these two dependent variables separately. Predictors of these two dependent variables included age at which the experience first occurred which was then re-categorised into four groups: whether the person knew the other person, whether they were family and so on. Various significant findings were reported. For example, 'participants who knew their perpetrator were 3.1 times more likely to non-disclose and 3.7 times more likely to delay disclosure than to disclose within a month' (p. 157).

Key points

- The power of multinomial logistic regression to help identify differences among psychologically interesting – but different – groups of individuals means that it has far greater scope within psychological research than has yet been fully appreciated by researchers.

- The unfamiliarity of some of the concepts should not be regarded as a deterrent. The key features of the analysis are accessible to any researcher no matter how statistically unskilled.

COMPUTER ANALYSIS

Multinomial logistic regression using SPSS

Data
- Name the variables in 'Variable View' of the 'Data Editor'.
- Enter the data under the appropriate variable names in 'Data View' of the 'Data Editor' (Screenshot 41.1).

Analysis
- Select 'Analyze', 'Regression' and 'Multinomial Logistic…' (Screenshot 41.2).

2
- Move dependent variable to 'Dependent:' box and predictors to the 'Factor(s):' box (Screenshot 41.3).
- Select 'Model', 'Main effects', move predictors into 'Stepwise Terms' and 'Continue'.

3
- Select 'Statistics …', 'Cell probabilities', 'Classification table', 'Goodness-of-fit', 'Continue' and 'OK' (Screenshot 41.4).

Output
- Check the way the dependent variable has been coded in the 'Dependent Variable Encoding' table.
- The 'Parameter Estimates' table gives the regression weights for the predictors together with their statistical significance (Screenshot 41.5).

FIGURE 41.4 SPSS steps for binomial logistic regression

Interpreting and reporting the output

- The Parameter Estimates table (Screenshot 41.5) provides the regression data for predicting the different types of offending. Each of the predictors is presented twice and you can ignore the rows which have 0^b towards the beginning under the B (regression weight) column. The significant predictors can be found from the Sig. column. Check the B weight for the direction of the relationship as you would with any form of regression.

- A brief write-up might be: 'Multinomial logistic regression showed that only some of the six predictors effectively predicted offence type (rapist, paedophile or incestuous abusers). The pseudo-r^2 (Cox & Snell) was .55 indicating a moderate fit between the model and the data. Rapists were different from the other types of offenders in that they had not spent time in a children's home and had been physically abused but not sexually abused. Incestuous offenders tended to be younger and their fathers were not hostile to them as a child.'

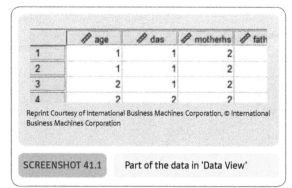

Reprint Courtesy of International Business Machines Corporation, © International Business Machines Corporation

SCREENSHOT 41.1   Part of the data in 'Data View'

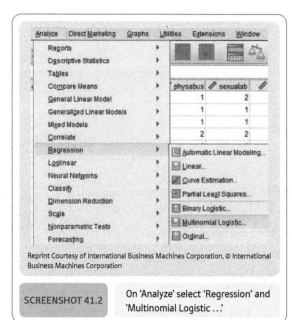

Reprint Courtesy of International Business Machines Corporation, © International Business Machines Corporation

SCREENSHOT 41.2   On 'Analyze' select 'Regression' and 'Multinomial Logistic …'

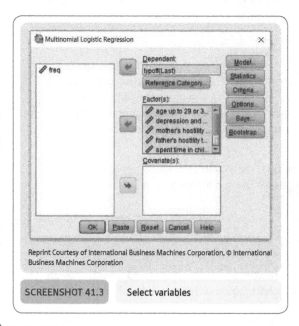

Reprint Courtesy of International Business Machines Corporation, © International Business Machines Corporation

SCREENSHOT 41.3   Select variables

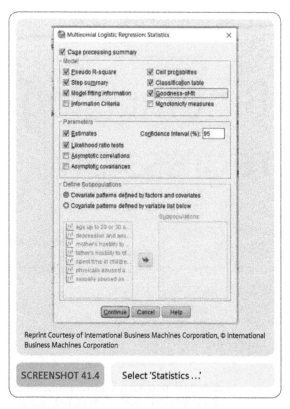

Reprint Courtesy of International Business Machines Corporation, © International Business Machines Corporation

SCREENSHOT 41.4   Select 'Statistics …'

Reprint Courtesy of International Business Machines Corporation, © International Business Machines Corporation

SCREENSHOT 41.5   Parameter Estimates table output

CHAPTER 42

Binomial logistic regression

Overview

- Binomial (or binary) logistic regression is a form of multiple regression which is applied when the dependent variable is dichotomous – that is, has only two different possible values.

- A set of predictors is identified which assesses the most likely of the two nominal categories a particular case falls into.

- The predictor variables may be any type of variable, including scores. However, in this chapter we concentrate on using dichotomous predictor variables.

- As in multiple regression, different ways of entering predictor variables are available. What is appropriate is determined partly by the purpose of the analysis. Blocks may be used in order to control for, or partial out, demographic variables for example.

- Classification tables compare the categories cases actually belong to with the categories predicted on the basis of the independent variables.

- Like other forms of regression, logistic regression generates *B*-weights (or slope) and a constant. However, these are used to calculate something known as the logit rather than scores. The logit is the natural logarithm of odds for the category. The percentage predicted in each category of the dependent variable can be calculated from this and compared with the actual percentage.

- As in all multivariate forms of regression, the final regression calculation provides information about the significant predictors among those being employed.

Preparation

Look back at Chapter 9 on simple regression, Chapter 18 on chi-square and Chapter 34 on multiple regression. Chapter 41 on multinomial logistic regression may be helpful in consolidating understanding of the material in this chapter.

42.1 Introduction

Binomial (or binary) logistic regression may be used to:

- determine a small group of variables which characterise the two different groups or categories of cases

- identify which other variables are ineffective in differentiating these two groups or categories of cases

- make actual predictions about which of the two groups a particular individual is likely to be a member given that individual's pattern on the other variables.

A simple way to understand binomial logistic regression is to regard it as a variant of linear multiple regression (Chapter 34). Binomial logistic regression, however, uses a dependent variable which is nominal and consists of just two categories. By employing a weighted pattern of predictor variables, binary logistic regression assesses a person's most likely classification on this binary dependent variable. This prediction is expressed as a probability or using some related concept. Other examples of possible binomial dependent variables include:

- success or failure in an exam

- suffering schizophrenia or not

- going to university or not.

If the dependent variable has three or more nominal categories, then multinomial logistic regression should be used (Chapter 41). In other words, if there are three or more groups or categories, multinomial logistic regression is the appropriate approach.

Often, but not necessarily, the independent variables are also binary nominal category variables. So gender and age group could be used as the predictor variables to estimate whether a person will own a mobile phone or not, for example.

Because the dependent variable is nominal data, regression weights are calculated which help calculate the probability that a particular individual will be in category *A* rather than category *B* of the dependent variable. More precisely:

- The regression weights and constant are used to calculate the logit.

- This in its turn is the natural logarithm of something called the odds.

- Odds are not very different from probability and are turned into probabilities using a simple formula.

This is a little daunting at first, but it is not that difficult in practice – especially given that one rarely would need to calculate anything by hand!

You may find it helpful to turn to Box 42.1 on simple logistic regression. Studying this will introduce you to most of the concepts in binomial logistic regression without too much confusing detail and complexity. Simple logistic regression would not normally be calculated since it achieves nothing computationally which is not more simply done in other ways. Box 42.2 explains natural logarithms.

Box 42.1	Focus on

Simple logistic regression

In this chapter we are looking at binomial logistic regression and applying it to predicting recidivism (re-offending by prisoners). We will take a simple example of this which uses one independent variable (whether the prisoner has previous convictions) and one dependent variable (whether or not prisoners re-offend). Table 42.1 illustrates such data. The table clearly shows that *prisoners who have previous convictions* are much more likely to re-offend than *prisoners who have not got previous convictions* (i.e. first-time offenders). If a prisoner has previous convictions, the odds are 40 to 10 that they will re-offend. This equates to a percentage of 80% (i.e. 40/40(40 + 10) × 100%). If a prisoner has no previous convictions then the odds are 15 to 30 that they will re-offend. This equates to a percentage of 33.33% (i.e. 15/(15 + 30) × 100%).

It would be a simple matter of predicting recidivism from these figures. Basically if a prisoner has previous convictions then they are very likely to re-offend (80% likelihood), but if they have no previous convictions then they are unlikely to re-offend (33% likelihood). Table 42.2 illustrates what we would expect on the basis of the data in Table 42.1. There is virtually no difference between the two tables – we have merely added the percentage of correct predictions for each row, that is, how easy the prediction is

in this simple case. Notice we are more accurate at predicting re-offending in those with previous convictions than we are at predicting no re-offending in those with no previous convictions. That is how simple the prediction is with just a single predictor variable.

In logistic regression, for mathematical computation reasons, calculations are carried out using odds rather than probabilities. However, odds and probability are closely related. The odds of re-offending *if the prisoner has previous convictions* is simply the numbers re-offending divided by the numbers not re-offending. That is, the odds of re-offending *if the prisoner has prior convictions* are $40 \div 10 = 4.0$. On the other hand, *if the prisoner has no previous convictions*, the odds for re-offending are $15 \div 30 = 0.50$.

A simple formula links probability and odds so it is very easy to convert odds into probabilities (and vice versa if necessary):

$$
\begin{aligned}
\text{probability (of re-offending)} &= \text{odds}/(1 + \text{odds}) \\
&= 40/(1 + 40) \\
&= 4.0 \div 5.0 \\
&= .80 \\
&(= 80\% \text{ as a percentage})
\end{aligned}
$$

Table 42.1	Tabulation of previous convictions against re-offending	
	Re-offends	**No re-offending**
Previous conviction	40	10
First offender	15	30

Table 42.2	Classification table including percentage of correct predictions		
	Re-offends	**No re-offending**	**Row correct**
Previous conviction	40	10	80.0%
First offender	15	30	66.7%

It should be stressed that in reality things are even easier since, apart from explanations of logistic regression such as this, all of the calculations are done by the computer program.

The concept of odds ratio occurs frequently in discussions of logistic regression. An odds ratio is simply the ratio of two sets of odds. Hence the odds ratio for 'has previous offences' against 'not having previous offences' is simply $4.0 \div 0.50 = 8.0$. This means that if a prisoner has previous convictions he is eight times more likely to re-offend than a prisoner who has no previous convictions. Of course, there are other odds ratios. For example, if the prisoner has no previous convictions he is $0.50 \div 4.0 = 0.125$ times as likely to re-offend than if he has previous convictions. An odds ratio of 0.125 seems hard to decipher, but it is merely the decimal value of the fraction $1 \div 8$. That seems more intuitively obvious to understand than the decimal. All that is being said is that there is eight times more chance of having outcome A than outcome B – which is the same thing as saying that there is an eighth of a chance of having outcome B rather than outcome A.

The actual calculations in logistic regression revolve around a concept known as the logit. A logit is simply the natural logarithm of the odds (or odds ratio). Box 42.2 gives an explanation of natural logarithms. For a short table of natural logarithms see Table 42.3. Most scientific calculators will provide the natural logarithm of any number – they are also known as Napierian logarithms.

If we run the data from Table 42.1 through the logistic regression program, a number of tables are generated. One of the most important tables will contain a B-weight and a constant. These are somewhat analogous to the b-weight and the constant that are obtained in linear regression (Chapter 9) and multiple regression (Chapter 34). For our data the B is 2.079 and the constant is -0.693. (If you try to reproduce this calculation using a computer program such as SPSS be very careful since programs sometimes impose different values for the cells from those you may be expecting.) The constant and B-weight are applied to the values of the dependent variable in order to indicate the likelihood of each of the two values occurring in offenders with previous convictions. Remember that the dependent variable is coded either 1 (if the offender has previous convictions) or 0 (if the offender has no previous convictions). The result of this calculation then gives us the logit from which a probability of either outcome may be calculated, though normally there is no need to do so.

So, if we wish to know the likelihood of re-offending, the dependent variable in our example variable has a value of 1 if the offender re-offends after release from prison. The logit (of the odds that the offender will re-offend) is calculated as:

$$\text{constant} + (1 \times B) = -0.693 + (1 \times 2.079)$$

$$= -0.693 + 2.079 = 1.386$$

Table 42.3	Some odds and their corresponding natural logarithm values		
Odds (or odds ratio)	Natural logarithm (logit)	Odds (or odds ratio)	Natural logarithm (logit)
0.10	−2.30	1.50	0.41
0.20	−1.61	2.00	0.69
0.25	−1.39	3.00	1.10
0.30	−1.20	4.00	1.39
0.40	−0.92	5.00	1.61
0.50	−0.69	6.00	1.79
0.60	−0.51	7.00	1.95
0.70	−0.36	8.00	2.08
0.80	−0.22	9.00	2.20
0.90	−0.11	10.00	2.30
1.00	0.00	100.00	4.61

This value of the logit can be turned into odds using the table of natural logarithms (Table 41.3). The odds for a logit of 1.386 is 4.00. This is no surprise as we calculated the odds for re-offending earlier in this box using very simple methods. Expressed as a probability, this is $4.00/(1 + 4.00) = 4.00/5.00 = .80$ or 80% as a percentage.

On the other hand, if the predictor variable has a value of 0 (i.e. the offender does not re-offend after leaving prison) then the calculation of the logit is as follows:

$$\text{logit} = \text{constant} + (0 \times B) = -0.693 + (0 \times 2.079)$$
$$= -0.693 + 0 = -0.693$$

Again Table 42.3 can be consulted to convert this logit (natural logarithm of the odds) into the odds. We find that the odds for a logit of 0.693 is 0.50. Remember what this means. We have calculated the odds that a prisoner who has no previous offences will re-offend on release to be 0.50. We can express this as a probability by applying the earlier formula. This is $0.50/(1 + 0.50) = 0.50 \div 1.50 = .33$ or 33% as a percentage. Thus, the probability of re-offending (if the prisoner has previous convictions) is .67 (or 67%) and the probability of not re-offending is .33 or 33%.

Unfortunately, binomial multiple regression is not quite that simple but only because it employs several predictor (independent variables) which may well be to a degree associated. Consequently, the prediction becomes much more complex and cannot be done without the help of a computer program because it is incredibly computationally intensive. But the main difference in practical terms is not great since the user rarely has to do even the most basic calculation. Instead of one B-weight, several regression weights may be produced – one for each predictor variable. This merely extends the calculation a little as you will see in the main text for this chapter.

Box 42.2   Key concepts

Natural logarithms

We do not really need to know about natural logarithms to use logistic regression, but the following may be helpful to those who want to dig a little deeper. Natural logarithms are also known as Napierian logarithms. A logarithm is simply the exponential power to which a particular base number (that can be any number) has to be raised in order to give the number for which the logarithm is required. Let us assume, for example, that the base number is 2.00 and we want to find the logarithm for the number 4.00. We simply have to calculate e (the exponential or power) in the following formula:

$$2.00^e = 4.00$$

It is probably obvious that in order to get 4.00, we have to square 2.00 (i.e. raise to the power of 2). So the logarithm to the base 2.00 for the number 4.00 is 2. Similarly, the logarithm of 8 to the base 2.00 is 3 and the logarithm of 16 is 4. Natural logarithms have as their base 2.71828. Table 42.3 gives some natural logarithms for a selection of numbers.

Natural logarithms are vital to the calculation of logistic regression because it is based on the Poisson distribution. Poisson distributions are largely used to calculate probabilities of rare occurrences in large populations. Multiple regression is based on the normal distribution, logistic regression is based on the Poisson distribution. One feature of logarithms is that they can be applied to any numerical measures in order to compact the distribution by making the large values relatively much smaller without affecting the small values so much. This can be seen in Table 42.3. Notice that if we take the odds ratios for 1 through to 100, the logit values only increase from 0 to 4.61. Also noteworthy is that the natural log of 1.00 (the point at which both outcomes are equally probable) is 0.0. In terms of the calculations, the main consequence of this is that the logistic regression B-weights have a greater influence when applied to a logit close to the midpoint (i.e. log of the odds ratio of 1.00) than they do higher on the natural logarithm scale.

42.2   Typical example

A typical use of binomial logistic regression would be in the assessment of the likelihood of re-offending if a prisoner is released from prison. This re-offending (i.e. recidivism) could be assessed as a binomial (i.e. dichotomous) variable. In this case, the variable re-offending simply takes one of two values – the prisoner re-offends or the prisoner does *not* re-offend (Table 42.4). (If one, for example, *counted* the number of times each prisoner re-offended in that period then regular multiple regression (Chapter 34) would be more appropriate since this would amount to a numerical score.) Decision-making about prisoner release is improved by knowing which of a set of variables are most associated with re-offending. Such variables (i.e. independent variables) might include:

- age (over 30 years versus 29 and under)

- whether they had previously been in prison

- whether they received treatment (therapy) in prison

- whether they express contrition (regret) for their offence

- whether they are married

- type of offender (sex offender or not).

Data on these variables plus re-offending (recidivism) are to be found in Table 42.5. There are only 19 different cases listed, but they have been reproduced five times to give a 'sample' of 95 cases. This helps make the output of the analysis more realistic for pedagogic purposes, though statistically and methodologically it is otherwise totally unjustified. Nevertheless, readers may find it easier to duplicate our analysis on the computer because one block of data can be copied several times. The basic structure of our data for this regression analysis is shown in Figure 42.1.

Although we have selected binary (i.e. dichotomous) variables as the predictors in our example, score variables can also be used as predictors in binomial logistic regression. Box 42.3 discusses score variables as predictors in logistic regression further. Equally, one could use nominal variables with three or more values though these have to be turned into dummy variables for the purpose of the analysis (see Section 41.2). A dummy variable is a binary variable taking the values of 0 or 1. Any nominal (category) variable having three or more values may be converted into several dummy variables. More than one type of variable can be used in any analysis. That is, the choice of types of predictor variables is very flexible. One thing is not flexible – the dependent variable can only be dichotomous; i.e. only two alternative values of the dependent variable are possible.

Table 42.4	Step 1 classification table		
	Predicted recidivist	Predicted non-recidivist	Percentage row correct
Actually re-offends	40	5	88.9%
Actually does not re-offend	5	45	90.0%

Table 42.5	Data for the study of recidivism – the data from 19 cases is reproduced five times to give realistic sample sizes but only to facilitate explanation

	Recidivism	Age	Previous prison term	Treatment	Contrite	Married	Sex offender
1	yes	younger	yes	no	no	no	yes
2	yes	older	yes	no	no	no	yes
3	yes	older	yes	yes	no	no	yes
4	yes	older	yes	yes	no	yes	no
5	yes	younger	yes	no	no	no	no
6	yes	younger	no	yes	yes	no	no
7	yes	older	no	yes	yes	yes	yes
8	yes	younger	yes	no	no	no	yes
9	yes	younger	no	no	no	yes	yes
10	yes	older	no	no	no	no	no
11	no	younger	no	yes	yes	no	no
12	no	older	no	yes	yes	no	no
13	no	older	yes	yes	yes	yes	yes
14	no	younger	no	yes	yes	yes	yes
15	no	younger	no	yes	yes	no	yes
16	no	younger	no	no	yes	yes	no
17	no	older	no	no	no	yes	no
18	no	older	yes	yes	yes	no	no
19	no	older	yes	yes	yes	no	no
etc.	yes	younger	yes	no	no	no	yes

Nominal predictor variables
Age of offender
Previous imprisonment
Therapy
Contrition
Married
Sex offender

Binary dependent variable
Recidivism

FIGURE 42.1	Structure of an example

Box 42.3   Focus on

Score variables as predictors in logistic regression

It is important to realise that score variables can be used as the independent or predictor variables in binomial logistic regression. In this chapter, we concentrate on nominal (category) variables as independent/predictor variables to avoid cluttering the chapter overly. Score variables used in this way can be interpreted more or less as a binomial category/nominal variable would be, so do not add any real complexity. The difficulties come in relation to using a program such as SPSS to carry out the analysis when the user has to specify which predictor variables are score variables and which are category/nominal variables (see also Box 41.1).

Table 42.6	Data from Table 42.5 coded in binary fashion as 0 and 1 for each variable					
	Recidivism	Age	Previous prison term	Treatment	Contrite	Married	Sex offender
1	1	0	1	0	0	0	1
2	1	1	1	0	0	0	1
3	1	1	1	1	0	0	1
4	1	1	1	1	0	1	0
5	1	0	1	0	0	0	0
6	1	0	0	1	1	0	0
7	1	1	0	1	1	1	1
8	1	0	1	0	0	0	1
9	1	0	0	0	0	1	1
10	1	1	0	0	0	0	0
11	0	0	0	1	1	0	0
12	0	1	0	1	1	0	0
13	0	1	1	1	1	1	1
14	0	0	0	1	1	1	1
15	0	0	0	1	1	0	1
16	0	0	0	0	1	1	0
17	0	1	0	0	0	1	0
18	0	1	1	1	1	0	0
19	0	1	1	1	1	0	0
etc.	1	0	1	0	0	0	1

As with any sort of regression, we work with known data from a sample of individuals. The relationships are calculated between the independent variables and the dependent variable using the data from this sample. The relationships (usually expressed as B-weights) between the independent and dependent variables are sometimes generalised to further individuals who were not part of the original sample. In our example, knowing the characteristics of prisoners who re-offend, we would be less likely to release a particular prisoner showing the pattern of characteristics which is associated with re-offending.

The terms independent and dependent variable are frequently used in regression. The thing being 'predicted' in regression is often termed the dependent variable. It is important not to confuse this with cause-and-effect sequences. Variations in the independent variables are not assumed to *cause* the variation in the dependent variable. There might be a causal relationship, but not necessarily so. All that is sought is an association. To anticipate a potential source of confusion, it should be mentioned that researchers sometimes use a particular variable as both an independent and a dependent variable at different stages of an analysis.

The data in Table 42.5 could be prepared for analysis by coding the presence of a feature as 1 and the absence of a feature as 0. In a sense, it does not matter which category of the two is coded 1. However, the category coded 1 will be regarded as the category having influence or being influenced. In other words, if recidivism is coded 1 then the analysis is about predicting recidivism. If non-recidivism is coded 1 then the

values you have coded 1 in order that you can later understand what the analysis means. If you do not use codes 0 and 1 then the computer program often will impose them (SPSS does this, for example) and you will need to consult the output to find out what codings have been used for each of the values. The coding of the data can be seen by comparing the entries for Tables 42.5 and 42.6 (e.g. a code of 1 is given if the person is a recidivist).

42.3 Applying the logistic regression procedure

Logistic binary regression is only ever calculated using computers. The key steps involved are outlined in Figure 42.2. The output largely consists of three aspects:

- Regression calculations involving a constant and *B*-weights as for any form of regression. Table 42.7 gives the constant and *B*-weights for our calculation.

- Classification tables which show how well cases are classified by the regression calculation. These are to be found in Table 42.8.

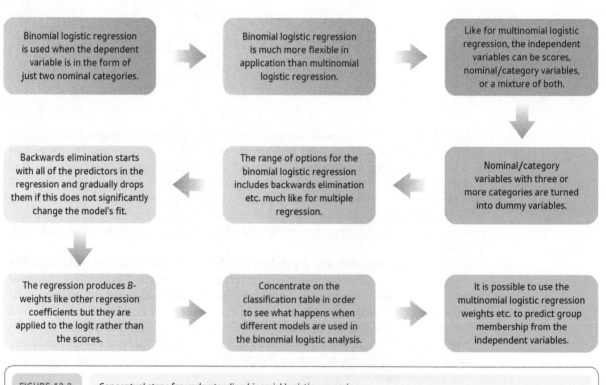

FIGURE 42.2   Conceptual steps for understanding binomial logistic regression

Table 42.7	Regression models for step 1 and step 2				
	B	Standard error	Wald	Degrees of freedom	Significance
Step 1					
Age (younger)	−2.726	0.736	13.702	1	.000
Previous convictions – yes	−1.086	0.730	2.215	1	.137
Treatment – no	19.362	8901.292	0.000	1	.998
Contrite – no	41.459	11325.913	0.000	1	.997
Married – no	−0.307	0.674	0.208	1	.648
Sex offender – no	−20.641	7003.92	0.000	1	.998
Constant	23.802	7003.92	0.000	1	.997
Step 2					
Age (younger)	−2.699	0.731	13.625	1	.000
Previous convictions – yes	−1.153	0.708	2.648	1	.104
Treatment – no	19.428	8895.914	0.000	1	.998
Contrite – no	−41.375	11337.365	0.000	1	.997
Sex offender – no	−20.475	7028.411	0.000	1	.998
Constant	23.542	7020.411	0.000	1	.997

Table 42.8	Classification tables having eliminated worst predictor		
	Not predicted recidivist	Predicted recidivist	Percentage correct
Step 1: *includes all predictor variables – age, previous imprisonment, treatment, contrition, married and sex offender*			
Not recidivist	45	5	90.0%
Recidivist	5	40	88.9%
			Overall correct 89.5%
Step 2: *married is dropped at this stage so age, previous imprisonment, contrition and sex offender remain in the analysis*			
Not recidivist	45	5	90.0%
Recidivist	5	40	88.9%
			Overall correct 89.5%
The analysis terminated at this stage.			

- Goodness-of-fit statistics which indicate, among other things, how much improvement (or worsening) is achieved in successive stages of the analysis. Some examples of these are presented in the text and in Table 42.9.

As with most forms of multiple regression, it is possible to stipulate any of a number of methods of doing the analysis. Entering all of the independent variables at one

Table 42.9	Omnibus tests of model coefficients		
	Chi-square	Degrees of freedom	Significance
Step 1			
Step	70.953	6	.000
Block	70.953	6	.000
Model	70.953	6	.000
Step 2			
Step	−0.210	1	.647
Block	70.743	5	.000
Model	70.743	5	.000

time is merely one of these options. Entering all predictors at the same time generally produces the simplest-looking computer output. Some of the alternatives to this method are discussed in Box 41.2 on discriminant function analysis on pp. 613–14 as they apply to many different forms of regression. To illustrate one of the possibilities, we will carry out *backwards elimination analysis* as our approach to the analysis of the data. There are several types of backwards elimination. Our choice is to use backwards stepwise conditional, which is one of the options readily available on SPSS. The precise mechanics of this form of analysis are really beyond a book of this nature.

In backwards elimination there is a minimum of three steps:

- Step 0 includes no predictors. Since we know the distribution of values on the *dependent* variable – in this case recidivism – then this would help us make an intelligent guess or prediction as to whether prisoners are likely to re-offend. Our study involves a sample of 95 prisoners. It emerged that 45 of them re-offended whereas the other 50 stayed on the straight and narrow. Hence, if we were to make a prediction in the absence of any other information, it would be that a prisoner will *not* re-offend since this is the most common outcome. This is shown in Table 42.10. Such a classification table indicates the accuracy of the prediction. If we predict that no prisoner will re-offend, then we are 100% correct for those who do not re-offend, and 0% correct (totally wrong) for those who do re-offend. The overall accuracy for the classification table (Table 42.8) is 52.6%. This is calculated from the total of correct predictions as a percentage of all predictions. That is, $50 \div 95 \times 100\% = 0.526 \times 100\% = 52.6\%$.

Table 42.10	Classification table based solely on distribution of re-offending – the step 0 classification table		
	Best prediction: re-offends	Best prediction: does not re-offend	% accuracy
Actually re-offends	0	45	0%
Actually no re-offending	0	50	100%
			Overall accuracy = 52.6%

- Step 1 (in backwards elimination) includes all of the predictors. That is, they are all entered at the same time. This step is to be found in Tables 42.7 and 42.8. This is a perfectly sound regression analysis in its own right. It is the simplest approach in order to maximise the classificatory power of the predictors.

- Step 2 involves the first stage of the backwards elimination. We obtain step 2 simply by eliminating the predictor which, if dropped from the step 1 model, makes no appreciable difference to the fit between the data and the predicted data (i.e. married – not). If omitting this predictor makes no difference to the outcome, it may be safely removed from the analysis. This is also illustrated in Tables 42.7 and 42.8. Dropping a variable means that the other values all have to be recalculated.

There may be further steps if it is possible to drop further ineffective predictors. The elimination of predictor variables in backwards elimination is not absolute. Instead, a predictor variable may be allowed back into the set of predictors at a later stage when other predictors have been eliminated. The reason for this is that the predictors are generally somewhat intercorrelated. As a consequence, the elimination of one predictor variable requires the recalculation of the predictive power associated with the other predictor variables. This means that sometimes a predictor which has previously been dropped from the analysis will return to the analysis at a later stage. There are no examples of the re-entry of variables previously dropped in our analysis – actually the analysis is now complete using our chosen method. Other methods of backwards elimination may involve more steps. There are criteria for the re-entry and dropping of predictors built into the statistical routine – the values of these may be varied.

The steps (step 0, step 1, step 2, etc.) could also be referred to as 'models'. A model is simply a (mathematical) statement describing the relationship of a set of predictors with what is being predicted. There are usually several ways of combining all or some of the predictor variables. What is the best model depends partly on the data but equally on the researcher's requirements. Often the ideal is a model that includes the minimum set of predictors that are correlated with (or predict) the dependent (predicted) variable.

Table 42.9 gives the goodness-of-fit statistics for the step 1 and step 2 models to the step 0 model. The significant value of chi-square indicates that the step 1 model is very different from the step 0 model. However, there is very little difference between the step 1 and step 2 models. Dropping the variable marital status from step 1 to give the step 2 model makes very little difference to the value of the chi-square – certainly not a significant difference. The computer output can be consulted to see the change if a particular predictor is removed though we have not reproduced such a table here. At step 2, having removed marital status makes a very small and non-significant change in fit. Indeed, marital status is selected for elimination because removing it produces the least change to the predictive power of the model. The chi-square value is -0.210 (the difference in the chi-square values) which indicates that the model is slightly less different from the step 0 model, but this chi-square is not significant (the probability is .647). Hence marital status was dropped from the model in step 2 because it makes little difference to the fit, whether included or not. The computer program then assesses the effect of dropping each of the predictors at step 2. Briefly, no further predictors could be dropped without significantly affecting the fit of the model to the data. So there is no step 3 to report in this example.

Table 42.8 gives the classification tables for steps 1 and 2. (Step 0 can be seen in Table 42.10.) At the step 1 stage, all of the predictors are entered because we are doing a backward elimination analysis. Comparing the step 0 and step 1 classification tables reveals that step 1 appears to be a marked improvement over the step 0 model. That is, the predictor variables in combination improve the prediction quite considerably. There are only 10 (i.e. 5 + 5) misclassifications and 85 (40 + 45) correct predictions using the step 1 model – an overall correct prediction rate of 85 ÷ 95 × 100% = 89.5%. If we released early, say, those prisoners predicted not to re-offend on the basis of our predictors then, overwhelmingly, they will not re-offend. At step 2, the classification table is exactly the same as for step 1. While the underlying model is clearly slightly different (see Table 42.7), in practical terms this is making no tangible difference in this case.

There is just one more useful statistic to be pulled from the computer output. This is known as the 'pseudo R^2' (see Section 41.6). It is roughly analogous to the multiple R^2 statistic used in multiple regression. It is a single indicator of how well the set of predictors predict. There are a number of such pseudo R^2. The Cox and Snell R-square and the Nagelkerke R-square are common ones. Several different ones may be given in the computer output. Although this is not shown in any of the tables, the value for the Cox and Snell R-square at step 2 is .525. This suggests a reasonably good level of prediction but there is clearly the possibility of finding further predictors to increase predictive power.

42.4 Regression formula

For most purposes, the above is sufficient. That is, we have generated reasonably powerful models for predicting the pattern of our data. The only really important task is making predictions about individuals based on their pattern on the predictor variables. If your work does not require individual predictions then there is no need for the following. Although we talk of prediction in relation to regression, this is often not the researcher's objective. Most typically, they are simply keen to identify the pattern of variables most closely associated with another variable (the dependent variable).

The predictor variables in our example are as follows:

- age – younger and older

- previous prison sentence or none

- treatment for offence or none

- contrition over offence or not

- marital status – married or not

- sex offender or not.

The dependent variable is recidivism (or not) following discharge from prison.

It is important to recall that all of the variables were coded in binary fashion using the following. That is:

- variables were coded as 1 if the characteristic is present

- variables were coded as 0 if the characteristic is absent.

By using these values, the predictors act as weights. It is important to note that multiplying by 0 means that we had nothing when we multiply values of 0 by their logistic regression weights. Computer programs such as SPSS usually recode binary variables for you in this way though care needs to be taken to check the output to find out just how the recoding has been done.

The basic formula for the prediction is:

predicted logit $=$ constant $+ (B_1 \times X_1) + (B_2 \times X_2) +$ etc.

That is, the formula predicts the logarithm of the odds of re-offending (recidivism) for an individual showing a particular pattern on the independent variables. X refers to the 'score' on a predictor variable (1 or 0 for a binary variable) which has to be multiplied by the appropriate regression weight (B). There is also a constant. It should be emphasised that this formula gives the predicted logit for a particular pattern of values on the independent variables. In other words, it is part of the calculation of the likelihood that a particular individual will re-offend though the predicted logit must be turned into odds and then probabilities before the likelihoods are known. It should be very clear from our step 2 model (Table 42.7) that the risk of re-offending is greater if the prisoner is young, has previous convictions, is undergoing treatment, is not contrite and is not a sex offender.

Just what is the likelihood that an individual with a particular pattern on the predictor variables will re-offend? Let us take a concrete example – an individual whose pattern is that he is younger, has previously been in prison, has undergone treatment, is not contrite and is not a sex offender. Younger, is not contrite and not a sex offender are coded 0 and has previously been in prison and has undergone treatment are coded 1. Using these codes and the regression weights form Table 42.7, the formula for the predicted logit then is:

$$\text{logit} = 23.542 + (0 \times -2.699) + (1 \times -1.153) + (1 \times 19.428) + (0 \times -41.375)$$
$$+ (0 \times -20.475)$$
$$= 23.542 + (0) + (-1.153) + (19.428) + (0) + (0)$$
$$= 41.817$$

This value for the logit of 41.817 translates approximately to odds of 3.733 of being in the re-offender rather than non-re-offender group with that pattern on the predictor variable. (That is, the natural logarithm of 3.733 is 41.817.) An odds ratio of 3.733 gives a probability of $3.733/(1 + 3.733) = 3.733 \div 4.733 = .79$ or 79%. This is rather approximate as the calculation has been subject to a rounding error. So a person with this particular pattern on the predictor variables is likely to re-offend.

42.5   Reporting the results

The reporting of any regression is somewhat dependent on the purpose of the analysis. Consequently, only the broad outlines can be given here. The final model has been chosen though there would be reason to choose some of the others in some circumstances. The following may be helpful as a structure for reporting one's findings:

A binomial logistic regression was conducted in order to find the set of predictors which best distinguish between the offending and re-offending group. All the predictor variables were binary coded as was the criterion predictors, offender group. The analysis employed backwards elimination of variables. The final model to emerge included five predictors of recidivism – being young, having previously been in prison, having undergone treatment, not being contrite and not being a sex offender. This model had a pseudo r -square of .53 using the Cox and Snell statistic which indicates that the fit of the model to the data possibly could be improved with the addition of further predictors. The success rate of the model was 90.0% for predicting non-re-offending and 88.9% for predicting re-offending.

Research examples

Binomial logistic regression

Dakwar and co-workers (2011) studied independent depression and substance-induced depression (the binomial dependent variable) in substance abusers. It is difficult to distinguish the two in clinical settings. Data were collected in a structured interview. Independent depression was found to be more likely if the individual's Hamilton Depression Scale score was higher and if there were a co-morbid diagnosis of post-traumatic stress disorder.

Ford, Howard and Oyebode (2012) investigated a number of psychological aspects of coeliac disease. This is an autoimmune medical condition which requires a lifelong diet free from gluten in the food. The condition has a number of unpleasant gastrointestinal ramifications and the other health risks associated. As a consequence, it can have a negative impact on the sufferer's feelings of psychological well-being. Some 288 sufferers were recruited for a postal questionnaire study which included dimensions such as health-related quality of life, self-efficacy, illness perceptions and dietary self-management. The researchers employed logistic regression to look at the factors which were associated with adherence to the gluten-free diet. The dependent variable was the measure of adherence to the diet split at the median to create two groups. Self-efficacy was lower in those who failed to adhere to the gluten-free diet. The measure of psychological well-being was unrelated to sticking to the diet or not.

Kenne, Boros and Fischbein (2010) studied factors associated with substance-dependent patients leaving detoxification against medical advice. This is a wasteful and costly outcome. The dependent variable was completion versus leaving against medical advice patients. Binomial logistic regression showed that 'the against medical advice leavers' were more likely to be unemployed and to claim that drug use did not impair their health. One suggestion is that extra effort could be made to identify those likely to leave treatment and put extra effort into retaining them in treatment.

Key points

- Given the power of binomial logistic regression to find the pattern of variables which are best able to differentiate two different groups of individuals in terms of their psychological characteristics, it might be regarded as a fundamental technique for any study comparing the characteristics of two groups of individuals. In other words, it is much more effective to use logistic regression than to carry out numerous t-tests on individual variables.

- Binomial logistic regression has great flexibility in the variety of variables used so long as the groups being compared are just two in number.

COMPUTER ANALYSIS

Binomial logistic regression using SPSS

Data
- Name the variables in 'Variable View' of the 'Data Editor'.
- Enter the data under the appropriate variables names in 'Data View' of the 'Data Editor' (Screenshot 42.1).

Analysis
- Select 'Analyze', 'Regression' and 'Binary Logistic...' (Screenshot 42.2).
- Move the dependent variable to the 'Dependent:' box, the predictors to the 'Covariate(s):' box and select 'Categorical...' (Screenshot 42.3).

2
- Move the categorical predictors to the 'Categorical Covariate(s):' box and select 'Continue' (Screenshot 42.4).

3
- Select the 'Method:' of entry from the dropdown menu next to this option (e.g. 'Backward conditional') and 'OK' (Screenshot 42.3).

Output
- Check the way the dependent variable has been coded in the 'Dependent Variable Encoding' table.

2
- Note the predictors in the 'Variables in the Equation' table for the final model and the direction of the association for the regression weights (Screenshot 42.5).

3
- Note the percentage of cases correctly identified in the 'Classification Table' for this model.

| FIGURE 42.3 | SPSS steps for binomial logistic regression |

Interpreting and reporting the output

- It is important that you know how the dependent variable has been coded so check in the output for this. The 'Variables in the Equation' output table (Screenshot 42.5) is the most important in terms of interpretation. Only the variable 'Age' is a significant predictor. The output removes the variable 'Married' in Step 2 but doing this makes no difference and the analysis stops. Thus only 'Age' is a significant predictor of the dependent variable which is 'Recidivist'.

- A brief report of the analysis might be: 'A backward conditional binomial logistic regression analysis examined which of the predictor variables predicted recidivism significantly. The only significant predictor was Age.'

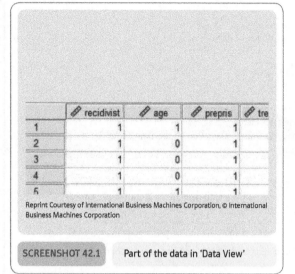

Reprint Courtesy of International Business Machines Corporation, © International Business Machines Corporation

| SCREENSHOT 42.1 | Part of the data in 'Data View' |

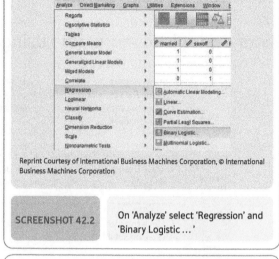

Reprint Courtesy of International Business Machines Corporation, © International Business Machines Corporation

| SCREENSHOT 42.2 | On 'Analyze' select 'Regression' and 'Binary Logistic ... ' |

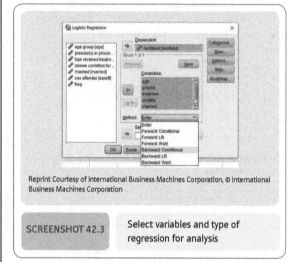

Reprint Courtesy of International Business Machines Corporation, © International Business Machines Corporation

| SCREENSHOT 42.3 | Select variables and type of regression for analysis |

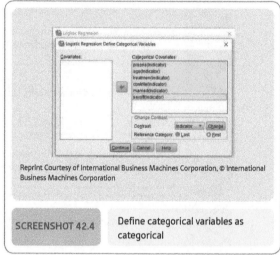

Reprint Courtesy of International Business Machines Corporation, © International Business Machines Corporation

| SCREENSHOT 42.4 | Define categorical variables as categorical |

Variables in the Equation

		B	S.E.	Wald	df	Sig.	Exp(B)
Step 1ᵃ	age group(1)	-2.726	.736	13.702	1	.000	.065
	previously in prison(1)	-1.086	.730	2.215	1	.137	.337
	has received treatment in prison(1)	19.362	8901.293	.000	1	.998	256354191.5
	shows contrition for offence(1)	-41.459	11325.914	.000	1	.997	.000
	married(1)	-.307	.674	.208	1	.648	.735
	sex offender(1)	-20.641	7003.093	.000	1	.998	.000
	Constant	23.802	7003.093	.000	1	.997	2.174E+10
Step 2ᵃ	age group(1)	-2.699	.731	13.625	1	.000	.067
	previously in prison(1)	-1.153	.708	2.648	1	.104	.316
	has received treatment in prison(1)	19.428	8895.914	.000	1	.998	273882274.4
	shows contrition for offence(1)	-41.375	11337.364	.000	1	.997	.000
	sex offender(1)	-20.475	7028.410	.000	1	.998	.000
	Constant	23.542	7028.410	.000	1	.997	1.675E+10

a. Variable(s) entered on step 1: age group, previously in prison, has received treatment in prison, shows contrition for offence, married, sex offender.

Reprint Courtesy of International Business Machines Corporation, © International Business Machines Corporation

| SCREENSHOT 42.5 | Important output |

CHAPTER 43

Data mining and big data

Overview

- Big data refers to the incredible amounts of digital information available as a result of social media, smart phones and other sources.

- Such data is regarded as being more action oriented compared to that provided in response to the research initiatives of researchers.

- The massive amounts of available data mean that samples are potentially very large and the numbers of possible variables similarly so. Statistical significance becomes much less important in this light than the magnitude of any relationships and their value. Furthermore, big data sets readily supply suitable large samples for cross validation. Weaknesses in traditional psychological research such as generally small sample sizes and the generality of null hypothesis significance testing may be corrected using big data.

- Consequently new analysis techniques are required to handle the sheer quantity of data as well as to capitalise on the advantages of this sort of data. Computers may have to be linked in order to cope with the potential data.

- Many of the statistics used with big data are similar to those that we have discussed in earlier chapters and should present no problems. However, few psychologists have the skills with computers involved in data scraping from websites, for example, and dealing with linking computers so as to cope with the storage and processing demands of big data. The answer is teamwork involving specialists.

Preparation

General familiarity with statistics from previous chapters.

43.1 Introduction

Many of the statistics commonly used by psychologists have a long history. Indeed, the statistical resources used in much psychological research are rarely state-of-the-art in terms of progress in the discipline of statistics. But this may change. The future of research in psychology may involve some radically different forms of data and statistics. This is not a prediction as there is evidence that these new approaches are already being deployed. The driving force for all of this literally lies in our hands. The digital world with which we are very familiar is massive in terms of the sheer quantity of available information. Whenever we use Facebook or Snapchat or any other digital platform including email and message boards, the stockpile of digitalised information is added too – multiply this by the number of users and the amount becomes colossal, if not unimaginable. In 2019, WhatsApp had 1 600 000 000 active users per month and Facebook Messenger 1 300 000 000 (https://www.statista.com/statistics/258749/most-popular-global-mobile-messenger-apps/). Startling figures, but only the beginning as there are many other platforms. There are probably more than 2 billion smart phone users worldwide (Arias, 2017) each generating masses of information. The world is awash with digital information and some fields have been quicker than psychology to utilise it. The commercial use of massive digital information is a good example. Consider the amount of data collected by supermarkets through the use of reward cards to realise its importance.

Digital information is data. Most of it, though, is not data as in the sense of a set of measurements (Chen & Wojciko, 2016) which constitutes the data for most psychological research. Initially, those trained in psychology may be reluctant to describe it as data. We are used to thinking of data as something which a researcher actively goes about creating, such as when an attitude questionnaire is developed and administered to participants. This data would not exist but for the active involvement of the researcher. Digital information is therefore almost entirely independent of the activities of researchers. Apart from this, the dividing line between information and data is otherwise hard to draw. There has been no reluctance in other disciplines to employ digital information as data and every reason why psychologists should do so too. Massive sets of digital data are generally termed big data though no precise definition is available in psychology but, at a minimum, it is an amount of data which could be stored by a one terabyte hard disc drive. There may be potential for big data to be turned into small data of the sort which most psychologists would be happy to analyse using their usual statistical resources. In relation to some research topics, big data may sometimes only contain a small amount of pertinent information. However, the fact that the research has sifted through a massive big data reserve means that specific research areas may be better serviced than in traditional research.

We have already hinted at possibly the most important reason for using digital information as data. It is not a response to the researcher but the result of the ordinary, everyday actions of large numbers of people. It might be asked, what is the best data – 1) the results of distributing questionnaire about anti-semitism to a sample of students or 2) identifying anti-semitic sentiments in Facebook messages? To be sure, they are not the same thing but the latter is behaviour instigated by the individual not by the researcher. While we may think that both have strengths and weakness, it is hard to deny the potential value of the digital information. Furthermore, it is unwise to ignore the increasing use of the digital media for purposes which would be tackled differently in the past. For example, Chhabra and Bryant (2016) point out that suicide notes seem to be increasingly left through the digital media rather than using pen and paper.

One important issue brought to the fore by the analysis of big data is that of data quality which may impact the extent to which research findings are generalisable (Cheung & Jak, 2018). It is difficult for the researcher to know the precise origins of the data and who controls the data. Although this is a common problem in psychological research in general, we cannot be sure about the nature of the population to which our findings may be legitimately applied. Cheung and Jak suggest that selection biases, even small ones, can materially affect outcomes since with massive samples the bias may erroneously generate significant findings. Of course, researchers who realise the importance of effect size may be less likely to be misled than those who regard statistical significance as king.

There are several obstacles in the way of using large-scale digital data:

1. By definition, there is so much of it that it would be hard for a researcher to store and process it on the typical workstation PC. The answer may lie in linking several computers together though, of course, sampling could work too.

2. Just how does the researcher obtain access to the digitalised information? The digital platforms may store the information but may be unwilling to share it with researchers for many reasons. For example, their users may not wish for what they see as private communications to be made available to researchers no matter how anonymised it is. Commercially valuable information is not likely to be shared. Of course, the obvious way of circumventing this problem is to collect information directly from the internet. There are techniques known as data scraping which do just that. You are probably familiar with the hotel booking sites which list the available prices of rooms. This information is almost certain to have come from data scraping off other websites.

3. Digital data are unlikely to be in the form that most psychologists would be happy to use. Mostly psychological data is collected in numerical form but digital data is frequently in verbal form. It is notable that most research publications in psychology use data in the form of scores and employ statistical analyses specifically geared to numerical scores. There are statistical techniques which can be used with verbal data. These mostly require that the verbal information is categorised. So statistics which deal with data in the form of categories are needed. Quite a few of these have been introduced in this book such as log linear analysis, etc.

4. The large number of variables and cases involved in digital data means that ordinary work-station computers need help, big time. So you will find that there are some statistical techniques which greatly reduce the amount of processing power needed. But ultimately linking computers is likely to be essential.

5. Few psychologists will have the ability with computers to cope with the demands for the analysis of large quantities of digital data. They should not be expected to have this expertise either. Dealing with big data almost invariably is a matter of teamwork. Quite clearly essential to this team will be experts in computing capable of linking computers, etc. Specialised statistical knowledge will almost certainly be required. Putting such a team together is a demanding task and not feasible for student research.

6. There are ethical and data protection implications when using big data for psychological research. So great care is needed to protect the identities of participants especially since they may inadvertently reveal rather a lot of identifying information about themselves (Oswald & Harlow, 2016).

Most psychologists will have at their fingertips the broad skills to analyse big data since they generally have experience of analytic strategies which are more or less similar from their training in traditional psychological research. Knowing about these is only of limited help since there is a great deal more to understand. Chen and Wojciko (2016) suggest that the real problem for psychologists is mastering just how Internet big data sources work from a software engineering perspective in order that they can be interfaced for data extraction. Not only this, detailed knowledge of the software employed to access the digital data may be demanding. Figure 43.1 lists just some of the steps needed by a psychologist planning big data research.

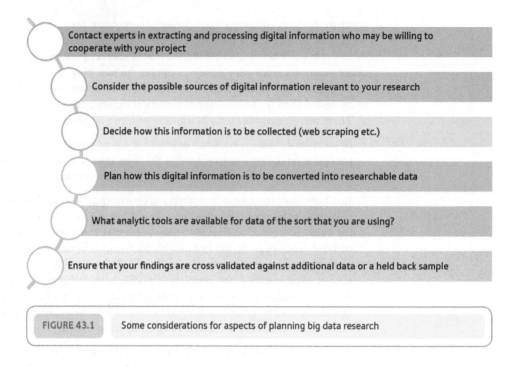

Contact experts in extracting and processing digital information who may be willing to cooperate with your project

Consider the possible sources of digital information relevant to your research

Decide how this information is to be collected (web scraping etc.)

Plan how this digital information is to be converted into researchable data

What analytic tools are available for data of the sort that you are using?

Ensure that your findings are cross validated against additional data or a held back sample

FIGURE 43.1   Some considerations for aspects of planning big data research

43.2   Adopting a new thinking mode

So what is data mining? This is perhaps the hardest thing to explain. It is difficult because there is no essential defining characteristic which separates data mining from data analysis in general. Some researchers have muddied the field a little by adopting the approach and its computing methods to the analysis of traditional forms of data set. Data mining is a data led approach to research. There is nothing complicated in this when we compare it with the traditional psychological approach to data analysis. Data mining highlights some of the problems with traditional data analysis. In this, data collection serves to evaluate a carefully defined research question or hypothesis developed on the basis of earlier research and theory. Whether explicitly stated or not, classical data collection advocates the rational and piece by piece development of understanding. It is a deductive process. Rampant empiricism is severely frowned upon as unfocused and lacking in a rational underpinning. Most psychologists will recognise the traditional approach from their training. It is an aspect of the academic approach which finds favour in academic circles. Despite this, is no other strategy possible?

Bear in mind that data mining does not originate from psychology or any closely related discipline. Data mining would not be possible without developments in computing and statistics. It was readily adopted by commercial interests in a quest for pragmatic and useful knowledge. All of this pushes us towards the idea that data mining simply trawls through massive data sets to find relationships which are of practical value. Some users of data mining are less concerned about academic niceties than others. For example, Brown (2014) takes a business oriented approach to data mining which can freely violate the normal assumptions of statistical techniques on the basis that what turns out to be useful is useful. Not surprisingly, some have referred to there being two distinct data analysis cultures (Cheung & Jak, 2018). A general definition of data mining involves a number of related aspects:

- The search for patterns (relationships) in massive data sets

- The integration of databases, statistics and intelligent machine learning techniques

- The presentation of the patterns in understandable ways including visual representations

One way of thinking about the differences is not that they lead to different knowledge but that the speed of travel to the destination is not the same. Using the traditional approach to data analysis – which involves the setting up of models or hypotheses about potential relationships – would scarcely touch the potential of big data. The careful steps involved are time consuming with no guarantee that the truly important relationships are identified with any alacrity. Data mining seeks a more direct route to finding relationships simply by encouraging the data to indicate what they are rather than confirm their existence.

Data mining should be rigorously distinguished from data dredging or data fishing. The latter concepts are essentially about capitalising on chance relationships in data sets. The researcher merely picks out substantial relationships between variables say from a correlation matrix and provides a story to explain why there should be a relationship. In the traditional academic model of data analysis, such practices are rewarded since statistically significant findings encourage journal editors to accept the ensuing paper for publication (Atkinson, Furlong & Wampold, 1982; Chan et al., 2004; Coursol & Wagner, 1986; Dickersin, Min & Meinert, 1992; Easterbrook et al., 1991). Data mining is actually substantially different from this. While ideas such as statistical significance are down-played in data mining for obvious reasons like the data sets involved are so large that statistical significance is not an issue, this does not mean that issues such as the reliability or replicability of the relationships found are ignored. With massive data sets, it is a quite easy to create two separate data sets or to split the data into two halves. One data set is known as the training set and is used to mine for relationships. This is sometimes referred to as the hold out sample in data mining. Once identified, the reliability or replicability of the findings may be assessed from whether they are found in the other data set; although this is generally referred to as cross-validation. Data mining therefore can have a built in reliability procedure or replication study. Traditional approaches to research may involve considerable delay before they are replicated, if at all. If data mining merely capitalised on chance relationships then the result would be useless relationships which fail to properly inform action.

Interestingly, qualitative methods in psychology often seek to find important relationships by starting with the data rather than the theory.

43.3 Dissatisfactions with traditional psychology

Substantial dissatisfaction has emerged over the years about the way in which psychologists do their statistical analyses. They do things which make a nonsense of their findings or, rather, find relationships which are nonsense. This goes far beyond obsession with null hypothesis significance testing or statistical significance. It is not a good idea to be overly obsessed with the statistical significance of one's research findings because there are more important things such as the size of the effect involved. If we take this for granted, then there are still other problems with much psychological research. For example, the common use of sample sizes which are inadequate to reliably detect statistically significant trends (Rossi, 1990). Also, there is the use of a number of informal procedures which have been described as researcher degrees of freedom. A good example of this might be termed sample size flexibility. This means that the researcher fails to stipulate the required sample size before commencing their study but runs the study for a while. Repeatedly, the researcher carries out a tentative data analysis and looks for statistically significant findings. When suitable ones are found, the collection of new data is stopped. The problem is that this procedure basically capitalises on chance trends which would disappear if data collection is continued. Another example is where the researcher uses several dependent variables but expunges those which show no significant trends: Again, this capitalises on chance trends. There are many other such examples (Kerr, 1998; John, Loewenstein & Prelec, 2012; Simmons, Nelson, & Simonsohn, 2011). The motivation for employing these procedures is unclear, but their use does help make sure that the researcher will have some significant findings to report even though these may not be the ones they were originally expecting. Statistically significant findings are at a premium in psychology since they increase the likelihood that a research paper will be accepted for publication in a journal (Smart, 1964; Wampold, Furlong, & Atkinson, 1983). Unfortunately, findings which simply exploit chance trends, will not be replicated in future research. While all of this may make sorry reading, the more important question is how research can be done better.

Yarkoni and Westfall (2017) are advocates of using big data approaches to psychological research. As part of this, they argue that the traditional approach to psychological research requires changing. In this, on the basis of background theory, researchers deduce what the likely relationships will be in their data. In other words, they build a model of the relationships likely to be found in the data. This is then tested statistically using a sample of data. If the model is effective then important relationships will be confirmed. However, there is no guarantee that this is the best model. Worst still, the researcher may find superficial evidence in favour of what is perceived as an entirely different model. This 'hallucination' may be adopted and written-up as if this was the intended model and the failed model forgotten. None of this is acceptable but examples are far from isolated. All of these things, and more, result in research findings exploiting chance trends. Models based on the exploitation (intended or not) of chance or error variation, are described as over determined in statistics. They may include real trends but definitely include chance trends. Tackling this general sort of problem can involve a variety of procedures including requiring the researcher to pre-register their planned analysis with the intended journal for the eventual publication before carrying out the research. Even ensuring that researchers are aware of the risk is a step forward. However, Yarkoni and Westfall suggest that the use of big data approaches may be preferable to traditional approaches to research and the risks that they entail. Moreover, despite the copious quantities of psychological research available on a wide variety of topics, predictions about new events are rarely made and generally are not too accurate.

43.4   Web scraping

There are many sources of big data, not all of them to be found on the Web. There may be considerable obstacles in the way of those wishing to use big data held by big organisations such as social media companies who may have little interest in cooperating with researchers for commercial as well as other reasons (Brown, 2014). One way of circumventing such gatekeepers is to employ Web scraping. This involves obtaining data directly from Web pages using automated processes which eventually turn the information on Web pages into structured data. Web scraping is quite common as a commercial practice such as when air tickets from many airlines are listed for sale by websites. Although they may not have come to your attention, there are substantial numbers of Web scraping programs available, many of them free. To review some of what is available, type 'Web scraping programs' into your favourite search engine and explore what it comes up with. There are several advantages in employing Web scraping in research. These include far larger sample sizes and the capability to have data ready for processing far more quickly than traditional survey methodologies would allow. Among the problems is that Web page owners can block the search process. For this reason, researchers are encouraged to limit the demand on the server's processing power which otherwise might result in blocking to protect the site.

There are archives which store, in snapshot form, Web pages from the past (e.g. http://archive.org/web/ or, alternatively, http://www.cachedpages.com/). As a consequence, it may be possible to introduce a longitudinal perspective to research. Automated web scraping is made possible because web pages are created using Hypertext Markup Language (HTML) such as used in HTML5. A web page can be regarded as a HTML file. Recent versions of HTML language indicate the semantic content of the webpage as well as containing meta information which is also machine readable.

You may find the following books also helping when starting with web scraping:

Aydin, O. (2018). *R Web Scraping Quick Start Guide*: *Techniques and tools to crawl and scrape data from websites*. Birmingham: Packt Publications.

Mitchell, R. (2018). *Web Scraping with Python*, Sebastopol, CA: O'Reilly Media.

43.5   Data mining and statistical techniques

There are no defining statistical techniques involved in data mining. And they are not necessarily complex either. For example, Landers, Brusso, Cavanaugh, and Collmus (2016) discuss many aspects of using scraped Web data. One thing which may be of particular interest to psychologists is their research case study which used Web scraping to test specific hypotheses derived from past research and preliminary perusal of the contents of a relevant depression message board. In other words, they adopted a hypothesis led approach typical of most psychological research. The hypothesis was that there is a gender difference in actively seeking social support to help deal with depression. They used the Web scraping tool 'Scrapy' which utilises the Python programing language to extract messages from the message board. Although the number of cases involved was very substantial compared with typical psychological research, the analysis employed the sort of statistics we discussed early in this book. So chi square (Chapter 18) was applied to show that females more commonly sought social support than males. At this stage in this book, you may be wondering why a test of significance was at all necessary since with a massive sample of messages in the analysis, even very minor trends are likely to be very significant as Landers et al. point out in their paper. The size of the trend is far more important with big data.

For reasons like this, graphic representations of data that we discussed early in this book – bar charts, scatterplots and the like – should never be overlooked or their importance downplayed. Many data miners, especially in commercial settings, would rely almost exclusively on graphical analyses. Data mining packages which use only graphical analysis techniques are not unknown. Quite often they get us closer to our data than a whole raft of numerically complex statistical techniques. Researchers using data mining approaches will eye-ball graphical representations of individual variables in the same way as any quantitative researcher should. They may be looking for data quality issues (Brown, 2014) but they may find surprising trends for some of the variables which otherwise might be overlooked. Of course, graphical methods include those showing relationships between variables which may also reveal important things in data. Many researchers may find graphical representations more informative than statistics like correlations, regression coefficients, and chi squares. Graphical methods are important for other reasons, not least of which they communicate clearly and effectively with clients and other audiences for research who lack statistical sophistication or an appetite for overly complex presentations. Given that data mining is intended to generate actionable findings, it may be essential for data miners to be convincing through the skilled use of graphical presentations. Big data research is almost certain to be sponsored research.

Quite a number of the statistics described earlier in this book have a role, especially when modified, in data mining. The various approaches to multiple regression would seem to be obvious contenders as statistical techniques for identifying patterns of relationships in data. The most likely form of multiple regression that would be recommended by statisticians in circumstances where the researcher has no hypotheses is stepwise multiple regression (Chapter 34). Although this may well identify a useful model to predict the criterion variable, it is not guaranteed. The reason is that stepwise multiple regression can only check out a few possibly satisfactory models. The more predictor variables there are the greater the chance that stepwise multiple regression will not include the ideal model – it is almost certain not to be included. The solution is obvious – try out all of the possible regression models. Given that we may have tens of different predictor variables in our data set, the number of separate multiple regressions which would have to be carried out is enormous as we have to analyse every possible subset of the predictor variables. This includes the model with all of the predictors, the models with all but one of the predictors, the models with all but two of the predictors, and so forth. Now you could do the required multiple regressions using SPSS one at a time but you would need multiple lifetimes. Davies (2008) suggests that a single computer would take a hundred years to complete the task for a model with 40 predictor variables. Things can be greatly speeded up by using several computers operating together which is known as parallel computing. The form of regression suitable for data mining purposes is known as all subsets regression. An extension of this called exhaustive regression (Davies, 2008) seeks to reduce the possibility of selecting spuriously good models which capitalise on chance. This is especially possible with very large data sets.

You will come across the term machine learning often in relation to big data. This is a distinctive field of computer science and statistics. It is not quite so difficult to understand its basics as to achieve the computer skills to carry it out. Sometimes the process is under the guidance of the researcher but it can be partially carried out by computers automatically. At root though, the idea is to establish the numerical values for a model linking a set of variables with outcomes. We did much the same thing, for example, when we discussed different forms of regression in earlier chapters. These numerical values are analogous to the regression weights we calculated in those chapters. Somewhat more technically, Hao and Ho (2019) describe machine learning as computer programming procedures '… that apply a mapping from a numerical representation of observations (also known as feature representation, typically as a fixed length feature vector) to some target values (as in regression) or categories (as in classification).' In machine learning, the learning process is the fitting of the numerical weights to models and is referred to as 'training'. Often, if not almost always, in traditional research, the end point of the analysis is when the parameters have been identified in the form of regression weights for each of the variables in the model. Not so in machine learning. Always in machine learning the model should be tested against new data to see if the model emerging out of the training phase is stable – that is, works much the same on the new data. With big data, there is almost certainly other data which can be used for this test process. It can be data held back from the available data specifically for this test phase. But it could be a totally different set of data or brand new data. It is possible to analyse the data using the test or held back data as if it were the training data and use the original training data as the test data. In other words, in machine learning as in all data mining, the initial analysis is immediately tested against other data. This is far from the case in traditional research even though it would be just as desirable to test the model before publishing the analysis.

A comprehensive guide to resources useful to psychologists seeking to use big data in their research or extract small data sets from it is Chen and Wojciko (2016). Quite often it is suggested that the Internet is a major resource for anyone interested in implementing a big data analysis. For example, Kosinski, Wang, Lakkaraju, and Leskovec (2016) use their Web based tutorial to describe forms of analysis. More generally, you may wish to study the following Website which identifies various free resources for data science in general: Elite Data Science. Free Data Science Resources for Beginners (https://elitedatascience.com/data-science-resources#technical-sk).

Key points

- The digital media social platforms and other sources of digital information, can provide data on a wide variety of topics relevant to psychologists. Although there are considerable problems to be faced in terms of the representativeness of these data, they are the result of people actively putting posts, etc. on to the internet in vast numbers. Researchers usually have no involvement in the creation of this information or data. The quantity of the information available far exceeds the typical data set for traditional psychological studies.

- Data mining and related approaches put the failings of traditional research into stark contrast with the advantages of large samples and free availability of checking samples when dealing with big data. Some of the poor practices of psychologists could be eliminated by the use of big data wherever possible including the use of inadequate sample sizes and the capitalising on chance trends.

- Big data approaches require analysis skills and computer knowledge which are well beyond the abilities of most psychologists because of the degree of specialisation involved. Hence psychologists wishing to engage in big data research need to be in a position to recruit the help of specialists in these fields. Big data related psychological publications are usually authored by a team of specialists in particular aspects of this challenging form of research.

Research examples

Big data, data mining and machine Learning

Schoedel, Au, Völkel et al. (2018) suggest that the use of digital data approaches could significantly contribute to psychological personality research. They identify sensation seeking as one such variable for which the internet has replaced more traditional expressions. Furthermore, much of the past research has concentrated on criminal exhibitions of sensation seeking. Most of the data was collected over a four week period via an app on volunteers' smart phones. Part of the data collected was based on aspects of smart phone and usage judged to be characteristic of sensation seeking. Things like the use of various apps thought to be sensation seeking related to variety of apps used, the variety of locations at which the phone was used, and so forth. They used machine learning and cross validation of the data. Although the relationship found between a questionnaire measure of sensation seeking and smart phone indicators of the same is interesting, the strength of the prediction from one to the other needs to be improved upon.

→

Song, Song, Seo and Jin (2016) analysed data for adolescents relevant to suicide data mined from South Korean websites including Twitter, for example. This country has a particularly high suicide rate. From over two billion items found using a Web crawler, they found almost 100,000 suicide related ones associated with adolescents. Terms such as hang oneself, kill oneself and suicide were the target. Automated text analysis was used to classify the Web content as pro, neutral or anti in relation to suicide. In addition, they had other data included on a monthly basis including number of bullying victims, employment rates, retail prices, and the suicide rate among young people. The analysis strategy included various structural models. The most important pathway led from education grade pressure through to depression to suicide risk. Suicide related words on the searched Website varied with monthly changes in employment, rental prices and bullying victimisation. The authors suggest that their research might lead to the automated identification of high suicide risk individuals and the possibility that they could be targeted with call-outs against suicide.

Symons, Feeney, Gallaher, et al. (2019) studied the effectiveness of clinicians compared to a substantial number of machine learning algorithms in terms of predicting the outcome of cognitive behavioural treatment for alcohol dependent people. The same data was used by the machine learning programs as the clinicians to make predictions about who would complete treatment and remain abstinent. The data included demographic, medical history, psychiatric history, family history of alcohol dependence, drinking history, and symptoms of alcohol dependence. There was very little difference between clinicians and computer programs in terms of the outcome variable prediction. The best of the algorithms was better than the worst of the clinicians though the signs were that this might not be a reliable finding.

Testing for excessively skewed distributions

The use of nonparametric tests (Mann–Whitney U-test, Wilcoxon matched pairs test) rather than parametric tests (unrelated t-test, related t-test) is conventionally recommended by some textbooks when the distribution of scores on a variable is significantly skewed (Chapter 21). There are a number of difficulties with this advice, particularly just how one knows that there is too much skew. It is possible to test for significant skewness. One simply computes skewness and then divides this by the standard error of the skewness. If the resulting value equals or exceeds 1.96 then your skewness is significant at the 5% level (two-tailed test) and the null hypothesis that your sample comes from a symmetrical population should be rejected.

A.1 Skewness

The formula for skewness is:

$$\text{skewness} = \frac{\left(\sum d^3\right)N}{SD^3 \times (N-1) \times (N-2)}$$

Notice that much of the formula is familiar: N is the number of scores, d is the deviation of each score from the mean of the sample, and SD is the estimated standard deviation of the scores (i.e. you use $N-1$ in the formula for standard deviation as described in Chapter 12).

What is different is the use of cubing. To cube a number you multiply it by itself twice. Thus the cube of 3 is $3 \times 3 \times 3 = 27$. A negative number cubed gives a negative number. Thus the cube of -4 is $(-4) \times (-4) \times (-4) = -64$.

We will take the data from Table 6.1 to illustrate the calculation of skewness. For simplicity's sake we will be using a definitional formula which involves the calculation of the sample mean. Table A.1 gives the data in column 1 as well as the calculation steps to be followed. The number of scores N equals 9.

Table A.1	Steps in the calculation of skewness		
Column 1 Age (years)	**Column 2** Scores – sample mean	**Column 3** Square values in column 2	**Column 4** Cube values in column 2
20	$20 - 23 = -3$	9	-27
25	$25 - 23 = 2$	4	8
19	$19 - 23 = -4$	16	-64
35	$35 - 23 = 12$	144	1728
19	$19 - 23 = -4$	16	-64
17	$17 - 23 = -6$	36	-216
15	$15 - 23 = -8$	64	-512
30	$30 - 23 = 7$	49	343
27	$27 - 23 = 4$	16	64
ΣX = sum of scores = 207		$\Sigma d^2 = 354$	$\Sigma d^3 = 1260$
$\bar{X}$ = mean score = 23			

For Table A.1,

$$\text{estimated standard deviation } (SD) = \sqrt{\frac{\Sigma d^2}{N - 1}}$$

$$= 6.652$$

Substituting this value and the values from the table in the formula for skewness we get:

$$\text{skewness} = \frac{1260 \times 9}{6.652^3 \times (9 - 1) \times (9 - 2)}$$

$$= \frac{11340}{16\,483.321}$$

$$= 0.688$$

(Skewness could have a negative value.)

A.2   Standard error of skewness

The standard error of skewness involves calculating the value of the following formula for our particular sample size ($N = 9$):

$$\text{standard error of skewness} = \sqrt{\frac{6 \times N \times (N - 1)}{(N - 2) \times (N + 1) \times (N + 3)}}$$

$$= \sqrt{\frac{432}{840}}$$

$$= \sqrt{0.514}$$

The significance of skewness involves a z-score:

$$z = \frac{\text{skewness}}{\text{standard error of skewness}}$$

$$= \frac{0.688}{0.717}$$

$$= 0.96$$

This value of z is lower than the minimum value of z (1.96) required to be statistically significant at the 5% level with a two-tailed test. Thus the scores are *not* extremely skewed. This implies that you may use parametric tests rather than nonparametric tests for comparisons involving this variable. Obviously you need to do the skewness test for the other variables involved.

For the related t-test, it is the skewness of the *differences* between the two sets of scores which needs to be examined, not the skewnesses of the two different sets of scores.

Large-sample formulae for the nonparametric tests

Sometimes you may wish to do a nonparametric test when the sample sizes exceed the tabulated values of the significance tables in Chapter 21. In these circumstances we would recommend using a computer. The reason is that ranking large numbers of scores is extremely time consuming and you risk making errors. However, if a computer is not available to do the analyses, you can make use of the following large-sample formulae for nonparametric tests.

B1.1 Mann–Whitney U-test

$$z = \frac{U - \dfrac{n_1 n_2}{2}}{\sqrt{\left(\dfrac{n_1 n_2}{N(N-1)}\right)\left(\dfrac{N^3 - N}{12} - \Sigma \dfrac{t^3 - 1}{12}\right)}}$$

U is as calculated in Chapter 21, n_1 and n_2 are the sizes of the two samples, and N is the sum of n_1 and n_2. t is a new symbol in this context: the number of scores tied at a particular value. Thus if you have three scores of 6 in your data, $t = 3$ for the score 6.

Notice that Σ precedes the part of the formula involving t. This indicates that for every score which has ties you need to do the calculation for the number of ties involved *and* sum all of these separate calculations. Where there are no ties, this part of the formula reduces to zero.

The calculated value of z must equal or exceed 1.96 to be statistically significant with a two-tailed test.

B1.2   Wilcoxon matched pairs test

$$z = \frac{T - \dfrac{N(N + 1)}{4}}{\sqrt{\dfrac{N(N + 1)(2N + 1)}{24}}}$$

T is the value of the Wilcoxon matched pairs statistic as calculated in Chapter 21. N is the number of pairs of scores in that calculation.

As before, z must equal or exceed 1.96 to be statistically significant with a two-tailed test.

APPENDIX B2

Nonparametric tests for three or more groups

Several nonparametric tests were described in Chapter 21. However, these dealt with circumstances in which only two sets of scores were compared. If you have three or more sets of scores there are other tests of significance which can be used. These are nowhere near so flexible and powerful as the analyses of variance described in Chapters 23–28.

B2.1 Kruskal–Wallis three or more unrelated conditions test

The Kruskal–Wallis test is used in circumstances where there are *more than two* groups of independent or unrelated scores. All of the scores are *ranked* from lowest to highest irrespective of which group they belong to. The average rank in each group is examined. If the null hypothesis is true, then all groups should have more or less the same average rank.

Imagine that the reading abilities of children are compared under three conditions: 1) high motivation, 2) medium motivation and 3) low motivation. The data might be as in Table B2.1. Different children are used in each condition so the data are unrelated. The scores on the dependent variable are on a standard reading test.

The scores are ranked from lowest to highest, ignoring the particular group they are in. Tied scores are given the average of the ranks they would have been given if they were different (Chapter 21). The results of this would look like Table B2.2, which also includes:

- Row A: the mean rank in each condition

- Row B: the square of the sum of the ranks in each condition

- Row C: the square of the sum of ranks from row B divided by the number of scores in each condition

- Row D: R which equals the sum of the squares of the sums of ranks divided by the sample size, i.e. the sum of the figures in row C.

Table B2.1	Reading scores under three different levels of motivation	
High motivation	**Medium motivation**	**Low motivation**
17	10	3
14	11	9
19	8	2
16	12	5
18	9	1
20	11	7
23	8	6
21	12	
18	9	
	10	

Table B2.2	Scores in Table B2.1 ranked from smallest to largest		
Row	**High motivation**	**Medium motivation**	**Low motivation**
	20	12.5	3
	18	14.5	10
	23	7.5	2
	19	16.5	4
	21.5	10	1
	24	14.5	6
	26	7.5	5
	25	16.5	
	21.5	10	
		12.5	
A	Mean ranks $= \dfrac{198}{9} = 22.0$	Mean ranks $= \dfrac{122}{10} = 12.20$	Mean ranks $= \dfrac{31}{7} = 4.43$
B	Sum of ranks$^2 = 198^2 = 39\,204$	Sum of ranks$^2 = 122^2 = 14\,884$	Sum of ranks$^2 = 31^2 = 961$
C	Mean ranks$^2 = \dfrac{39\,204}{9} = 4356.00$	Mean ranks$^2 = \dfrac{14\,884}{10} = 1488.40$	Mean ranks$^2 = \dfrac{961}{7} = 137.29$
D	R = sum of calculations in row C = 4356.00 + 1488.40 + 137.29 = 5981.69		

The statistic H is calculated next using the following formula:

$$H = \frac{12R}{N(N+1)} - 3(N+1)$$

where R is the sum of the mean rank squared in Row D in Table B2.2 and N is the number of scores ranked. Substituting,

$$H = \frac{12 \times 5981.69}{26(26 + 1)} - 3(26 + 1)$$

$$= \frac{71780.28}{702} - 81$$

$$= 102.251 - 81$$

$$= 21.25$$

The distribution of H approximates that of chi-square. The degrees of freedom are the number of different groups of scores minus one. Thus the significance of H can be assessed against Significance Table 18.1 which tells us that our value of H needs to equal or exceed 6.0 to be significant at the 5% level (two-tailed test). Thus we reject our null hypothesis that reading was unaffected by levels of motivation.

B2.2 Friedman three or more related samples test

This test is used in circumstances in which you have three or more *related* samples of scores. The scores for each participant in the research are ranked from smallest to largest separately. In other words, the scores for Joe Bloggs are ranked from 1 to 3 (or however many conditions there are), the scores for Jenny Bloggs are also ranged from 1 to 3 and so forth for the rest. The test essentially examines whether the average ranks in the several conditions of the experiment are more or less equal, as they should be if the null hypothesis is true.

Table B2.3 gives the scores in an experiment to test the recall of pairs of nonsense syllables under three conditions – high, medium and low distraction. The same participants were used in all conditions of the experiment.

Table B2.4 shows the scores ranked from smallest to largest for each participant in the research separately. Ties are given the average of the ranks that they would have otherwise been given.

- Row A gives the sums of the ranks for each condition or level of distraction.

- Row B gives the square of each sum of ranks for each condition.

- Row C gives the total, R, of the squared sums of ranks from row B.

Table B2.3	Scores on memory ability under three different levels of distraction		
	Low distraction	**Medium distraction**	**High distraction**
John	9	6	7
Mary	15	7	2
Shaun	12	9	5
Edmund	16	8	2
Sanjit	22	15	6
Ann	8	3	4

Table B2.4	Scores ranked separately for each participant		
	Low distraction	**Medium distraction**	**High distraction**
John	3	1	2
Mary	3	2	1
Shaun	3	2	1
Edmund	3	2	1
Sanjit	3	2	1
Ann	3	1	2
Row A	Sum of ranks = 18	Sum of ranks = 10	Sum of ranks = 8
Row B	Square = $18^2 = 324$	Square = $10^2 = 100$	Square = $8^2 = 64$
Row C	R = sum of above squares = $324 + 100 + 64 = 488$		

The value of R is entered in the following formula:

$$\chi_r^2 = \frac{12R}{nK(K+1)} - 3n(K+1)$$

where n is the number of participants (i.e. of rows of scores) = 6, and K is the number of columns of data (i.e. of different conditions) = 3. Therefore,

$$\chi_r^2 = \frac{12 \times 488}{6 \times 3 \times (3+1)} - 3 \times 6 \times (3+1)$$

$$= \frac{5856}{72} - 72$$

$$= 9.33$$

The statistical significance of χ_r^2 is assessed using the chi-square table (Significance Table 18.1). The degrees of freedom are the number of conditions − 1 = 3 − 1 = 2. This table tells us that a value of 6.0 or more is needed to be statistically significant at the 5% level (two-tailed test). Thus, it appears that the null hypothesis that the conditions have no effect should be rejected in favour of the hypothesis that levels of distraction influence memory.

COMPUTER ANALYSIS

Kruskal–Wallis and Friedman nonparametric tests using SPSS

Data
- Name the variables in 'Variable View' of the 'Data Editor'.
- Enter the data under the appropriate variable names in 'Data View' of the 'Data Editor'.

Analysis
- For the Kruskal–Wallis unrelated test, select 'Analyze', 'Nonparametric Tests' 'Legacy Dialogs' and 'K Independent Samples. . .' (Screenshot B2.1).

2
- Move the appropriate test (dependent) and grouping (independent) variables to the two boxes to the right, defining the range for the grouping variables (Screenshot B2.2).

3
- For the Friedman related test, select 'Analyze', 'Nonparametric Tests' 'Legacy Dialogs' and 'K Related Samples. . .' (Screenshot B2.3).

4
- Move the appropriate variables to the box to the right and ensure 'Friedman' is selected (Screenshot B2.4).

Output
- Check to see if the p value is significant at .05 or less (Screenshots B2.5 and B2.6).
- If it is, conduct further tests to see where the significant difference are.

FIGURE B2.1   SPSS steps for Kruskal–Wallis and Friedman nonparametric tests

Interpreting and reporting the output

- We could report the Kruskal–Wallis results for the data in Screenshot B2.5 for the data in Table B2.1 as follows: 'The Kruskal–Wallis test found that the reading scores in the three motivation conditions differed significantly, $\chi^2(2) = 21.31$, two-tailed $p = .001$.' We would then follow this with reporting the results of further tests to determine which groups differed significantly and in what direction.

- We could report the Friedman results of the data in Screenshot B2.6 for the data in Table B2.3 as follows: 'There was a significant difference in recall in the three conditions, Friedman $\chi^2(n = 6) = 9.33, p < .009$.' We would then need to report the results of further tests to determine which groups differed significantly and in what direction.

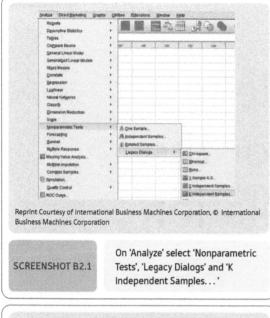

Reprint Courtesy of International Business Machines Corporation, © International Business Machines Corporation

| SCREENSHOT B2.1 | On 'Analyze' select 'Nonparametric Tests', 'Legacy Dialogs' and 'K Independent Samples. . .' |

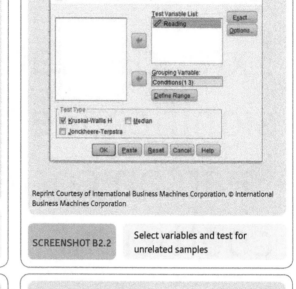

Reprint Courtesy of International Business Machines Corporation, © International Business Machines Corporation

| SCREENSHOT B2.2 | Select variables and test for unrelated samples |

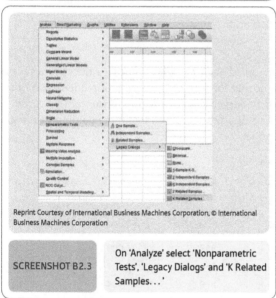

Reprint Courtesy of International Business Machines Corporation, © International Business Machines Corporation

| SCREENSHOT B2.3 | On 'Analyze' select 'Nonparametric Tests', 'Legacy Dialogs' and 'K Related Samples. . .' |

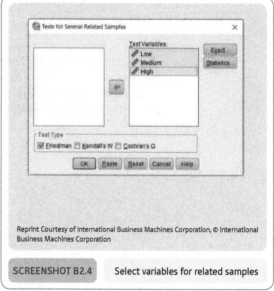

Reprint Courtesy of International Business Machines Corporation, © International Business Machines Corporation

| SCREENSHOT B2.4 | Select variables for related samples |

Kruskal-Wallis Test

Ranks

	Conditions	N	Mean Rank
Reading	High	9	22.00
	Medium	10	12.20
	Low	7	4.43
	Total	26	

Test Statistics[a,b]

	Reading
Chi-Square	21.317
df	2
Asymp. Sig.	.000

a. Kruskal Wallis Test

b. Grouping Variable: Conditions

Reprint Courtesy of International Business Machines Corporation, © International Business Machines Corporation

Ranks

	Mean Rank
Low	3.00
Medium	1.67
High	1.33

Test Statistics[a]

N	6
Chi-Square	9.333
df	2
Asymp. Sig.	.009

a. Friedman Test

Reprint Courtesy of International Business Machines Corporation, © International Business Machines Corporation

Extended table of significance for the Pearson correlation coefficient

The following table gives both two-tailed and one-tailed values for the significance of the Pearson correlation coefficient. Ignoring the sign of the correlation coefficient obtained, your value has to be equal to, or be larger than, the value in the table in order to be statistically significant at the level of significance stipulated in the column heading.

Sample size	Two-tailed: 10% One-tailed: 5%	Two-tailed: 5% One-tailed: 2.5%	Two-tailed: 2% One-tailed: 1%	Two-tailed: 1% One-tailed: 0.5%
3	.988	.997	1.000	1.000
4	.900	.950	.980	.990
5	.805	.878	.934	.959
6	.729	.811	.882	.917
7	.669	.754	.833	.875
8	.621	.707	.808	.834
9	.582	.666	.750	.798
10	.549	.632	.715	.765
11	.521	.602	.685	.735
12	.497	.576	.658	.708
13	.476	.553	.634	.684
14	.458	.532	.612	.661
15	.441	.514	.592	.641
16	.426	.497	.574	.623
17	.412	.482	.558	.606

Sample size	Two-tailed: 10% One-tailed: 5%	Two-tailed: 5% One-tailed: 2.5%	Two-tailed: 2% One-tailed: 1%	Two-tailed: 1% One-tailed: 0.5%
18	.400	.468	.543	.590
19	.389	.456	.529	.575
20	.378	.444	.516	.561
21	.369	.433	.503	.549
22	.360	.423	.492	.537
23	.352	.413	.482	.526
24	.344	.404	.472	.515
25	.337	.396	.462	.505
26	.330	.388	.453	.496
27	.323	.382	.445	.487
28	.317	.374	.437	.479
29	.311	.367	.430	.471
30	.306	.361	.423	.463
31	.301	.355	.416	.456
32	.296	.349	.409	.449
33	.291	.344	.403	.442
34	.287	.339	.397	.436
35	.283	.334	.392	.430
36	.279	.329	.386	.424
37	.275	.325	.381	.418
38	.271	.320	.376	.413
39	.267	.316	.371	.408
40	.264	.312	.367	.403
41	.260	.308	.362	.398
42	.257	.304	.358	.393
43	.254	.301	.354	.389
44	.251	.297	.350	.384
45	.248	.294	.346	.380
46	.246	.291	.342	.376
47	.243	.288	.338	.372
48	.240	.285	.335	.368
49	.238	.282	.331	.365
50	.235	.279	.328	.361
51	.233	.276	.325	.358
52	.231	.273	.322	.354
53	.228	.271	.319	.351
54	.226	.268	.316	.348
55	.224	.266	.313	.345
56	.222	.263	.310	.341
57	.220	.261	.307	.339
58	.218	.259	.305	.336
59	.216	.256	.302	.333
60	.214	.254	.300	.330

Sample size	Two-tailed: 10% One-tailed: 5%	Two-tailed: 5% One-tailed: 2.5%	Two-tailed: 2% One-tailed: 1%	Two-tailed: 1% One-tailed: 0.5%
62	.211	.250	.295	.325
63	.209	.248	.293	.322
64	.207	.246	.290	.320
65	.206	.244	.288	.317
66	.204	.242	.286	.315
67	.203	.240	.284	.313
68	.201	.239	.282	.310
69	.200	.237	.280	.308
70	.198	.235	.278	.306
71	.197	.234	.276	.304
72	.195	.232	.274	.302
73	.194	.230	.272	.300
74	.193	.229	.270	.298
75	.191	.227	.268	.296
76	.190	.226	.266	.294
77	.189	.224	.265	.292
78	.188	.223	.263	.290
79	.186	.221	.261	.288
80	.185	.220	.260	.286
81	.184	.219	.258	.285
82	.183	.217	.257	.283
83	.182	.216	.255	.281
84	.181	.215	.253	.280
85	.180	.213	.252	.278
86	.179	.212	.251	.276
87	.178	.211	.249	.275
88	.176	.210	.248	.273
89	.175	.208	.246	.272
90	.174	.207	.245	.270
91	.174	.206	.244	.269
92	.173	.205	.242	.267
93	.172	.204	.241	.266
94	.171	.203	.240	.264
95	.170	.202	.238	.263
96	.169	.201	.237	.262
97	.168	.200	.236	.260
98	.167	.199	.235	.259
99	.166	.198	.234	.258
100	.165	.197	.232	.256
200	.117	.139	.164	.182
300	.095	.113	.134	.149
400	.082	.098	.116	.129
500	.074	.088	.104	.115

Table of significance for the Spearman correlation coefficient

The following table gives both two-tailed and one-tailed values for the significance of the Spearman correlation coefficient. Ignoring the sign of the correlation coefficient obtained, your value has to equal or be larger than the value in the table in order to be statistically significant at the level of significance stipulated in the column heading. If there are ties then the significance level becomes increasingly inaccurate.

Sample size	Two-tailed: 10% One-tailed: 5%	Two-tailed: 5% One-tailed: 2.5%	Two-tailed: 2% One-tailed: 1%	Two-tailed: 1% One-tailed: 0.5%
5	.900	–	–	–
6	.829	.886	.943	–
7	.714	.786	.893	–
8	.643	.738	.833	.881
9	.600	.683	.783	.833
10	.564	.648	.745	.858
11	.520	.620	.737	.814
12	.496	.591	.703	.776
13	.475	.566	.673	.743
14	.456	.544	.646	.714
15	.440	.524	.623	.688
16	.425	.506	.602	.665
17	.411	.490	.583	.644
18	.399	.475	.565	.625
19	.388	.462	.549	.607

Sample size	Two-tailed: 10% One-tailed: 5%	Two-tailed: 5% One-tailed: 2.5%	Two-tailed: 2% One-tailed: 1%	Two-tailed: 1% One-tailed: 0.5%
20	.377	.450	.535	.591
21	.368	.438	.521	.576
22	.359	.428	.508	.562
23	.351	.418	.497	.549
24	.343	.409	.486	.537
25	.336	.400	.476	.526
26	.329	.392	.466	.515
27	.323	.384	.457	.505
28	.317	.377	.448	.496
29	.311	.370	.440	.487
30	.305	.364	.433	.478
31	.300	.358	.425	.470
32	.295	.352	.418	.462
33	.291	.346	.412	.455
34	.286	.341	.406	.448
35	.282	.336	.400	.442
36	.278	.331	.394	.435
37	.274	.327	.388	.429
38	.270	.322	.383	.423
39	.267	.318	.378	.418
40	.263	.314	.373	.412
41	.260	.310	.368	.407
42	.257	.306	.364	.402
43	.254	.302	.360	.397
44	.251	.299	.355	.393
45	.248	.295	.351	.388
46	.245	.292	.347	.384
47	.243	.289	.344	.380
48	.240	.286	.340	.376
49	.237	.283	.336	.372
50	.235	.280	.333	.368
51	.233	.277	.330	.364
52	.230	.274	.326	.361
53	.228	.272	.323	.357
54	.226	.269	.320	.354
55	.224	.267	.317	.350
56	.222	.264	.314	.347
57	.220	.262	.311	.344
58	.218	.260	.309	.341
59	.216	.257	.306	.338
60	.214	.255	.303	.335
61	.212	.253	.301	.332
62	.211	.251	.298	.330

Sample size	Two-tailed: 10% One-tailed: 5%	Two-tailed: 5% One-tailed: 2.5%	Two-tailed: 2% One-tailed: 1%	Two-tailed: 1% One-tailed: 0.5%
63	.209	.249	.296	.327
64	.207	.247	.294	.324
65	.206	.245	.291	.322
66	.204	.243	.289	.319
67	.202	.241	.287	.317
68	.201	.239	.285	.315
69	.199	.238	.283	.312
70	.198	.236	.280	.310
71	.197	.234	.278	.308
72	.195	.233	.277	.306
73	.194	.231	.275	.303
74	.193	.229	.273	.301
75	.191	.228	.271	.299
76	.190	.226	.269	.297
77	.189	.225	.267	.295
78	.187	.223	.266	.293
79	.186	.222	.264	.292
80	.185	.221	.262	.290
81	.184	.219	.261	.288
82	.183	.218	.259	.286
83	.182	.216	.257	.284
84	.181	.215	.256	.283
85	.179	.214	.254	.281
86	.178	.213	.253	.279
87	.177	.211	.251	.278
88	.176	.210	.250	.276
89	.175	.209	.248	.274
90	.174	.208	.247	.273
91	.173	.207	.246	.271
92	.172	.205	.244	.270
93	.172	.204	.243	.268
94	.171	.203	.242	.267
95	.170	.202	.240	.266
96	.169	.201	.239	.264
97	.168	.200	.238	.263
98	.167	.199	.237	.261
99	.166	.198	.235	.260
100	.165	.197	.234	.259
200	.117	.139	.165	.183
300	.095	.113	.135	.149
400	.082	.098	.117	.129
500	.074	.088	.104	.115
1000	.052	.062	.074	.081

APPENDIX E

Extended table of significance for the *t*-test

The following table gives two-tailed and one-tailed significance values for the *t*-test. The value of *t* which you obtain (ignoring sign) in your calculation has to equal or be larger than the listed value in order to be statistically significant at the level of significance given in each column heading.

For the related *t*-test the degrees of freedom are the *number of pairs* of scores −1.

For the unrelated *t*-test the degrees of freedom are the number of scores −2.

Degrees of freedom	Two-tailed: 10% One-tailed: 5%	Two-tailed: 5% One-tailed: 2.5%	Two-tailed: 2% One-tailed: 1%	Two-tailed: 1% One-tailed: 0.5%
1	6.314	12.706	31.820	63.657
2	2.920	4.303	6.965	9.925
3	2.353	3.182	4.541	5.841
4	2.132	2.776	3.747	4.604
5	2.015	2.571	3.365	4.032
6	1.943	2.447	3.143	3.708
7	1.895	2.365	2.998	3.500
8	1.860	2.306	2.897	3.355
9	1.833	2.262	2.821	3.250
10	1.813	2.228	2.764	3.169
11	1.796	2.201	2.718	3.106
12	1.782	2.179	2.681	3.055
13	1.771	2.160	2.650	3.012
14	1.761	2.145	2.625	2.977
15	1.753	2.132	2.603	2.947
16	1.746	2.120	2.583	2.921
17	1.740	2.110	2.567	2.898
18	1.734	2.101	2.552	2.878

Degrees of freedom	Two-tailed: 10% One-tailed: 5%	Two-tailed: 5% One-tailed: 2.5%	Two-tailed: 2% One-tailed: 1%	Two-tailed: 1% One-tailed: 0.5%
19	1.729	2.093	2.539	2.861
20	1.725	2.086	2.528	2.845
21	1.721	2.080	2.518	2.831
22	1.717	2.074	2.508	2.819
23	1.714	2.069	2.500	2.807
24	1.711	2.064	2.492	2.797
25	1.708	2.064	2.485	2.787
26	1.706	2.055	2.479	2.779
27	1.703	2.052	2.473	2.771
28	1.701	2.048	2.467	2.763
29	1.699	2.045	2.462	2.756
30	1.697	2.042	2.457	2.750
31	1.696	2.039	2.453	2.744
32	1.694	2.037	2.449	2.739
33	1.692	2.035	2.445	2.733
34	1.691	2.032	2.441	2.728
35	1.690	2.030	2.438	2.724
36	1.688	2.028	2.434	2.720
37	1.687	2.026	2.431	2.715
38	1.686	2.024	2.429	2.712
39	1.685	2.023	2.426	2.708
40	1.684	2.021	2.423	2.704
41	1.683	2.020	2.421	2.701
42	1.682	2.018	2.418	2.698
43	1.681	2.017	2.416	2.695
44	1.680	2.017	2.414	2.692
45	1.679	2.014	2.412	2.690
46	1.679	2.013	2.410	2.687
47	1.678	2.012	2.408	2.685
48	1.677	2.011	2.408	2.682
49	1.677	2.010	2.405	2.680
50	1.676	2.009	2.403	2.678
51	1.675	2.008	2.402	2.676
52	1.675	2.007	2.400	2.674
53	1.674	2.006	2.399	2.672
54	1.674	2.005	2.397	2.670
55	1.673	2.004	2.396	2.668
56	1.672	2.003	2.395	2.667
57	1.672	2.002	2.394	2.665
58	1.672	2.002	2.392	2.663
59	1.671	2.001	2.391	2.662
60	1.671	2.000	2.390	2.660
61	1.670	2.000	2.389	2.659
62	1.670	1.999	2.388	2.658

Degrees of freedom	Two-tailed: 10% One-tailed: 5%	Two-tailed: 5% One-tailed: 2.5%	Two-tailed: 2% One-tailed: 1%	Two-tailed: 1% One-tailed: 0.5%
63	1.669	1.998	2.387	2.656
64	1.669	1.998	2.386	2.655
65	1.669	1.997	2.385	2.654
66	1.668	1.997	2.384	2.652
67	1.668	1.996	2.383	2.651
68	1.668	1.995	2.383	2.650
69	1.667	1.995	2.382	2.649
70	1.667	1.994	2.381	2.648
71	1.667	1.994	2.380	2.647
72	1.666	1.994	2.379	2.646
73	1.666	1.993	2.379	2.645
74	1.666	1.993	2.378	2.644
75	1.665	1.992	2.377	2.643
76	1.665	1.992	2.376	2.642
77	1.665	1.991	2.376	2.641
78	1.665	1.991	2.375	2.640
79	1.664	1.990	2.375	2.640
80	1.664	1.990	2.374	2.639
81	1.664	1.990	2.373	2.638
82	1.664	1.989	2.373	2.637
83	1.663	1.989	2.372	2.636
84	1.663	1.989	2.372	2.636
85	1.663	1.988	2.371	2.635
86	1.663	1.988	2.370	2.634
87	1.663	1.988	2.370	2.634
88	1.662	1.987	2.369	2.633
89	1.662	1.987	2.369	2.632
90	1.662	1.987	2.369	2.632
91	1.662	1.986	2.368	2.631
92	1.662	1.986	2.368	2.630
93	1.661	1.986	2.367	2.630
94	1.661	1.986	2.367	2.629
95	1.661	1.985	2.366	2.629
96	1.661	1.985	2.366	2.628
97	1.661	1.985	2.365	2.627
98	1.661	1.984	2.365	2.627
99	1.660	1.984	2.365	2.626
100	1.660	1.984	2.364	2.626
200	1.653	1.972	2.345	2.601
300	1.650	1.968	2.339	2.592
400	1.649	1.966	2.336	2.588
500	1.648	1.965	2.334	2.586
1000	1.646	1.962	2.330	2.581
	1.645	1.960	2.326	2.576

APPENDIX F

Table of significance for chi-square

The following table gives one-tailed and two-tailed significance values for chi-square. The obtained value of chi-square has to equal or exceed the listed value to be statistically significant at the level in the column heading.

Degrees of freedom	5%	1%
1 (1-tailed)[a]	2.705	5.412
1 (2-tailed)	3.841	6.635
2 (2-tailed)	5.992	9.210
3 (2-tailed)	7.815	11.345
4 (2-tailed)	9.488	13.277
5 (2-tailed)	11.070	15.086
6 (2-tailed)	12.592	16.812
7 (2-tailed)	14.067	18.475
8 (2-tailed)	15.507	20.090
9 (2-tailed)	16.919	21.666
10 (2-tailed)	18.307	23.209
11 (2-tailed)	19.675	24.725
12 (2-tailed)	21.026	26.217

[a] It is correct to carry out a one-tailed chi-square only when there is just one degree of freedom.

Extended table of significance for the sign test

Your value must be smaller than or equal to the listed value to be significant at the level stipulated in the column heading.

N	Two-tailed: 5% One-tailed: 2.5%	Two-tailed: 2% One-tailed: 1%	Two-tailed: 1% One-tailed: 0.5%
5	0		
6	0	0	
7	0	0	
8	1	0	0
9	1	1	0
10	1	1	0
11	2	1	0
12	2	2	1
13	3	2	1
14	3	2	1
15	3	3	2
16	4	3	2
17	4	4	2
18	5	4	3
19	5	4	3
20	5	5	3
21	6	5	4
22	6	5	4
23	7	6	5
24	7	6	5
25	7	7	5

N	Two-tailed: 5% One-tailed: 2.5%	Two-tailed: 2% One-tailed: 1%	Two-tailed: 1% One-tailed: 0.5%
26	8	8	6
27	9	8	6
28	9	8	7
29	10	9	7
30	10	9	7
31	10	10	8
32	11	10	8
33	11	10	9
34	12	11	9
35	12	11	9
36	13	12	10
37	13	12	10
38	13	12	11
39	14	13	11
40	14	13	11
41	15	14	12
42	15	14	12
43	16	15	13
44	16	15	13
45	16	15	13
46	17	16	14
47	17	16	14
48	18	17	15
49	18	17	15
50	19	18	15
51	19	18	16
52	20	18	16
53	20	19	17
54	20	19	17
55	21	20	17
56	21	20	18
57	22	21	18
58	22	21	19
59	23	21	19
60	23	22	19
61	24	22	20
62	24	23	20
63	24	23	21
64	25	24	21
65	25	24	22
66	26	25	22
67	26	25	22
68	27	25	23

N	Two-tailed: 5% One-tailed: 2.5%	Two-tailed: 2% One-tailed: 1%	Two-tailed: 1% One-tailed: 0.5%
69	27	26	23
70	28	26	24
71	28	27	24
72	28	27	24
73	29	28	25
74	29	28	25
75	30	29	26
76	30	29	26
77	31	29	27
78	31	30	27
79	32	30	27
80	32	31	28
81	33	31	28
82	33	32	29
83	33	32	29
84	34	32	30
85	34	33	30
86	35	33	30
87	35	34	31
88	36	34	31
89	36	35	32
90	37	35	32
91	37	36	33
92	38	36	33
93	38	36	34
94	38	37	34
95	39	37	34
96	39	38	35
97	40	38	35
98	40	39	36
99	41	39	36
100	41	40	37
200	88	86	81
300	135	132	127
400	183	180	174
500	231	228	221
1000	473	468	459

Table of significance for the Wilcoxon matched pairs test

Your value must be smaller than or equal to the listed value to be significant at the level stipulated in the column heading.

Number of pairs of scores	Two-tailed: 10% One-tailed: 5%	Two-tailed: 5% One-tailed: 2.5%	Two-tailed: 1% One-tailed: 0.5%
6	2	0	–
7	4	2	–
8	6	4	0
9	8	6	2
10	11	8	3
11	14	11	5
12	17	14	7
13	21	17	10
14	26	21	13
15	31	25	16
16	36	30	20
17	42	35	24
18	47	40	28
19	54	46	33
20	60	52	37
21	68	59	42
22	76	66	47
23	84	74	54
24	92	81	60
25	101	90	67
26	111	98	74

→

Number of pairs of scores	Two-tailed: 10% One-tailed: 5%	Two-tailed: 5% One-tailed: 2.5%	Two-tailed: 1% One-tailed: 0.5%
27	121	107	82
28	131	117	90
29	141	127	99
30	153	137	108
31	164	148	117
32	176	159	127
33	188	171	137
34	201	183	147
35	215	195	158
36	228	208	169
37	242	222	181
38	257	235	193
39	272	250	206
40	288	264	219
41	304	279	232
42	320	295	246
43	337	311	260
44	354	327	275
45	372	344	290
46	390	361	305
47	409	379	321
48	428	397	337
49	447	415	354
50	467	434	371
51	488	454	389
52	508	474	407
53	530	494	425
54	551	515	444
55	574	536	463
56	596	558	483
57	619	580	503
58	643	602	524
59	667	625	545
60	692	649	566
61	716	673	588
62	742	697	610
63	768	722	633
64	794	747	656
65	821	773	679
66	848	799	703
67	876	825	728
68	904	852	752
69	932	880	778

Number of pairs of scores	Two-tailed: 10% One-tailed: 5%	Two-tailed: 5% One-tailed: 2.5%	Two-tailed: 1% One-tailed: 0.5%
70	961	908	803
71	991	936	829
72	1021	965	856
73	1051	994	883
74	1082	1024	910
75	1113	1054	938
76	1145	1084	967
77	1178	1115	995
78	1210	1147	1025
79	1243	1179	1054
80	1277	1211	1084
81	1311	1244	1115
82	1346	1278	1146
83	1381	1311	1177
84	1416	1346	1209
85	1452	1380	1241
86	1488	1415	1274
87	1525	1451	1307
88	1563	1487	1340
89	1600	1523	1374
90	1639	1560	1409
91	1677	1598	1444
92	1717	1636	1479
93	1756	1674	1515
94	1796	1713	1551
95	1837	1752	1588
96	1878	1792	1625
97	1919	1832	1662
98	1961	1872	1700
99	2004	1913	1739
100	2047	1955	1778
200	8702	8444	7944
300	20101	19628	18710
400	36294	35565	34154
500	57308	56290	54318
1000	235222	232344	226772

APPENDIX I

Tables of significance for the Mann–Whitney *U*-test

Table I.1 5% significant values level for the Mann–Whitney *U*-statistic (one-tailed test)

See Table I.1 opposite: Your value must be in the listed ranges for your sample sizes to be significant at the 5% level; i.e. to accept the hypothesis. In addition, you should have predicted which group would have the smaller sum of ranks.

Table I.2 1% significant values level for the Mann–Whitney *U*-statistic (two-tailed test)

See Table I.2 on page 682: Your value must be in the listed ranges for your sample sizes to be significant at the 1% level; i.e. to accept the hypothesis at the 1% level.151–220

Table I.1   5% significant values level for the Mann–Whitney U-statistic (one-tailed test)

Sample size for smaller group	Sample size for larger group											
	5	6	7	8	9	10	11	12	13	14	15	20
5	0–4 / 21–25	0–5 / 25–30	0–6 / 29–35	0–8 / 32–40	0–9 / 36–45	0–11 / 39–50	0–12 / 43–55	0–13 / 47–60	0–15 / 50–65	0–16 / 54–70	0–18 / 57–75	0–25 / 75–100
6	0–5 / 25–30	0–7 / 29–36	0–8 / 34–42	0–10 / 38–48	0–12 / 42–54	0–14 / 46–60	0–16 / 50–66	0–17 / 55–72	0–19 / 59–78	0–21 / 61–82	0–23 / 67–90	0–32 / 88–120
7	0–6 / 29–35	0–8 / 34–42	0–11 / 38–49	0–13 / 43–56	0–15 / 48–63	0–17 / 53–70	0–19 / 58–77	0–21 / 63–84	0–24 / 67–91	0–26 / 72–98	0–28 / 77–105	0–39 / 101–140
8	0–8 / 32–40	0–10 / 38–48	0–13 / 43–56	0–15 / 49–64	0–18 / 54–72	0–20 / 60–80	0–23 / 65–88	0–26 / 70–96	0–28 / 76–104	0–31 / 81–112	0–33 / 87–120	0–47 / 113–160
9	0–9 / 36–45	0–12 / 42–54	0–15 / 48–63	0–18 / 54–72	0–21 / 60–81	0–24 / 66–90	0–27 / 72–99	0–30 / 78–108	0–33 / 84–117	0–36 / 90–126	0–39 / 96–135	0–54 / 126–180
10	0–11 / 39–50	0–14 / 46–60	0–17 / 53–70	0–20 / 60–80	0–24 / 66–90	0–27 / 73–100	0–31 / 79–110	0–34 / 86–120	0–37 / 93–130	0–41 / 99–140	0–44 / 106–150	0–62 / 138–200
11	0–12 / 43–55	0–16 / 50–66	0–19 / 58–77	0–23 / 65–88	0–27 / 72–99	0–31 / 79–110	0–34 / 87–121	0–38 / 94–132	0–42 / 101–143	0–46 / 108–154	0–50 / 115–165	0–69 / 151–220
12	0–13 / 47–60	0–17 / 55–72	0–21 / 63–84	0–26 / 70–96	0–30 / 78–108	0–34 / 86–120	0–38 / 94–132	0–42 / 102–144	0–47 / 109–156	0–51 / 117–168	0–55 / 125–180	0–77 / 163–240
13	0–15 / 50–65	0–19 / 59–78	0–24 / 67–91	0–28 / 76–104	0–33 / 84–117	0–37 / 93–130	0–42 / 101–143	0–47 / 109–156	0–51 / 118–169	0–56 / 126–182	0–61 / 134–195	0–84 / 176–260
14	0–16 / 54–70	0–21 / 61–82	0–26 / 72–98	0–31 / 81–112	0–36 / 90–126	0–41 / 99–140	0–46 / 108–154	0–51 / 117–168	0–56 / 126–182	0–61 / 135–196	0–66 / 144–210	0–92 / 188–280
15	0–18 / 57–75	0–23 / 67–90	0–28 / 77–105	0–33 / 87–120	0–39 / 96–135	0–44 / 106–150	0–50 / 115–165	0–55 / 125–180	0–61 / 134–195	0–66 / 144–210	0–72 / 153–225	0–100 / 200–300
20	0–25 / 75–100	0–32 / 88–120	0–39 / 101–140	0–47 / 113–160	0–54 / 126–180	0–62 / 138–200	0–69 / 151–220	0–77 / 163–240	0–84 / 176–260	0–92 / 188–280	0–100 / 200–300	0–138 / 262–400

Source: The above table has been adapted from Table I of *Fundamentals of behavioral statistics*, The McGraw Hill Companies Inc. (Runyon, R.P. and Haber, A., 1989).

Table I.2 1% significant values level for the Mann–Whitney U-statistic (two-tailed test)

Sample size for smaller group	Sample size for larger group											
	5	6	7	8	9	10	11	12	13	14	15	20
5	0 25	0–1 29–30	0–1 34–35	0–2 38–40	0–3 42–45	0–4 46–50	0–5 50–55	0–6 54–60	0–7 58–65	0–7 63–70	0–8 67–75	0–13 87–100
6	0–1 29–30	0–2 34–36	0–3 39–42	0–4 44–48	0–5 49–54	0–6 54–60	0–7 59–66	0–9 63–72	0–10 68–78	0–11 71–82	0–12 78–90	0–18 102–120
7	0–1 34–35	0–3 39–42	0–4 45–49	0–6 50–56	0–7 56–63	0–9 61–70	0–10 67–77	0–12 72–84	0–13 78–91	0–15 83–98	0–16 89–105	0–24 116–140
8	0–2 38–40	0–4 44–48	0–6 50–56	0–7 57–64	0–9 63–72	0–11 69–80	0–13 75–88	0–15 81–96	0–17 87–104	0–18 94–112	0–20 100–120	0–30 130–160
9	0–3 42–45	0–5 49–54	0–7 56–63	0–9 63–72	0–11 70–81	0–13 77–90	0–16 83–99	0–18 90–108	0–20 97–117	0–22 104–126	0–24 111–135	0–36 144–180
10	0–4 46–50	0–6 54–60	0–9 61–70	0–11 69–80	0–13 77–90	0–16 84–100	0–18 92–110	0–21 99–120	0–24 106–130	0–26 114–140	0–29 121–150	0–42 158–200
11	0–5 50–55	0–7 59–66	0–10 67–77	0–13 75–88	0–16 83–99	0–18 92–110	0–21 100–121	0–24 108–132	0–27 116–143	0–30 124–154	0–33 132–165	0–48 172–220
12	0–6 54–60	0–9 63–72	0–12 72–84	0–15 81–96	0–18 90–108	0–21 99–120	0–24 108–132	0–27 117–144	0–31 125–156	0–34 134–168	0–37 143–180	0–54 186–240
13	0–7 58–65	0–10 68–78	0–13 78–91	0–17 87–104	0–20 97–117	0–24 106–130	0–27 116–143	0–31 125–156	0–34 135–169	0–38 144–182	0–42 153–195	0–60 200–260
14	0–7 63–70	0–11 71–82	0–15 83–98	0–18 94–112	0–22 104–126	0–26 114–140	0–30 124–154	0–34 134–168	0–38 144–182	0–42 154–196	0–46 164–210	0–67 213–280
15	0–8 67–75	0–12 78–90	0–16 89–105	0–20 100–120	0–24 111–135	0–29 121–150	0–33 132–165	0–37 143–180	0–42 153–195	0–46 164–210	0–51 174–225	0–73 227–300
20	0–13 87–100	0–18 102–120	0–24 116–140	0–30 130–160	0–36 144–180	0–42 158–200	0–48 172–220	0–54 186–240	0–60 200–260	0–67 213–280	0–73 227–300	0–105 295–400

Source: The above table has been adapted from Table I of *Fundamentals of behavioral statistics*, The McGraw Hill Companies Inc. (Runyon, R.P. and Haber, A., 1989).

Tables of significance values for the *F*-distribution

J.1 5% significance values for the *F*-distribution (one-tailed test)

Your value has to equal or be larger than the tabled value to be significant at the 5% level for an effect to be significant.

Degrees of freedom for error or within-cells mean square (or variance estimate)	Degrees of freedom for between-treatments mean square (or variance estimate)					
	1	2	3	4	5	∞
1	161.448	199.500	215.707	224.583	230.162	254.314
2	18.513	19.000	19.165	19.247	19.297	19.496
3	10.128	9.553	9.277	9.118	9.014	8.527
4	7.709	6.945	6.592	6.389	6.257	5.628
5	6.608	5.787	5.410	5.193	5.051	4.365
6	5.988	5.144	4.758	4.534	4.388	3.669
7	5.592	4.738	4.347	4.121	3.972	3.230
8	5.318	4.459	4.067	3.838	3.688	2.928
9	5.118	4.257	3.863	3.634	3.482	2.707
10	4.965	4.103	3.709	3.479	3.326	2.538
13	4.668	3.806	3.411	3.180	3.026	2.207
15	4.544	3.683	3.288	3.056	2.902	2.066
20	4.352	3.493	3.099	2.867	2.711	1.844
30	4.171	3.316	2.923	2.690	2.534	1.623
60	4.002	3.151	2.759	2.526	2.369	1.390
∞	3.842	2.996	2.605	2.372	2.215	1.000

J.2   1% significance values for the *F*-distribution (one-tailed test)

Your value has to equal or be larger than the tabled value to be significant at the 1% level for an effect to be significant.

Degrees of freedom for error or within-cells mean square (or variance estimate)	Degrees of freedom for between-treatments mean square (or variance estimate)					
	1	2	3	4	5	∞
1	4052.180	4999.500	5403.350	5624.580	5763.650	6365.860
2	98.503	99.000	99.167	99.250	99.300	99.500
3	34.117	30.817	29.457	28.710	28.238	26.126
4	21.198	18.000	16.695	15.977	15.522	13.464
5	16.259	13.274	12.060	11.392	10.967	9.021
6	13.745	10.925	9.780	9.149	8.746	6.880
7	12.247	9.547	8.452	7.847	7.461	5.650
8	11.259	8.650	7.591	7.007	6.632	4.859
9	10.562	8.022	6.992	6.423	6.057	4.311
10	10.045	7.560	6.553	5.995	5.637	3.909
13	9.074	6.701	5.740	5.206	4.862	3.166
15	8.684	6.359	5.417	4.894	4.556	2.869
20	8.096	5.849	4.939	4.431	4.103	2.422
30	7.563	5.391	4.510	4.018	3.699	2.007
60	7.078	4.978	4.126	3.650	3.339	1.607
∞	6.635	4.606	3.782	3.320	3.018	1.000

J.3 10% significance values for the *F*-distribution for testing differences between two groups (one-tailed test)

This table is only to be used for determining whether an *F*-value which is not significant at the 5% level for two groups is significant at the 10% level which is the equivalent to a one-tailed *t*-test. You should only do this if you have good grounds for predicting the direction of the difference between the two means. Your value has to equal or be larger than the tabled value to be significant at the one-tailed 10% level for the *t*-test.

Degrees of freedom for error or within-cells mean square (or variance estimate)	Minimum value of *F*-ratio to be significant at the 10% level
1	39.864
2	8.527
3	5.539
4	4.545
5	4.061
6	3.776
7	3.590
8	3.458
9	3.361
10	3.285
13	3.137
15	3.074
20	2.975
30	2.881
60	2.792
∞	2.706

APPENDIX K

Table of significance values for *t* when making multiple *t*-tests

The following table gives the 5% significance values for two-tailed *t*-tests when you are making up to 10 unplanned comparisons. The number of comparisons you decide to make is up to you and does not have to be the maximum possible. This table can be used in any circumstances where you have multiple *t*-tests.

Degrees of freedom	Number of comparisons being made									
	1	2	3	4	5	6	7	8	9	10
1	12.706	25.452	38.188	50.923	63.657	76.390	89.124	101.856	114.589	127.321
2	4.303	6.205	7.649	8.860	9.925	10.886	11.769	12.590	13.360	14.089
3	3.182	4.177	4.857	5.392	5.841	6.231	6.580	6.895	7.185	7.453
4	2.776	3.495	3.961	4.315	4.604	4.851	5.067	5.261	5.437	5.598
5	2.571	3.163	3.534	3.810	4.032	4.219	4.382	4.526	4.655	4.773
6	2.447	2.969	3.288	3.521	3.708	3.863	3.997	4.115	4.221	4.317
7	2.365	2.841	3.128	3.335	3.500	3.636	3.753	3.855	3.947	4.029
8	2.306	2.752	3.016	3.206	3.355	3.479	3.584	3.677	3.759	3.833
9	2.262	2.685	2.933	3.111	3.250	3.364	3.462	3.547	3.622	3.690
10	2.228	2.634	2.870	3.038	3.169	3.277	3.368	3.448	3.518	3.581
11	2.201	2.593	2.820	2.981	3.106	3.208	3.295	3.370	3.437	3.497
12	2.179	2.560	2.780	2.934	3.055	3.153	3.236	3.308	3.371	3.428
13	2.160	2.533	2.746	2.896	3.012	3.107	3.187	3.257	3.318	3.373
14	2.145	2.510	2.718	2.864	2.977	3.069	3.146	3.213	3.273	3.326
15	2.132	2.490	2.694	2.837	2.947	3.036	3.112	3.177	3.235	3.286
16	2.120	2.473	2.673	2.813	2.921	3.008	3.082	3.146	3.202	3.252
17	2.110	2.458	2.655	2.793	2.898	2.984	3.056	3.119	3.174	3.222

Degrees of freedom	Number of comparisons being made									
	1	2	3	4	5	6	7	8	9	10
18	2.101	2.445	2.639	2.774	2.878	2.963	3.034	3.095	3.149	3.197
19	2.093	2.433	2.625	2.759	2.861	2.944	3.014	3.074	3.127	3.174
20	2.086	2.423	2.613	2.744	2.845	2.927	2.996	3.055	3.107	3.153
21	2.080	2.414	2.601	2.732	2.831	2.912	2.980	3.038	3.090	3.135
22	2.074	2.406	2.591	2.720	2.819	2.898	2.966	3.023	3.074	3.119
23	2.069	2.398	2.582	2.710	2.807	2.886	2.953	3.010	3.059	3.104
24	2.064	2.391	2.574	2.700	2.797	2.875	2.941	2.997	3.047	3.091
25	2.060	2.385	2.566	2.692	2.787	2.865	2.930	2.986	3.035	3.078
26	2.055	2.379	2.559	2.684	2.779	2.856	2.920	2.975	3.024	3.067
27	2.052	2.373	2.553	2.676	2.771	2.847	2.911	2.966	3.014	3.057
28	2.048	2.369	2.547	2.670	2.763	2.839	2.902	2.957	3.005	3.047
29	2.045	2.364	2.541	2.663	2.756	2.832	2.894	2.949	2.996	3.038
30	2.042	2.360	2.536	2.657	2.750	2.825	2.887	2.941	2.988	3.030
31	2.039	2.356	2.531	2.652	2.744	2.818	2.880	2.934	2.981	3.022
32	2.037	2.352	2.526	2.647	2.739	2.812	2.874	2.927	2.974	3.015
33	2.035	2.348	2.522	2.642	2.733	2.807	2.868	2.921	2.967	3.008
34	2.032	2.345	2.518	2.638	2.728	2.801	2.863	2.915	2.961	3.002
35	2.030	2.342	2.515	2.633	2.724	2.797	2.857	2.910	2.955	2.996
36	2.028	2.339	2.511	2.630	2.720	2.792	2.853	2.905	2.950	2.990
37	2.026	2.336	2.508	2.626	2.715	2.788	2.848	2.900	2.945	2.985
38	2.024	2.334	2.505	2.622	2.712	2.784	2.844	2.895	2.940	2.980
39	2.023	2.331	2.502	2.619	2.708	2.780	2.839	2.891	2.936	2.976
40	2.021	2.329	2.499	2.616	2.704	2.776	2.836	2.887	2.931	2.971
41	2.020	2.327	2.496	2.613	2.701	2.772	2.832	2.883	2.927	2.967
42	2.018	2.325	2.494	2.610	2.698	2.769	2.828	2.879	2.923	2.963
43	2.017	2.323	2.491	2.607	2.695	2.766	2.825	2.875	2.920	2.959
44	2.015	2.321	2.489	2.605	2.692	2.763	2.822	2.872	2.916	2.955
45	2.014	2.319	2.487	2.602	2.690	2.760	2.819	2.869	2.913	2.952
46	2.013	2.317	2.485	2.600	2.687	2.757	2.816	2.866	2.910	2.949
47	2.012	2.316	2.483	2.598	2.685	2.755	2.813	2.863	2.907	2.946
48	2.011	2.314	2.481	2.595	2.682	2.752	2.810	2.860	2.904	2.943
49	2.010	2.312	2.479	2.593	2.680	2.750	2.808	2.857	2.901	2.940
50	2.009	2.311	2.477	2.591	2.678	2.747	2.805	2.855	2.898	2.937
51	2.008	2.309	2.476	2.589	2.676	2.745	2.803	2.853	2.896	2.934
52	2.007	2.308	2.474	2.588	2.674	2.743	2.801	2.850	2.893	2.932
53	2.006	2.307	2.472	2.586	2.672	2.741	2.798	2.848	2.891	2.929
54	2.005	2.306	2.471	2.584	2.670	2.739	2.797	2.846	2.889	2.927
55	2.004	2.304	2.469	2.583	2.668	2.737	2.795	2.844	2.887	2.925
56	2.003	2.303	2.468	2.581	2.667	2.735	2.793	2.842	2.885	2.922
57	2.003	2.302	2.467	2.579	2.665	2.734	2.791	2.840	2.882	2.920
58	2.002	2.301	2.465	2.578	2.663	2.732	2.789	2.838	2.881	2.918
59	2.001	2.300	2.464	2.577	2.662	2.730	2.787	2.836	2.879	2.916

Degrees of freedom	Number of comparisons being made									
	1	2	3	4	5	6	7	8	9	10
60	2.000	2.299	2.463	2.575	2.660	2.729	2.786	2.834	2.877	2.915
61	2.000	2.298	2.462	2.574	2.659	2.727	2.784	2.833	2.875	2.913
62	1.999	2.297	2.461	2.573	2.658	2.726	2.782	2.831	2.873	2.911
63	1.998	2.296	2.460	2.571	2.656	2.724	2.781	2.829	2.872	2.909
64	1.998	2.295	2.459	2.570	2.655	2.723	2.779	2.828	2.870	2.908
65	1.997	2.295	2.458	2.569	2.654	2.721	2.778	2.826	2.869	2.906
66	1.997	2.294	2.457	2.568	2.652	2.720	2.777	2.825	2.867	2.905
67	1.996	2.293	2.456	2.567	2.651	2.719	2.775	2.824	2.866	2.903
68	1.995	2.292	2.455	2.566	2.650	2.718	2.774	2.822	2.864	2.902
69	1.995	2.291	2.454	2.565	2.649	2.716	2.773	2.821	2.863	2.900
70	1.994	2.291	2.453	2.564	2.648	2.715	2.772	2.820	2.862	2.899
71	1.994	2.290	2.452	2.563	2.647	2.714	2.770	2.818	2.860	2.898
72	1.994	2.289	2.451	2.562	2.646	2.713	2.769	2.817	2.859	2.896
73	1.993	2.289	2.450	2.561	2.645	2.712	2.768	2.816	2.858	2.895
74	1.993	2.288	2.450	2.560	2.644	2.711	2.767	2.815	2.857	2.894
75	1.992	2.287	2.449	2.559	2.643	2.710	2.766	2.814	2.856	2.893
76	1.992	2.287	2.448	2.559	2.642	2.709	2.765	2.813	2.854	2.891
77	1.991	2.286	2.447	2.558	2.641	2.708	2.764	2.812	2.853	2.890
78	1.991	2.285	2.447	2.557	2.640	2.707	2.763	2.811	2.852	2.889
79	1.990	2.285	2.446	2.556	2.640	2.706	2.762	2.810	2.851	2.888
80	1.990	2.284	2.445	2.555	2.639	2.705	2.761	2.809	2.850	2.887
81	1.990	2.284	2.445	2.555	2.638	2.705	2.760	2.808	2.849	2.886
82	1.989	2.283	2.444	2.554	2.637	2.704	2.759	2.807	2.848	2.885
83	1.989	2.283	2.444	2.553	2.636	2.703	2.759	2.806	2.847	2.884
84	1.989	2.282	2.443	2.553	2.636	2.702	2.758	2.805	2.846	2.883
85	1.988	2.282	2.442	2.552	2.635	2.701	2.757	2.804	2.845	2.882
86	1.988	2.281	2.442	2.551	2.634	2.701	2.756	2.803	2.845	2.881
87	1.988	2.281	2.441	2.551	2.634	2.700	2.755	2.803	2.844	2.880
88	1.987	2.280	2.441	2.550	2.633	2.699	2.755	2.802	2.843	2.880
89	1.987	2.280	2.440	2.550	2.632	2.699	2.754	2.801	2.842	2.879
90	1.987	2.280	2.440	2.549	2.632	2.698	2.753	2.800	2.841	2.878
91	1.986	2.279	2.439	2.548	2.631	2.697	2.752	2.800	2.841	2.877
92	1.986	2.279	2.439	2.548	2.630	2.696	2.752	2.799	2.840	2.876
93	1.986	2.278	2.438	2.547	2.630	2.696	2.751	2.798	2.839	2.876
94	1.986	2.278	2.438	2.547	2.629	2.695	2.750	2.797	2.838	2.875
95	1.985	2.277	2.437	2.546	2.629	2.695	2.750	2.797	2.838	2.874
96	1.985	2.277	2.437	2.546	2.628	2.694	2.749	2.796	2.837	2.873
97	1.985	2.277	2.436	2.545	2.627	2.694	2.748	2.795	2.836	2.873
98	1.984	2.276	2.436	2.545	2.627	2.693	2.748	2.795	2.836	2.872
99	1.984	2.276	2.435	2.544	2.626	2.692	2.747	2.794	2.835	2.871
100	1.984	2.276	2.435	2.544	2.626	2.692	2.747	2.793	2.834	2.871
∞	1.960	2.241	2.394	2.498	2.576	2.638	2.690	2.734	2.773	2.807

GLOSSARY

− 2 log likelihood (ratio) test: Used in logistic regression, it is a form of chi-square test which compares the goodness of fit of two models where one model is a part of (i.e. nested or a subset of) the other model. The chi-square is the difference in the −2 log likelihood values for the two models.

A priori test: A test of the difference between two groups of scores when this comparison has been planned ignorant of the actual data. This contrasts with a *post hoc* test which is carried out after the data have been collected and which has no particularly strong expectations about the outcome.

Adjusted mean: A mean score when the influence of one or more covariates have been removed, especially in analysis of covariance.

Alpha level: The level of risk that the researcher is prepared to mistakenly accept the hypothesis on the basis of the available data. Typically this is set at a maximum of 5% or .05 and is, of course, otherwise referred to as the level of significance.

Analysis of covariance (ANCOVA): A variant of the analysis of variance (ANOVA) in which scores on the dependent variable are adjusted to take into account (control) a covariate(s). For example, differences between conditions of an experiment at pre-test can be controlled for.

Analysis of variance (ANOVA): An extensive group of tests of significance which compare means on a dependent variable. There may be one or more independent (grouping) variables or factors. ANOVA is essential in the analysis of most laboratory experiments.

Association: A relationship between two variables.

Bar chart: A picture in which frequencies are represented by the height of a set of bars. It should be the areas of a set of bars but SPSS ignores this and settles for height.

Bartlett's test of sphericity: A test used in MANOVA of whether the correlations between the variables differ significantly from zero.

Beta level: The risk that we are prepared to accept rejecting the null hypothesis when it is in fact true.

Beta weight: The standardised regression weight in multiple regression. It corresponds to the correlation coefficient in

Between-groups design: Basically a design where different participants are allocated to different groups or conditions.

Between-subjects design: *see* Between-groups design.

Big data: Data sets too large for traditional forms of data analysis and often requiring multiple linked computers for extraction, storage and analysis.

Bimodal: A frequency distribution with two modes.

Bivariate: Involving two variables as opposed to univariate which involves just one variable.

Bivariate correlation: A correlation between two variables.

Block: A subset of variables which will be analysed together in a sequence of blocks.

Bonferroni adjustment: A method of adjusting significance levels for the fact that many statistical analyses have been carried out on the data.

Bootstrapping: A method of creating sampling distributions from the basic sample which is reproduced numerous times to approximate the 'population'. This allows repeated sampling and hence the calculation of sampling distributions for all sorts of statistics.

Boxplot: A diagram indicating the distribution of scores on a variable. It gives the median in a box, the left and right hand sides of which are the lower and upper values of the interquartile range. Lines at each side of the box identify the largest and smallest scores.

Box's M: A statistical test which partly establishes whether the data meet the requirements for a MANOVA analysis. It examines the extent to which the covariances of the dependent variables are similar for each of the groups in the analysis. Ideally, then, Box's *M* should not be significant. The test is used in MANOVA though its interpretation is complex.

Case: The basic unit of analysis on which data are collected such as individuals or organisations.

Categorical variable: A nominal or category variable.

Category variable: A variable which consists of categories rather than numerical scores. The categories have no particular quantitative order. However, usually on SPSS they will be coded as numbers.

Cell: The intersection of one category of a variable with

variable has categories A, B and C and the other variable has categories X, Y and Z, then the cells are A with X, A with Y, A with Z, B with X, B with Y, etc. It is a term frequently used in ANOVA as well as with chi-square tables (i.e. crosstabulation and contingency tables).

Chart: A graphical or pictorial representation of the characteristics of one's data.

Chart Editor window: In SPSS it is a window which can be opened to refine a chart.

Chi-square distribution: A set of theoretical probability distributions which vary according to the degrees of freedom and which are used to determine the statistical significance of a chi-square test.

Chi-square test, Pearson's: A test of goodness-of-fit or association for frequency data. It compares the observed data with the estimated (or actual) population distribution (this is usually based on combining two or more samples).

Cluster analysis: A variety of techniques which identify the patterns of variables or cases that tend to be similar to each other. No cluster analysis techniques are dealt with in this book as they are uncommon in psychology. Often factor analysis, which is in this book, does a similar job.

Cochran's Q test: A test of whether the frequencies of a dichotomous variable differ significantly for more than two related samples or groups.

Coefficient of determination: The square of Pearson's correlation coefficient. So a correlation of .4 has a coefficient of determination of .16. It is useful especially since it gives a numerically more accurate representation of the relative importance of different correlation coefficients than the correlation coefficients themselves do.

Common variance: The variance that two or more variables share.

Communality: The variance that a particular variable in an analysis shares with other variables. It is distinct from error variance and specific variance (which is confined to a particular variable). It mainly appears in factor analysis.

Component matrix: A table showing the correlations between components and variables in factor analysis.

Compute: In SPSS, this procedure allows the researcher to derive new variables from the original variables. For example, it would be possible to sum the scores for each participant on several variables.

Condition: One of the groups in ANOVA or the *t*-test.

Confidence interval: A more realistic way of presenting the outcomes of statistical analysis than, for example, the mean or the standard deviation would be. It gives the range within which 95% or 99% of the most common means, standard deviations, etc. would lie. Thus instead of saying that the mean is 6.7 we would say that the 95% confidence interval for the mean is 5.2 to 8.2.

Confirmatory factor analysis: A test of whether a particular model or factor structure fits a set of data satisfactorily.

Confounding variable: Any variable which clouds the interpretation of a correlation or any other statistical relationship. Once the effects of the confounding variable are removed, the remaining relationship presents a truer pic-

Contingency table: A frequency table giving the frequencies in all of the categories of two or more nominal (category) variables tabulated together.

Correlation coefficient: An index which gives the extent and the direction of the linear association between two variables.

Correlation matrix: A matrix of the correlations of pairs of variables.

Count: The number of times (frequency) a particular observation (score or category, for example) occurs.

Counterbalancing: If some participants take part in condition A of a study first, followed by condition B later, then to counterbalance any time or sequence effects other participants should take part in condition B first followed by condition A second.

Covariance: The variance which two or more score variables have in common (i.e. share). It is basically calculated like variance but instead of squaring each score's deviation from the mean the deviation of variable X from its mean is multiplied by the deviation of variable Y from its mean.

Covariate: A variable which correlates with the variables that are the researcher's main focus of interest. In the analysis of covariance it is the undesired influence of the covariate which is controlled for.

Cox and Snell's R^2: The amount of variance in the criterion variable accounted for by the predictor variables. It is used in logistic regression.

Cramér's V: Also known as Cramér's phi, this correlation coefficient is usually applied to a contingency or crosstabulation table greater than 2 rows × 2 columns.

Critical value: Used when calculating statistical significance with statistical tables such as those in the Appendices. It is the minimum value of the statistical calculation which is statistically significant (i.e. which rejects the null hypothesis).

Cronbach's alpha: A measure of the extent to which cases respond in a similar or consistent way on all the variables that go to make up a scale.

Data Editor window: The data spreadsheet in which data items are entered in SPSS.

Data handling: The various techniques to deal with data from a study excluding its statistical analysis. It would include data entry into the spreadsheet, the search for errors in data entry, recoding variables into new values, computing new variables and so forth.

Data mining: The search for patterns in massive data sets combining advances combining statistics and machine learning in particular.

Data View: The window in SPSS which allows you to see the data spreadsheet.

Degrees of freedom: The number of components of the data that can vary while still yielding a given population value for characteristics such as mean scores. All other things being equal, the bigger the degrees of freedom the more likely it is that the research findings will be statistically significant.

Dependent variable: A variable which potentially may be affected or predicted by other variables in the analysis. It is

Descriptive statistics: Indices which describe the major characteristics of variables or the relationships between variables. It includes measures of central tendency (mean, median and mode for example) and measures of spread (range, variance, etc.).

Deviation: Usually the difference between a score and the mean of the set of scores.

Dialog or Dialogue box: A rectangular picture in SPSS which allows the user to select various procedures.

Dichotomous: A nominal (category) variable with just two categories. Gender (male/female) is an obvious example.

Direct Oblimin: A rotation procedure for making factors in a factor analysis more meaningful or interpretable. Its essential characteristic is that the factors are not required to be uncorrelated (independent) of each other.

Discriminant (function) analysis: A statistical technique for score variables which maximises the difference(s) between two or more groups of participants on a set of variables. It generates a set of 'weights' which are applied to these variables.

Discriminant function: Found mainly in discriminant (function) analysis. A derived variable based on combining a set of variables in such a way that groups are as different as possible on the discriminant function. More than one discriminant function may emerge but each discriminant function is uncorrelated with the others.

Discriminant score: An individual's score on a discriminant function.

Dummy coding: Used when analysing nominal (category) data to allow such variables to be used analogously to scores. Each category of the nominal (category) variable is made into a separate dummy variable. If the nominal (category) variable has three categories A, B and C then two new variables, say A versus not A and B versus not B are created. The categories may be coded with the value 1 and 0. It would not be used where a variable has only two different categories.

Dummy variable: A variable created by dummy coding.

Effect size: A measure of the strength of the relationship between two variables. Most commonly used in meta-analysis. The Pearson correlation coefficient is a very familiar measure of effect size. Also commonly used is Cohen's *d*. The correlation coefficient is recommended as the most user-friendly measure of effect size as it is very familiar to most of us and easily understood.

Eigenvalue: The variance accounted for by a factor. It is simply the sum of the squared factor loadings. The concept is also used for discriminant functions.

Endogenous variable: Any variable in path analysis that can be explained on the basis of one or more variables in that analysis.

Eta: A measure of association for non-linear (curved) relationships.

Exact significance: The precise significance level at and beyond which a result is statistically significant.

Exogenous variable: A variable in path analysis which is not

Exploratory factor analysis: The common form of factor analysis which finds the major dimensions of a correlation matrix using weighted combinations of the variables in the study. It identifies combinations of variables which can be described as one or more superordinate variable or factor.

Exponent or power: A number with an exponent or power superscript is multiplied by itself by that number of times. Thus 3^2 means 3×3 whereas 4^3 means $4 \times 4 \times 4$.

Extraction: The process of obtaining factors in factor analysis.

F-ratio: The ratio of two variances. It can be used to test whether these two variances differ significantly using the *F*-distribution. It can be used on its own but is also part of the *t*-test and ANOVA.

Factor matrix: A table showing the correlations between factors and the variables.

Factor scores: Standardised scores for a factor. They provide a way of calculating an individual's score on a factor which precisely reflects that factor.

Factor, factor analysis: A variable derived by combining other variables in a weighted combination. A factor seeks to synthesise the variance shared by variables into a more general variable to which the variables relate.

Factor, in analysis of variance: An independent or subject variable but is best regarded as a variable on which groups of participants are formed. The variances of these groups are then compared using ANOVA. A factor should consist of a nominal (category) variable with a small number of categories.

Factorial ANOVA: An analysis of variance with two or more independent or subject variables.

Family error rate: The probability or significance level for a finding when a family or number of tests or comparisons are being made on the same data.

Fisher test: Tests of significance (or association) for 2×2 and 2×3 contingency tables.

Frequency: The number of times a particular category occurs.

Frequency distribution: A table or diagram giving the frequencies of values of a variable.

Friedman's test: A nonparametric test for determining whether the mean ranks of three or more related samples or groups differ significantly.

Goodness-of-fit index: A measure of the extent to which a particular model (or pattern of variables) designed to describe a set of data actually matches the data.

Graph: A diagram for illustrating the values of one or more variables.

Grouping variable: A variable which forms the groups or conditions which are to be compared.

Harmonic mean: The number of scores, divided by the sum of the reciprocal ($1/x$) of each score.

Help: A facility in software with a graphical interface such as SPSS which provides information about its features.

Hierarchical agglomerative clustering: A form of cluster ana-

with the most similar variable or cluster until one cluster remains.

Hierarchical or sequential entry: A variant of regression in which the order in which the independent (predictor) variables are entered into the analysis is decided by the analyst rather than mathematical criteria.

Hierarchical regression: *see* Hierarchical or sequential entry.

Histogram: A chart which represents the frequency of particular scores or ranges of scores in terms of a set of bars. The height of the bar represents the frequency of this score or range of scores in the data.

Homogeneity of regression slope: The similarity of the regression slope of the covariate on the criterion variable in the different groups of the predictor variable.

Homogeneity of variance: The similarity of the variance of the scores in the groups of the predictor variable.

Homoscedasticity: The similarity of the scatter or spread of the data points around the regression line of best fit in different parts of that line.

Hypothesis: A statement expressing the expected or predicted relationship between two or more variables.

Icicle plot: A graphical representation of the results of a cluster analysis in which crosses (x) are used to indicate which variables or clusters are paired at which stage.

Identification: The extent to which the parameters of a structural equation model can be estimated from the original data.

Independence: Events or variables being unrelated to each other.

Independent groups design: A design in which different cases are assigned to different conditions or groups.

Independent *t*-test: A parametric test for determining whether the means of two unrelated or independent groups differ significantly.

Independent variable: A variable which may affect (predict) the values of another variable(s). It is used to form the groups in experimental designs. It is also used in regression for the variables used to predict the dependent variable.

Inferential statistics: Statistical techniques which help predict the population characteristics from the sample characteristics.

Interaction: This describes outcomes in research which cannot be accounted for on the basis of the separate influences of two or more variables. So, for example, an interaction occurs when two variables have a significant influence when combined.

Interaction graph: A graph showing the relationship of the means of two or more variables.

Interquartile range: The range of the middle 50% of a distribution. By ignoring the extreme quarter in each direction from the mean, the interquartile range is less affected by extreme scores.

Interval data: Data making up a scale in which the distance or interval between adjacent points is assumed to be the same or equal but where there is no meaningful zero point.

Just-identified model: A structural equation model in which the data are just sufficient to estimate its parameters.

Kaiser or Kaiser–Guttman criterion: A statistical criterion in factor analysis for determining the number of factors or components for consideration and possible rotation in which factors or components with eigenvalues of one or less are ignored.

Kendall's tau (τ): An index of the linear association between two ordinal variables. A correlation coefficient for nonparametric data in other words.

Kolmogorov–Smirnov test for two samples: A nonparametric test for determining whether the distributions of scores on an ordinal variable differ significantly for two unrelated samples.

Kruskal–Wallis test: A nonparametric test for determining whether the mean ranked scores for three or more unrelated samples differ significantly.

Kurtosis: The extent to which the shape of a bell-shaped curve is flatter or more elongated than a normal distribution.

Latent variable: An unobserved variable that is measured by one or more manifest variables or indicators.

Level: Used in analysis of variance to describe the different conditions of an independent variable (or factor). The term has its origins in agricultural research where levels of treatment would correspond to, say, different amounts of fertiliser being applied to crops.

Levels of measurement: A four-fold hierarchical distinction proposed for measures comprising nominal, ordinal, equal interval and ratio.

Levene's test: An analysis of variance on absolute differences to determine whether the variances of two or more unrelated groups differ significantly.

Likelihood ratio chi-square test: A form of chi-square which involves natural logarithms. It is primarily associated with log-linear analysis.

Line graph: A diagram in which lines are used to indicate the frequency of a variable.

Linear association or relationship: This occurs when there is a straight line relationship between two sets of scores. The scattergram for these data will be represented best by a straight line rather than a curved line.

Linear model: A model which assumes a linear relationship between the variables.

LISREL: The name of a particular software designed to carry out *li*near *s*tructural *rel*ationship analysis also known as structural equation modelling.

Loading: An index of the size and direction of the association of a variable with a factor or discriminant function of which it is part. A loading is simply the correlation between a variable and the factor or discriminant function.

Log likelihood: An index based on the difference between the frequencies for a category variable(s) and what is predicted on the basis of the predictors (i.e. the modelled data). The bigger the log likelihood the poorer the fit of the model to the data.

Logarithm: The amount to which a given base number (e.g. 10) has to be multiplied by itself to obtain a particular number. So in the expression 3^2, 2 would be the logarithm for the base 3 which makes 9. Sometimes it is recommended that scores are converted to their logarithms if this results in the data fitting the requirements of the statistical procedure better.

Logistic or logit regression: A version of multiple regression in which the dependent, criterion or outcome variable takes the form of a nominal (category) variable. Any mixture of scores and nominal (category) variables can act as predictors. The procedure uses dummy variables extensively.

Log-linear analysis: A statistical technique for nominal (category) data which is essentially an extension of chi-square where there are three or more independent variables.

Main effect: The effect of an independent or predictor variable on a dependent or criterion variable.

Manifest variable: A variable which directly reflects the measure used to assess it.

Mann–Whitney test: A nonparametric test for seeing whether the number of times scores from one sample are ranked significantly higher than scores from another unrelated sample.

Marginal totals: The marginal totals are the row and column total frequencies in crosstabulation and contingency tables.

Matched-subjects design: A related design in which participants are matched in pairs on a covariate or where participants serve as their own control. In other words, a repeated or related measures design.

Matrix: A rectangular array of rows and columns of data.

Mauchly's test: A test for determining whether the assumption that the variance–covariance matrix in a repeated measures analysis of variance is spherical or circular.

Maximum likelihood method: A method for finding estimates of the population parameters of a model which are most likely to give rise to the pattern of observations in the sample data.

McNemar test: A test for assessing whether there has been a significant change in the frequencies of two categories on two occasions in the same or similar cases.

Mean: The everyday numerical average score. Thus the mean of 2 and 3 is 2.5.

Mean square: A term for variance estimate used in analysis of variance.

Measure of dispersion: A measure of the variation in the scores such as the variance, range, interquartile range and standard error.

Median: The score which is halfway in the scores ordered from smallest to largest.

Mediating variable: One which is responsible for the relationship between two other variables.

Mixed ANOVA: An ANOVA in which at least one independent variable consists of related scores and at least one other variable consists of uncorrelated scores.

Mixed design: *see* Mixed ANOVA.

Mode: The most commonly occurring score or category.

Moderating or moderator effect: A relationship between two variables which differs according to a third variable. For example, the correlation between age and income may be moderated by a variable such as gender. In other words, the correlation for men and the correlation for women between age and income is different.

Multicollinearity: When two or more independent or predictor variables are highly correlated.

Multimodal: A frequency distribution having three or more modes.

Multiple correlation or R: A form of correlation coefficient which correlates a single score (A) with two or more other scores ($B + C$) in combination. Used particularly in multiple regression to denote the correlation of a set of predictor variables with the dependent (or outcome) variable.

Multiple regression: A parametric test to determine what pattern of two or more predictor (independent) variables is associated with scores on the dependent variable. It takes into account the associations (correlations) between the predictor variables. If desired, interactions between predictor variables may be included.

Multivariate: Involving more than two variables.

Multivariate analysis of variance (MANOVA): A variant of analysis of variance in which there are two or more *dependent* variables combined. MANOVA identifies differences between groups in terms of the combined dependent variable.

Nagelkerke's R^2: The amount of variance in the criterion variable accounted for by the predictor variables.

Natural or Napierian logarithm: The logarithms calculated using 2.718 as the base number.

Nested model: A model which is a simpler subset of another model and which can be derived from that model.

Nonparametric test: A statistical test of significance which requires fewer assumptions about the distribution of values in a sample than a parametric test.

Normal distribution: A mathematical distribution with very important characteristics. However, it is easier to regard it as a bell-shaped frequency curve. The tails of the curve should stretch to infinity in both directions but this, in the end, is of little practical importance.

Numeric variables: Variables for which the data are collected in the form of scores which indicate quantity.

Oblique factors: In factor analysis, oblique factors are ones which, during rotation, are allowed to correlate with each other. This may be more realistic than orthogonal rotations. One way of looking at this is to consider height and weight. These are distinct variables but they correlate to some degree. Oblique factors are distinct but they can correlate.

Odds: Obtained by dividing the probability of something occurring by the probability of it not occurring.

Odds ratio: The number by which the odds of something occurring must be multiplied for a one unit change in a predictor variable.

One-tailed test: A version of significance testing in which a strong prediction is made as to the direction of the relationship. This should be theoretically and empirically well founded on previous research. The prediction should be made prior to examination of the data.

Ordinal data: Numbers for which little can be said other than the numbers give the rank order of cases on the variable from smallest to largest.

Orthogonal: Essentially means at right angles.

Orthogonal factors: In factor analysis, orthogonal factors are factors which do not correlate with each other.

Outcome variable: A word used especially in medical statistics to denote the dependent variable. It is also the criterion variable. It is the variable which is expected to vary with variation in the independent variable(s).

Outlier: A score or data point which differs substantially from the other scores or data points. It is an extremely unusual or infrequent score or data point.

Output window: The window of computer software which displays the results of an analysis.

Over-identified model: A structural equation model in which the number of data points is greater than the number of parameters to be estimated, enabling the fit of the model to the data to be determined.

Paired comparisons: The process of comparing each variable mean with every (or most) other variable mean in pairs.

Parameter: A characteristic such as the mean or standard deviation which is based on the population of scores. In contrast, a statistic is a characteristic which is based on a sample of scores.

Parametric: To do with the characteristics of the population.

Parametric test: A statistical test which assumes that the scores used come from a population of scores which is normally distributed.

Part or semi-partial correlation: The correlation between two variables (X and Y) when a third variable Z is held constant for either X or Y but not both.

Partial correlation: The correlation between a criterion and a predictor when the criterion's and the predictor's correlation with other predictors have been partialled out.

Participant: Someone who takes part in research. A more appropriate term than the archaic and misleading 'subject'.

PASW Statistics: The name for SPSS in 2008–9.

Path diagram: A diagram in which the relationships (actual or hypothetical) between variables are presented.

Pathway: A line in a path diagram depicting a relationship between two variables.

Phi: A measure of association between two binomial or dichotomous variables.

Pivot table: A table in SPSS which can be edited.

Planned comparisons: Testing whether a difference between two groups is significant when there are strong grounds for expecting such a difference.

Point-biserial correlation: A correlation between a score variable and a binomial (dichotomous) variable – i.e. one with two categories.

Population: All of the scores from which a sample is taken. It is erroneous in statistics to think of the population as people since it is the population of scores on a variable.

Post hoc **test:** A test to see whether two groups differ significantly predicting or expecting that they will. Essentially they are unplanned tests which were not stipulated prior to the collection of data.

Power: In statistics the ability of a test to reject the null hypothesis when it is false.

Principal components analysis: Primarily a form of factor analysis in which the variance of each variable is set at the maximum value of 1 as no adjustment has been made for communalities. Probably best reserved for instances in which the correlation matrix tends to have high values which is not common in psychological research.

Probability distribution: The distribution of outcomes expected by chance.

Promax: A method of oblique rotation in factor analysis.

Quantitative research: Research which at the very least involves counting the frequency of categories in the main variable of interest.

Quartimax: A method of orthogonal rotation in factor analysis.

Randomisation: The assignment of cases to conditions using some method of assigning by chance.

R: Refers to a popular computer programing language and a collection of statistical analysis software which is available for use without charge.

Range: The difference between the largest and smallest score of a variable.

Ratio data: A measure for which it is possible to say that a score is a multiple of another score such as 20 being twice 10. Also there should be a zero point on the measure. This is a holy grail of statistical theory which psychologists will never find unless variables such as time and distance are considered.

Recode: Giving a value, or set of values, another value such as recoding age into ranges of age.

Regression coefficient: The weight which is applied to a predictor variable to give the value of the dependent variable.

Related design: A design in which participants provide data in more than one condition of the experiment. This is where participants serve as their own controls. More rarely, if samples are matched on a pairwise basis to be as similar as possible on a matching variable then this also constitutes a related design if the matching variable correlates with the dependent variable.

Related factorial design: A design in which there are two or more independent or predictor variables which have the same or similar cases in them.

Reliability: Internal reliability is the extent to which items which make up a scale or measure are internally consistent. It is usually calculated either using a form of split-half reliability in which the score for half the items is correlated with the score for the other half of the items (with an adjustment for the shortened length of the scale) or using Cronbach's alpha (which is the average of all possible split-half reliabilities). A distinct form of reliability is test–retest

Repeated measures ANOVA: An analysis of variance which is based on one or more related factors having the same or similar cases in them.

Repeated measures design: A design in which the groups of the independent variables have the same or similar cases in them.

Residual: The difference between an observed and expected score.

Residual sum of squares: The sum of squares that are left over after other sources of variance have been removed.

Rotation: *see* Rotation of factors.

Rotation of factors: This adjusts the factors (axes) of a factor analysis in order to make the factors more interpretable. To do so, the numbers of high and low factor loadings are maximised whereas the numbers of middle-sized factor loadings are made minimal. Originally it involved plotting the axes (factors) on graph paper and rotating them physically on the page, leaving the factor loadings in the same points on the graph paper. As a consequence, the factor loadings change since these have not moved but the axes have.

Sample: A selection or subset of scores on a variable. Samples cannot be guaranteed to be representative of the population but if they are selected at random then there will be no systematic difference between the samples and the population.

Sampling distribution: The theoretical distribution of a particular size of sample which would result if samples of that size were repeatedly taken from that population.

Saturated model: A model (set of variables) which fully accounts for the data. It is a concept used in log-linear analysis.

Scattergram: *see* Scatterplot.

Scatterplot: A diagram or chart which shows the relationship between two score variables. It consists of a horizontal and a vertical scale which are used to plot the scores of each individual on both variables.

Scheffé test: A *post hoc* test used in analysis of variance to test whether two group means differ significantly from each other.

Score statistic: A measure of association in logistic regression.

Scree test: A graph of the eigenvalues of successive factors in a factor analysis. It is used to help determine the 'significant' number of factors prior to rotation. The point at which the curve becomes flat and 'straight' determines the number of 'significant' factors.

Select cases: The name of an SPSS procedure for selecting sub-samples of cases based on one or more criteria such as the gender of participants.

Sign test: A nonparametric test which determines whether the number of positive and negative differences between the scores in two conditions with the same or similar cases differ significantly.

Significance level: The probability level at and below which an outcome is assumed to be unlikely to be due to chance.

Simple regression: A test for describing the size and direction of the association between a predictor variable and a criterion variable.

Skew: A description given to a frequency distribution in which words, it is a lop-sided frequency distribution compared to a normal (bell-shaped) curve.

Sort cases: The name of an SPSS procedure for ordering cases in the data file according to the values of one or more variables.

Spearman's correlation coefficient: A measure of the size and direction of the association between two variables rank ordered in size.

Sphericity: Similarity of the correlations between the dependent variable in the different conditions.

Split-half reliability: The correlation between the two halves of a scale adjusted for the number of variables in each scale.

SPSS: A statistical computer package which in 2008–9 was renamed PASW Statistics. In 2010 it was renamed SPSS Statistics. It is still generally referred to as SPSS.

Squared Euclidean distance: The sum of the squared differences between the scores on two variables for the sample.

Standard deviation: Conceptually, the average amount by which the scores differ from the mean.

Standard error: Conceptually, the average amount by which the means of samples differ from the mean of the population.

Standard or direct entry: A form of multiple regression in which all of the predictor variables are entered into the analysis at the same time.

Standardised coefficients or weights: The coefficients or weights of the predictors in an equation are expressed in terms of their standardised scores.

Stepwise entry: A form of multiple regression in which variables are entered into the analysis one step at a time. In this way, the most predictive predictor is chosen first, then the second most predictive predictor is chosen second having dealt with the variance due to the first predictor and so forth.

Sum of squares: The total obtained by adding up the squared differences between each score and the mean of that set of scores. The 'average' of this is the variance.

Syntax: Statements or commands for carrying out various procedures in computer software.

Test–retest reliability: The correlation of a measure taken at one point in time with the same (or very similar) measure taken at a different point in time.

Transformation: Ways of adjusting the data to meet the requirements for the data for a particular statistical technique. For example, the data could be changed by taking the square root of each score, turning each score into a logarithm and so forth. Trial and error may be required to find an appropriate transformation.

Two-tailed test: A test which assesses the statistical significance of a relationship or difference in either direction.

Type I error: Accepting the hypothesis when it is actually false.

Type II error: Rejecting the hypothesis when it is actually true.

Under-identified model: A structural equation model in which there are not enough data points to estimate its parameters.

Unique variance: Variance of a variable which is not shared

Univariate: Involving one variable.

Unplanned comparisons: Comparisons between groups which were not stipulated before the data were collected but after its collection.

Unstandardised coefficients or weights: The coefficients or weights which are applied to scores (as opposed to standardised scores).

Value label: The name or label given to the value of a variable such as 'Female' for '1'.

Variable label: The name or label given to a variable.

Variable name: The name of a variable.

Variable View: The window in SPSS Data Editor which shows the names of variables and their specification.

Variance: The mean of the sum of the squared difference between each score and the mean of the set of scores. It constitutes a measure of the variability or dispersion of scores on a quantitative variable.

Variance–covariance matrix: A matrix containing the variance of the variables (in the diagonal) and the covariances between pairs of variables in the rest of the table.

Variance estimate: The variance of the population of scores calculated from the variance of a sample of scores from that population.

Variance ratio: The ratio between two variances, commonly referred to in ANOVA (analysis of variance).

Varimax: In factor analysis, a procedure for rotating the factors to simplify understanding of the factors which maintains the zero correlation between all of the factors.

Wald statistic: The ratio of the beta coefficient to its standard error. Used in logistic regression.

Web scraping: The process of extracting information from numerous websites for eventual analysis.

Weights: An adjustment made to reflect the size of a variable or sample.

Wilcoxon signed-rank test: A nonparametric test for assessing whether the scores from two samples that come from the same or similar cases differ significantly.

Wilks' lambda: A measure, involving the ratio of the within-groups to the total sum of squares, used to determine if the means of variables differ significantly across groups.

Within-subjects design: A correlated or repeated measures design.

Yates's continuity correction: An outmoded adjustment to a 2×2 chi-square test held to improve the fit of the test to the chi-square distribution.

z-score: A score expressed as the number of standard deviations a score is from the mean of the set of scores.

REFERENCES

Abeyta, A. A., Routledge, C., & Juhl, J. (2015). Looking back to move forward: Nostalgia as a psychological resource for promoting relationship goals and overcoming relationship challenge. *Journal of Personality and Social Psychology, 109*, 1029–1044.

Ahrens, C., Campbell, R., Ternier-Thames, N., Wasco, S., & Sefl, T. (2007). Deciding whom to tell: Expectations and outcomes of rape survivors' first disclosures. *Psychology of Women Quarterly, 31*, 38–49.

Aitken, L. S., & West, S. G. (1991). *Multiple regression: Testing and interpreting interactions*. Newbury Park, CA: Sage.

Aksentijevic, A. (2015). Statistician, heal thyself: Fighting statophobia at the source. *Frontiers of Psychology, 6*, 1–5.

Ang, R. P., & Huan, V. S. (2006). Relationship between academic stress and suicidal ideation: Testing for depression as a mediator using multiple regression. *Child Psychiatry and Human Development, 37*, 133–143.

APA (2010). *Publication Manual of the American Psychological Association* (6th ed.). Washington, DC: American Psychological Association.

Arias, J. M. C. (2017). Big data for use in psychological research. *International Journal of Psychological Research, 10*, 6–7.

Atkinson, D. R., Furlong, M. J., & Wampold, B. E. (1982). Statistical significance, reviewer evaluations, and the scientific process: Is there a (statistically) significant relationship? *Journal of Counseling Psychology, 29*, 189–194.

Baron, L., & Straus, M. (1989). *Four theories of rape: A state-level analysis*. New Haven, CT: Yale University Press.

Baron, R. M., & Kenny, D. A. (1986). The moderator–mediator variable distinction in social psychological research: Conceptual, strategic, and statistical considerations. *Journal of Personality and Social Psychology, 51*, 1173–1182.

Ben-Zvi, D., & Garfield, J. (Eds.) (2004). *The challenge of developing statistical literacy, reasoning, and thinking*. Dordrecht, Netherlands: Kluwer Academic Publishers.

Bierie, D. M. (2013). Procedural justice and prison violence: Examining complaints among federal inmates (2000–2007). *Psychology, Public Policy, and Law, 19*, 15–29.

Blackmore, E. R., Jones, I., Doshi, M., Haque, S., Holder, R., Brockington, I., & Craddock, N. (2006). Obstetric variables associated with bipolar affective puerperal psychosis. *British Journal of Psychiatry, 188*, 32–36.

Blalock, H. M. (1972). *Social statistics*. New York, NY: McGraw-Hill.

Blankenship, K. L., Wegener, D. T., & Murray, R. A. (2012). Circumventing resistance: Using values to indirectly change attitudes. *Journal of Personality and Social Psychology, 103*, 606–621.

Blom, D., van Middendorp, H., & Geenen, R. (2012). Anxious attachment may be a vulnerability factor for developing embitterment. *Psychology and Psychotherapy: Theory, Research and Practice, 85*, 351–355.

Bourne, V.J. (2018). Does mathematical ability predict performance in the research components of an undergraduate psychology degree? Only a little bit, for a little while, and in specific ways. *Scholarship of Teaching and Learning in Psychology, 4*(3), 181–188.

Brasel, A., & Gips, J. (2011). Media multitasking behavior: Concurrent television and computer usage. *Cyberpsychology, Behavior, and Social Networking, 14*, 527–534.

Bridges, F. S., Williamson, C. B., Thompson, P. C., & Windsor, M. A. (2001). Lost letter technique: Returned responses to battered and abused women, men, and lesbians. *North American Journal of Psychology, 3*, 263–276.

Brown, M. S. (2014). *Data mining for dummies*. Hoboken, NJ: John Wiley and Sons.

Butler, C. (1995a). Teachers' qualities, resources and involvement of special needs children in mainstream classrooms. Unpublished thesis, Department of Social Sciences, Loughborough University.

Butler, R. (1995b). Motivational and informational functions and consequences of children's attention to peers' work. *Journal of Educational Psychology, 87,* 347–360.

Carlson, E. N., Vazire, S., & Oltmanns, T. F. (2011). You probably think this paper's about you: Narcissists' perceptions of their personality and reputation. *Journal of Personality and Social Psychology, 101,* 185–201.

Carolan, L. A., & Power, M. J. (2011). What basic emotions are experienced in bipolar disorder? *Clinical Psychology & Psychotherapy, 18,* 366–378.

Casidy, R. (2012). Discovering consumer personality clusters in prestige sensitivity and fashion consciousness context. *Journal of International Consumer Marketing, 24,* 291–299.

Castell, S., Charlton, A., Clemence, M., Pettigrew, N., Pope, S., Quigley, A., Shah, J. N., & Silman, T. (2014). *Public Attitudes to Science 2014 Main Report.* London: Department of Business, Education, and Skills.

Chan, A., Hróbjartsson, A., Haahr, M. T., Gøtzsche, P. C., & Altman, D. G. (2004). Empirical evidence for selective reporting of outcomes in randomized trials: Comparison of protocols to published articles. *Journal of the American Medical Association, 291,* 2457–2465.

Chen, E. E., & Wojcik, S. P. (2016). A practical guide to big data research in psychology. *Psychological Methods, 21,* 458–474.

Cheung, M.W.-L., & Jak, S. (2018). Challenges of big data analyses and applications in psychology. *Zeitschrift für Psychologie, 226,* 209–211.

Chew, P. K. H., & Dillon, D. B. (2014). Statistics anxiety update: refining the construct and recommendations for a new research agenda. *Perspectives on Psychological Science, 9,* 196–208.

Chhabra, N., & Bryant, S.M. (2016). Snapchat toxicology: Social media and suicide. *Annals of Emergency Medicine, 68,* 527.

Childs, A., & Klimoski, R. J. (1986). Successfully predicting career success: An application of the biographical inventory. *Journal of Applied Psychology, 71,* 3–8.

Cohen, J. (1988). *Statistical power analysis for the behavioural sciences* (2nd ed.). Hillsdale, NJ: Lawrence Erlbaum Associates.

Cohen, J., Cohen, P., West, S. G., & Aiken, L. S. (2003). *Applied multiple regression/correlation analysis for the behavioral sciences* (3rd ed.). Hillsdale, NJ: Lawrence Erlbaum Associates.

Contador, I., Fernández-Calvo, B., Cacho, L. J., Ramos, F., & López-Rolón, A. (2010). Non-verbal memory tasks in early differential diagnosis of Alzheimer's disease and unipolar depression. *Applied Neuropsychology, 17,* 251–261.

Coursol, A., & Wagner, E. E. (1986). Effect of positive findings on submission and acceptance rates: A note on meta-analysis bias. *Professional Psychology: Research and Practice, 17,* 136–137.

Cramer, D. (1992). *Personality and psychotherapy.* Milton Keynes, UK: Open University Press.

Crighton, D., & Towl, G. (1994). The selection and recruitment of prison officers. *Forensic Update: A*

Critcher, C. R., & Dunning, D. (2013). Predicting persons' versus a person's goodness: Behavioral forecasts diverge for individuals versus populations. *Journal of Personality and Social Psychology, 104,* 28–44.

Cumming, G., & Calin-Jageman, R. (2017). *Introduction to the new statistics: Estimation, open science, and beyond.* New York, NY: Routledge.

Cumming, S. P., Sherar, L. B., Hunter Smart, J. E., Rodriques, A. M. M., Standage, M., Gillson, F. B., & Malina, R. M. (2012). Physical activity and physical self-concept in adolescence: A comparison of girls at the extremes of the biological maturation continuum. *Journal of Research on Adolescence, 22,* 746–757.

Curseu, P. L., Schruijer, S. G. L., & Boros, S. (2012). Socially rejected while cognitively successful: The impact of minority dissent on groups' cognitive complexity. *British Journal of Social Psychology, 51,* 570–582.

Dakwar, E., Nunes, E. V., Bisaga, A., Carpenter, K. C., Mariani, J. J., Sullivan, M. A., Raby, W. N., & Levin F. R. (2011). A comparison of independent depression and substance-induced depression in cannabis-, cocaine-, and opioid-dependent treatment seekers. *American Journal on Addictions, 20,* 441–446.

Davies, A. (2008). Exhaustive regression: An exploration of regression-based data mining techniques using super computation. RPF Working Paper No. 2008-008 http://www.gwu.edu/~forcpgm/2008-008.pdf

Deary, I. J., Hunter, R., Langan, S. J., & Goodwin, G. M. (1991). Inspection time, psychometric intelligence and clinical estimates of cognitive ability in pre-senile Alzheimer's disease and Korsakoff's psychosis. *Brain, 114,* 2543–2554.

Dickersin, K., Min, Y. I., & Meinert, C. L. (1992). Factors influencing publication of research results: Follow-up of applications submitted to two institutional review boards. *Journal of the American Medical Association, 263,* 374–378.

Di Filippo, G., de Luca, M., Judica, A., Spinelli, D., & Zoccolotti, P. (2006). Lexicality and stimulus length effects in Italian dyslexics: Role of overadditivity effect. *Child Neuropsychology, 12,* 141–149.

Drees, M. J., & Mack, M. G. (2012). An examination of mental toughness over the course of a competitive season. *Journal of Sport Behavior, 35,* 377–386.

Dumont, K., & Louw, J. (2009). The recognition of Henri Tajfel's work on intergroup relations. *International Journal of Psychology, 44,* 46–59.

Easterbrook, P. J., Berlin, J. A., Gopalan, R., & Matthews, D. R. (1991). Publication bias in clinical research. *Lancet, 337,* 867–872.

Edenfield, J. L., Adams, K. S., & Briihl, D. (2012). Relationship maintenance strategy use by romantic attachment style. *North American Journal of Psychology, 14,* 149–162.

Estevis, E., Basso, M. R., & Combs, D. (2012). Effects of practice on the Wechsler Adult Intelligence Scale–IV across 3- and 6-month intervals. *Clinical*

Eysenck, H. J., & Eysenck, S. B. G. (1976). *Psychoticism as a dimension of personality*. London, UK: Hodder & Stoughton.

Faust, M. E., Balota, D. A., Spieler, D. H., & Ferraro, F. R. (1999). Individual differences in information processing rate and amount: Implications for group differences in response latency. *Psychological Bulletin*, *125*, 777–799.

Fayed, N., Klassen, A. F., Dix, D., Klaassen, R., & Sung, L. (2011). Exploring predictors of optimism among parents of children with cancer. *Psycho-Oncology*, *20*, 411–418.

Fitneva, S. A., Lam, N. H., & Dunfield, K. A. (2013). The development of children's information gathering: To look or to ask? *Developmental Psychology*, *49*, 533–542.

Ford, S., Howard, R., & Oyebode, J. (2012). Psychosocial aspects of coeliac disease: A cross-sectional survey of a UK population. *British Journal of Health Psychology*, *17*, 743–757.

Frank, G. K. W., Roblek, T., Shott, M. E., Jappe, L. M., Rollin, M. D. H., Hagman, J. O., & Pryor, T. (2012). Heightened fear of uncertainty in anorexia and bulimia nervosa. *International Journal of Eating Disorders*, *45*, 227–232.

Freund, P. A., & Kasten, N. (2012). How smart do you think you are? A meta-analysis on the validity of self-estimates of cognitive ability. *Psychological Bulletin*, *138*, 296–321.

Friedrich, J., Childress, J., & Cheng, D. (2018). Replicating a National Survey on Statistical Training in undergraduate psychology programs: Are there "New Statistics" in the New Millennium? *Teaching of Psychology*, *45*, 312–323.

Gallagher, P., Yancy, W. S. Jr, Jeffreys, A. S., Coffman, C. J., Weinberger, M., Bosworth, H. B., & Voils, C. I. (2013). Patient self-efficacy and spouse perception of spousal support are associated with lower patient weight: Baseline results from a spousal support behavioral intervention. *Psychology, Health & Medicine*, *18*, 175–181.

Gannon, T. A., & Barrowcliffe, E. (2012). Firesetting in the general population: The development and validation of the Fire Setting and Fire Proclivity Scales. *Legal and Criminological Psychology*, *17*, 105–122.

Gervais, S. J., Vescio, T. K., & Allen, J. (2012). When are people interchangeable sexual objects? The effect of gender and body type on sexual fungibility. *British Journal of Social Psychology*, *51*, 499–513.

Gibbs, S., & Powell, B. (2012). Teacher efficacy and pupil behaviour: The structure of teachers' individual and collective beliefs and their relationship with numbers of pupils excluded from school. *British Journal of Educational Psychology*, *82*, 564–584.

Gillis, J. S. (1980). *Child Anxiety Scale Manual*. Champaign, IL: Institute of Personality and Ability Testing.

Glantz, S. A., & Slinker, B. K. (1990). *Primer of applied regression and analysis of variance*. New York, NY: McGraw-Hill.

Gordon, S. (1995). A theoretical approach to understanding [Online], *3*(3) http://www.amstat.org/publications/jse/v3n3/gordon.html

Gordon, S. (2004). Understanding students' experiences of statistics in a service course. *Statistics Education Research Journal*, *3*, 40–59.

Gotwals, J. K., Stoeber, J., Dunn, J. G. H., & Stoll, O. (2012). Are perfectionistic strivings in sport adaptive? A systematic review of confirmatory, contradictory, and mixed evidence. *Canadian Psychology*, *53*, 263–279.

Gray, H. M., LaPlante, D. A., & Shaffer, H. J. (2012). Behavioral characteristics of Internet gamblers who trigger corporate responsible gambling interventions. *Psychology of Addictive Behaviors*, *26*, 527–535.

Griffin, B., & Hesketh, B. (2008). Post-retirement work: The individual determinants of paid and volunteer work. *Journal of Occupational and Organizational Psychology*, *81*, 101–121.

Guzman, J. F., & Kingston, K. (2012). Prospective study of sport dropout: A motivational analysis as a function of age and gender. *European Journal of Sports Science*, *12*, 431–442.

Hannaford, P.C., Thompson, C., & Simpson, M. (1996). Evaluation of an educational programme to improve the recognition of psychological illness by general practitioners. *British Journal of General Practice*, *46*(407), 333–337.

Hao, J., & Ho, T. K. (2019). Machine learning made easy: A review of Scikit-learn Package in Python Programming Language. *Journal of Educational and Behavioral Statistics*, *44*, 348–361.

Harinck, F., & Van Kleef, G. A. (2012). Be hard on the interests and soft on the values: Conflict issue moderates the effects of anger in negotiations. *British Journal of Social Psychology*, *51*, 741–752.

Harlow, L. L., & Oswald, F. L. (2016). Big data in psychology: Introduction to the Special Issue. *Psychological Methods*, *21*, 447–457.

Hoenig, J. M., & Heisey, D. M. (2001). The abuse of power: The pervasive fallacy of power calculations for data analysis. *The American Statistician*, *55*, 19–24.

Hoicka, E., & Akhtar, N. (2012). Early humour production. *British Journal of Developmental Psychology*, *30*, 586–603.

Howell, D. (2013). *Statistical methods for psychology* (8th ed.). Belmont, CA: Cengage.

Howitt, D. (2013). *Introduction to qualitative methods in psychology* (3rd ed.). Harlow, UK: Pearson Education.

Howitt, D., & Cramer, D. (2020). *Introduction to research methods in psychology* 5th ed. Harlow, UK: Pearson.

Howitt, D., & Cumberbatch, G. (1990), *Pornography: Impacts and influences*. London, UK: Home Office Research and Planning Unit.

Huck, S. W. (2009). *Statistical misconceptions*. New York: Routledge.

Huisman, A., van Houwelingen, C. A. J., & Kerkhof, A. J. F. M. (2010). Psychopathology and suicide method in mental health care. *Journal of Affective Disorders*, *121*,

Huitema, B. E. (1980). *The analysis of covariance and its alternatives.* New York, NY: Wiley.

Hunter, P. G., Schellenberg, E. G., & Griffith, A. T. (2011). Misery loves company: Mood-congruent emotional responding to music. *Emotion, 11,* 1068–1072.

Ingravallo, F., Vignatelli, L., Brini, M., Brugaletta, C., Franceschini, C., Lugaresi, F., Manca, M. C., Garbarino, S., Montagna, P., Cicognani, A., & Plazzi, G. (2008). Medico-legal assessment of disability in narcolepsy: An interobserver reliability study. *Journal of Sleep Research, 17,* 111–119.

Ivancevich, J. M. (1976). Effects of goal setting on performance and job satisfaction. *Journal of Applied Psychology, 61,* 605–612.

Jafari, N., Zamani, A., Farajzadegan, Z., Bahrami, F., Emami, H., & Loghmani, A. (2013). The effect of spiritual therapy for improving the quality of life of women with breast cancer: A randomized controlled trial. *Psychology, Health and Medicine, 18,* 56–69.

John, L. K., Loewenstein, G., & Prelec, D. (2012). Measuring the prevalence of questionable research practices with incentives for truth telling. *Psychological Science 23,* 524–532.

Kenne, D. R., Boros, A. P., & Fischbein, R. L. (2010). Characteristics of opiate users leaving detoxification treatment against medical advice. *Journal of Addictive Diseases, 29,* 283–294.

Kerlinger, F. N. (1986). *Foundations of behavioural research.* New York, NY: Holt, Rinehart & Winston.

Kerr, N. L. (1998). HARKing: Hypothesizing After the Results are Known. *Personality and Social Psychology Review, 2,* 196–217.

Kogan, S. M. (2004). Disclosing unwanted sexual experiences: Results from a national sample of adolescent women. *Child Abuse & Neglect, 28,* 147–165.

Kois, L., Pearson, J., Chauhan, P., Goni, M., & Saraydarian, L. (2013). Competency to stand trial among female inpatients. *Law and Human Behavior, 37,* 231–240.

Kosinski, M., Wang, Y., Lakkaraju, H., & Leskovec, J. (2016). Mining big data to extract patterns and predict real-life outcomes. *Psychological Methods, 21,* 493–506.

Kuhnle, C., Hofer, M., & Kilian, B. (2012). Self-control as predictor of school grades, life balance, and flow in adolescents. *British Journal of Educational Psychology, 82,* 533–548.

Laaksonen, M. A., Lindfors, O., Knekt, P., & Aalberg, V. (2012). Suitability for Psychotherapy Scale (SPS) and its reliability, validity, and prediction. *British Journal of Clinical Psychology, 51,* 351–375.

Lalonde, R. N., & Gardner, R. C. (1993). Statistics as a second language? A model for predicting performance in psychology students. *Canadian Journal of Behavioural Science, 25,* 108–125.

Lamoureux, B. E., Palmieri, P. A., Jackson, A. P., & Hobfoll, S. E. (2012). Child sexual abuse and adulthood-interpersonal outcomes: Examining pathways for

intervention. *Psychological Trauma: Theory, Research, Practice, and Policy, 4,* 605–613.

Lampropoulos, G. K., Schneider, M. K., & Spengler, P. M. (2009). Predictors of early termination in a university counseling training clinic. *Journal of Counseling and Development, 87,* 36–46.

Landers, R. N., Brusso, R. C., Cavanaugh, K. J., & Collmus, A. B. (2016). A primer on theory-driven web scraping: Automatic extraction of big data from the Internet for use in psychological research. *Psychological Methods, 21,* 475–49.

Lautamo, T., Laakso, M. L., Aro, T., Ahonen, T., & Törmäkangas, K. (2011). Validity of the play assessment for group settings: An evaluation of differential item functioning between children with specific language impairment and typically developing peers. *Australian Occupational Therapy Journal, 58,* 222–230.

Levine, T. R., Asada, K. J., & Carpenter, C. (2009). Sample size and effect size are negatively correlated in meta-analysis: Evidence and implications of a publication bias against non-significant findings. *Communication Monographs, 76,* 286–302.

Lipsey, M. W., & Wilson, D. B. (1993). The efficacy of psychological, educational, and behavioral treatment: Confirmation from meta-analysis. *American Psychologist, 48,* 1181–1209.

Lowe, P., & Ang, R. (2012). Cross-cultural examination of test anxiety among US and Singapore students on the Test Anxiety Scale for Elementary Students (TAS-E). *Educational Psychology, 32,* 107–126.

MacCabe, J. H., Brebion, G., Reichenber, A., Ganguly, T., McKenna, P. J., Murray, P. J., & David, A. S. (2012). Superior intellectual ability in schizophrenia: Neuropsychological characteristics. *Neuropsychology, 26,* 181–190.

Maguire-Jack, K., Gromoske, A. N., & Berger, L. M. (2012). Spanking and child development during the first five years of life. *Child Development, 83,* 1960–1977.

Meeten, F., & Davey, G. C. L. (2012). Mood as input and perseverative worrying following the induction of discrete negative moods. *Behavior Therapy, 43,* 393–406.

Mercer, S. H., Harpole, L. L., Mitchell, R. R., McLemore, C., & Hardy, C. (2012). The impact of probe variability on brief experimental analysis of reading skills. *School Psychology Quarterly, 27,* 223–235.

Meyer, M. M., Bell, R., & Buchner, A. (2015). Remembering the snake in the grass: Threat enhances recognition but not source memory. *Emotion, 15,* 721–730.

Mitsumatsu, H. (2013). Stronger discounting of external cause by action in human adults: Evidence for an action-based hypothesis of visual collision perception. *Journal of Experimental Psychology: General, 142,* 101–118.

Motes, M. A., Hubbard, T. L., Courtney, J. R., & Rypma, B. (2008). A principal components analysis of dynamic spatial memory biases. *Journal of Experimental*

Psychology: Learning, Memory, & Cognition, 34, 1076–1083.

Munford, M. B. (1994). Relationship of gender, self-esteem, social class and racial identity to depression in blacks. *Journal of Black Psychology, 20,* 157–174.

Murphy, K. R., & Myors, B. (2004), *Statistical power analysis: A simple and general model for traditional and modern hypothesis tests* (2nd ed.). Mahwah, NJ: Lawrence Erlbaum Associates.

Mutsvunguma, P., & Gwandure, C. (2011). The psychological well-being of employees who handle cash in a bank in inner city Johannesburg. *Psychology, Health & Medicine, 16,* 430–436.

Nair, U. S., Collins, B. N., & Napolitano, M. A. (2012). Differential effects of a body image exposure session on smoking urge between physically active and sedentary female smokers. *Psychology of Addictive Behaviors, 27,* 322–327.

Nicholas, M. K, Coulston, C. M., Asghari, A., & Malhi, G. S. (2009). Depressive symptoms in patients with chronic pain. *Medical Journal of Australia, 190,* S66–S70.

Niemeier, J. P., Marwitz, J. H., Lesher, K., Walker, W., & Bushnik, T. (2007). Gender differences in executive functions following traumatic brain injury. *Neuropsychological Rehabilitation, 17,* 293–313.

Norman, G. J., Hawkley, L., Ball, A., Berntson, G. G., & Cacioppo, J. T. (2013). Perceived social isolation moderates the relationship between early childhood trauma and pulse pressure in older adults. *International Journal of Psychophysiology, 88,* 334–338.

Onwuegbuzie, A. J. (2004). Academic procrastination and statistics anxiety. *Assessment & Evaluation in Higher Education, 29,* 3–19.

Otgaar, H., Horselenberg, R., van Kampen, R., & Lalleman, K. (2012). Clothed and unclothed human figure drawings lead to more correct and incorrect reports of touch in children. *Psychology, Crime & Law, 18,* 641–653.

Passmore, J., & Rehman, H. (2012). Coaching as a learning methodology – a mixed methods study in driver development using a randomised controlled trial and thematic analysis. *International Coaching Psychology Review, 7,* 166–184.

Pechey, R., & Halligan, P. (2011). The prevalence of delusion-like beliefs relative to sociocultural beliefs in the general population. *Psychopathology, 44,* 106–115.

Perlman, D. (2011). Examination of self-determination within the sport education model. *Asia-Pacific Journal of Health, Sport and Physical Education, 2,* 79–92.

Peters, M., & Durding, B. M. (1978). Handedness measured by finger tapping: A continuous variable. *Canadian Journal of Psychology, 32,* 257–261.

Pituch, K. A., & Stevens, J. P. (2016). *Applied multivariate statistics for the social sciences: Analyses with SAS and IBM's SPSS.* (6th ed.). Hove, UK: Routledge.

Potter, G. G., Hartman, M., & Ward, T. (2009). Perceived stress and everyday memory complaints among older adult women. *Anxiety, Stress and Coping, 2,* 475–81.

Ridenour, T. A., McCoy, K. D., & Dean, R. S. (1996). An exploratory stepwise discriminant function analysis of malingered and nondistorted responses to the Neuropsychological Symptom Inventory. *International Journal of Neuroscience, 87,* 91–95.

Rohmer, O., & Louvet, E. (2012). Implicit measures of the stereotype content associated with disability. *British Journal of Social Psychology, 51,* 732–740.

Rossi, J. S. (1990). Statistical power of psychological research: What have we gained in 20 years? *Journal of Consulting and Clinical Psychology, 58,* 646–656.

Rothbard, N., & Wilk, S. L. (2011). Waking up on the right or wrong side of the bed: Start-of-workday mood, work events, employee affect, and performance. *Academy of Management Journal, 54,* 959–980.

Rowe, M. L. (2012). A longitudinal investigation of the role of quantity and quality of child-directed speech in vocabulary development. *Child Development, 83,* 1762–1774.

Rubin, J., Wynn, J., & Moscovitch, M. (2016). The spatial scaffold: The effects of spatial context on memory for events. *Journal of Experimental Psychology: Learning, Memory, and Cognition, 42,* 308–315.

Ruggeri, K., Dempster, M., & Hanna, D. (2011). The impact of misunderstanding the nature of statistics. *Psychology Teaching Review, 17,* 33–38.

Ruscio, J., & Roche, B. (2012). Variance heterogeneity in published psychological research: A review and a new index. *Methodology: European Journal of Research Methods for the Behavioral and Social Sciences, 8,* 1–11.

Schau, C. (2003). Students' attitudes: The 'other' important outcome in statistics education. http://www.statlit.org/pdf/2003SchauASA.pdf. Accessed 11 November 2016.

Schimmack, U. (2012). The ironic effect of significant results on the credibility of multiple-study articles. *Psychological Methods, 17,* 551–566.

Schoedel, R., Au, Q., Volkel, T. S., Lehmann, F, Becker, D, Buhner, M., Bischl, B., Hussmann, H., & Stachl, C. (2018). Footprints of sensation seeking: A traditional concept in the big data era. *Zeitschrift für Psychologie, 226,* 232–24.

Schulenberg, S. E., & Yutrzenka, B. A. (2001). Equivalence of computerized and conventional versions of the Beck Depression Inventory-II (BDI-II). *Current Psychology, 20,* 216–230.

Sedlmeier, P., Eberth, J., Schwarz, M., Zimmermann, D., Haarig, F., Jaeger, S., & Kunze, S. (2012). The psychological effects of meditation: A meta-analysis. *Psychological Bulletin, 138,* 1139–1171.

Sierra, P., Livianos, L., & Rojo, L. (2005). Quality of life for patients with bipolar disorder: Relationship with clinical and demographic variables. *Bipolar Disorders, 7,* 159–165.

Siew, C. S. Q., McCartney, M. J., & Vitevitch, M. S. (2019). Using network science to understand statistics anxiety among college students. *Scholarship of Teaching and Learning in Psychology, 5,* 75–89.

Signal, T. L., van den Berg, M. J., Mulrine, H. M., & Gander, P. H. (2012). Duration of sleep inertia after napping during simulated night work and in extended operations. *Chronobiology International, 29*, 769–779.

Simmons, J. P., Nelson, L. D., & Simonsohn, U. (2011). False-positive psychology: Undisclosed flexibility in data collection and analysis allows presenting anything as significant. *Psychological Science, 22*, 1359–1366.

Simpson, S., & Karageorghis, C. I. (2006). The effects of synchronous music on 400-m sprint performance. *Journal of Sports Sciences, 24*, 1095–1102.

Siy, J. O., & Cheryan, S. (2013). When compliments fail to flatter: American individualism and responses to positive stereotypes. *Journal of Personality and Social Psychology, 104*, 87–102.

Skinner, B. F. (1948). 'Superstition' in the pigeon. *Journal of Experimental Psychology, 38*, 168–172.

Smart, R. G. (1964). The importance of negative results in psychological research. *Canadian Psychologist, 5a*, 226–232.

Smith-Bell, C. A., Burhans L. B., & Schreurs B. G. (2012). Predictors of susceptibility and resilience in an animal model of posttraumatic stress disorder. *Behavioral Neuroscience, 126*, 749–761.

Song, J., Song, T.M., Seo, D-C., & Jin, J. (2016). Data mining of web-based documents on social networking sites that included suicide-related words. *Journal of Adolescent Health 59*, 668–673.

Sprung, J. M., Sliter, M. T., & Jex, S. M. (2012). Spirituality as a moderator of the relationship between workplace aggression and employee outcomes. *Personality and Individual Differences, 53*, 930–934.

Symons, M., Feeney, G. F. X., Gallagher, M. R., Young, R. McD., & Connor, J.P. (2019). Machine learning vs addiction therapists: A pilot study predicting alcohol dependence treatment outcome from patient data in behavior therapy with adjunctive medication. *Journal of Substance Abuse Treatment 99*, 156–162.

Szostak, H. (1995). Competitive performance, anxiety and perceptions of parental pressure in young tennis players. Unpublished thesis, Department of Social Sciences, Loughborough University.

Taylor, J. S., Rastle, K., & Davis, M. H. (2013). Can cognitive models explain brain activation during word and pseudoword reading? A meta-analysis of 36 neuroimaging studies. *Psychological Bulletin, 139*, 766–791.

Teissedre, F., & Chabrol, H. (2004). Detecting women at risk for post-natal depression using the Edinburgh Postnatal Depression Scale at 2 to 3 days post-partum. *Canadian Journal of Psychiatry, 49*, 51–54.

Testa, M., Van Zile-Tamsen, C., & Livingston, J. A. (2007). Prospective prediction of women's sexual victimization by intimate and nonintimate male perpetrators. *Journal of Consulting and Clinical Psychology, 75*, 52–60.

Tonsing, K. N. (2018). Instructor immediacy and statistics anxiety in social work undergraduate students, *Social Work Education, 37*, 223–233.

Touliatos, J., & Lindholm, B. W. (1981). Congruence of parents' and teachers' ratings of children's behavior problems. *Journal of Abnormal Child Psychology, 9*, 347–354.

Tracey, T. J., Sherry, P., Bauer, G. P., Robins, T. H., Todaro, L., & Briggs, S. (1984). Help seeking as a function of student characteristics and program description: A logit-loglinear analysis. *Journal of Counseling Psychology, 31*, 54–62.

Tremont, G., & Alosco, M. L. (2011). Relationship between cognition and awareness of deficit in mild cognitive impairment. *International Journal of Geriatric Psychiatry, 29*, 299–306.

Tyson, P., Wilson, K., Brailsford, R., & Law, K. (2010). Physical activity and mental health in a student population. *Journal of Mental Health, 19*, 492–499.

Vallat-Azouvi, C., Pradat-Diehl, P., & Azouvi, P. (2012). The Working Memory Questionnaire: A scale to assess everyday life problems related to deficits of working memory in brain injured patients. *Neuropsychological Rehabilitation: An International Journal, 22*, 634–649.

van Schaik, P., & Ling, J. (2012). An experimental analysis of experiential and cognitive variables in web navigation. *Human Computer Interaction, 27*, 199–234.

Vassari, M., & Crosby, J. W. (2008). A reliability generalization study of coefficient alpha for the UCLA Loneliness Scale. *Journal of Personality Assessment, 90*, 601–607.

Vista, A., & Care, E. (2011). Gender differences in variance and means on the Naglieri Non-verbal Ability Test: Data from the Philippines. *British Journal of Educational Psychology, 81*, 292–308.

Wagner, U., & Zick, A. (1995). The relation of formal education to ethnic prejudice: Its reliability, validity and explanation. *European Journal of Social Psychology, 25*, 41–56.

Wampold, B. E., Furlong, M. J., & Atkinson, D. R. (1983). Statistical significance, power, and effect size: A response to the reexamination of reviewer bias. *Journal of Counseling Psychology, 30*, 459–463.

Wickham, L. H., Morris, P. E., & Fritz, C. O. (2000). Facial distinctiveness: Its measurement, distribution and influence on immediate and delayed recognition. *British Journal of Psychology, 91*, 99–123.

Wilkes, S., Cordier, R., Bundy, A., Docking, K., & Munro, N. (2011). A play-based intervention for children with ADHD: A pilot study. *Australian Occupational Therapy Journal, 58*, 231–240.

Woods, S. P., Rippeth, J. D., Conover, E., Carey, C. L., Parsons, T. D., & Troster, A. I. (2006). Statistical power of studies examining the cognitive effects of subthalamic nucleus deep brain stimulation in Parkinson's disease. *The Clinical Neuropsychologist, 20*, 27–38.

Wright, L., & Hardie, S. M. (2012). Are left-handers really more anxious? *Laterality, 17,* 629–642.

Wyrick, D. L., & Bond, L. (2011). Reducing sensitive survey response bias in research on adolescents: A comparison of web-based and paper-and-pencil administration. *American Journal of Health Promotion, 25,* 349–352.

Yarkoni, T., & Westfall, J. (2017). Choosing prediction over explanation in psychology: lessons from machine learning. *Perspectives on Psychological Science, 12,* 1100–1122.

Yildirim, İ. (2008). Relationships between burnout, sources of social support and sociodemographic variables. *Social Behavior and Personality, 36,* 603–616.

Zhang, Y., & Risen, J. L. (2014). Embodied motivation: Using a goal systems framework to understand the preference for social and physical warmth. *Journal of Personality and Social Psychology, 107,* 965–977.

Ziegler, R. H., & Britta Diehl, M. (2012). Relationship between job satisfaction and job performance: Job ambivalence as a moderator. *Journal of Applied Social Psychology, 42,* 2019–2040.

Zimprich, D. (2012). Attitudes toward statistics among Swiss psychology students. *Swiss Journal of Psychology, 71,* 149–155.

INDEX

Note: Glossary page numbers appear in **bold**.

−2 log likelihood 619, **689**

a priori statistical power analysis 568–70
a priori test **689**
Abeyta, A. A. 213
addition rule 246, 247
adjusted mean **689**
advanced correlational statistics 429–99
    factor analysis 444–66
    multiple regression and multiple correlation 466–83
    partial correlation 431–43
    path analysis 484–99
advanced qualitative or nominal techniques 581–652
    analysis of complex contingency tables 583–608
    binomial logistic regression 626–42
    data mining and big data 643–52
    multinomial logistic regression 609–25
advanced techniques 501–80
    meta-analysis 503–21
    moderator effects 536–57
    reliability in scales and measurement 522–35
    statistical power analysis 558–80
agreement between raters 529–32
    kappa coefficient calculation 530–2
Agresti, A. 608
Ahrens, C. 605
Aiken, L. S. 544, 546, 551, 557
Akhtar, N. 254
Aksentijevic, A. 4, 7
all subsets regression 650
Allen, J. 223
Alosco, M. L. 87
alpha level 565, **689**
alpha reliability 526–8
alternative hypothesis 147, 148
alternatives to chi-square 235–7
American Psychological Association (APA) 198, 200–2
    analysis of covariance (ANCOVA) 381, 383
    chi-square 233, 238
    confidence intervals 205, 213
    discriminant function analysis 411
    effect size 221
    Fisher exact probability test 237

Mann–Whitney *U* test 265
mixed design 265
multivariate analysis of variance (MANOVA) 397
one-way analysis of variance 298
path analysis 497
Pearson correlation coefficient 151
related *t*-test 175
sign test 261
Spearman's rho correlation coefficient 155
unrelated *t*-test 192
variance ratio test 278
Wilcoxon matched pairs test 263
analysis of complex contingency tables 583–608, **690**
    degrees of freedom 593
    hierarchical models 634
    key points 605
    lambda 634
    log-linear methods 584–5
    reporting results 634
    three-variable example 593–603
    two-variable example 586–93
analysis of covariance (ANCOVA) 370–85, 388, **689**
    calculation: one-way analysis of covariance 373–81
    computer analysis 383–5
    key points 382
    research examples 382
analysis of variance (ANOVA) 11, **689**
    effect size 219–31
    moderator effects 541, 551–4
    reporting 202
analysis of variance (ANOVA): correlated scores/repeated measures 300–14
    calculation 305–11
    computer analysis 313–14
    dependent variable 301
    examples 304–11
    key points 312
    matched sets 302
    research examples 311–12
    theory 303–4
analysis of variance (ANOVA): mixed design 353–69
    calculation 358–65
    cell sizes 354
    computer analysis 367–9

fixed vs random effects 355
key points 367
mixed designs and repeated measures 354–66
research examples 366
simpler alternative 365
analysis of variance (ANOVA): multiple comparisons 342–52
computer analysis 350–2
contrasts 346–8
Duncan multiple range test 344
F-ratio significance 344
key points 349
methods 345
multifactorial ANOVA 345–6
Newman–Keuls test 344
planned (*a priori*) vs unplanned (*post hoc*) comparisons 344
research examples 349
trends 348
analysis of variance (ANOVA): one-way unrelated/ uncorrelated 282–99
calculation 291–4
computer analysis 297–9
degrees of freedom 284, 288–91
key points 296–7
research examples 296
revision and new material 283–4
sum of squares 284
summary table 294–6
theory 284–8
variance 283
analysis of variance (ANOVA): two-way for unrelated/ uncorrelated scores 315–41
calculation 323–31
computer analysis 339–41
interactions 331–4
key points 338
research examples 337–8
steps 318–31
theory 317–18
three or more independent variables 334–7
ANCOVA *see* analysis of covariance
Anderson, E. B. 608
Anderson, R. E. 401, 415
Ang, R. P. 132, 212, 398, 480
ANOVA *see* analysis of variance
anxiety about statistics 4–5
applications of statistics 2–3
Arden, R. 279
Arias, J. M. C. 644
arithmetic mean 48–9, 51
calculation 49
Asada, K. J. 223
assessing change over time 422
association **689**
Atkinson, D. R. 647
attitudes towards statistics 2, 4–5, 7–8
Au, Q. 651
averages, variation and spread 46–61
calculation: numerical or arithmetic mean 49
calculation: variance using computational formulae 56–7
computer analysis 60–1
key points 59

mean, median and mode 48–51
mean, median and mode comparison 51
numerical indexes 47
research examples 58–9
spread of scores: range and interquartile range 51–5
spread of scores: variance 55–8
variance estimate 57
see also variables
Aydin, O. 649
Azouvi, P. 155

backwards elimination analysis, logistic regression procedure 636–7
bands of scores 39–40
bar charts 36, 37–8, **689**
compound 96–7, 99–101
computer analysis 99–101
pictogram 38
Baron, L. 438
Baron, R. M. 551
Barrowcliffe, E. 155, 412
Bartlett's test of sphericity **689**
Basso, M. R. 382
Bell, R. 221
Ben-Zvi, D. 4
Berger, L. M. 496
beta level **689**
beta weight **689**
between-groups design **689**
between-subjects design **689**
bidirectional relationships 486
Bierie, D. M. 163
big data 23, 643–52, **689**
key points 651
problems 645
research examples 651–2
traditional psychology, dissatisfactions with 647–8
Web scraping 648–9
bilateral relationships 486
bimodal **689**
bimodal and multimodal frequency distributions 68
binomial logistic regression 626–42
computer analysis 641–2
example 631–4
key points 640
logistic regression procedure 634–8
natural logarithms 630
odds ratio 629
regression formula 638–9
reporting findings 639
research examples 640
simple logistic regression 628–30
uses 627
bivariate **689**
bivariate correlation **689**
Black, W. C. 401, 415
Blackmore, E. R. 267
Blalock, H. M. 194
Blankenship, K. L. 366
block **689**
Blom, D. 117
Bond, L. 338
Bonferroni adjustment 345, 389, **689**

bootstrapping 11, 258–9, 475, **689**
Boros, A. P. 640
Boros, S. 337
Bourne 5
Box's test of equality 397, **689**
boxplot 53–5, **689**
Brasel, A. 71
Bridges, F. S. 605
Britta Diehl, M. 555
Brown, M. S. 646, 648, 649
Brusso, R. C. 649
Bryant, S. M. 644
Bryman, A. 466 499
Buchner, A. 221, 578
Burhans, L. B. 41
Butler, C. 439–40
Butler, R. 458–61

Calin-Jageman, R. 2
canonical correlations 405
Care, E. 279
Carlson, E. N. 117
Carpenter, C. 223
case **689**
Casidy, R. 398
Castellan, N. J. 270
categorical variable **689**
categories/groups *see* multinomial logistic regression
category variables (categorical variables, nominal variables)
    12, **689**
Cattell, R. 446
causality 432
Cavanaugh, K. J. 649
cell **689–90**
censuses 22
centroids 404, 614
Cetinkalp, Z. K. 58
Chabrol, H. 117
Chan, A. 647
change in − 2 log likelihood 619
chart **690**
Chart Editor window **690**
checklist 418–21
Chen, E. E. 644, 645, 651
Cheryan, S. 201
Cheung, M. W.-L. 644–5
Chew, P. K. H. 3
Chhabra, N. 644
chi-square 225–43, 259, 345, **690**
    alternatives 235–7
    calculation 231–3
    calculation: Fisher exact probability test 236–7
    calculation: one sample 237–8
    computer analysis 241–3
    crosstabulation/contingency table 227
    effect size 217–18
    Fisher exact probability test 236–7
    key points 241
    and known populations 237
    McNemar test 239
    one sample 237–8
    partitioning 233–4
    reporting 202

research examples 240
    table of significance 673
    theory 227–33
    warnings 234–5
    Yates's correction 235
Child, D. 466
cluster analysis **690**
Cochran's Q test **690**
coefficient alpha 526–8
coefficient of attenuation 223
coefficient of determination 112, 217, **690**
Cohen, J. 550, 557, 572, 574
Cohen, P. 557
Cohen's d 506–7, 508–9, 565, 567–8, 572
Collins, B. N. 440
Collmus, A. B. 649
Combs, D. 382
common variance **690**
communality 453–6, **690**
    iteration 455
comparison of studies 517–18
complex data *see* factor analysis
component matrix **690**
compound bar chart 96–7, 99–101
    computer analysis 99–101
compound histogram 97–8
Compute **690**
condition **690**
confidence intervals 131–2, 141, 204–14, **690**
    calculation: Pearson correlation coefficient 210–11
    calculation: predicted score 211–12
    calculation: related t-test 209–10
    calculation: single sample 208
    calculation: unrelated t-test 209
    computer analysis 214
    confidence limits 207
    key points 214
    parameters 141
    point estimates 205
    regression 211
    relationship between significance and confidence intervals
        208
    reporting 198, 201, 213
    research examples 212–13
    standard error 205
    statistics 141
confidence limits 207
confirmatory factor analysis **690**
confounding variable **690**
consistency and agreement *see* reliability in scales and
    measurement
Contador, I. 87
contingency tables *see* analysis of complex contingency
    tables
contrasts 346–8
correlated scores designs 168
correlation
    and causality 112
    reporting 200, 202
correlation coefficients 102–21, **690**
    calculation: Pearson correlation coefficient 108–10
    calculation: Spearman's rho with/without tied ranks
        114, 116

coefficient of determination 112
computer analysis 118–21
covariance 106–10
example 116
key points 117
principles 104–12
research design issue 112
research examples 117
rules 111
significance testing 113
Spearman's rho 113–16
and *t*-test 11
see also statistical significance of correlation coefficient
correlation matrix 433, **690**
count **690**
counterbalancing 168, **690**
Coursol, A. 647
covariance 106–10, **690**
covariate **690**
Cox and Snell's R^2 617, 618, 638, **690**
Cramer, D. 385, 415, 446, 466, 483, 499, 504, 514, 518, 521
Cramer's *V* **690**
Crighton, D. 239
Critcher, C. R. 201
critical value **690**
Cronbach's alpha **690**
computer analysis 534–5
research examples 533
Crosby, J. W. 533
cross-validation 647
crosstabulation (contingency) tables 94, 95, 96, 227
computer analysis 99–101
research examples 98
Cumberbatch, G. 438
Cumming, G. 2
Cumming, S. P. 382
cumulative frequency curves 68–70
Curseu, P. L. 337

Dakwar, E. 640
data
dredging 647
exploration techniques 22
fishing 647
handling **690**
scraping 645
types *see* statistics
see also big data; data mining; factor analysis
Data Editor window **690**
data mining 23, 643–52, **690**
dissatisfactions with traditional psychology 647–8
graphical methods 649–50
key points 651
new thinking mode 646–7
problems 645
research examples 651–2
and statistical techniques 649–51
Web scraping 648–9
Data View **690**
Davey, G. C. L. 98, 254, 296
Davies, A. 650
Davis, M. H. 519

Dean, R. S. 412
Deary, I. J. 98
decisions in factor analysis 449–56
communality 453–6
factor scores 456
number of factors 452–3
orthogonal or oblique rotation 451–2
rotated or unrotated factors 451
degrees of freedom 284, 288–91, 593, **690**
quick formulae 291
researcher 648
t-test 171, 172
Dempster, M. 4
dependent and independent variables 169
dependent variable 301, **690**
descriptive statistics 19–134, **691**
averages, variation and spread 46–61
correlation coefficients 102–21
regression 122–34
relationships between variables 90–101
shapes of distributions of scores 62–74
standard deviation 75–89
statistics 21–30
tables and diagrams 31–45
deviation **691**
Di Filippo, G. 87
diagrammatic and tabular presentation 92
diagrams and tables *see* relationships between variables
Dialogue box **691**
dichotomous **691**
Dickersin, K. 647
Diekhoff, G. 401, 415
differences between Pearson and likelihood ratio chi-square 585
Dillon, D. B. 3
direct entry **695**
Direct Oblimin **691**
discriminant function **691**
discriminant function analysis 402–15, 613–14, **691**
computer analysis 413–14
key points 412
MANOVA and 395–6, 403–5
reporting your findings 411–12
research examples 412
stepwise 411
using 405–11
discriminant score **691**
distinguishing between categories/groups *see* multinomial logistic regression
distorted curves 66–8
kurtosis (steepness/shallowness) 66, 67–8
skewness 66–7
distributions of scores *see* shapes of distributions of scores
disturbance term 486
Drees, M. J. 176
dummy coding **691**
dummy variables 612, **691**
Dumont, K. 311
Duncan multiple range test 344
Dunfield, K. A. 366
Dunning, D. 201
Durding, B. M. 72

Easterbrook, P. J. 647
effect size 215–24, **691**
    analysis of variance (ANOVA) 219–31
    approximation for nonparametric tests 219
    chi-square 217–18
    key points 224
    large, medium or small? 221–2
    meta-analysis 506–7, 508–14
    method and statistical efficiency 222–3
    Pearson correlation coefficient as 506
    reporting 198, 201, 221
    research examples 223
    statistical power analysis 565, 567–8, 572
    statistical significance 216–17
    in studies 217–19
    t-test 218–19
effects of different characteristics of studies 507–8
eigenvalues 451, **691**
Emery, P. J. 520
endogenous variable 486, **691**
equal frequencies model 586, 587–8, 595
    proportionate frequencies 587
equal-interval measurement 26, 27, 28
Erdfelder, E. 578
Estevis, E. 382
estimated standard deviation 80
eta 219–31, **691**
Evartt, D. L. 520
exact significance **691**
exhaustive regression 650
exogenous variable 486, **691**
exploratory and confirmatory factor analysis 410,
    457–8, **691**
exponent **691**
extraction **691**
Eysenck, H. J. 9, 446
Eysenck, S. B. G. 9

F-distribution table of significance values 683–5
F-ratio 390, 392, 393, **691**
    significance 344
    see also variance ratio test
factor **691**
factor analysis 9, 404, 444–66, **691**
    computer analysis 464–5
    concepts 447–9
    data issues in 450–1
    decisions 449–56
    exploratory and confirmatory factor analysis 457–8
    history 446
    key points 463
    literature example 458–61
    principal components analysis 464–5
    reporting results 461–2
    research examples 462–3
    second-order 452
factor loadings 448–9
factor matrix **691**
factor scores **691**
factorial ANOVA **691**
factorials 236
family error rate **691**
Faul, F. 578

Faust, M. E. 87
Fayed, N. 132
Feeney, G. F. X. 652
Fidell, L. S. 401, 415, 466, 483
findings 622
    see also meta-analysis; statistical power analysis
Fischbein, R. L. 640
Fisher exact probability test 236–7, 240
    literature example 240
    research examples 240
Fisher's *z* 512
Fisher test **691**
Fitneva, S. A. 366
Ford, S. 640
Frank, G. K. W. 296
frequencies 25, **691**
    computer analysis 72–3
    percentage 35
    simple 35
frequency curves 68–71
    bimodal and multimodal frequency distributions 68
    cumulative frequency curves 68–70
    percentiles 70–1
frequency data *see* chi-square
frequency distribution **691**
Freund, P. A. 519
Friedman test 267, 660–1, 660–1, **691**
    computer analysis 662–3
Fritz, C. O. 72
Furlong, M. J. 647

G*Power 475, 507, 571, 572–6, 578–80
Gallagher, M. R. 652
Gallagher, P. 132
Gannon, T. A. 155, 412
Gardner, R. C. 5
Garfield, J. 4
Geenen, R. 117
General Linear Model (GLM) 125
generalising and inferring *see* samples from populations
Gervais, S. J. 223
Gibbs, S. 462
Gillis, J. S. 116
Gips, J. 71
Glantz, S. A. 365, 369, 385, 483
Glass, G. V. 520
goodness-of-fit 584, **691**
Gordon, S. 3, 4
Gosset, William 7–8
Gotwals, J. K. 440
graph **691**
Gray, H. M. 412
Griffin, B. 623
Griffith, A. T. 312
Gromoske, A. N. 496
grouping variable **691**
Guzman, J. F. 398
Gwandure, C. 193

Hair, J. F., Jr 401, 415
Halligan, P. 462–3
Hanna, D. 4
Hannaford, P. C. 212–13

Hao, J. 650
Hardie, S. M. 382
Harinck, F. 337
Harlow, L. L. 645
harmonic mean **691**
Hartman, M. 440
Heisey, D. M. 570
Help **691**
Hesketh, B. 623
hierarchical agglomerative clustering **691–2**
hierarchical entry **692**
hierarchical models 634
hierarchical multiple regression approach to identifying
    moderator effects 541–51
    computer analysis 497–8
hierarchical regression **692**
hierarchical selection 471, 472
histograms 39–40, **692**
    compound 97–8
    and frequency curves 63–4
Ho, T. K. 650
Hoenig, J. M. 570
Hofer, M. 495
Hoicka, E. 254
homogeneity of regression slope **692**
homogeneity of variance **692**
homoscedasticity **692**
Hotelling's trace 392, 394
Hotelling's two sample t^2 388
Howard, R. 640
Howell, D. 352, 355
Howitt, D. 438, 504, 514, 518, 521
Huan, V. S. 132, 212, 480
Huck, S. W. 65
Huisman, A. 213, 240, 623
Huitema, B. E. 380
Hunter, P. G. 312
hypothesis **692**

icicle plot **692**
identification 491, **692**
independence **692**
independent groups design **692**
independent t-test **692**
independent variable **692**
inference *see* statistical significance of correlation
    coefficient
inferential statistics 22, 138, **692**
Ingravallo, F. 532
inter-rater reliability 529–32
interaction graph **692**
interactions 584, 587, **692**
    moderator effects 542, 543–4
internal consistency of scales and measurements 523
interquartile range 51–5, **692**
interval data **692**
interval measurement 26, 27, 28
interval scores 11
intervals for population mean based on single sample 208
Introduction to Research Methods in Psychology 518, 521
item analysis using item–total correlation 523–5
iteration 455
Ivancevich, J. M. 349

Jafari, N. 176
Jak, S. 644–5
Jex, S. M. 555
Jin, J. 652
John, L. K. 648
Juhl, J. 213
just-identified model 491, **692**

Kaiser or Kaiser–Guttman criterion **692**
Kaiser test 452
kappa coefficient
    calculation 530–2
    computer analysis 534–5
    research examples 532
Karageorghis, C. I. 577
Kasten, N. 519
Kendall's tau **692**
Kenne, D. R. 640
Kenny, D. A. 551
Kenyon, M. 267
Kerkhof, A. J. F. 213, 240, 623
Kerlinger, F. N. 249
Kerr, N. L. 648
Kilian, B. 495
Kingston, K. 398
Kline, P. 466
Kogan, S. M. 240, 623
Kois, L. 240
Kolmogorov–Smirnov test for two samples **692**
Kosinski, M. 651
Kruskal–Wallis test 267, 658–60, **692**
    computer analysis 662–3
Kuhnle, C. 495
kurtosis (steepness/shallowness) 66, 67–8, **692**
    leptokurtic curve 67
    mesokurtic curve 67
    platykurtic curve 67
    research examples 71–2

Laaksonen, M. A. 532
Lakkaraju, H. 651
Lalonde, R. N. 5
Lam, N. H. 366
lambda 634
Lamoureux, B. E. 496
Landers, R. N. 649
Lang, A.-G. 578
LaPlante, D. A. 412
large-sample formulae for nonparametric tests
    656–7
    Mann–Whitney U-test 656
    Wilcoxon matched pairs test 657
latent variable **692**
Lautamo, T. 223
learning statistics
    difficulties 4–6
    research 3–4
Leskovec, J. 651
level **692**
levels of measurement **692**
Levene's test 392, **692**
Levine, T. R. 223
likelihood ratio chi-square 585, **692**

Likert questionnaires 39
limitations of statistics 9–11
Lindholm, B. W. 349
line graph **692**
linear association or relationship **692**
linear model **692**
Ling, J. 59
Lipsey, M. W. 572
LISREL **692**
Livianos, L. 98
loading **692**
Loewenstein, G. 648
log likelihood **692**
log-linear methods 583–608
   analysis 602–3, **693**
   computer analysis 606–7
   differences between Pearson and likelihood ratio
     chi-square 585
   goodness-of-fit 584
   interactions 584
   likelihood ratio chi-square 585
   models 584
   natural logarithm 585
   Pearson chi-square 584, 585
   research examples 605
   see also analysis of complex contingency tables
logarithm 6, **693**
logistic regression procedure 634–8, **693**
   backwards elimination analysis 636–7
logit 620, 629–30
Lounsbury, J. W. 480
Louvet, E. 155
Louw, J. 311
Lowe, P. 398

machine learning 650–1
Mack, M. G. 176
Maguire-Jack, K. 496
main effects model 586–7, 589–93, 596–8,
   693
manifest variable **693**
Mann–Whitney U-test 264–6, 513–14, 656, **693**
   computer analysis 268–70
   effect size 219
   table of significance 680–2
MANOVA *see* multivariate analysis of variance
marginal totals **693**
Mariscuilo, L. A. 270
matched sets 302
matched-subjects design 169, **693**
matching 168–9
mathematical ability 4–6
mathematics anxiety 5
matrix **693**
Mauchly's test **693**
maximum likelihood method **693**
Maxwell, A. E. 243
McCartney, M. J. 5
McCoy, K. D. 412
McFadden's R^2 617, 618
McNemar test 239, 260, **693**
McSweeney, M. 270
mean **693**

mean, median and mode 48–51
   arithmetic mean 48–9, 51
   comparison 51
   confidence intervals 208
   median 49–50
   mode 50–1
   reporting 201, 202
mean square **693**
measure of dispersion **693**
measurement theory
   interval/equal-interval measurement 26, 27, 28
   nominal categorisation 26, 27, 28
   ordinal (rank) measurement 26, 27, 28
   ratio measurement 26, 27, 28
measurement types 24–8
   measurement theory 26–8
   nominal/categorical/category measurement 24
   score/numerical measurement 24, 25
median 49–50, 51, **693**
mediator variables 433–4, 537–9, **693**
Meeten, F. 98, 254, 296
Meinert, C. L. 647
Mercer, S. H. 163
meta-analysis 503–21
   calculator 520
   comparison of studies 517–18
   computer analysis 520–1
   difficulties 504–5
   effects of different characteristics of studies 507–8
   example 514–17
   first steps in meta-analysis 508–14
   key points 520
   objectives 504
   other measures of effect size 506–7
   Pearson correlation coefficient as effect size 506
   reporting results 518–19
   research examples 519
Meta-Analyst 520
Meta-Stat 520
Meyer, M. M. 221
Milgram, S. 605
Min, Y. I. 647
Mitchell, R. 649
Mitsumatsu, H. 203
MIX 520
mixed ANOVA **693**
mixed designs and repeated measures **693**
   fixed vs random effects 355
   risks in related subjects designs 365–6
mode 50–1, **693**
model 584, 637
model building 9
moderator variables and effects 433–4, 536–57, **693**
   ANOVA approach 551–4
   calculation: identifying moderator effects using ANOVA
     approach 552–4
   calculation: identifying moderator effects using
     hierarchical multiple regression approach 545–51
   computer analysis 556–7
   hierarchical multiple regression approach 541–51
   key points 555
   research design issue 544
   research examples 555

Morris, P. E. 72
Moscovitch, M. 213
Motes, M. A. 462
multicollinearity 477–8, 612, **693**
multifactorial ANOVA 345–6
multimodal **693**
multimodal frequency distributions 68
multinomial logistic regression 609–25
    change in −2 log likelihood 619
    computer analysis 624–5
    discriminant function analysis 613–14
    dummy variables 612
    findings 622
    key points 623
    pattern of variables 611
    prediction 620–1
    prediction accuracy 616–17
    predictors 617–20
    reporting findings 622–3
    research examples 623
    score variables 611
    uses 613–14
    Wald statistic 621
    worked example 615–16
multiple comparison tests, recoding groups for 426–7
multiple control variables 437
    first-order partial correlation 437
    second-order partial correlation 437
    zero-order correlation 437
multiple correlation *see* multiple regression and multiple
    correlation
multiple items to measure same variable 422
multiple regression and multiple correlation 404,
    466–83, **693**
    assumptions 474–5
    computer analysis 481–3
    data mining 650
    different approaches 473–4
    hierarchical selection 471, 472
    key points 481
    literature example 479–80
    multicollinearity 477–8
    prediction and 478
    regression equations 470–1
    reporting results 478–9
    research design issues 473–4
    research examples 480
    selection 471–3
    setwise selection 472
    standardised vs unstandardised regression weights 468
    stepwise selection 471, 472, 475–7, 481–3
    theory 468–74
multiple responses 32
multiplication rule 246, 248
multivariate **693**
multivariate analysis of variance (MANOVA) 386–401, **693**
    combining dependent variables 389
    computer analysis 399–401
    discriminant function analysis and 395–6
    key points 398
    reporting findings 397
    research examples 398
    vs several ANOVAs 389

    two stages 390–1
    using 392–7
multivariate tests 392–4
Munford, M. B. 479–80
Murphy, K. R. 571
Murray, R. A. 366
Mutsvunguma, P. 193
Myors, B. 571

Nagelkerke's R^2 617, 618, 638, **693**
Nair, U. S. 440
Napierian logarithms *see* natural logarithms
Napolitano, M. A. 440
natural logarithms 585, 629, 630, **693**
    Poisson distribution 630
negative (−) values 6, 54, 86
Nelson, L. D. 648
nested model **693**
Newman–Keuls test 344
Nicholas, M. K. 480
nominal categories 95–7
nominal categories/numerical scores 97–8
    compound histogram 97–8
    crosstabulation tables 98
nominal categorisation 26, 27, 28
nominal (category) data 33, 34–8
    bar charts 36, 37–8
    frequencies 34
    percentage frequencies 35
    pie diagrams 36–7
    simple frequencies 35
nominal variables *see* category variables
non-recursive relationships 486
nonparametric statistical tests 11, 257, 258, 259–66,
    693
    effect size 219
    related samples 259–64
    unrelated samples 264–6
    see also large-sample formulae for nonparametric
    tests
nonparametric statistics *see* ranking tests
nonparametric tests for three or more groups 658–63
    computer analysis 662–3
    Friedman three or more related samples test 660–3
    Kruskal–Wallis three or more unrelated conditions test
    658–60, 662–3
normal curve 11, 64–5, **693**
null hypothesis 147–9
number of factors 452–3
numeric variables **693**
numerical indexes 47
numerical mean *see* arithmetic mean
numerical score data 38–41
    bands of scores 39–40
    histogram 39–40
numerical scores 93–5
    scattergram 93–4

oblique factors **693**
oblique rotation 451–2
observed power 570
odds **693**
odds ratio 629, **693**

Oltmanns, T. F. 117
one-tailed test **693**
one-tailed vs two-tailed significance testing 250–5
    computer analysis 255
    further requirements 253–4
    key points 254
    research examples 254
    theory 251–3
Onwuegbuzie, A. J. 5
ordinal data **694**
ordinal (rank) measurement 11, 26, 27, 28
orthogonal **694**
orthogonal factors **694**
orthogonal rotation 451–2
Oswald, F. L. 645
Otgaar, R. 59
outcome variable **694**
outliers, identifying 52–3, **694**
output window **694**
over-identified model 491, **694**
Oyebode, J. 640

paired comparisons **694**
parallel computing 650
parameters 141, **694**
parametric **694**
parametric tests 257, **694**
part correlation **694**
partial correlation 431–43, **694**
    calculation 439
    calculation: partial correlation coefficient 435
    calculation: statistical significance of partial correlation
        436–7
    computer analysis 441–3
    interpretation 436
    key points 440–1
    literature example 438
    multiple control variables 437
    research design issue 433
    research examples 440
    student example 439–40
    suppressor variables 437–8
    theory 433–4
participant **694**
Passmore, J. 193
PASW Statistics **694**
path analysis 484–99
    computer analysis 497–8
    generalisation 490–1
    key points 496
    path coefficients 487–90
    reporting results 494–5
    research design issue 491
    research examples 492–4, 495–6
    theory 485–91
path coefficients 487–90
path diagram **694**
pathway **694**
pattern of variables 611
Pearson chi-square 584, 585, **690**
Pearson correlation coefficient 103, 108–10, 149–53,
        210–11, 509
    calculation 108–10, 151–2

    as effect size 217, 506
    extended table of significance 664–6
    research examples 117
    statistical power analysis 565, 567–8
    statistical significance of 151–2, 155
    see also correlation coefficients
Pechey, R. 462–3
Pedhazur, E. J. 483, 499
percentage frequencies, calculation 35
percentages, reporting 202
percentiles 70–1
Perlman, D. 312
Peters, M. 72
phi **694**
pictogram 38
pie diagrams 36–7
Pillai's trace 392, 393, 394
Pituch, K. A. 453
pivot table **694**
planned (*a priori*) vs unplanned (*post hoc*) comparisons
        344, **694**
Plomin, R. 279
point-biserial correlation **694**
point estimates 205
Poisson distribution 630
populations **694**
    see also samples from populations
post hoc statistical power analysis 568–70
post hoc test **694**
Potter, G. G. 440
Powell, B. 462
power 691, **694**
    see also statistical power analysis
Pradat-Diehl, P. 155
pre-test/post-test design 355–6
predicted score 211–12
prediction 620–1
    accuracy 616–17
    see also regression
predictors 617–20
Prelec, D. 648
principal component analysis **694**
    computer analysis 464–5
probability 244–9
    calculation: addition rule 247
    calculation: multiplication rule 248
    implications 247
    key points 240
    principles 245–6
    regression to the mean 245
    repeated significance testing 247
    significance testing across different studies 247
probability distribution **694**
promax **694**
pseudo R^2 statistics 617–18, 638
psychology, dissatisfactions with traditional 647–8
*Publication Manual of the American Psychological
        Association* 198, 200–2

quantitative research **694**
quartimax **694**

R **694**

random samples 139, 140–1
   computer analysis 142–3
   standard error 140
randomisation **694**
range 51–5, **694**
rank measurement (ordinal) 26, 27, 28
ranking tests 256–70
   calculation: Mann–Whitney U test 264–6
   calculation: sign test 260–1
   calculation: Wilcoxon matched pairs test 262–3
   computer analysis 268–70
   key points 268
   nonparametric statistical tests 259–66
   parametric tests 257
   research examples 267
   theory 257–9
   three or more groups of scores 267
Rastle, K. 519
ratio data **694**
ratio measurement 26, 27, 28
ratio scores 11
reciprocal relationships 486
recode **694**
regression 122–34, 211, 466–83
   calculation 128–30
   calculation: confidence intervals for predicted score
      211–12
   computer analysis 133–4
   equations 125–30
   formula 638–9
   key points 132
   line 123–4, 125–7
   to the mean 245
   reporting 202
   research design issues 127, 130
   research examples 132
   standard error 130–2
   see also multiple regression and multiple correlation
regression coefficient **694**
regression equations 125–30, 470–1
   least squares solutions 126
Rehman, H. 193
related factorial design **694**
related measures designs 168, **694**
related research designs 12–13
related samples
   sign test 260–1
   Wilcoxon matched pairs test 261–4
related t-test (correlated/paired t-test) 166–79
   calculation 173–5
   cautionary note 175–6
   computer analysis 178–9
   confidence intervals 209–10
   degrees of freedom 171, 172
   dependent and independent variables 169
   key points 177
   related (correlated/paired) t-test 167, 178–9
   repeated measures designs 168
   research design issues 168–9
   research examples 176
   theory 170–5
relationship between significance and confidence intervals
   208

   calculation: confidence 208
   calculation: confidence intervals for unrelated t-test 209
   calculation: Pearson correlation coefficient 210–11
   calculation: related t-test 209–10
relationships between variables 90–101
   computer analysis 99–101
   diagrammatic and tabular presentation 92
   key points 99
   nominal categories 95–7
   nominal categories/numerical scores 97–8
   numerical scores 93–5
   research examples 98
reliability in scales and measurement 522–35, **694**
   agreement between raters 529–32
   alpha reliability 526–8
   calculation: kappa coefficient 531–2
   calculation: split-half reliability 526
   computer analysis 534–5
   internal consistency of scales and measurements 523
   item-analysis using item–total correlation 523–5
   key points 533
   research examples 532–3
   split-half reliability 525–6
repeated measures ANOVA **695**
repeated measures designs 168, **695**
repeated significance testing 247
reporting statistical analyses 197–203, 639
   analysis of variance (ANOVA): one-way unrelated/
      uncorrelated 295–6
   APA style 200–2
   confidence intervals 213
   discriminant function analysis 411–12
   effect size 221
   key points 203
   multivariate analysis of variance (MANOVA) 397
   research examples 203
   results 461–2, 478–9, 494–5, 604, 622–3
   shortened forms 199–200
   significance levels *see* significance level reporting
   statistical significance 199
research designs, importance of understanding 6–7
research methods and statistical efficiency 222–3
researcher degrees of freedom 648
residual 486, 587, 602–3, **695**
residual sum of squares **695**
Ridenour, T. A. 412
Risen, J. L. 221
risks in related subjects designs 365–6
Roche, B. 279
Rohmer, O. 155
Rojo, L. 98
Rosenthal, R. 521
Rossi, J. S. 647
rotated or unrotated factors 451, **695**
Rothbard, N. 41
rounding errors 192
Routledge, C. 213
Rowe, M. L. 203
Roy's largest root 392, 394
Rubin, J. 213
Rudner, L. M. 520
Ruggeri, K. 4
Ruscio, J. 279

sample size 8–9
  flexibility 648
samples 22, **695**
  development of sampling 7
samples from populations 137–43
  computer analysis 142–3
  confidence intervals 141
  inferential statistics 138
  key points 142
  random samples 140–1
  theory 138–9
sampling distribution **695**
saturated model 588, 596, **695**
scattergram **695**
  computer analysis 120–1
  crosstabulation (contingency) tables 94
  frequencies 94
  overlaps 94
  regression line 93
scatterplot **695**
Schau, C. 4
Scheffé test 344, **695**
Schellenberg, E. G. 312
Schimmack, U. 576–7
Schoedel, R. 651
Schreurs, B. G. 41
Schruijer, S. G. L. 337
Schulenberg, S. E. 193
Schwarzer, R. 520
score/numerical measurement 23–4, 25
score variables 12
scores 48–51
  central tendency 48
  logistic regression 611, 632, **695**
  see also shapes of distributions of scores
Scrapy 649
scree test 453, **695**
Sedlmeier, P. 519
select cases **695**
semi-partial correlation **694**
Seo, D.-C. 652
sequential entry **692**
setwise selection 472
Shaffer, H. J. 412
Shafran, R. 267
shapes of distributions of scores 62–74
  computer analysis 72–3
  distorted curves 66–8
  histograms and frequency curves 63–4
  key points 72
  normal curve 64–5
  other frequency curves 68–71
  research examples 71–2
shortened forms in research reports 199–200
Siegel, S. 270
Sierra, P. 98
Siew, C. S. Q. 5
sign test 259, 260–1, 264, **695**
  extended table of significance 674–6
Signal, T. L. 366
significance level reporting **695**
significance testing 7, 113, 135–270
  across different studies 247

chi-square 225–43
confidence intervals 204–14
effect size 215–24
one-tailed vs two-tailed 250–5
probability 244–9
ranking tests 256–70
related (correlated/paired) *t*-test 166–79
reporting statistical analyses 197–203
samples from populations 137–43
standard error 158–65
statistical significance of correlation coefficient 144–57
unrelated (uncorrelated/independent) *t*-test 180–96
Simmons, J. P. 648
Simonsohn, U. 648
simple logistic regression 628–30, **695**
Simpson, S. 212–13, 577
Siy, J. O. 201
skewness 66–7, **695**
  negative skew 66, 67
  positive skew 66, 67
  research examples 71–2
  see also testing for excessively skewed distributions
Skinner, B. F. 41
Slinker, B. K. 365, 369, 385, 483
Sliter, M. T. 555
Smart, R. G. 648
Smith-Bell, C. A. 41
Song, J. 652
Song, T. M. 652
sort cases **695**
Spearman's rho correlation coefficient 113–16, 153–5, 259, **695**
  calculation: with/without tied ranks 114, 116
  research examples 117
  statistical significance 153–5
  table of significance 667–9
  see also correlation coefficients
sphericity **695**
split-half reliability 525–6, **695**
  calculation 526
spread of scores
  range and interquartile range 51–5
  variance 55–8
Sprung, J. M. 555
SPSS 13, **695**
  Analyze, Graphs and Transform drop-down menus 17–18
  ANCOVA 383–5
  binomial logistic regression 641–2
  chi-square 241–3
  confidence intervals 214
  correlated ANOVA 313–14
  correlation coefficients 118–21
  Cronbach's alpha and kappa 534–5
  crosstabulation and compound bar charts 99–101
  data entry basics 29–30
  descriptive statistics 60–1
  discriminant function analysis 413–14
  frequencies 72–3
  Friedman test 662–3
  Kruskal–Wallis test 662–3
  log-linear analysis 606–7
  MANOVA 399–401
  Measure drop-down menu 26

meta-analysis 520–1
mixed design ANOVA 367–9
moderator variables 556–7
multinomial logistic regression 624–5
multiple comparison tests 350–2
one-tailed vs two-tailed significance testing 255
one-way analysis of variance 297–9
partial correlation 441–3
path analysis 497–8
principal components analysis 464–5
random samples 142–3
ranking tests 268–70
recoding groups for multiple comparison tests 426–7
regression 133–4
related (correlated/paired) *t*-test 178–9
reliability in scales and measurement 534–5
scattergrams 120–1
selecting subsamples of data 424–5
standard deviation and *z*-scores 88–9
standard error 164–5
statistical significance of correlation coefficient 156–7
stepwise multiple regression 481–3
tables and diagrams 42–5
two-way analysis of variance 339–41
unrelated *t*-test 194–6
Variable View 27
variance ratio (*F*-ratio) test 280–1
spurious correlation, third or confounding variables,
    suppressor variables *see* partial correlation
spurious relationships 486
square root of a number 6
squared Euclidean distance **695**
squaring a number 6
standard deviation 58, 75–89, 186–9, **695**
    calculation 79–80
    calculation: converting score into *z*-score 81–2
    calculation: table of standard normal distribution 84–5
    computer analysis 88–9
    estimated standard deviation 80
    key points 87–8
    reporting 201, 202
    research examples 87
    standard normal distribution 83–6
    theoretical background 76–80
    z-score 80–2
    z-score: important feature 86
    z-score: use 82–3
    see also standard error
standard entry **695**
standard error 130–2, 158–65, 186–9, 205, **695**
    calculation 162–3
    computer analysis 164–5
    confidence interval 131–2
    estimated standard deviation and standard error 161–3
    key points 163
    random samples 140
    research examples 163
    sampling distribution 160
    theory 159–60
    unrelated *t*-test 171, 186–9
standard normal distribution 83–6
    calculation 84–5
standardisation, moderator effects 542–3

standardised coefficients or weights **695**
statistical approaches to finding moderator effects 541
statistical efficiency and research methods 222–3
statistical inference *see* statistical significance of correlation
    coefficient
statistical power analysis 8, 558–80
    calculating power 572–6
    computer analysis 578–80
    effect size 567–8
    key points 577
    research design issues 559–60, 567–8
    research examples 576–7
    Type I and II errors 560, 561–2, 563–4, 565, 566
    types and limitations 568–70
    using 571–2
statistical significance 8
    big data 648
    effect size 216–17
    relationship with confidence intervals 208
    reporting 199, 200
statistical significance of correlation coefficient 144–57
    alternative hypothesis 147, 148
    calculation: Pearson correlation coefficient 151–2
    computer analysis 156–7
    key points 155
    null hypothesis 147–9
    Pearson correlation coefficient 149–53
    population 145, 147
    research design issues 149
    research examples 155
    Spearman's rho correlation coefficient 153–5
    theory 145–7
    Type I error 152–3
    Type II error 152–3
statistics 21–30, 141
    big data 23
    computer analysis 29–30
    data exploration techniques 22
    data mining 23
    descriptive statistics 22, 33
    inferential statistics 22
    key points 28
    measurement types 24–8
    samples 22
    variables and measurement 23–4
statistics and analysis of experiments 416–27
    checklist 418–21
    computer analysis 424–7
    key points 422
    Patent Stats Pack 417
    research design issues 418, 423
    special cases 422
Statistics Software for Meta-Analysis 520
stepwise discriminant function analysis 411
stepwise entry **695**
stepwise multiple regression 475–7
    computer analysis 481–3
    data mining 650
stepwise selection 471, 472
Stevens, J. P. 453
Straus, M. 438
Student *t*-test *see* unrelated *t*-test
students and statistics 2

sum of squares 284, **695**
sunflowers 94
suppressor variables 437–8
Survey of Attitudes Toward Statistics 5
Symons, M. 652
syntax **695**
systematic reviews 504
Szostak, H. 82

t-test
    and correlation coefficient 11
    development 7
    effect size 218–19
    extended table of significance 670–2
    meta-analysis 513–14
    related/correlated/paired scores *see* related t-test
    reporting 202
    table of significant values for multiple *t*-tests 686–8
    unrelated/uncorrelated/independent scores *see* unrelated
      t-test
Tabachnick, B. G. 401, 415, 466, 483
tables and diagrams 31–45
    computer analysis 42–5
    nominal (category) data 34–8
    numerical score data 38–41
    using 41
    see also relationships between variables
Tajfel, H. 311
Tatham, R. L. 401, 415
Taylor, J. S. 519
Teissedre, F. 117
test–retest reliability **695**
testing for excessively skewed distributions 653–5
    skewness 653–4
    standard error of skewness 654–5
Thompson 212–13
three-variable example 593–603
    data components 601–2
    equal frequencies model 595
    frequencies 594
    log-linear analysis 602–3
    main effects model 596–8
    saturated model 596
    two-variable interactions 598–601
Tinsley, H. E. A. 535
Touliatos, J. 349
Towl, G. 239
Tracey, T. J. 605
traditional psychology, dissatisfactions with 647–8
training set 647
transformation **695**
Tremont, G. 87
trends in data 8
trivial factors 453
two-tailed test **695**
two-variable example 586–93
    equal frequencies model 586, 587–8
    interactions 587
    main effects model 586–7, 589–93
    saturated model 588
two-way relationships 486
Type I error 152–3, 389, 391, **695**
    statistical power analysis 560, 561–2, 563, 565

Type II error 152–3, **695**
    statistical power analysis 560, 566
Tyson, P. 296

under-identified model 491, **695**
unique variance **695**
univariate 41, **696**
unplanned comparisons **696**
unrelated research designs 12–13
unrelated samples 264–6
    Mann–Whitney *U*-test 264–6
unrelated *t*-test (uncorrelated/independent *t*-test) 180–96
    calculation 189–92
    cautionary note 192
    computer analysis 194–6
    confidence intervals 209
    key points 193–4
    Mann–Whitney *U*-test 192
    research examples 193
    rounding errors 192
    standard deviation and standard error 186–9
    theory 182–6
unstandardised coefficients or weights **696**
uses of statistics 2–3

Vallat-Azouvi, C. 155
value label **696**
van Houwelingen, C. A. J. 213, 240, 623
van Kleef, G. A. 337
van Middendorp, H. 117
van Schaik, P. 59
variability
    calculation: variance using computation formulae 56–7
    mean deviation 55
    range and interquartile range 51–5
    standard deviation 58
    using negative (−) values 54
    variance 51
variable label **696**
variable name **696**
Variable View **696**
variables 31–45
    calculation: percentage frequencies 35
    calculation: slices for pie diagram 36
    computer analysis 42–5
    errors to avoid 41
    key points 42, 59
    and measurement 23–4
    raw data 32
    research design issue 12–13
    statistics 32
    tables and diagrams 33–41
    using graphs and tables 41
    see also averages, variation and spread
variance 55–8, 283, **696**
    estimate 57, 284, **696**
variance analysis 271–427
    analysis of covariance (ANCOVA) 370–85, 388
    analysis of variance (ANOVA) 282–99
    analysis of variance (ANOVA): correlated scores/repeated
      measures 300–14
    analysis of variance (ANOVA): mixed design 353–69
    analysis of variance (ANOVA): multiple comparisons 342–52

analysis of variance (ANOVA): one-way unrelated/ uncorrelated ANOVA 282–99
analysis of variance (ANOVA): two-way for unrelated/ uncorrelated scores 315–41
discriminant function analysis 402–15, 613–14
multivariate analysis of variance (MANOVA) 386–401
statistics and analysis of experiments 416–27
variance ratio test 273–81
variance–covariance matrix 110, **696**
variance ratio test 273–81, **696**
    calculation 276–8
    computer analysis 280–1
    key points 279
    research examples 279
    theory and application 275–8
Varimax **696**
Vassari, M. 533
Vazire, S. 117
Vescio, T. K. 223
Vista, A. 279
Vitevitch, M. S. 5
Völkel, T. S. 651

Wagner, E. E. 647
Wagner, U. 492–4, 495
Wald statistic 621, **696**
Wampold, B. E. 647, 648
Wang, Y. 651
Ward, T. 440
Warren, C. S. 555
Web scraping 648–9, **696**
Wegener, D. T. 366
weights **696**

Weiss, D. J. 535
West, S. G. 544, 546, 551, 557
Westfall, J. 648
Wickham, L. H. 72
Wilcoxon matched pairs test 259, 261–4, 657
    computer analysis 268–70
    table of significance 677–9
Wilcoxon signed-rank test **696**
Wilk, S. L. 41
Wilkes, S. 176
Wilks' lambda 392, 393, 408, **696**
Wilson, D. B. 572
within-subjects design **696**
Wojcik, S. P. 644, 645, 651
Woods, S. P. 577
Wright, L. 382
Wynn, J. 213
Wyrick, D. L. 338

Yarkoni, T. 648
Yates's correction 235, **696**
Yildirim, I. 349
Yutrzenka, B. A. 193

z-scores 80–2, 86, 169–70, 509–13, **696**
    calculation: converting score into z-score 81–2
    computer analysis 88–9
    important feature 86
    research examples 87
    use 82–3
Zhang, Y. 221
Zick, A. 492–4, 495
Ziegler, R. H. 555
Zimprich, D. 5